FUNDAMENTALS
OF PLANT
SCIENCE

FUNDAMENTALS OF PLANT SCIENCE

Richard M. Klein
University of Vermont

Deana T. Klein
St. Michael's College

1817

HARPER & ROW, PUBLISHERS, New York
Cambridge, Philadelphia, San Francisco, Washington,
London, Mexico City, São Paulo, Singapore, Sydney

Sponsoring Editor: Claudia M. Wilson
Project Editor: Joan Gregory
Text Design Adaptation and Cover Design: Lucy Zakarian
Text Art: Veronica LeBlanc and Linda E. Jones
Production Manager: Kewal Sharma
Compositor: Black Dot, Inc.
Printer and Binder: R. R. Donnelley & Sons Company

Cover Illustration: Follower of Michelangelo da Caravaggio.
Still Life—Fruit and Flowers. Oil on canvas. 29⅛″ × 39⅜″.
Wadsworth Atheneum, Hartford, Ella Gallup Sumner and Mary
Catlin Sumner Collection.

FUNDAMENTALS OF PLANT SCIENCE

Library of Congress Cataloging in Publication Data

Klein, Richard M.
  Fundamentals of plant science.

  Includes index.
  1. Plants, Cultivated. 2. Botany. 3. Agriculture.
I. Klein, Deana T. II. Title. III. Title: Plant
science.
SB91.K57 1988   631   87-8698
ISBN 0-06-043707-3
87 88 89 90 9 8 7 6 5 4 3 2 1

CONTENTS

Chapter 6/Water   129

Chapter 7/Mineral Nutrition   157

PREFACE

For many years there has been considerable controversy about the relative values of "pure" and "applied" science. The physicist tends to look down on the engineer, the physiologist on the medical practitioner and, regrettably, the botanist on the forester and the horticulturist. Obviously, this is nonsense. There is, in reality, absolutely no way that the theoretical and the practical can be separated. Advances in knowledge come from all aspects of science. The fundamental basis for our understanding of the relationship between the seasons of the year and the flowering of plants was obtained by plant scientists working for the U.S. Department of Agriculture on very practical matters concerned with the breeding of tobacco. A good deal of our knowledge of mineral nutrition, water relations, and many other aspects of plant science has been derived from field studies with economically important plants. A plant scientist studying, say, the relation of a particular source of nitrogen to the yield of wheat, contributes as much to our fundamental knowledge of mineral nutrition and plant growth as the scientist in a laboratory. Since the laboratory is not the real world, scientific information obtained under laboratory conditions must be evaluated in the field. The conditions and techniques of field research are different from those in the laboratory and the thrust of the experiments is different, but the value of the work to both science and to human affairs is unquestionable.

In order to develop experimental approaches to problems that are important for the well-being of people, the horticulturist, forester, or agronomist must possess a comprehensive background in many areas of science. The physical sciences—chemistry, physics, and mathematics—and their application to plant science research must be understood. All of the biological sciences are a base for plant research. A working knowledge of both theoretical and practical entomology is clearly needed for disease control work, whether in research or in the vitally important area of consultation with producers. Soils, water, light, and the other factors that comprise the plant's environment must also be understood, not just on a theoretical level, but also from the point of view of how these factors affect the growth of crops. A laboratory scientist can, unfortunately, become so specialized that little attention is paid to other areas of the broad topic of plant biology, but the practitioner can never neglect such matters. County agents and extension personnel are frequently confronted with situations where the advice that the producer needs requires a broad plant science background.

To a large extent, these considerations underlie this book. Since the plant scientist, whether a professional or a person growing plants for food or fun, is working with plants, a fundamental knowledge of a number of aspects of plant science must be mastered. Knowledge of the structure, growth and development, and physiology of green plants is necessary. It is, we believe, not enough to know that nitrogen is required for plant growth. The physiology, perhaps the biochemistry, and certainly the role of nitrogen in the economy of the individual plant and the plant population that constitutes a crop must all be considered. A general botanical background is necessary to understand and to integrate the large amount of applied plant science information now available. Plants do not live in a vacuum, but are always interacting with their physical and biological environments. Through these interactions, they utilize radiant energy for photosynthesis and deploy the accumulated energy-rich compounds for maintenance and growth. Soil, water, temperature and other factors in the plant's world modify or even control how plants respond to energy, nutrients, and other facets of their environment. The theoretical and the applied are two sides of the same coin—and maybe both are on the same side of the coin.

Some books are designed to tell the reader how to do something, and many of these are highly detailed and very accurate. Few, however, attempt to provide the reader with the reasons behind any particular practice or technique, nor should they attempt to do so; this is the role of a textbook. Where applicable, reference to manuals dealing with procedures in plant sciences have been provided.

Plant science is almost impossible to define with any precision. Because of the breadth and depth of knowledge a plant scientist needs to function effectively, plant science has been subdivided into areas of specialization. Horticulture, for example, has three major subdivisions. Ornamental horticulture includes floriculture, nursery production, and landscaping, which embraces turf science, design and maintenance, and arboriculture. Olericulture covers vegetable production from the level of home gardens to field crops and also includes storage, processing and marketing. Pomology is concerned with fruit and nut production, processing, and marketing. Agronomy, like horticulture, is a major area of plant science devoted to the production of cereal grains and a few important noncereals, forage grasses, and the production of the food and forage legumes. The commercial production of many other field crops, some of which are also of interest to the horticulturist, is usually considered to be the responsibility of the agronomist.

Closely associated with the plant scientist are specialists in related fields. Soil scientists, meteorologists and climatologists, chemists who determine plant composition and who make agricultural chemicals, and engineers who design farm and garden machinery, although not trained as plant scientists, interact with them to study economically important plants. Foresters are plant scientists, although forestry has become so specialized and diverse that it has been separated from the other plant sciences.

Since conditions differ greatly in various parts of the world, plant scientists have acquired knowledge and skills that enable them to work with particular crops, particular aspects of plant growth and development, and conditions particular to dry or wet climates, to the tropics, or to the harsh conditions of mountainous regions. Nevertheless, the fundamentals of plant science are the same whether one is working on millet in central Africa, potatoes in the Peruvian mountains, or wheat in North America.

Acquisition of knowledge is not a linear process wherein one goes from A to B to C, but it is cyclic in that an understanding of C is needed for evaluation of A. This is a problem that all instructors face and we are facing in this book. Of course, one needs chemistry and physics to appreciate how light or temperature or wind or water affects plant growth processes. It would be the best of possible academic worlds if each student came into plant science with degrees in chemistry, physics, and math plus a background in meteorology. Recognizing that this is impossible, we have written this book on the assumption that readers do not necessarily have a comprehensive background in physical and biological sciences. It was, frankly, something of a challenge to provide you with accurate, up-to-date, and useful information on topics in plant science and to present that information with the physical and biological science backgrounds that may still be in your future. Any science can, if one works at it, be presented in terms and with concepts that do not require the advanced material that, in time and with continued interest, you will acquire.

This may be your first in-depth acquaintance with biological sciences. We hope that your experience will be as pleasant, indeed as intellectually stimulating, as was ours. Plants are alive; they are exciting to study and to work with. They are the basic living entities in the world, their importance in our lives and in the life of all Mankind is a justification for studying them. We need plants and we need people to study plants and to use the knowledge obtained from research to provide plants and their products to the people who are alive now and those who will be alive in the future.

ACKNOWLEDGMENTS

We appreciate the time and effort given us by many individuals. Critical reviews of all or parts of the manuscript were provided by Drs. Robert J. Bauske, Department of Horticulture, Iowa State University; James W. Boodley, Department of Floriculture and Ornamental Horticulture, Cornell University; Jerry Brand, Botany Department, University of Texas; William F. Campbell, Department of Plant Science, Utah State University; William L. Culbertson, Botany Department, Duke University; Frank H. Emerson, Department of Horticulture, Purdue University; W. C. Fontano, Department of Horticultural Science, North Carolina State University; John E. Greenaway, Mount Hood Community College; E. Jay Holcomb, Department of Horticulture, Pennsylvania State University; John F. Kelly, Department of Horticulture, Michigan State University. We are, however, responsible for errors of fact and interpretation.

RICHARD M. KLEIN
DEANA T. KLEIN

FUNDAMENTALS
OF PLANT
SCIENCE

PART ONE

A
BOTANICAL
BACKGROUND

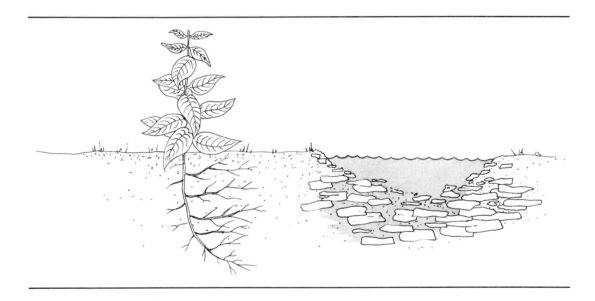

C H A P T E R 1

THE PLANT KINGDOM

INTRODUCTION

Geological Perspective

Our planet, earth, is considered to be between 4.6 and 4.7 billion years old. The eras and periods of geological time and the epochs of the most recent era, the Cenozoic, are listed in Table 1-1. Most of the geological information is derived from patterns of rock formation created during the last 570 million years, a time during which organisms left a good fossil record. During these millions of years all of the present mountain ranges were formed, and most of the deposits of plant material—the source of potential fossil fuels—accumulated. The middle Pleistocene epoch is considered to be especially important for the evolution of animals and humans. For this epoch the fossil record is supplemented by newer methodologies for the estimation of time. Potassium-argon dating is adequate for the early Pleistocene, and analyses of sedimentary rocks and radiocarbon dating are used to date events of the later Pleistocene. These accurate methods have also indicated that the time spread for the epochs of the Tertiary period may be longer than was formerly considered to be the case.

The geography of the earth is thought to have changed constantly during these billions of years. The paleogeography of the continental masses during the Paleozoic era is quite difficult to determine. Nevertheless, conclusions based upon paleomagnetic, paleoclimatic, and plate tectonic data indicate that 550 million years ago there were widely separated continental blocks that moved around and that by 260 to 240 million years ago these had grouped together into the supercontinent Pangaea (Figure 1-1).

Plate tectonics, or continental drift, originally proposed by Alfred Wegener in 1912, was accepted in the 1960s by earth scientists as a reasonable way of explaining how the geological features of the earth were and are formed. The theory also contributes to our knowledge and understanding of plant distribution and has helped to solve several mysteries. The theory of plate tectonics states that the continents are riding or "floating" on the outermost layer of the earth, the 15

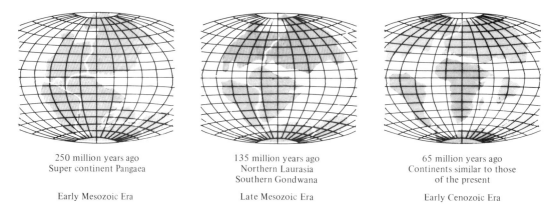

250 million years ago
Super continent Pangaea

Early Mesozoic Era

135 million years ago
Northern Laurasia
Southern Gondwana

Late Mesozoic Era

65 million years ago
Continents similar to those
of the present

Early Cenozoic Era

Figure 1-1   Position of the continental masses from the early Mesozoic era to the present.

Table 1-1 GEOLOGICAL TIMETABLE

Era	Period	Epoch	Years since beginning of period	Events
Cenozoic	Quarternary	Recent	10,000	Agriculture
		Pleistocene	1–1.8 million	Glaciation
	Tertiary	Pliocene	11 million	Diversification
		Miocene	25 million	of angiosperms
		Oligocene	40 million	
		Eocene	60 million	
		Paleocene	70 million	
Mesozoic	Cretaceous		135 million	Evolution of angiosperms
	Jurassic		180 million	Earliest angiosperms
	Triassic		230 million	Gymnosperm forests
Paleozoic	Permian		280 million	Conifers, cycads
	Carboniferous			
	Pennsylvanian		310 million	Primitive seed
	Mississippian		345 million	plants
	Devonian		405 million	Primitive vascular plants
	Silurian		425 million	Early land plants
	Ordovician		500 million	Diverse algae
	Cambrian		600 million	Marine algae
Precambrian			1.2 billion	Eukaryotic algae, fungi
			3–3.5 billion	Prokaryotes
			4.6–4.7 billion	Origin of earth

or so crustal plates. Some plates move past each other and others move over or under each other. The midocean ridge running north–south in the Atlantic Ocean is the site of upwelling of molten rock and contributes to the drifting apart of the North American and African plates and to the widening of the Atlantic Ocean. The Himalayan Mountain chain was created when India moved northward against the Asian continent and slipped (subducted) under it.

Pangaea began to split apart by about 225 to 200 million years ago into a massive southern area called Gondwana and an equally massive northern area called Laurasia (or Laurussia). Gondwana included the future areas of South America, Africa, Antarctica, Australia, and India. Laurasia was composed of the future land masses of North America, Europe, Asia, and Greenland. About 135 million years ago, Laurasia and Gondwana began to drift apart into continental masses, and by 65 million years ago the continents were pretty much as we see them today.

The effect of continental drift and mountain building and also of major climatic changes, such as the glaciation of the Pleistocene, has had an enormous impact on plant distribution. One example will illustrate this. Our modern food yams in the family Dioscoreaceae are divided into Old World and New World species. Ancestral Dioscoreaceae, thought to be among the earliest flowering plants (angiosperms), probably appeared in the early Jurassic in Southeast Asia and spread from there. Separation into Old World (Southeast Asia and Africa) and New World species (Caribbean) is considered to be due to the formation of the Atlantic Ocean after the Cretaceous period.

Fossil Record

The origin of cellular life occurred at least as long ago as 2 to 3 billion years, in the Precambrian era. There are fossils of bacteria-like forms in rock formations that are at least 2 billion years old. These organisms must have been prokaryotic (not having a true nucleus) and heterotrophic (requiring complex organic compounds of nitrogen and carbon for normal metabolism). Their source of energy, nitrogen and carbon compounds, was the organic soup of the primitive oceans—a rich supply of carbon-containing molecules accumulated during the previous millions of years of abiotic synthesis. The origin of bacteria may well be even earlier, since a microfossil very much like one of our modern blue-green algae has been discovered and its age radiocarbon dated at 3.4 billion years. Since bacteria are more primitive than blue-green algae, it can be argued that, if sufficiently old rocks could be found, fossils of bacteria should be discovered that date to more than 3.4 billion years ago.

Autotrophic bacteria, utilizing inorganic molecules as a source of energy, evolved, and at some point a few of these bacteria began to be able to use energy from the sun. A dramatic turning point took place about 2.8 billion years ago that made life a self-sustaining, permanent part of the sea when later autotrophic forms, resembling modern, blue-green algae, developed a type of photosynthesis that produced oxygen. Free oxygen, released into the atmosphere over millions of years, slowly increased in concentration. The availability of oxygen set the stage for the later evolution of aerobic forms of life on land.

The main fossil record for the eukaryotic algae begins at about the Precambrian-Cambrian time boundary. The first single-celled eukaryotic organism evolved some time between 1.5 and 1.0 billion years ago. During the Cambrian period prokaryotic and eukaryotic algae were clinging to moist rocks and soil surfaces, as were bacteria and simple fungi. While the blue-green algae have a fairly continuous geological record from the Precambrian, many of the other algal groups do not appear until the Cambrian or Ordovician periods. Near the end of the Silurian, small, simple plants made their first appearance on land, and from that time on there is a continuous record of progressive evolution of most major groups of land plants leading to the flowering plants (angiosperms).

The first land plants, now extinct, were certainly very small ones. Fossil materials, found in Europe, Siberia, and Canada, show a slender, leafless stem, less than 2 mm (¼ in.) in diameter. These and other early land plants must have been confined to swamps and other wet areas. Their internal organization (at least what we know of it) indicates that they could not survive or reproduce under dry conditions. From these simple beginnings evolved all higher plants —club mosses, horsetails, ferns, gymnosperms, flowering plants.

More complex land plants were evolving during the 50 million years of the Devonian. The forests of the late Devonian were quite varied and the Carboniferous was characterized by a tremendous increase in number and variety of plants. But the harsher, drier climate of the Permian led to a reduction in this diversity. The gymnosperms, capable of surviving and reproducing during this time of change in climate, became the dominant land plant during most of the Mesozoic era.

Sometime in the Mesozoic, the ancestral flowering plant evolved. A variety of geological events affected the development of angiosperms as well as their spread into a wide range of habitats. The supercontinent Pangaea began to split apart during the Triassic, mountain-building processes began, and the temperature of the earth was in a cooling phase. The Mesozoic era was also a time of extinction. Many cycads died out, all the *Ginkgos* died out except one relic species, *G. biloba,* and some of the conifers disappeared. The early Cenozoic era saw the evolution of angiosperm tree species and annual herbaceous grasses.

There are at least 300,000 plant species alive today of which some 220,000 are angiosperms. The angiosperms are divided into several hundred families. These plants come in every size and shape from trees that are as large as many gymnosperm trees to a floating aquatic plant that is only 1 mm ($\frac{1}{8}$ in.) in diameter. They are capable of growing and reproducing in every habitat on earth: wet, dry, temperate, arctic, tropical. There is little evidence that they were in existence much before the Jurassic, but since that time they have shown a remarkable spread throughout our land masses.

Life on Land

What was it that made the land a more difficult environment for plant survival than the ocean? The answer is the availability of water. In a moist or aquatic environment the organism is surrounded by water or a film of water. Dissolved in the water are the various inorganic minerals the plant requires for its nutrition (Chapter 7) as well as the carbon dioxide required for photosynthesis (Chapter 11) and the oxygen required for aerobic respiration (Chapter 12). In a land environment the water is in the soil, and the above-ground, or aerial, parts of the plant lose water by evaporation. The loss of water from the aerial parts of the plant was a most serious barrier to the adaptation to a land habitat. What permitted the plant to survive out of water and to become a successful land plant was the development of a relatively waterproof outer protective layer called a cuticle. The cuticle forms a solid covering, but contains holes or pores, the stomata, through which gases and water vapor easily diffuse. The size of the stomata is regulated by a pair of cells called the guard cells. Thus, the cuticle and stomatal apparatus form a relatively impervious barrier that can reduce water loss to a minimum and at the same time permit gas exchange.

A variety of evolutionary adaptations permitted land plants to grow larger and more complex. Specialized structures to absorb water and minerals from the soil developed; these were simple rhizoids in the bryophytes and true roots in higher plants. Larger size required a system to transport water and minerals from the soil to all parts of the plant and to transport the organic molecules formed in the leaves during photosynthesis to other parts of the plant. The higher plants evolved such a system, the vascular tissue (Chapter 4). Another adaptation was the ability to synthesize lignin, a compound that adds strength and rigidity to the cell wall. The ability to detect and to respond to gravity ensured that roots would grow downward into the soil where water is available and the stem with its attached leaves would grow upward into the atmosphere where light is available for photosynthesis. And lastly, unique reproductive structures developed. In aquatic habitats motile zoospores and motile gametes are produced by most algae. Although these had limited value for most land plants, motile male sperm persisted for millions of years. Only in the most highly evolved gymnosperms, the conifers, and in all angiosperms did a mechanism finally develop that was not dependent on water but still ensured that the male sperm cell would reach the female egg cell to complete the sexual reproductive phase. This independence from water is achieved through the male pollen grain. When the grain germinates, it forms the pollen tube containing the sperm nuclei (Chapter 3). All other land plants require water or a film of water to permit the motile sperm cell to swim to reach the egg.

HOW PLANTS ARE CLASSIFIED

Hierarchical Ranking

Mankind has for centuries kept records of useful plants and animals. A Chinese herbal attributed to Emperor Sheng-nung and thought to be about 5000 years old describes medicinal and food plants; an Assyrian herbal, at least 2500 years old, lists the names of more than 900 plants categorized into oil, drug, and vegetable crops. Numerous ancient books and treatises on plants have survived and become part of our botanical heritage.

Giving names to plants has always been something of a problem since it was recognized, early on, that to avoid confusion everyone should call a particular plant by the same name. Since Latin was the most universally known scholarly language, it was natural to use Latin for naming plants, and scientific names are still Latinized. But there was still no accepted system for assigning names. The name of one plant often contained several descriptive terms (referred to as a polynomial system) and names became quite clumsy. With the publication of *Species Plantarum* in 1753 by Carl Linnaeus, the naming of plants was put on a firm basis—the binomial system—with each species of plant having two names. Many of these names are still used today. A plant name is a combination of the genus name and a species name (or specific epithet). The specific epithet is frequently a descriptive term.

Within a genus there may be many species; for example, the phlox genus (*Phlox*) contains about 60 species, but only one species in that genus can have a particular specific epithet. There is only one *P. maculata,* wild sweet william. But the common name of another plant, *Dianthus barbatus,* is also sweet william. This example points up the value of scientific nomenclature—positive identification of a particular plant can be made even though two different plants have the same common name or one plant has several different common names.

The science of taxonomy is concerned with the concepts and methods of classification. A set of rankings, or hierarchies, has been devised: kingdom, division, class, order, family, genus, species. All green plants are usually placed in the plant kingdom. There are many divisions in this kingdom, the number depending upon which authority is followed. A group of classes makes up a division and so on for order, family, genus, and species. Names designating these hierarchies have specific endings so that their taxonomic rank is immediately apparent. For example, names of divisions end in *-phyta,* and family names end in *-aceae.* The names of eight families do not follow this rule and although new names with appropriate endings have been proposed, the use of these older, historical names continues (Table 1-2). Any of these taxonomic groupings is referred to as a taxon.

Genus and species names are written in italics or are underlined; common names and taxa other than genus or species appear in roman type or are not underlined. The genus name is always capitalized. The specific name is generally not capitalized, but occasionally it is. Hortus Third, the authority on plant names used in this book, gives the Latin name of corn (maize) as *Zea Mays,* but the specific epithet is sometimes lower cased as *Zea mays.* A species name is sometimes capitalized if it is the name of a person, a noun, or a non-Latin name, although this practice is optional. The abbreviation, sp., refers to a single species, and spp. refers to more than one species; neither is italicized nor underlined.

All of the rules regarding botanical names are codified in the International Code of Botanical Nomenclature and the rules governing horticultural names are found in the International Code of Nomenclature of Cultivated Plants. Both of these references are used worldwide by plant scientists.

The taxon genus may be defined as a group of closely related species having certain characteristics in common that indicate and reflect their similar genetic heritage. The most difficult taxon to define is that of the fundamental rank of species, and while the definition used here may not be totally satisfactory, it does present a modern conceptual framework. A species is the smallest group of individuals that are genetically similar in their characteristics, form interbreeding populations producing fertile offspring, and remain distinct from closely related species. Two closely related species may hybridize and the offspring of

Table 1-2   HISTORICAL NAMES OF EIGHT ANGIOSPERM FAMILIES AND PROPOSED NEW NAMES WITH STANDARD TAXON ENDINGS

Older name	Alternative name	Common name
Compositae	Asteraceae	Sunflower or aster
Cruciferae	Brassicaceae	Mustard
Gramineae	Poaceae	Grass
Guttiferae	Clusiaceae	Hypericum
Labiatae	Lamiaceae	Mint
Leguminosae	Fabaceae	Bean or pea
Palmae	Arecaceae	Palm
Umbelliferae	Apiaceae	Carrot

such an interspecific cross may or may not be fertile. The horticultural and agricultural geneticist takes advantage of this possibility of hybridization in attempting to produce better crop plants. Intergeneric crosses are much less usual, but they do occur between closely related genera; examples are found in the orchid family. An unusual, and potentially important, intergeneric hybrid is the cross between wheat and rye, *Triticale.* This newly created genus is a cereal grain that is capable of growing under unfavorable environmental conditions and that contains the high total protein level of wheat and the high level of the essential amino acid lysine of rye (Chapter 21).

Variety is a botanical taxon corresponding to the category of subspecies used by zoologists. A varietal population differs from other populations within the species, but obviously belongs to the same species. The usual reason for assigning varietal status is geographical separation of populations. The horticulturist, unfortunately, has been guilty of using the varietal designation very loosely.

Another taxonomic category is form. Members of one form within a species differ from other members of the species by only one or a very few visible characteristics, for example, a rare white-flowered form in a blue-flowered species.

Variety and form epithets appear in the following way. The actual epithet, or descriptive term, is written in italics or underlined, and the type of taxon is included. For example, cherry tomato is *Lycopersicon esculentum* var. *cerasiforme* and pear tomato is *L. esculentum* var. *pyriforme. Tillandsia fasciculata* var. *densispica* forma *alba* is the white form of a particular variety of wild pineapple. The names of hybrid plants are preceded by the multiplication sign (X) as in the hybrid genus of the painted feather bromeliad, X*Guzvriesea* or the hybrid species of house geranium, *Pelargonium* X*hortorum.*

These taxonomic terms designate natural or wild plants as well as domesticated ones. But one term, cultivar, is applicable only to cultivated plants—those valuable horticultural or agricultural plants which must be propagated in a manner so as to maintain their uniqueness. Cultivar is a contraction of "cultivated variety." It is abbreviated cv. (singular) or cvs. (plural). The first letter of the cultivar name is always capitalized, and the name itself appears in roman type and is not underlined. The cultivar name may also be set off by a single quotation marks: *Phaseolus vulgaris* 'Kentucky Wonder.' *Phaseolus vulgaris* cv. Kentucky Wonder is one of many pole-type green or kidney beans.

Another term, cultigen, is occasionally used. This refers to a cultivated plant that is known only as a cultivated form, the wild ancestor being lost or unknown (Chapter 2). Corn and cabbage are such cultigens.

Significance of Genetic Uniformity and Heterosis

Cultivars are propagated by two main methods. Those which are sexually reproduced by means of seeds include most common garden flowers, cereal grains, and most vegetable crops. When crop plants are propagated by means of seed, basic concepts and methods of breeding are employed, not only to maintain

Table 1-3   GROUPS OF _BRASSICA OLERACEA_

Group	Vegetable
Acephala	Kale, collards
Alboglabra	Chinese kale
Botrytis	Broccoli, cauliflower
Capitata	Cabbage, head cabbage, savoy cabbage
Gemmifera	Brussels sprouts, sprouts
Gongylodes	Kohlrabi
Italica	Italian broccoli, asparagus broccoli
Tronchuda	Portuguese kale, tronchuda kale

their uniformity, but also to improve them. Plants grown from hybrid seed (interspecific or other crosses) may show enhanced size, more robustness, and increased yield, that is, hybrid vigor, or heterosis.

Hybrid seed is often designated in seed catalogs as F_1, which means that these are first filial generation offspring resulting from a cross between two parents differing in one or more characteristics. Most of the cultivars of corn grown in the United States today are F_1 hybrids as are some other cereal grains, vegetable crops such as tomatoes, and some annual garden flowers. Plants grown from seeds obtained from these F_1 plants will not show the same characteristics as the hybrid parent. Principles of classical Mendelian genetics explain this; this next generation of plants may show the hereditary characters of the original parents, not of the F_1 hybrid. The uniformity of the parent plants is carefully maintained in order to cross them yearly for obtaining the new crop of F_1 seed.

Cultivars propagated vegetatively using cuttings, grafts, or other asexual methods (Chapter 15) are called _clones._ Examples include potatoes, rhubarb roots, asparagus roots, and apple and other fruit trees. Grafts between tomato and potato can be made and are called pomato or topato. The progeny are genetically uniform and have the same hereditary characteristics as the individual source plant.

Some species of cultivated plants have many cultivars and similar cultivars are put together in a category called a group. For example, the cultivated varieties of beet (_Beta vulgaris)_ are divided into two groups. The cicla group are those cultivars used as leafy vegetables, including leaf beet, spinach beet, chard, and swiss chard. The crassa group are those grown primarily for their roots including garden beet, red beet, yellow beet, sugar beet, beetroot, mangel, mangel-worzel, and mangold. Cultivars of cole vegetables (_Brassica oleracea)_ have also been so categorized (Table 1-3).

MAJOR GROUPS OF PLANTS

Phylogenetic Classification

Living organisms were traditionally divided into two categories or kingdoms: plants and animals. As our knowledge increased and as technological advances, such as the electron microscope, enhanced our ability to see within cells, it became apparent that the traditional division was too simple. In fact, instead of two kingdoms, three, four, or even five have been proposed. The ideal is to group together similar organisms using all available information and then place these groups into larger groups. This natural or phylogenetic classification will then reflect evolutionary development from primitive to advanced organisms. Table 1-4 summarizes such a phylogenetic classification of plants.

In contrast are artificial classification schemes which are arbitrary, but may be very convenient. Vegetables may be classified according to their edible parts. Flowers are classified according to their bloom time or whether they are annuals or perennials or whether they are herbaceous or woody. Trees may be classified as to whether they are evergreen or deciduous or hardwood or softwood.

Some Characteristics of Major Plant Groups

Viruses Classification of the plant kingdom does not include the viruses because they are not cellular organisms (the cytosol is not surrounded by a membrane; see Chapter 4), and they do not exhibit characteristics that could be used to position them with similar organisms. They have only one type of nucleic acid and do not have a true metabolism. They are not plants. It is, however, appropriate to consider them since they are a major cause of plant diseases (Chapter 10).

Viruses are so small that they are below the limit of the resolving power of the light microscope and therefore can be seen only through the electron microscope. Plant viruses, with rare exceptions, contain ribonucleic acid (RNA); examples include tobacco mosaic virus, turnip yellows mosaic virus, tomato bushy stunt virus, wound tumor virus. A virus that contains deoxyribonucleic acid (DNA) is cauliflower mosaic virus. The plant viruses are among the smallest of viruses and primarily parasitize the nucleus of infected cells. A newly discovered category of viral plant pathogens, viroids, are one-tenth the size of the smallest plant virus; these include potato spindle tuber virus and chrysanthemum stunt virus.

Prokaryota Bacteria and blue-green algae (cyanobacteria), the prokaryotes, share a set of characteristics that distinguish them from all other living organisms. Their cells do not contain a true nucleus because a membrane does not surround the nuclear material nor is protein combined with the nucleic acid molecules. Prokaryotic cells do not contain other major organelles (Chapter 4), although enzymes or pigments associated with membranes within the cytoplasm confer on these regions specific functions such as aerobic metabolism (Chapter 12) or photosynthesis (Chapter 11).

Bacteria Bacterial cells are typically round, rod-shaped, or curved. With rare exceptions, the living protoplast is surrounded by a rigid cell wall containing complex molecules. Cellulose is not found in the cell wall.

Bacteria, as a group, show the greatest ability to survive unusual environ-

Table 1-4 CLASSIFICATION OF PLANTS

Taxonomic categories	Common name	Number of species
Kingdom plantae		
Prokaryota		
Division Schizophyta	Bacteria	1,600
Division Cyanophyta	Blue-green algae	1,500
Eukaryota		
Algae		
Division Euglenophyta	Euglenoids	450
Division Chrysophyta	Diatoms, golden algae	6,300
Division Xanthophyta	Yellow-green algae	5,800
Division Pyrrophyta	Dinoflagellates	1,000
Division Phaeophyta	Brown algae	1,500
Division Rhodophyta	Red algae	4,000
Division Chlorophyta	Green algae, desmids	7,000
The Embryophytes		
Nonvascular plants		
Division Bryophyta	Mosses, liverworts, hornworts	23,600
Vascular plants		
Primitive vascular plants		
Division Psilophyta	Whisk ferns	3
Division Lycophyta	Club mosses, spike mosses, quillworts	1,200
Division Equisetophyta	Horsetails	40
Advanced vascular plants		
Division Polypodiophyta	Ferns	10,000
Seed plants		
Gymnosperms		
Division Cycadophyta	Cycads	100
Division Ginkgophyta	Ginkgo	1
Division Coniferophyta	Conifers	520
Angiosperms		
Division Angiospermae (Magnoliophyta)	Flowering plants	
Class Dicotyledonae (Magnoliopsida)	Dicots	165,400
Class Monocotyledonae (Liliopsida)	Monocots	54,000
Kingdom fungi		
Division Myxomycota	Slime molds	500
Division Eumycota	True fungi	100,000
Subdivision Mastigomycotina	Water molds, damping-off fungi, downy mildews	
Subdivision Zygomycotina	Bread molds	
Subdivision Ascomycotina	Sac (cup) fungi, morels, truffles, powdery mildews	
Subdivision Basidiomycotina	Club fungi, rusts, smuts, mushrooms, puffballs	
Subdivision Deuteromycotina	Imperfect fungi	

mental conditions. Most microorganisms grow and reproduce in a milieu where the pH is between 5.5 and 7.5, but the thiobacilli can grow at a pH below 3.0 and urea-decomposing bacteria grow only above pH 8.0. Some bacteria survive a temperature above 80° C (176° F); these thermophiles (heat-loving) are inhabitants of hot springs and compost piles. Most organisms have an absolute requirement for molecular oxygen as aerobic respiration is their only method for obtaining energy (Chapter 12). Others, the obligate anaerobes, are poisoned by oxygen. Some anaerobes are more tolerant and can grow in the presence or absence of oxygen.

Bacteria must find in their environment nutrients which, when broken down, provide energy to be used to synthesize their own unique molecules. The variety of molecules bacteria can utilize range from simple inorganic ones, such as ammonia or hydrogen, to complex sugars. Those bacteria which utilize inorganic molecules in the presence of oxygen are called aerobic chemolithotrophs; those which carry out their reactions in the absence of oxygen are anaerobic chemolithotrophs. Several species of bacteria that participate in the nitrogen cycle (Chapter 7) belong to these two groups. Most species of bacteria are aerobic or anaerobic chemoorganotrophs, that is, they derive their primary energy from organic, carbon-containing compounds (Chapter 12).

Bacteria are the causal agents of diseases in plants as well as in people. Some species can fix atmospheric nitrogen as well as participate in the nitrogen cycle.

Blue-green algae (cyanobacteria)   Blue-green algae are prokaryotes and are thus related to the bacteria because of similarities in their internal organization. They are, as are the bacteria, primitive organisms. They all have chlorophyll *a* and are capable of a type of photosynthesis exactly like that of the eukaryotic plants (Chapter 11). Their yellow pigments are similar to those found in eukaryotic plants. The cell wall of these organisms is similar to that of the bacteria, but it may contain cellulose. Each cell has a colorless central area where DNA is found and a peripheral area where photosynthetic pigments are located. The simplest species, referred to as cyanoplankton, are unicellular and free-floating; many species are filamentous. They show no true sexual reproduction, but have a variety of ways of reproducing asexually, forming several types of reproductive structures that are resistant to drying out. One such reproductive structure is called a heterocyst. Some species are able to fix nitrogen and in those species that form a heterocyst, the nitrogen fixation occurs specifically in this structure (Chapter 7). A few species are thermophiles growing in hot springs, but they do not survive as high a temperature as do the thermophilic bacteria.

The blue-green algae are a source of food for marine and fresh water animals. They are also a source of pollution; when their growth rate is high, forming "blooms," they can give a disagreeable taste and odor to water, and two species form poisonous compounds.

Eukaryota   The algae, fungi, higher plants, and animals are called eukaryotes because the hereditary nuclear material is associated with protein and is surrounded by a membrane that separates this organelle, the nucleus, from the cytoplasm of the cell. The nuclear material condenses into structures called chromosomes which divide in a process referred to as mitosis. A variety of other organelles are also present in the eukaryotic cell (Chapter 4).

Eukaryotic algae The eukaryotic algae, varying in size from the small, single-celled greens to the gigantic brown kelps, are found in a variety of moist or aquatic habitats from tree trunks to the relatively shallow waters along the edge of the continents. They all have chlorophyll *a* and one other type of chlorophyll, *b, c, d,* or *e.* Their cells contain a variety of yellow pigments and algae in some divisions also have other pigments which give a characteristic color to the cell. Sexual reproduction is common.

A few green, a few brown, and many red algae are sources of food for people. The Pyrrophyta and Chrysophyta are members of the phytoplankton and provide food for animals from microscopic invertebrates to whales. The kelps are harvested and used as cattle feed and as a soil mulch. The bulk of our atmospheric oxygen comes from the photosynthesis of marine algae. Eukaryotic algae have many industrial uses. Diatomaceous earth (the silica-containing cell walls of diatoms) is a fine abrasive in silver polish and toothpaste and a filter for liquids (beer). Emulsifiers and stabilizers in various foods are derived from brown algae; and thickeners, carrageenan and agar, are products of red algae. Members of two divisions, Pyrrophyta and Chrysophyta, form poisonous compounds. The red tide organism, a dinoflagellate, forms a toxin that is poisonous for shellfish and, ultimately, for people who eat such shellfish.

Fungi The fungi are put in a separate kingdom because they do not have chlorophyll and cannot photosynthesize and thus may not be plants in the usual sense of that term. Some fungi are parasitic, obtaining their nutrients from living organisms, but most are saprobic, utilizing already dead organisms as a source of food. The body of the fungus is called a thallus; it may be a single cell, as in yeasts, or a tube filled with cytoplasm called a filament or hypha. Most fungi are filamentous. Their cell wall may contain cellulose or, more usually, chitin, which is also found in insects.

Fungi are important decomposers, playing a basic role in nutrient recycling processes and humus formation (Chapter 5). Thermophilic fungi are essential decomposers in compost piles and rotting manure. Fungi associated with the roots of most higher plants are called mycorrhizal fungi (Chapter 6); some mushrooms (Basidiomycotina) are important mycorrhizal partners. Some species of fungi live symbiotically in association with species of blue-green algae or green algae; this partnership forms the organism called a lichen.

Fungi cause a number of diseases in plants (Chapter 10). Beer and wine are end products of alcoholic fermentation by some species of yeasts, and one species of yeast is used in baking. A few fungi are eaten for their delicate flavor or for their hallucinogenic effects; some are poisonous. Single-cell protein (SCP), derived mostly from yeasts, is a high quality protein with good levels of B vitamins; it is being used in animal feed. A few fungi synthesize poisonous substances called mycotoxins; one, aflatoxin, is a cancer-causing compound.

Embryophytes   The remaining divisions of plants (all eukaryotes) are categorized as embryophytes because of the common characteristic of the presence of an embryo in the process of reproduction. The embryo is formed as a result of sexual reproduction and is protected by and retained within a jacket of cells within or on the female parent. This evolutionary development provided a significant increase in the organism's opportunity for survival on land.

Other general characteristics of embryophytes include chlorophylls *a* and *b,* an array of yellow pigments, multicellular reproductive structures, and a sexual reproductive cycle in which two phases or generations, the gametophyte and the sporophyte, alternate with each other. In all embryophytes except the conifers and the flowering plants, successful sexual reproduction requires the presence of water to enable the motile male sperm to swim to the female egg.

Nonvascular Plants: Bryophytes   Mosses, liverworts, and hornworts form the Division Bryophyta. They are all rather small and generally live in shady, moist habitats. They dry out easily, becoming shriveled and brown, but if water is again available, their tissues quickly absorb it, and they seem miraculously to come back to life.

These plants do not have vascular tissues, the specialized systems for transporting water and food (Chapter 4). The typical green leafy bryophytes seen in shady woods are the gametophyte generation and, if carefully observed, the brownish or greenish sporophyte attached to the gametophyte may be seen.

Bryophytes are among the first plants to colonize bare rocks and soil and, when they die, provide organic material in which other plants may grow. They are easily killed by environmental pollutants and are sensitive indicators for such compounds. Peat mosses are commonly used in gardening as a way of enhancing the waterholding capacity of sandy soil (Chapter 5). Peat coal, formed by peat mosses, is still burned as a low-grade fuel.

Vascular Plants   Vascular plants, or tracheophytes, are those advanced plants that possess xylem and phloem tissues (vascular tissues), a relatively recent evolutionary development. These transporting systems gave a tremendous advantage to these plants and were instrumental in their success in a land environment as well as permitting them to grow to such a large size as some coniferous and flowering trees.

Primitive vascular plants   Included in this general category are the Psilophyta, the whisk ferns; Lycophyta, which includes club mosses, quillworts, and spike mosses; and Equisetophyta, the horsetails (or scouring rushes). Whisk ferns have little or no economic value, but living and extinct species show important evolutionary relationships. Club mosses were prominent in the geological past, some fossil species being large and treelike, and were important in coal formation. Living spike mosses occur in a wide range of habitats and have some economic importance as ornamental house plants. The horsetails were also more prominent in the geological past than they are today and, along with the lycopods, were important in the formation of coal. Living species are found in moist environments; they have little or no economic value. Their other common name, scouring rushes, comes from their use as an abrasive, their cell walls containing silica.

Advanced vascular plants: Polypodiophyta   The many species of ferns are widely distributed in a variety of habitats, although most are found in the subtropics and tropics. They can be recognized by their large fronds or leaves and the coiled appearance of their immature leaves, called fiddleheads. Ferns have economic importance; fiddleheads of some species are considered a delicacy; the trunks of tropical tree ferns are employed in house building; osmunda fiber is used for growing bromeliads and orchids in greenhouses; and many are important foliage plants in homes and are important components of shade gardens.

Seed Plants: Gymnosperms   The Cycadophyta (cycads) Ginkgophyta (ginkgo), and Coniferophyta (conifers) are grouped together as gymnosperms, plants that form seeds (structures containing an embryo) that are covered by only a few layers of tissue, the seed coats. Thus, gymnosperms form unprotected or "naked" seeds.

The cycads have a tropical to subtropical distribution; a few species such as *Cycas revoluta,* the Sago palm, are important house and garden plants. Ginkgo, the only surviving representative of the division, is an important ornamental tree, particularly useful for polluted environments, and is grown worldwide. Conifers were the source of most of the world's coal. They are still distributed widely but particularly in temperate regions. They are the most important of the gymnosperms, being sources of lumber, turpentine, paper pulp, Christmas trees, and landscape plants.

Angiosperms   The largest and most advanced group of seed plants is the Angiospermae (Magnoliophyta), the angiosperms or flowering plants. The evolution of a new structure, the flower, contributed to the outstanding success of this division. The flower contains an ovary, inside of which the seeds are formed and mature (Chapter 3). The enclosure of the seeds by the ovary wall added a new dimension of protection, a major factor in the survival of the organism and also a factor in expanding its distribution. Birds and other animals eat fruit and seeds, the seeds pass through their digestive tracts unharmed, and they are deposited at a distance from the parent plant. A portion of the seed is nutritive tissue (more than is found in the gymnosperm seed) which provides sufficient food for the germination and early growth of the seedling until it is large enough to engage in photosynthesis and survive on its own.

The flower, a thing of beauty to people, has intrinsic value in the success of the angiosperms. Flowers form pollen, as do cones of conifers. Pollen grains, containing male sperm nuclei, are carried by the wind or by animals to the female part of the structure (Chapter 3). The evolutionary development of the pollen grain meant that the angiosperms became independent of water for their sexual reproduction. In species in which pollen distribution depends upon the wind, as in many tree species and the grasses, the flowers tend to be small,

Table 1-5 CHARACTERISTICS OF THE DICOTYLEDONAE AND MONOCOTYLEDONAE CLASSES OF ANGIOSPERMS

Characteristic	Dicots	Monocots
Seed leaves or cotyledons	2 (rare: 1, 3, 4)	1
Venation of leaves	Usually net pattern	Usually parallel pattern
Cambium	Present	Absent
Vascular bundles in stem	Arranged as ring	Generally scattered
Flower parts (or multiples of basic number)	Sets of 5, less often 4	Sets of 3
Mature root system	Tap or fibrous	Fibrous
Habit	Woody (about half)	Rarely woody

inconspicuous, and not brightly colored. Species that rely upon animals—from carrion flies to hummingbirds—tend to have large, brightly colored, showy, and odiferous flowers, an attractant for their pollinators.

A large body of information has accumulated on pollinating animals and the plants they visit. The primary pollinating agent for many flowering plants, such as fruit trees and berries, is the honeybee which collects both nectar and pollen. Hummingbirds patronize, almost exclusively, those tubular, bright red to orange flowers that form copious amounts of nectar. Carrion flies and beetles are attracted to, and hence pollinate, such flowers as the starfish plant *(Stapelia)* which produces an intense odor of rotting flesh.

Another factor contributing to the success of the flowering plants was the development of vessel cells in the water-conducting system (see Chapter 4). This type of cell is analogous to a water pipe capable of moving large amounts of water from the soil, through the stem, and into the leafy area.

The angiosperms are divided into two groups, the dicots (Dicotyledonae) and the monocots (Monocotyledonae), on the basis of a number of distinctive visible and microscopic attributes (Table 1-5). The number of seed leaves, or cotyledons, is the principal distinguishing trait, although the type of leaf venation is the most readily recognized.

The angiosperms are the most successful of the land plants, the most numerous in terms of numbers of species, and the source of food, fiber, drugs, shelter, and clothing. The next section of this chapter will explore the characteristics and contributions of the families of flowering plants most used by humans.

ECONOMICALLY IMPORTANT FAMILIES

Structural Characteristics

A taxon made up of related genera of flowering plants is called a family, distinguished from all other families primarily on the basis of the characteristics of flowers and fruits (Chapter 3). Other informational characteristics are less consistent, but nevertheless useful for constructing a phylogenetic tree of the various families and determining the closeness of their relation to one another. These include habit (tree, shrub, or herb), structure and arrangement of leaves, size, unique chemical compounds, and others. There are 315 dicot and 65 monocot families and most plants are easily categorized by their general appearance: grasses (Gramineae), cacti (Cactaceae), legumes (Leguminosae), palms (Palmae). The identification of a family is a shorthand way of stating the criteria which differentiate one from another. If a flowering plant is a legume, a member of the pea or pulse family, we know that it is likely to have a butterfly-like flower, a pod-type fruit, and roots with nodules in which nitrogen fixation occurs.

Knowing criteria for distinguishing families has predictive value for determining the possible usefulness of other species or those newly brought into cultivation. Members of the spurge family (Euphorbiaceae) often contain a milky juice. For example, the Para rubber tree *(Hevea brasiliensis)* forms abundant amounts of latex, which is processed into natural rubber. Are there as yet undiscovered euphorbs which could be so utilized? Milkweed family members (Asclepiadaceae) also have a milky sap; the nightshade or potato family (Solanaceae) has many species that form alkaloids with medicinal or poisonous properties. The mustard family (Cruciferae) is noted for its pungent herbs and oil seeds. The pea family (Leguminosae) is of economic importance because many of its members are a source of high quality proteins and oils. The grass family (Gramineae) is the most important of all flowering plant families; the cereal grains are the major source of food for people.

There are many families in which only one or a few species or only one genus is of agricultural or horticultural importance. In others potential uses are as yet unrecognized or undeveloped. For example, members of the amaranth family (Amaranthaceae) are grown mostly as ornamentals, such as Joseph's Coat *(Amaranthus tricolor)* or green vegetables, such as Love-Lies-Bleeding *(A. caudatus),* or are weeds, such as tumbleweed *(A. albus).* But the grain amaranths (several species) are little utilized, even though their seeds, ground for use as a flour or cereal, have a good flavor, high nutritional value, and a yield which compares favorably with corn (maize) and other true cereals.

Selected Economically Important Families

Gramineae   The grass family contains some 10,000 species. They are, for the most part, annual or perennial herbs. Their round stems have hollow internodes but solid nodes. Their quite inconspicuous flowers are grouped to form spikes, racemes, or panicles (Chapter 3). The fruit is a grain, or caryopsis. The endosperms of the seeds contain starch and in some cases protein and oil; the seeds have a low water content and therefore a long storage life. The cereal grains belong to this family as do sugar cane, bamboo, and the grasses, important as forage crops and for lawns. The importance of the cereal grains is due directly to the storage products found in the seeds—high quality carbohydrate, protein, and oil.

Wheat and rice are the most valuable of the cereal grains as a source of food (Chapter 21). Wheat, derived from wild grass ancestors (Chapter 2), has been used as a food grain for more than 10,000 years, and there are today more than 17,000 cultivated varieties. During this long history the wild characteristic of seed dispersal (shattering) has been eliminated by selection and breeding. Wheat, along with other cereal grains, depends upon people for its dispersal. Wheat is highly valued in making bread—the staff of life—because of its high protein content (8–15 percent), while rice has a lower protein level. Corn (maize), sorghum, and other grains are utilized in the United States mostly to feed livestock; and corn, because of its oily embryo, yields high levels of edible oils.

Cereal grains show environmental adaptability and grow over a wide range of climates. Rye and oats tolerate a wider temperature range than do wheat, corn, or barley; barley will grow in salty, irrigated areas (Chapter 5) where other cereal grains will not survive. Millets and sorghum are adapted to arid regions.

Other species of this family—temperate, tropical, and subtropical grasses —are food for wild animals as well as domesticated range animals (cattle, sheep) that roam freely on natural grassland areas. Several species of grasses are now being deliberately planted to reestablish overgrazed natural grasslands. Horticulturally important species include lawn grasses. A few species of bamboo and certain grasses are grown as ornamentals. Bamboo is important as a building material because its stems become woody.

Leguminosae The pea family, about 13,000 species, is made up of three subfamilies or three separate families depending upon your taxonomic persuasion. All three subfamilies form a podlike fruit. Most of the economically important species belong to one group, the subfamily Papilionoideae (or family Fabaceae). The plants are trees, shrubs, or herbs; the cotyledons are the storage site for carbohydrate, high levels of protein (up to 45 percent), and oil. Most members of the family form nodules on their roots in which symbiotic bacteria fix nitrogen. The host plant can use this nitrogen for making protein and thus is less dependent on nitrogen fertilizer (Chapter 7). Nitrogen-containing compounds not taken up by the plant remain in the soil, a not inconsiderable factor in maintaining soil fertility.

The seeds of soybean, bean, pea, lentil, peanut, broad bean, chick-pea, and other peas and beans are highly important as human food; soybeans are economically valuable as a source of oils and protein (see Chapter 22). Many species are grown for their seed and leafy parts as livestock fodder or as forage legumes such as alfalfa (lucerne) and various clovers. Some legumes are grown as cover crops to prevent soil erosion, to keep out weeds, to add organic matter to the soil when plowed back in as a green manure, and to add nitrogen from their root nodules and vegetative parts. A few legumes are used as ornamentals such as sweet pea, lupines, wisteria, and several trees including black locust, honey locust, redbud, and carob. Some species are the source of the insecticide rotenone.

Solanaceae Members of the nightshade or potato family, about 2000 species, are mostly herbaceous, although some are shrubs and small trees. The fruit is a berry or capsule. The Irish or white potato tuber, an underground stem, is an important vegetable. Tobacco leaves are made into cigars and cigarettes which are smoked for their nicotine effect. Other members are economically important for their fruits. These include the most popular garden "vegetables"—the tomato, eggplant, and the various capsicum peppers (sweet, chili, and hot peppers). Several species are sources of medically useful alkaloids such as belladonna from which atropine is derived. Others contain toxic alkaloids including jimson weed, deadly nightshade, black nightshade, henbane, and Jerusalem cherry. Several are popular garden plants: flowering tobacco, petunia, butterfly flower, Chinese lantern plant, and bush violet.

Rosaceae The rose family is composed of 2000 species of herbs, shrubs, and trees growing mostly in north temperate areas. It is usually divided into four subfamilies on the basis of the type of fruit formed: follicle or capsule, pome, achene, or drupe (Chapter 3). Many of the fruits are commercially important. The pome fruits include pear and apple; the drupe or stone fruits include almond, peach, cherry, several plums, apricot, and loquat; and the achenes in or on a fleshy receptacle include red and black raspberry, blackberry, and strawberry. Horticulturally important representatives are the many popular roses and cinquefoil; the shrubby ones include bridal wreath, firethorn, hawthorn, and flowering quince. Ornamental trees include mountain ash, serviceberry, flowering almond, and flowering crabs.

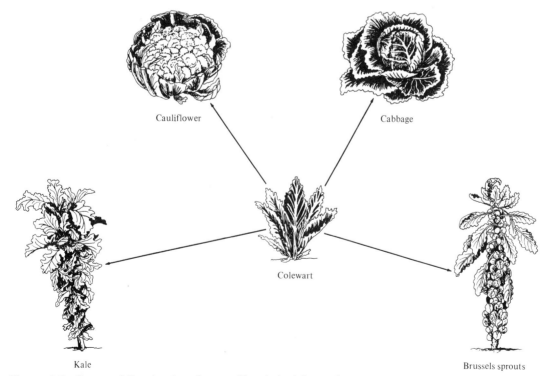

Figure 1-2 Groups of *Brassica*, the cole vegetables, derived from colewort.

Cruciferae The mustard family contains 3200 species of annual, biennial, and perennial herbs. They have a pungent or bitter flavor due to the sulfur-containing compounds in their watery juice. The fruit is a silique or silicle (Chapter 3). Black mustard seeds are ground to make salad mustard, and nasturtium is a source of mustard oil. Many important food crops are members of this family including the cole vegetables: cabbage, cauliflower, broccoli, and others (Figure 1-2). Garden radishes, horseradish, and watercress are also important. A number of ornamentals are garden favorites including honesty, stocks, candytuft, rock cress, lady's smock or meadow cress, wallflower, sweet alyssum, and penny cress. Weeds that can become noxious pests are weedy mustards, shepherd's purse, and peppergrass.

SUPPLEMENTARY READINGS

Bailey, L. H., E. Z. Bailey, and Staff of the L. H. Bailey Hortorium. 1976. *Hortus Third.* Macmillan, New York.

Bamback, R. K., C. R. Scotese, and A. M. Ziegler. 1980. Before Pangaea: The geographies of the Paleozoic world. *Amer. Sci.* 68:26–38.

Coombes, A. J. 1985. *Dictionary of Plant Names.* ISBS/Timber Press, Beaverton, Ore.

Cronquist, A. 1971. *Introductory Botany.* 2nd ed. Harper & Row, New York.

Ferguson, N. 1984. *Ferguson's Garden Plant Directory.* Pan Books, Hingham, Mass.

Gilmour, J. S. L. (ed.). 1969. *International Code of Nomenclature of Cultivated Plants.* International Bureau for Plant Taxonomy and Nomenclature of the International Association for Plant Taxonomy. Utrecht, Netherlands.

Grant, W. 1984. *Plant Biosystematics.* Academic Press, New York.

Hallam, A. 1975. Alfred Wegener and the hypothesis of continental drift. *Sci. Amer.* 232:88–97.

Healy, B. J. 1972. *A Gardener's Guide to Plant Names.* Scribner, New York.

Heiser, C. B., Jr. 1981. *Seed to Civilization.* 2nd ed. Freeman, San Francisco.

Heywood, V. H. 1974. *Flowering Plants of the World.* Mayflower Books, New York.

Hulse, J. H., and D. Spurgeon. 1974. Triticale. *Sci. Amer.* 231(2):72–80.

Jeffrey, C. 1982. *An Introduction to Plant Taxonomy.* 2nd ed. Cambridge University Press, New York.

Jones, S. B., Jr., and A. E. Luchsinger. 1979. *Plant Systematics.* McGraw-Hill, New York.

Little, R. J., and C. E. Jones. 1980. *A Dictionary of Botany.* Van Nostrand Reinhold, New York.

Parker, S. P. (ed.). 1982. *Synopsis and Classification of Living Organisms.* McGraw-Hill, New York.

Radford, A. E., W. C. Dickinson, J. R. Massey, and C. R. Bell. 1974. *Vascular Plant Systematics.* Harper & Row, New York.

Ray, P. M., T. A. Steeves, and S. A. Fultz. 1983. *Botany.* Saunders, Philadelphia.

Sclater, J. R., and T. Tapscott. 1979. The history of the Atlantic. *Sci. Amer.* 240:156–175.

Tarling, D. H. 1980. *Continental Drift and Biological Evolution.* Carolina Biology Reader, Burlington, N.C.

C H A P T E R 2

ORIGINS OF
CULTIVATED PLANTS

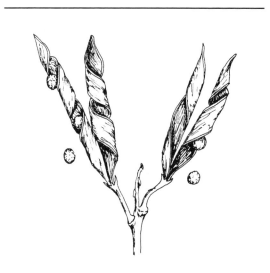

ORIGIN OF AGRICULTURE

Invention of Agriculture

Fifty thousand or more years ago bands of ancient Manlike creatures wandered throughout the Old World. We know they could make tools since hand axes and flake tools have been found by archeologists throughout a vast area of Africa and western Eurasia. The size and shape of these tools are thought to correspond to "food gathering" practices; tools that cut or dug were of value to the gatherers in obtaining sufficient quantities of food. Finally, between 15,000 and 10,000 years B.P. (before the present) some of the more settled bands or communities of people arrived at the threshold of food production—deliberate planting (Table 2-1).

Our present knowledge indicates that primitive agriculture developed in the Old World. The impetus was not a shortage of food; starving people do not have the time or energy for the necessary experimentation. Improvement of those wild plants gathered for food occurred when people had sufficient food and the leisure time for trial-and-error testing. The primitive people who changed from gathering to planting were probably not nomadic hunters. They most likely were already living in woodland areas as settled bands or groups, hunting game and

Table 2-1   EARLIEST EVIDENCE OF AGRICULTURAL DEVELOPMENT

Date (years B.P.)	Culture period	Technological developments	Agricultural developments
2,000	Bronze		Planting of *Triticum durum,* durum wheat 2,000 B.P.
4,000			
6,000	Final Neolithic 6,000–5,000		*T. dicoccum,* emmer wheat 6,000
	Late Neolithic 6,500–6,000	Bronze casting	*T. monococcum,* einkorn wheat 6,750
	Middle Neolithic 7,000–6,5000	Copper metallurgy	*T. aestivum,* bread wheat 7,500
8,000	Early Neolithic 8,000–7,000	Sophisticated pottery decorations	Irrigation Rice
	Upper Mesolithic 9,250–8,000		Planting of barley
10,000	Lower Mesolithic 10,333–9,250		Early farming Plant and animal domestication
12,000		Invention of pottery	
20,000	Upper Paleolithic 20,000–10,300	Edge-ground stone tools	Hunting and gathering
30,000		Many wooden tools	
40,000	Lower to Middle Paleolithic	Simple stone tools	

catching fish in nearby rivers. It was a small step to the deliberate planting for a later harvest.

Primitive agriculture required well-diversified land area and a suitable climate. Such suitable sites are areas where the soil does not need drainage or irrigation, eliminating bogs and deserts as likely sites of the earliest agriculture, and where the soil can be broken with primitive tools. Agriculture most probably began in wooded areas, where the soil was easier to break or cultivate, than in grasslands, where the root mass formed by grasses is difficult to penetrate. (The western grasslands in the United States were not opened up to agriculture until the invention of a plow with a sharp steel blade, the moldboard plow originated by John Deere.)

The early farmers took advantage of asexual or vegetative reproduction, planting pieces of the desired plant to establish a variety of crops useful for both food and fiber. A large number of flowering plants, both monocots and dicots, are known to be ancient and easily propagated vegetatively. Early vegecultures grew bananas, aroids, yams, palms, vines, breadfruit, citrus, persimmon, and others. These plants, while good sources of carbohydrate, are generally low in protein and fat; fish and small game were a necessary addition to the diet. Primitive vegeculture eventually led to primitive agriculture—the deliberate planting of seeds. When protein-rich seeds were used as a source of food, dependence on animal protein decreased.

The invention of agriculture probably occurred several times. Among the earliest archeological explorations were those in the Fertile Crescent, the well-drained, hilly upland areas east of the Mediterranean including the present western Israel, western Lebanon, western Syria, southeastern Turkey, northeastern Iraq, and southeastern Iran (Figure 2-1). The area of the Fertile Crescent has been explored intensively, and we know a great deal about the life of the people inhabiting the region. An agricultural revolution occurred there about 10,000 years B.P. Jarmō, a village in eastern Iraq, was inhabited at least as early as 9000 years B.P. Kernels of carbonized wheat were found which resemble kernels of wild wheat growing there today. Carbonized barley grains, similar to modern barley, were also found. Carbonized wheat grains also have been discovered in northern Syria, and these are even older, having an estimated age of 10,000 years B.P.

It was thought initially that the Fertile Crescent was the cradle of early agriculture. It now appears that the earliest agricultural revolution took place in southeast Asia where settled villages dating to perhaps 15,000 years B.P. have been found. Agriculture in the New World was invented independently some thousands of years ago, after migrating bands of people crossed the land bridge connecting eastern Siberia to western Alaska. The Caribbean basin is the most probable site of the earliest farming villages, where agricultural activity dates to 5000 to 9000 years B.P.

The information gleaned from both Old World and New World archeological sites shows that there was a long transition time from gatherers to the earliest vegeculturists and eventually to agriculturists. Each geographical region domesticated its own unique food plants, a reflection of the indigenous or endemic plants available to the inhabitants. But all show several similar characteristics that

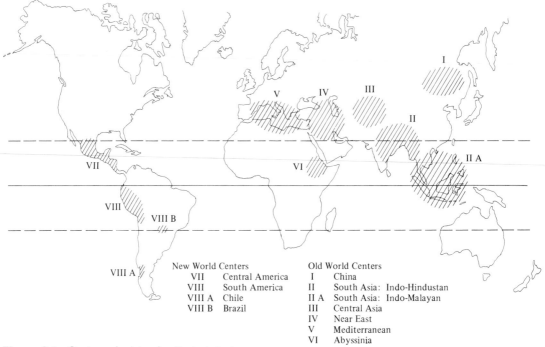

New World Centers
VII	Central America
VIII	South America
VIII A	Chile
VIII B	Brazil

Old World Centers
I	China
II	South Asia: Indo-Hindustan
II A	South Asia: Indo-Malayan
III	Central Asia
IV	Near East
V	Mediterranean
VI	Abyssinia

Figure 2-1   Centers of origin of cultivated plants.

undoubtedly played a major role in the establishment of permanent settlements: a mild climate, good soil, and alternating rainy and dry seasons.

Origin and Development of Cultivated Plants

During the early years of the twentieth century the Russian geneticist N. I. Vavilov explored the world looking for potential new cultivars or new crops to enhance the food-growing potential of his country. On the basis of this undertaking, he described eight centers of species formation. These were regions where various plants were first cultivated and therefore, in his view, must be endemic. They were areas of natural distribution (that is, areas in which the plants grew naturally) and where natural hybridization seemed to be occurring. The modern geography of plants shows that the distribution of plant species is not uniform. An unusually large number of species and varieties of plants are found in southeast China, Indochina, India, the Malay Archipelago, southwest Asia, tropical Africa, the Cape region, Abyssinia (Ethiopia), Central America, South America, southern Mexico, countries bordering the Mediterranean Sea, and the Near East. A paucity of varieties is seen in Siberia, central and northern Europe, and temperate North America.

A map of these centers (see Figure 2-1) shows that the origin and development of most of the important cultivated plants occurred in a strip between 20° and 45° north latitude. A number of food plants seem to have originated in several regions or centers, but different species are characteristic of each center. The differences are in part genetic with different species having different numbers of chromosomes. For example, the common wheat endemic to the mountainous areas of northwest India has 21 pairs of chromosomes, while other wheat species with 14 pairs of chromosomes are endemic in Ethiopia and the Near East (Figure 2-2).

Many of our modern cultivated plants have been domesticated for thousands of years and some have no recognizable wild ancestor. These include wheat, barley, corn, soybean, peanut, flax, and cotton. Other crops were derived from weeds growing among the planted ones. Rye is such an example. With the northward movement of winter barley and wheat from southwest Asia to Europe and Siberia, rye, because of its winter hardiness and tolerance of adverse soil conditions, began to replace wheat. Human intervention helped rye to become an independent crop.

Not all cultivated crops are ancient in origin. Common beet has been

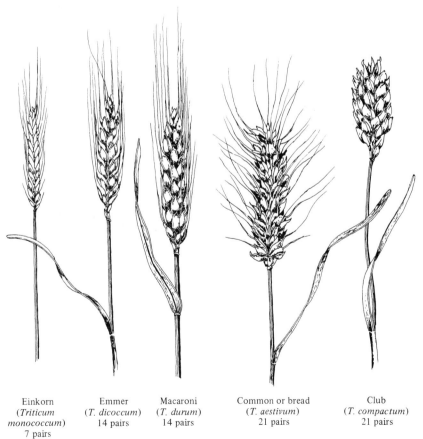

| Einkorn (*Triticum monococcum*) 7 pairs | Emmer (*T. dicoccum*) 14 pairs | Macaroni (*T. durum*) 14 pairs | Common or bread (*T. aestivum*) 21 pairs | Club (*T. compactum*) 21 pairs |

Figure 2-2 Five types of cultivated wheat (*Triticum* spp.) and their chromosome numbers.

cultivated since prehistoric times for its leaves, but its usefulness as a potential source of sugar was not recognized until the middle of the eighteenth century. Since that time intensive breeding and selection have led to the development of the sugar beet, a highly important source of commercial sugar competing favorably with sugar cane.

Another example of a plant that began to be cultivated only recently is pyrethrum, the source of the insecticidal pyrethrins. These compounds, widely used because of their toxicity for insects, are essentially nontoxic for warm-blooded animals and, in addition, are biodegradable. The earliest record of this plant's use as an insecticide is about 2000 years B.P., but its domestication dates only from about the middle of the nineteenth century. Derris, the source of rotenone, another natural insecticide and fish poison, has, on the other hand, been cultivated since ancient times.

Old World Centers of Origin of Cultivated Plants   The China center, one of the earliest and largest independent centers of agricultural activity, encompasses the mountainous regions of central and western China and the adjacent lowlands. Indigenous plants include broomcorn millet and other millets, barleys, soybean and other bean genera, Chinese yam, rhubarb, many fruits such as apricot, plum, cherry, and lichi, tea bush, opium poppy, and hemp. The Indo-Hindustan center of South Asia, including Burma and Assam, is considered, along with southern China, as the primary center of domestication of rice, since a large number of wild species as well as common rice, growing wild, are found here. Sugar cane, a large number of legumes, a variety of tropical fruits, including orange and lemon, yam, Oriental cotton, and hemp also originated here. The Indo-Malayan center —the Malay archipelago—considered a subdivision of the South Asia center, is rich in several cultivated fruits.

The Central Asia center—northwest India, all of Afghanistan, Tadjikistan and Uzbekistan of the U.S.S.R., and western Tien Shan—is a native home of wheat and an important source of varieties of wheat such as common wheat, club wheat, and shot wheat. Major leguminous species are found here as well as cotton, carrot, and garlic. The apple was first cultivated here.

The Near-East center—interior of Asia Minor, all of Transcaucasia, Iran, and the highlands of Turkmenistan—is noted for the number of species of cultivated wheat including einkorn wheat, durum wheat, and several others. Rye, barley, and oats originated here. It is also the home of grape, pear, cherry, pomegranate, almond, fig, and many other fruits. The first orchards may well have been located in this area.

The Mediterranean center ranks with China as an important center of origin for vegetables and for the olive.

The Abyssinia center, mainly Ethiopia, is a probable center of origin of cultivated barley and the primary center of several varieties of coffee. It may also be the region where sorghum was domesticated.

New World Centers of Origin of Cultivated Plants   The Central America center—South Mexico and Central America—is the primary center of origin of corn (maize) and the most closely related wild species, teosinte. It is also the home of the major American species of bean, squash, pepper, sweet potato, arrowroot, agave, cacao, and avocado. Upland cotton, the most important cotton fiber used for cloth, originated in south Mexico. Other plants unique to Central America are curare and datura.

The South America center, which includes Peru, Ecuador, and Bolivia, is noted for several varieties of potato, the tomato, quinine, tobacco, peanut, and the rubber tree; manioc originated in Brazil.

Temperate North America is home to few cultivated plants. Sunflower, cranberry, blueberry, strawberry, nut trees such as pecan, hickory, and black walnut, and American grape are indigenous.

HOW NEW CULTIVATED PLANTS ARE OBTAINED

As many as 3000 plant species have served as primary sources of food, but only about 200 have been domesticated. Even more surprising, less than a dozen major crops are now grown as sources of protein for human consumption. In the New World the only important wild grass to be domesticated and transformed into a food grain is corn (maize or Indian corn). There is archeological evidence that as many as 150 varieties of Indian corn were used by pre-Columbian people. Tiny cobs of primitive corn have been found that are about 7000 years old. In the Old World, on the other hand, a variety of native grasses have been domesticated: wheat, barley, rye, oats, and millet.

Worldwide movement of cultivated plants began only when people began to migrate, taking their supplies of food with them, particularly easily stored seed and root crops. Those who opened up the major trade routes, such as the Silk Route through Central Asia, carried silk, spices, and other plant material to Europe and European products back to Asia. The Spanish and Portuguese explorers, who accidentally found Central America in their search for a sea route to Asia, were instrumental in bringing a number of cultivars of wheat as well as limes and olives to the New World.

The place where a plant was initially domesticated from wild ancestors and today's center of production may be vastly different. The potato was a prominent cultivated plant in the Andes Mountains in the sixteenth century when the Spanish explorers arrived in the New World, yet the major production area is now in Europe. Cultivated varieties of wheat originated in Asia and arrived in the New World with the Spanish. Today, the Soviet Union, the United States, Canada, and Argentina are major producers of wheat, growing a large number of cultivars developed for different climatic conditions. The original home of corn was tropical Central America, but the center of production today is midwestern United States.

PROTECTION OF GERMPLASM

The introduction of food crops, as well as ornamental plants, into the United States from other parts of the world began when the Pilgrims arrived. Benjamin

Franklin continued this practice by sending seeds and cuttings from Europe, and President John Quincy Adams formalized this activity. This plant material is a source of germplasm—the germ cells that are bearers of the genetic material—or genes that can combine to form new and different varieties of plants. Under the direction of the U.S. Department of Agriculture new agricultural or horticultural plants brought into the United States, whether seed, plant, or cutting, are grown in one of the Plant Introduction stations and can be assigned a plant introduction number; almost 500,000 PI's have been issued. These plant introductions contribute germplasm which may increase the disease resistance of currently grown cultivars, increase yield, increase tolerance to low soil moisture, or enhance other desired qualities.

The USDA Germplasm Resources Laboratory at Beltsville, Maryland, is the agency responsible for assigning PI numbers and maintaining appropriate records. The USDA National Seed Storage Laboratory at Fort Collins, Colorado, stores seeds of plants that are normally propagated by seeds. These agencies, under the National Plant Germplasm System, have, as their responsibility, not only the introduction and maintenance of germplasm that has potential value, but also its evaluation, testing, and distribution.

The United States, although it is in a region with few endemic cultivated plants, is now the home for an infinite variety of useful flowering plants.

SUPPLEMENTARY READINGS

Cobley, J. S., and W. M. Steele. 1977. *An Introduction to the Botany of Tropical Crops.* 2nd ed. Longman, New York.

Evans, L. T. (ed.). *Crop Physiology.* Cambridge University Press, New York.

Harlan, J. R. 1955. The plants and animals that nourish man. *Sci. Amer.* 235(3):88–97.

Harlan, J. R. 1975. *Crops and Man.* American Society of Agronomy, Madison, Wis.

Harris, D. R. 1972. The origins of agriculture in the tropics. *Amer. Sci.* 60:180–193.

Heiser, C. B., Jr. 1979. Origins of some cultivated new world plants. *Annu. Rev. Ecol. System.* 10:309–326.

Jarrige, J. F., and R. H. Meadow. 1980. The antecedents of civilization in the Indus Valley. *Sci. Amer.* 243(2):122–133.

Poincelot, R. P. 1986. *Towards a More Sustainable Agriculture.* Avi Books, Westport, Conn.

Rindos, D. 1984. *The Origins of Agriculture: An Evolutionary Perspective.* Academic Press, Orlando, Fla.

Schery, W. 1972. *Plants for Man.* 2nd ed. Prentice-Hall, Englewood Cliffs, N.J.

Schwanitz, F. 1966. *The Origin of Cultivated Plants.* Harvard University Press, Cambridge, Mass.

Solheim, W. G., II. 1972. An earlier agricultural revolution. *Sci. Amer.* 226(4):34–41.

Soule, J. 1985. *Glossary for Horticultural Crops.* Wiley, New York.

Vavilov, N. I. 1950. *The Origin, Variation, Immunity and Breeding of Cultivated Plants.* Chronica Botanica, Vol. 13. Chronica Botanica, Waltham, Mass.

Waterworth, H. E. 1981. Our plant's ancestors migrated too. *BioScience* 31(9):698.

Zeven, A. C., and P. M. Zhukovsky. 1975. *Dictionary of Cultivated Plants and Their Centres of Diversity.* Centre for Agricultural Publishing, Wageningen, Netherlands.

C H A P T E R 3

STRUCTURE OF CULTIVATED PLANTS

THE BODY PLAN OF PLANTS

A cultivated plant is most easily defined as one that is deliberately grown and used by people. Clearly, many plants fall under this broad definition, since plants are used to supply food, shelter, clothing, medicine, industrial products, and many other products. Many plants are now under cultivation, but some economically important plants grow in the wild and the usable product is gathered. Maple sugar is an example. Of the approximately 220,000 flowering plants, fewer than 200 are used directly as basic food, perhaps another 150 form part of the culture of various groups of people, and several hundred have ornamental value.

Because of this diversity, it is impossible here to provide detailed descriptions of all the plants used by people. There is, fortunately, a great deal of structural and functional similarity among all of the flowering plants. Light microscopic and electron microscopic views of plant cells show a fundamental unity, the various types of plant cells fall into identical categories, the organization of cell types into tissues and organ systems is similar, and even the gross structure of plants shows similarities. To have the necessary grasp of the structure of economic plants, it is logical to discuss a "typical" flowering plant. Of course, the details of plant structure, from the submicroscopic to the whole-plant level, do show considerable variation. The gross form of a pea plant *(Pisum sativum)* and that of the sugar maple tree *(Acer saccharum)* are quite different. However, both have the same organ systems, and this similarity extends to the cell constitutents, cell types, and tissues. It is as if one had a limited number of different brick types and wanted to build a warehouse or a cathedral. The final shape and the proportions of the buildings would differ, but the bricks would be the same in both structures.

In discussing the organization of plants, one can start either at the microscopic level and move to the gross or visually apparent level of the organs and the whole plant or one can do the reverse. For a variety of reasons, including the fact that most people are more familiar with intact or whole plants than with plants seen microscopically, we have chosen to start with whole plants and then look at their components and how they are fitted together.

BODY PLAN OF THE ENTIRE PLANT

The typical flowering plant (Figure 3-1) has five major organ systems: root, stem, leaf, flower, and fruit. The root system anchors the plant within its substrate (usually soil), is the primary organ for the uptake of water and dissolved minerals from the soil water, provides a storage region for substances produced by photosynthesis, and produces compounds needed for the growth and development of the entire plant.

The stem system is the structural support of the plant, maintains the plant in a position to capture solar radiation for photosynthesis, is the major conduit for root-absorbed water to and through the leaves, and is the conduit for the movement of materials formed in photosynthesis to the rest of the plant. In many

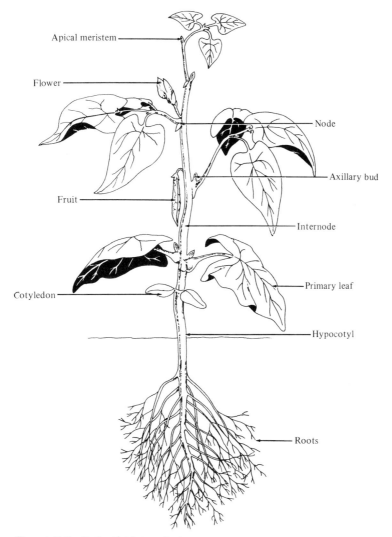

Figure 3-1 Parts of a bean plant.

plants stems can elongate or enlarge laterally to increase the storage and transmission capacity and the mechanical strength of the plant.

The leaf system is, in most plants, the primary organ for photosynthesis. It plays basic roles in the movement of water and, like the root and stem, it makes compounds needed for the growth and development of the plant as a whole.

The two other organ systems, flower and fruit, function in sexual reproduction. Although other organs can reproduce the plant through asexual reproduction, there are certain advantages conferred by sexual reproduction, a process that permits the exchange of genetic information. The fruit is the structure in which seeds develop. Seeds have been defined as the young plant in a box with its lunch, an apt description. The food reserves in cotyledons or endosperm are the lunch and the seed coat is the box in which the new generation is contained.

As you can see simply by looking around you, natural selection over long periods of evolution has produced considerable variation in the structure of each of these organ systems and of their parts. Many of these adaptive modifications are of economic and practical significance. For example, the elongated leaf stalk (petiole) of celery *(Apium graveolens* var. *dulce)* and rhubarb *(Rheum Rhabarbarum)* and the enlarged root system of carrot *(Daucus carota)* provide us with the edible parts of these plants. The stem of the carrot is compressed, with the leaves being borne very close together; the edible root has been selected for its greatly enhanced storage capacity. The horticulturist can further modify the size and form of plant organs with environmental controls; celery petioles can be made lighter in color, longer, and more succulent (juicier and more tender) by covering them with soil during their growth. The position on the plant, its size, and other valuable characteristics of plant organs can also be manipulated by selection and selective breeding. However, the fundamental organization into organ systems cannot be completely overwhelmed.

ROOTS

Root Types

With some important exceptions, the root is an underground plant organ that plays a variety of roles in the growth of the plant. Its internal organization (described more fully in Chapter 4) is designed to enable it to fulfill these various functions.

Roots originate by one of two processes. The most common is initiation in the embryo within the seed. During embryo development certain cells are programmed to become the primordial root, or radicle, which develops along with the other parts of the embryo. At germination the radicle grows through the seed coat to form the primary root. This primary root is usually round in cross section and tapers to a point, the root tip. Its subsequent growth and development is determined by the type of root system that is characteristic of the species.

Roots may also be initiated in other organs. In some plants root growth can be induced in cuttings from parts of mature plants, such as roots, stems, and leaves, a phenomenon of great horticultural importance in producing clones of plants. When cuttings are rooted, a single dominant tap root does not form, but a number of approximately equal roots develop. Roots also form on intact stems or leaves of plants in some, but not all families of horticultural plants. Such roots, called adventitious roots, are common on members of the nightshade family (Solanaceae) and can be seen easily as bumps or as vertical rows of short roots on tomato stems. This is useful when transplanting tomatoes. Tomatoes may (and should) be transplanted deeper than they had been growing in the flat or seed bed; these adventitious roots will develop quickly to provide excellent anchoring and an increased root system for absorption of water and nutrients. Many vines have adventitious roots on their stems which cling to trees, rocks or walls. The common English ivy *(Hedera helix)* has many groups of roots produced at intervals along the stem (Figure 3-2).

The radicle or primary root may develop into one of several different root types (Figure 3–2). It can remain the dominant axis of the root system as a tap root with some side (lateral) roots. More frequently, the primary root initiates large numbers of lateral roots, the primacy of the tap root is lost, and the root mass becomes a highly branched, fibrous root system in which no single root is dominant. In some plants, corn *(Zea Mays)* being an outstanding example, roots may develop above the soil line and grow out at angles into the soil. These prop roots function much as do the guy ropes on a tent; they stabilize the upright structure.

Inspection of a young root with a hand lens will show that the lateral roots do not develop from the youngest portions of the root, but can be found only at a distance from the tip. These lateral roots do not appear at random on the root, but are found in definite vertical rows. This is because lateral roots are initiated from only certain cell types within the root and these types are found only at specific locations of the maturing root.

As discussed later (Chapter 6), roots of many plants form mutually beneficial associations with certain species of fungi. These mycorrhizal associations usually cause some modification of the shape of the young root. It becomes somewhat club-shaped rather than tapering to a point, and it is frequently possible to see filaments of the fungal partner protruding from the root.

Structural variations on these three general root types have been exploited horticulturally in the selection and breeding of economic plants. The function of

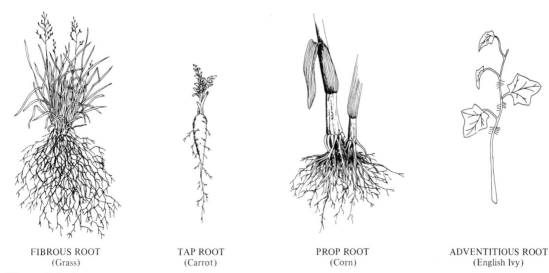

| FIBROUS ROOT | TAP ROOT | PROP ROOT | ADVENTITIOUS ROOT |
| (Grass) | (Carrot) | (Corn) | (English Ivy) |

Figure 3-2 Root systems.

Begonia   Dahlia

Figure 3-3 Tuberous roots.

a root as a starch storage organ has been enhanced by selection and breeding to result in a root that is used for food. These are usually known as root crops since they develop underground. This is a term of convenience, since some of our root crops are not roots at all. The white potato (*Solanum tuberosum*) is an underground stem; the yam (*Dioscorea* spp.) and the sweet potato (*Ipomoea Batatas*) are true roots. The young fruit (a legume) of the peanut (*Arachis hypogaea*) turns down and is forced into the soil and, clearly, is not a root.

Of the true roots used as food, the most important on a worldwide base, although not too well known in North America, is the cassava (*Manihot esculenta*) or manioc (Figure 11-14). We know it as tapioca, the washed, dried starch of the root, but manioc is a staple carbohydrate food for people of tropical parts of the world. The sweet potato (*Ipomoea Batatas*), also of tropical origin, is a true root. Beets, both the familiar red table beet and the much larger sugar beet (both are *Beta vulgaris*) are primarily roots, although the upper portion of the root where the leaves appear is a greatly compressed stem. The edible carrot *(Daucus carota)*, the parsnip (*Pastinaca sativa*), the radish (*Raphanus sativus*), and the turnip (*Brassica rapa*) are also examples of swollen tap roots with compressed stems. Begonia and dahlia have tuberous roots (Figure 3-3).

There are a number of true roots used as food in tropical regions which are of limited availability in North America. Most of them are swollen tap roots, although a few fibrous root crops are known. The fibrous storage roots of the pond or water lilies (*Nuphar* spp.) have been used by American Indians, Chinese, and other cultures. Fibrous roots of some trees have been used as rope and even as thread.

Penetration and Distribution

There is a general belief that roots grow down (positive geotropism) and that stems grow up (negative geotropism). There are, as a casual examination will show, as many exceptions to this rule as there are examples. In fact, most roots

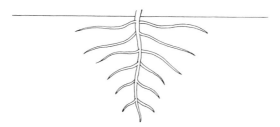

Figure 3-4 Geotropic angles formed by lateral roots.

do not grow straight down, but actually grow laterally at some given angle (Figure 3-4). Only the tap root shows strict positive geotropism. The geotropically regulated angle assumed by a root is determined at the time of its initiation by control mechanisms that are not understood. Once a root has been programmed relative to geotropic response, its subsequent growth pattern is permanently fixed, and a vertical root usually will not become horizontal. Tap roots can, depending on the species, grow down as much as 10 to 15 m (30 to 45 ft) and, in a few desert plants, may grow to a vertical depth of 30 m (95 ft). Most horticultural and agronomic plants, however, have relatively shallow roots systems (Table 3-1). Even tap roots may not grow straight down. The root tip is sensitive to physical barriers to growth and to chemicals and has the ability to bend to one side to avoid a rock or pebble or a toxic chemical (such tropic movements are discussed in Chapter 13). As a consequence, to avoid misshapen, split, and small root crops, there is a considerable advantage in preparing the soil to below the depth to which the roots may be expected to grow (by sifting to eliminate clumps and pebbles, by adding sand to lighten the soil).

The ability of roots to show lateral spread has, over evolutionary time, proved to be beneficial to the plant. The mass of lateral roots increases the area of soil available for water and mineral uptake, and, where soils are shallow to a hardpan or bedrock, they allow a broad area for stabilization and anchoring of the plant.

Table 3-1 AVERAGE ROOT-ZONE DEPTHS OF MATURE PLANTS GROWN IN DEEP, PERMEABLE, WELL-DRAINED LOAM SOIL

Crop plant	Root depth (m)	Crop plant	Root depth (m)
Asparagus	1.8	Parsnip	1.0
Bean	1.0	Pea	1.3
Beet (table)	0.75	Potato	1.3
Broccoli	0.6	Pumpkin	2.0
Cabbage	0.6	Radish	0.3
Cantaloupe	2.0	Spinach	0.6
Carrot	0.75	Squash	0.6
Corn (sweet)	1.0	Sweet potato	1.5
Lawn grass	0.5	Tomato	2.0
Lettuce	0.2	Turnip	1.0
Onion	0.3	Strawberry	1.0

Table 3-2   SIZE OF ROOT SYSTEM OF A RYE PLANT *(SECALE CEREALE)*

Kind of root	Number	Length	
		Meters	Feet
Main roots	143	65	214
Secondary roots	35,600	5,181	17,000
Tertiary roots	2,300,000	174,947	574,000
Quarternary roots	11,500,000	441,938	1,450,000
Total root	14,000,000	609,570	2,041,214
			(380 miles)

The volume of soil occupied by the root system of a fibrous-rooted plant is variable, but it frequently is greater than the aerial volume of the stem and leaves. The volume or weight of the shoot relative to the volume or weight of the roots is called the shoot/root ratio. Many forest or ornamental trees have root systems that extend considerably beyond the width of the crown of the tree. This is an important consideration when plants are to be fertilized or are to be dug for transplanting. The total length of a fibrous root system has been painstakingly measured in several economically important plants. For example, a rye plant (*Secale cereale*) growing under optimum conditions has a total root length of close to 600 km (380 mi) and, when a calculation of the average cross-sectional diameter of the root is used, the volume of the root system is over 200 m^3 (Table 3-2).

The mechanical pressure developed by a root to allow it to penetrate through soil is extremely high, so high in some plants that roots can fracture concrete. The advantages that this can confer upon the plant are obvious. Although clay hardpans do present a severe barrier to penetration of roots, a thin hardpan can sometimes be penetrated.

When roots of two or more identical species of plant touch, they may fuse or graft together. Almost all of the trees in a plantation or orchard are interconnected and the same may be true for some crop plants. The potential advantage of this can only be speculated upon, but the possible dangers have been studied in relation to the movement of root disease organisms in tree plantations, and in orchards, and in rows of trees along roadsides. An infection of one plant may quickly spread to the others.

STEMS

The stem is, for all practical purposes, the plant organ that holds leaves up into the light. In order to do so, it must possess other structural and functional attributes. It must have a vascular or plumbing system to permit the passage of water and dissolved substances from the soil through the root and to the leaves. The stem's vascular system must also move the products of photosynthesis from the leaves down to the rest of the plant. In large plants the stem must be sufficiently strong to resist the pressures of wind and sufficiently large to store sugars formed in photosynthesis. In plants that live for more than one year (biennials and perennials), growth of the stem provides for both increased resistance to wind and increased girth, as well as for extension in length so that the leaves are not shaded excessively.

In general, stems are round in cross section, although there are exceptions; the stems of alfalfa (*Medicago sativa*) and members of the mint family (Labiat- ae), which include a number of cooking herb species, are square. The develop- ment of stems is most easily seen in younger plants where increases in girth by secondary thickening do not complicate the picture.

The primary stem is formed during the development of the embryo within the seed. At seed maturity the young stem consists of a region above the root that has the seed leaves (cotyledons) and a short stem axis, the epicotyl. When the seed germinates and begins to develop, the shoot assumes its typical, usually erect form with one or more pairs of leaves.

The young stem is usually a single, elongated axis. The place where a leaf is attached is called a node, and a stem region between two nodes is called an internode (Figure 3-1). A good deal of the elongation of a stem is due to the elongation of the cells comprising the internodes. An examination of a bean plant (*Phaseolus*) will show that the young internodes toward the top of the stem are shorter than those closer to the base of the plant since the younger internodes have not yet fully elongated.

Stem Types

Not all plants have a single main stem. Shrubs are woody perennials that have more than one stem. Some stems are derived from shoot buds that are initiated on the stem; plants having this type of shoot initiation are called stoloniferous. Closely related species may exhibit either the shrub habit or the single-stem, tree habit. *Amelanchier canadensis* (shadbush) is a large shrub, while the closely related species *A. arborea* is a single-stemmed tree growing to 15 m (46 ft) in height.

Suckers are shoots arising from subterranean buds that form on roots that may have extended several meters away from the primary trunk or stem. Not all plants have the ability to form suckers; indeed, suckering is more the exception than the rule. Suckers can, in plants like blackberry, serve as propagating material, being cut from the parent plant after they have formed their own root system.

Herbaceous plants, particularly members of the grass family including both lawn grasses and cereal grains such as wheat, can form new stems from the crown (root-shoot junction) of the plant (Figure 3-5). These tillers serve to increase the number of stems and hence fruiting stalks of the plant. Promotion of tillering in lawn grasses is a valuable practice in developing a good lawn (Chapter 18).

In addition to leaves, stems bear other appendages. Flowers and fruit are obvious, but buds are much less obvious. Two types of buds are found on stems (see Figure 3-1). One, the terminal bud or apical meristem, is the region where new primary stem cells and leaves are formed (Chapter 4). The second type, the axillary bud, is less apparent. It is a small bud nestled in the junction of the leaf stalk and stem axil; it is formed at the same time as the leaf. The axillary bud is essentially a lateral apical meristem, containing the tissues necessary for the development of a shoot. During the growing season it may remain undeveloped, but under special circumstances it can develop into a shoot bearing leaves. Most lateral and side branches of many perennial plants originate in the axillary buds. The pattern of branching is determined by the position of the buds. This fact is important in applying the techniques of pruning (Chapter 14).

Although it is usual for stems to bear leaves, at least during part of an annual life cycle, plants such as the cacti rarely or never form leaves. The stem is the primary or sole photosynthetic organ. The edible and ornamental species of asparagus have finely divided branches that are green and photosynthetic. Such branches are called cladophylls (Figure 3-6). A number of plants initiate thorns from tissues below the epidermis or bark of the stem (Figure 3-7).

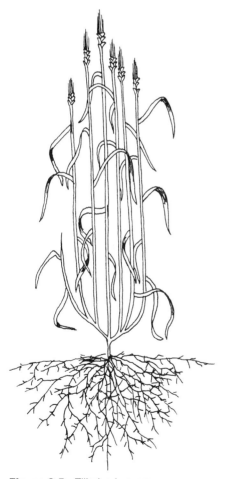

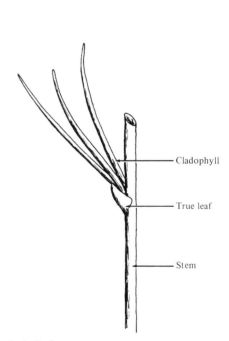

Cladophyll

True leaf

Stem

Figure 3-5   Tillering in a grass.   **Figure 3-6**   Cladophyll of asparagus.

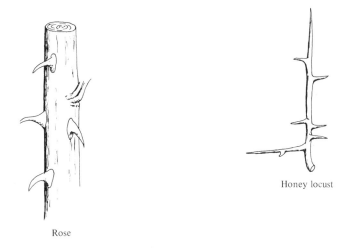

Honey locust

Rose

Figure 3-7 Stem thorns.

The longevity of stems varies. Annual plants generally live for only one season and the entire plant dies at the end of the growing and reproductive phases. Perennial plants may live for only two years (biennial) or for many years, but only those plants classified as woody perennials retain living stems for several years. Plants with stems that die back to the ground and are replaced by new stems each year are called herbaceous perennials. They are common in temperate zones.

During the early period of the growth of a stem, the exterior cell layer is composed of epidermal cells. The cells immediately interior to the epidermal cells may be green and carry on photosynthesis. In many annuals the stem is photosynthetic during the entire life of the plant. As stems age, however, the epidermis is replaced by bark. The bark may be smooth and relatively thin or may become deeply ridged in species-specific patterns as the stem increases in diameter. Many woody perennials can be identified easily by their bark patterns.

The bark of plants, particularly those of thin-barked woody perennials, may have small, usually horizontal raised areas called lenticels. They are composed of loosely arranged groups of cells that provide a pathway for gas exchange into the stem.

In temperate regions, where there are seasonal changes in temperature and light, many plants form winter buds. As the growing season begins to come to an end, terminal and axillary buds are signaled by light and temperature to develop heavy bud scales (modified leaves) about the bud. Winter buds, protected by these bud scales and sometimes by woolly mats of hairs, enclose the potential new shoots that develop as the bud "breaks" in the spring (Figure 3-8). The lateral or side branches of many perennial plants are due to the growth of these axillary buds.

Although there are variations in branching, plants can be classified into

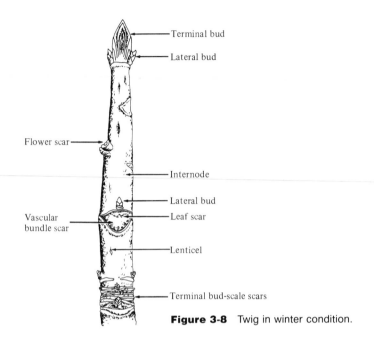

Terminal bud

Lateral bud

Flower scar

Internode

Lateral bud

Leaf scar

Vascular
bundle scar

Lenticel

Terminal bud-scale scars

Figure 3-8 Twig in winter condition.

three major groups (Figure 3-9). Dichotomous branching results when a single axis divides into two equal axes with each of the new stems dividing again. Excurrent or monopodial branching is a branching pattern in which many of the axillary buds develop into side branches, but the main stem axis remains dominant. In the decurrent or sympodial pattern a number of axillary buds

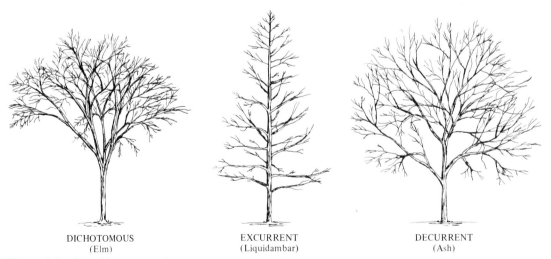

DICHOTOMOUS
(Elm)

EXCURRENT
(Liquidambar)

DECURRENT
(Ash)

Figure 3-9 Branching patterns in tree stems.

develop into approximately equal-sized branches, giving a bushy appearance to the plant. Branching is not necessarily fixed according to species; a maple or oak tree in a forest will usually grow in the monopodial form, while the umbrella-shaped sympodial form dominates in trees growing in the open. Some plants, if not injured, will never show branching. The sunflower *(Helianthus annuus)* may reach 2 m (6.5 ft) in height without any branches, while a coleus and other bedding plants will branch freely while still quite young. The suppression of branching, called apical dominance, is discussed in Chapter 14.

Growth Habits

Although we usually think of stems as being vertical and aerial, this is not always the case (Figure 3-10). Many stems are horizontal, running along the soil surface and forming roots at their tips. The runners or stolons of cultivated strawberry *(Fragaria Xananassa),* which can reproduce the plant, exhibit this growth habit. Rhizomes are stems that grow parallel to and beneath the soil surface, forming roots and leaves at intervals; the fleshy rhizomes of some iris species and of many native and ornamental ferns are typical examples. The tuber of the white potato *(Solanum tuberosum)* is not a root, but a fleshy, starch-storing underground stem. The true yam *(Dioscorea* spp.) is a root tuber, and the sweet potato *(Ipomoea Batatas)* is also a root. Two other stem forms are of considerable horticultural importance. The bulbs of onion and related vegetables *(Allium* spp.) and many other members of the lily family (Liliaceae) have greatly compressed stems; the

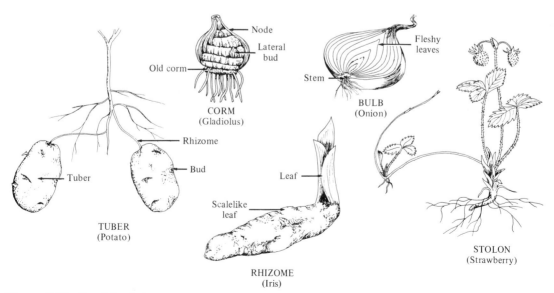

Figure 3-10 Specialized stems.

fleshy leaves are borne at the nodes of the dome-shaped stem and enclose it. The corms of gladiolus *(Gladiolus* spp.) and crocus *(Crocus* spp.) are also stems.

Many stems are very flexible when young, and with the aid of roots developed at their nodes, are capable of climbing. Vines such as kudzu *(Pueraria lobata)* and tropical lianas such as the strangler fig *(Ficus aurea)* are serious pests in their native habitats and when introduced into other countries. Others, like the common ivy *(Hedera helix)* and the morning glory *(Ipomoea purpurea)* are extensively planted as indoor and outdoor ornamentals.

LEAVES

Leaves are usually flattened organs attached to stems. A leaf has two major parts: the blade, which is the light-capturing area, and a usually thin, cylindrical stalk or petiole, which attaches the leaf to the stem (Figure 3-11). Leaves are not borne randomly on the stem, but appear at particular sites, the nodes of the stem. In some, but not all leaves, there may be small green appendages, called stipules, at the base of the petiole where it joins the stem. In some plants they may be modified into spines (Figure 3-12) or sheaths about the petiole-stem juncture. The stipules are capable of photosynthesis. Leaves without petioles are called

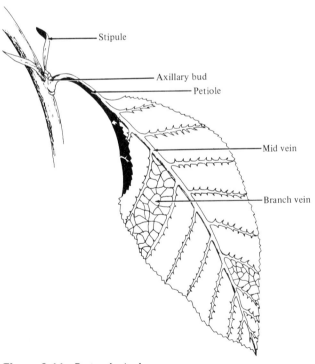

Figure 3-11 Parts of a leaf.

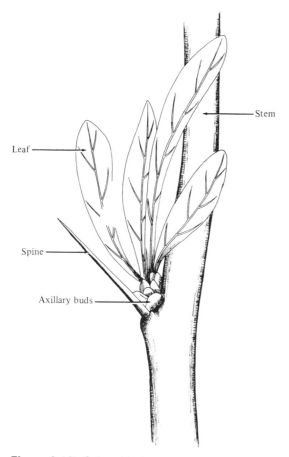

Figure 3-12   Spine of barberry.

sessile. Cereal grain leaves are often ligulate, that is, there is no petiole and the base of the leaf encircles the stem (Figure 3-13).

At the base of the petiole, usually in the internal angle between the petiole and the stem, there is an axillary bud. The axillary bud is formed at the time the leaf forms on the apical meristem of the stem. It is an inactive, but fully developed apical meristem, capable when activated of developing into a shoot. When this bud is forced into development by growth substances, the new stems can make the plant bushier.

The veins of a leaf are, anatomically, bundles of vascular tissue that carry water and dissolved substances into the tissues of the leaf and remove the products of photosynthesis from the leaf. The pattern of venation is genetically determined and is of considerable utility in identifying plants. In the dicots there are two major venation patterns (see Figure 3-13): pinnate venation, in which small veins branch from a single main vein, and palmate venation, in which small veins branch out from several main veins that fan out over the leaf. With a

PINNATE
(Elm)

PALMATE
(Sugar maple)

PARALLEL
(Corn)

Figure 3-13   Leaf venation patterns.

few exceptions, leaves of the grasses and other monocots (lilies, orchids, etc.) have parallel venation, that is, the veins run parallel to the long axis of the leaf. The veins coalesce at the base of the leaf blade and extend through the petiole where they connect with the vascular system of the stem and of the root. Thus, there is a continuity of vascular tissues from the tip of the roots up to the leaves.

At the stem nodes leaves may occur in several different arrangements (Figure 3-14). An alternate arrangement has only one leaf at each node; an opposite arrangement has two leaves, one on either side of the stem, at each node; and a whorled arrangement has more than two leaves at each node. In the

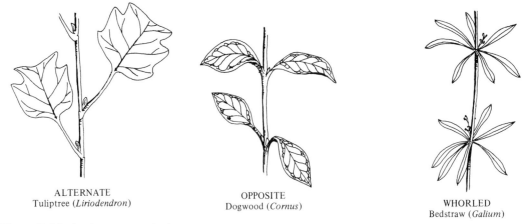

ALTERNATE
Tuliptree (*Liriodendron*)

OPPOSITE
Dogwood (*Cornus*)

WHORLED
Bedstraw (*Galium*)

Figure 3-14   Leaf arrangement.

Figure 3-15 Leaf orientation in a phyllotactic pattern.

alternate and opposite arrangements each leaf or leaf pair comes off from the stem in a spiral pattern descending from the stem tip (Figure 3-15). The pattern ensures that a lower leaf or leaf pair is not directly below the leaves immediately above it and so is not completely shaded by them. The spirals are easily seen in pine cones, whose scales are modified leaves. This fixed order, called phyllotaxy, is laid down at the time of the origin of the leaf in the apical meristem.

A leaf is called simple when only one blade is attached to the stem by a single petiole. Aspens *(Populus)* and willows *(Salix)* are trees with simple leaves. If there is more than one blade, the leaf is compound (Figure 3-16). In a pinnate-compound leaf the blades emerge from several different points along the

SIMPLE
Linden (*Tilia*)

PINNATE-COMPOUND
Ash (*Fraxinus*)

PALMATE-COMPOUND
Horsechestnut (*Aesculus*)

Figure 3-16 Leaf types.

petiole; in a palmate-compound leaf the blades all emerge from one point at the end of the petiole. Honeylocust *(Gleditsia)* and walnut *(Juglans)* trees and pea *(Pisum)* and bean *(Phaseolus)* plants have compound leaves. The blades of a compound leaf are called leaflets. Although each leaflet may have its own stalk, the stalk is technically not a petiole and is called a petiolule or rachis. It does not carry a vascular strand directly to the stem, but instead is connected to the true petiole of the whole compound leaf. It is usually easy to determine if a leaf is simple or compound; an axillary bud is always present at the base of a petiole, but is not found at the base of a rachis or a petiolule (Figure 3-17).

Shapes and sizes of leaves vary considerably. These differences from species to species, or even from cultivar to cultivar, are genetically determined and are sufficiently stable to be of taxonomic value, although nutritional or other environmental conditions may cause some variations. For example, leaves deprived of adequate nitrogen may be smaller than normal, and shade frequently causes the development of thin, large leaves. Tobacco growers take advantage of this and grow plants under tents of mesh cloth to obtain the thin leaves needed to make cigar wrappers. Shapes vary from narrow, almost ribbonlike to completely round. Leaf shapes may change with the developmental stage of the plant. In the common English ivy *(Hedera helix)* the juvenile, vining, and nonsexual phase of the plant bears deeply lobed leaves, while those of the mature, bushy, and sexual plant are much less lobed.

The margins of leaves may be smooth or toothed, and special names have been given to each of the large number of margin types. This characteristic is species specific and usually does not vary greatly with environmental changes.

Leaf surfaces show considerable variation depending on the species or cultivar. The surface may be smooth to the touch without hairs (glabrous) or rough (glaucous) due to waxes excreted by the epidermis. The leaves may be covered with hairs that are developed from the epidermal cells. Depending on

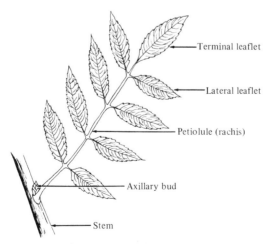

Terminal leaflet

Lateral leaflet

Petiolule (rachis)

Axillary bud

Stem

Figure 3-17 Axillary bud of the compound leaf of white ash *(Fraxinus americana)*.

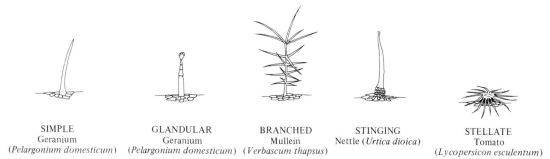

SIMPLE
Geranium
(*Pelargonium domesticum*)

GLANDULAR
Geranium
(*Pelargonium domesticum*)

BRANCHED
Mullein
(*Verbascum thapsus*)

STINGING
Nettle (*Urtica dioica*)

STELLATE
Tomato
(*Lycopersicon esculentum*)

Figure 3-18 Leaf hairs.

the species, hairs may be thick or thin, simple or complex, sparse or dense (Figure 3-18). They may be found on the upper or the lower leaf-blade surface. In some plants, particularly some that are native to hot, dry areas, long white hairs cover the leaf surface. These reflect the sun's rays, preventing possible damage to the leaf caused by excessive heat.

In some plants evolutionary development has modified some leaves into thin, filiform structures called tendrils (Figure 3-19). Tendrils have the capacity to coil when they touch a surface, so that they can help support the plant. This can be seen in peas or in grapes.

Not all leaves are thin. Many plants of harsh environments evolved with

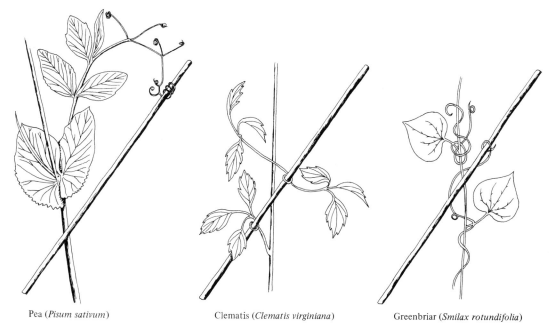

Pea (*Pisum sativum*)

Clematis (*Clematis virginiana*)

Greenbriar (*Smilax rotundifolia*)

Figure 3-19 Tendrils.

leaves that help the plant to survive under the existing environmental conditions. Plants in very humid or wet conditions tend to have deeply lobed or even feathery leaves. Such a shape increases the air flow about the leaf thereby assisting in the removal of water by transpiration (Chapter 6). In very dry (xeric) habitats the leaves are modified to lessen the removal of water. Some become leathery or succulent, others have heavy waxy coatings on the leaf surface, and others show anatomical alterations in the numbers or architecture of the stomata. Under drought conditions some leaves show modifications that allow them to curl which decreases the surface area available for water loss. And, of course, some desert plants have dispensed entirely with leaves and depend, like the cacti, upon their photosynthetic stems.

Although there are differences in the size and shape, most of these structures are immediately recognizable as leaves. Bracts, however, are not usually recognized as leaves (Figure 3-20). Bracts occur below the flowers of many plants, and they tend to be small, green, and inconspicuous. In some plants the bracts become fleshy; the globe artichoke, a food plant, has an inedible flower surrounded and protected by green bracts that are edible. In other plants the bracts grow large and have a color other than green; in the poinsettia *(Poinsettia)* and in dogwood *(Cornus* spp.) the bracts may be white, pink, or red and are incorrectly assumed to be the petals of the flower rather than specialized leaves.

The average life of a leaf depends upon both genetic and environmental factors. In temperate areas many leaves are deciduous, initiated in the spring or at the beginning of a rainy season and dying in the fall or during the dry season. Other plants have leaves that shrivel or wither at the end of the growing season, but are not shed until the beginning of the next growing season. This condition, called marcescence, is common in many trees that have a juvenile phase. Young oaks *(Quercus* spp.) usually retain their dead leaves throughout the winter.

Dogwood (*Cornus*)

Globe artichoke (*Helianthus*)

Figure 3-20   Leaf bracts.

Persistent (evergreen) leaves may remain functional throughout the year for two or many years. The needles of many conifers are able to photosynthesize, even in the depths of winter, when their temperature is raised by the sun. Plants with persistent leaves are at risk of desiccation during winter when soil water is frozen and hence unavailable and water loss through the leaves occurs on windy or sunny days (Chapter 6). Some desert plants, the ocotillo *(Fouquieria splendens)* being an outstanding example, shed their leaves when the soil dries out and can grow a new set—sometimes within a few days—when rain falls.

FLOWERS

Floral Parts

The flower is the organ in which sexual reproduction and the development of the seed occurs. It is derived by alteration of a vegetative bud meristem, either the terminal apical meristem of the stem or a lateral meristem further down on the plant. If the terminal apical meristem is converted into a floral meristem, the plant will not continue to grow in height. Such a plant is usually called determinant or bush type. Many cultivars have been selected or bred to be determinant or indeterminant; most tomato cultivars used for commercial processing are of the determinant type since the fruits mature all at once instead of being spaced out over time as are the fruits of indeterminant cultivars. The pineapple *(Ananas* spp.) is another example of a determinant plant with the flower, and eventually the fruit, being formed at the shoot apex. Factors that activate and regulate conversion of a vegetative meristem into a flowering meristem are discussed in Chapter 15.

Examination of the structure of the parts of a flower shows that they are all modified leaves. This is most obvious for petals, in which veins are easily seen, but all parts of a flower show the stages in development typical of leaves.

The structure of a typical, although theoretical, flower is shown in Figure 3-21. The flower stalk or pedicel, directly comparable to a leaf petiole, connects the flower to the stem or, in the case of multiple flowers, to other flowers. This broadens out to form a flower receptacle which, in some plants like apple *(Malus* spp.), becomes a part of the edible fruit. Arising from the receptacle are four subparts of the flower. The outside ring consists of leaflike structures, sepals, which together form the calyx. Inside of the calyx is the corolla, composed of a ring of petals.

The numbers of sepals and petals, collectively the perianth, and their arrangement is of great taxonomic importance. Petals may be free and unattached to each other or they may fuse during early development to form a tube as in morning glory *(Ipomoea* spp.) or fuchsia *(Fuchsia* spp.) In general, the dicots have sepals and petals in sets of four or five or multiples thereof, while the

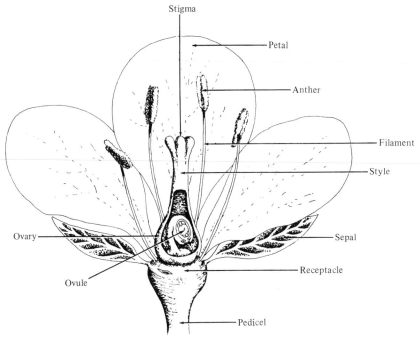

Figure 3-21 Parts of a flower.

monocots have sets of three or multiples of three (Figure 3-22). Through selection and breeding, the number and size of petals can be modified; wild species of rose *(Rosa* spp.) have 5 petals, but cultivated roses *(Rosa* spp.) have up to 25. Petals and sepals have two functions. They protect the sexual parts from damage and, by virtue of their colors and odors, they attract animals that are involved in pollination. Not all flowers have both sepals and petals; flowers lacking one or both of these parts are called incomplete.

The remaining two subparts of the flower are the sexual parts. The stamen is the male apparatus and the pistil the female. The male sexual entity, the pollen grain, is produced within the anther portion of the stamen attached to the receptacle or to the petals by a long filament (essentially a leaf midrib). The ovary consists of one or more seed-forming units, called carpels, and within each carpel there may be one or more ovules each enclosing an egg, the female entity. The female apparatus, sometimes called the pistil, is divided into three major portions. Attached to the upper portion of the ovary is a stalk, the style, that is usually expanded at its top to form the stigma surfaces, sometimes sticky, on which pollen is deposited in pollination. The typical flower contains both male and female parts and is called a perfect flower. Flowers that contain either stamens or pistils, but not both, are imperfect, or unisexual, and are not capable of self-fertilization. In many cases avoiding self-fertilization is advantageous in that the cross-fertilization facilitates the interchange of genetic materials among members of a population.

REGULAR
Sedum (*Sedum* spp.)

IRREGULAR
Iris (*Iris* spp.)

Figure 3-22   Form of dicot and monocot flowers.

Both male and female imperfect flowers can be borne on the same plant (monoecious plants); the tassels of corn *(Zea Mays)* are anthers and the silks are the stigma and style of the pistil. Imperfect flowers may also be borne on different plants (dioecious plants). A number of ornamental plants, including hollies *(Ilex* spp.), oaks *(Quercus* spp.), and maples *(Acer* spp.) are dioecious and to obtain fruit, both male and female specimens must be planted together. Many cultivars of cucumber and other gourd and squash plants have imperfect flowers (Figure 3-23) which may, depending on the cultivar, be borne on the same or on different plants. Plants with female flowers are called gynoeceous, and those bearing male flowers are called androeceous. Some plants are in effect dioecious even though they bear perfect flowers, because the pollen produced by the flowers cannot pollinate and fertilize any other flower on the same plant.

The functionally important parts of a flower are the stamen and pistil. In many plants, including most of the grasses and cereal grains plus trees such as maples, oaks, pines, and the nut trees, the transfer of pollen from anther to stigma occurs by movement of pollen on the wind. Most wind-pollinated plants have small, uncolored, and inconspicuous flowers (Figure 3-24). The flowers of plants pollinated by birds and insects are larger, frequently colored, and usually showy. The color pigments of petals and, less frequently, of sepals are found in the surface layer of cells, the epidermal layer. They are chemically quite varied, although most red and blue pigments are anthocyanins. The anthocyanins may be red, blue, or even purple depending on the acid-alkali balance of the pigmented cells. It is usually not possible to modify the color of these pigments by changing the acidity of the soil (Chapter 5), but this can be done with hydrangea *(Hydrangea macrophylla),* whose flowers are light blue under alkaline soil conditions and pink under acid conditions.

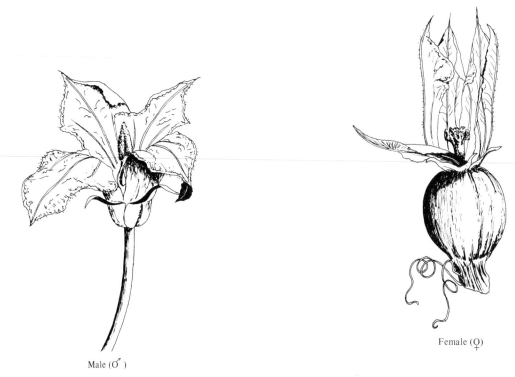

Male (♂)

Female (♀)

Figure 3-23   Dioecious flowers of squash (*Cucurbita* spp.).

Pollination

A diagrammatic representation of the reproduction of a flowering plant is presented in Figure 3-25. We can follow the cycle starting from the transfer of pollen from the anther to the stigma of a receptive pistil. This process, known as pollination, has received a good deal of research attention, because of its importance and because it illustrates some of the most fascinating aspects of evolution of flowering plants. In some plants the pollination process is simple. The anthers of the garden pea *(Pisum sativum)* are close to the stigma of the same flower and pollination frequently occurs prior to the opening of the flower. This ensures self-pollination, and all seeds within a pod are genetically identical.

In cross-pollination pollen must be physically transported to the stigma of another flower. All of the cultivated plants that are not self-pollinated utilize wind, water, or animals as the vectors or transporters of pollen. Appropriate mechanisms for cross-pollination must exist, requiring that there be structural and, in the case of animals, behavioral adaptations. Bright petal colors attract pollinating birds and insects. The odor of the flowers is also an attractant as is the nectar produced in glands at the base of the flower. The odor of rotting meat given off by skunk cabbage *(Symplocarpus foetidus)* attracts pollinating flies.

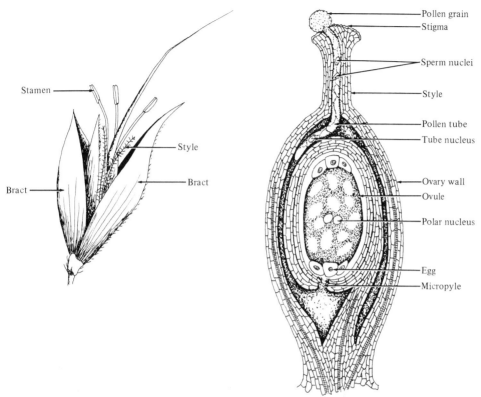

Figure 3-24 Floret of a wind-pollinated oat *(Avena)* plant

Figure 3-25 Pistil and fertilization.

Pollinators have evolved structures and behaviors to correspond to the floral adaptations. The length of the bill and tongue of hummingbirds matches the length of the flower tube that must be entered to obtain nectar and the birds are attracted to bright red flowers. Bees are instinctively programmed for their nectar- and pollen-gathering chores as are other insect pollinators.

Pollen transfer by the wind is an inefficient process, and wind-pollinated plants produce huge numbers of pollen grains to ensure pollination. In addition, the stigma-style apparatus has to have efficient pollen capturing structures. Grasses, for example, have feathery stigmas (see Figure 3-24), and in other plants the stigmas are broad and sticky. Wind-pollinated plants have reduced corollas or may lack them entirely. It is frequently difficult to obtain pollination, fertilization, and fruit set in greenhouse and house plants that are usually cross-pollinated by the wind. In some self-pollinated plants wind shakes pollen out of the anthers onto the stigma. For such plants grown indoors, pollination and flower and fruit development may be increased by shaking the plants.

When a pollen grain that is compatible with the plant lands on the stigma, it germinates by growing a pollen tube which enters the stigmatic tissues and

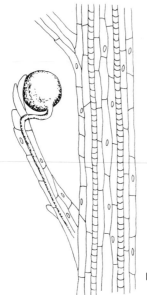

Figure 3-26 Pollination and pollen tube germination on the stigma-style of
the silk of corn *(Zea Mays).*

continues to grow down the style to the ovary (Figure 3-26). The pollen tube
contains three nuclei, two of which are sperm nuclei and the third, which does
not participate in reproduction, is the pollen tube nucleus. When the tube
reaches an ovule within one of the carpels of the ovary, it bursts, releasing the
two sperm nuclei. One of these fuses with the egg nucleus to form the first cell
(zygote) of the next generation (which produces the embryo), and the other
sperm nucleus fuses with a pair of nuclei in the egg sac (the polar nuclei) to
initiate the endosperm tissue system that will nourish the developing embryo.

Inflorescences

Individual flowers may be radially symmetrical, that is actinomorphic, which
means that the flower is divisible into equal halves along any radius. Some
flowers, like those of the bean or the iris, can be divided into two equal halves
only with a cut along a single plane along the axis of the flower. These are
bilaterally symmetrical, or zygomorphic (see Figure 3-22).

Flowers may be borne singly or in larger numbers on a single stalk. Groups
of flowers on one main stalk are called inflorescences. Inflorescences are
separated into two groups; the individual flowers of an indeterminate inflorescence mature from the lower or outer ones to the upper or inner ones, and those
of a determinate inflorescence mature from the upper to the lower (Figures 3-27
and 3-28).

The basic type of indeterminate inflorescence is the raceme in which there
is a single flower stalk and branching of this stalk to give the flower head (see

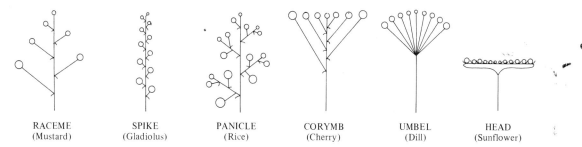

| RACEME | SPIKE | PANICLE | CORYMB | UMBEL | HEAD |
| (Mustard) | (Gladiolus) | (Rice) | (Cherry) | (Dill) | (Sunflower) |

Figure 3-27   Indeterminate inflorescences.

Figure 3-27). There are a number of variations on the raceme pattern. The spike has flowers that do not have pedicels, but are borne directly on the flower stalk. The catkins (aments) of willow *(Salix* spp.) are pendulous spikes of imperfect flowers. Panicles, the inflorescences of many cereal grains, are branched. Corymbs have a short axis and long stalks, and umbels are corymbs in which the stalks are of varying lengths with all the flowers on the same horizontal plane. A head is essentially a corymb without individual flower stalks. In the aster family (Compositae or Asteraceae) the flower head usually has sterile or ray flowers around the periphery of the head.

The basic type of determinant inflorescence is the dichasium in which all stalks arise from one common stalk (see Figure 3-28). Variations include the cyme and the sympodial cyme. The spadix of Jack-in-the-pulpit *(Arisaema* spp.) and other aroids (members of the arum or Araceae family) is placed with the determinate inflorescences. All of these variations are employed in plant classification and are considerations in landscape and garden planning.

FRUITS

Following pollination and fertilization, the ovary develops into a fruit. A fruit is a ripened ovary. Fruits are formed only in angiosperms, although fruitlike structures may be found in some gymnosperms, such as the junipers and yews.

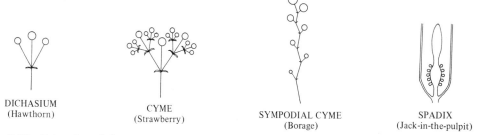

| DICHASIUM | CYME | SYMPODIAL CYME | SPADIX |
| (Hawthorn) | (Strawberry) | (Borage) | (Jack-in-the-pulpit) |

Figure 3-28   Determinate inflorescences.

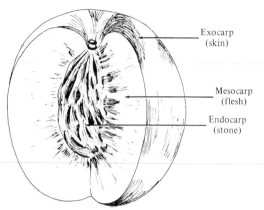

Exocarp
(skin)

Mesocarp
(flesh)

Endocarp
(stone)

Figure 3-29   Peach *(Amygdalus persica)* fruit.

The word *fruit* is here used botanically, rather than in the common, everyday sense. Many of our vegetables are technically fruits; the tomato, bell pepper, green bean, and the cereal grains are fruits because they are matured ovaries containing seeds.

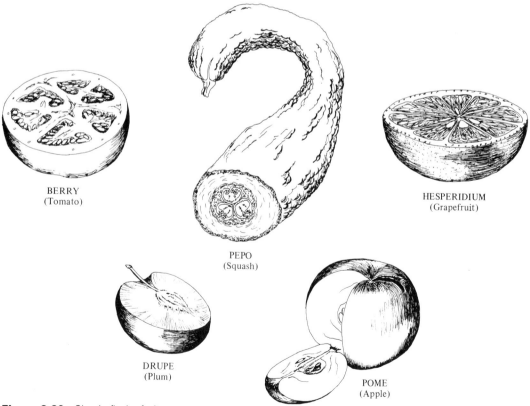

BERRY
(Tomato)

PEPO
(Squash)

HESPERIDIUM
(Grapefruit)

DRUPE
(Plum)

POME
(Apple)

Figure 3-30   Simple fleshy fruits.

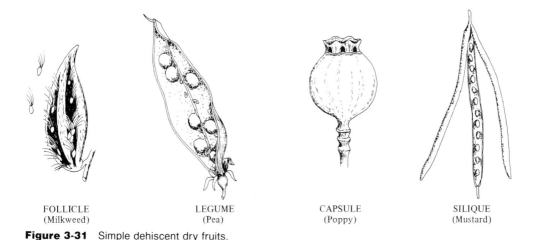

FOLLICLE
(Milkweed)

LEGUME
(Pea)

CAPSULE
(Poppy)

SILIQUE
(Mustard)

Figure 3-31   Simple dehiscent dry fruits.

In a few plants, notably the navel orange *(Citrus sinensis* cv. Washington) and seedless grapefruits *(Citrus paradisi),* pollination occurs and the fruit develops, but no mature seeds are formed. This is called parthenocarpy. Seedless watermelon *(Citrullus lanatus)* and seedless tomatoes *(Lycopersicon esculentum)* have been produced through the use of growth-regulating substances, but the characteristic of seedlessness is not genetically fixed in these plants. This, and other evidence, demonstrates that the maturation of the fruit depends to some extent upon the presence of growth substances which, in normal development, appear to be derived from the growing seeds within the fruit. In some fruits, the banana *(Musa* sp.) and seedless grapes *(Vitis* spp.) being familiar examples, fertilization may occur, but the developing seed aborts and all that remains is a small, dark-colored speck.

The ovary wall (pericarp) of most fruits varies with the species under consideration. It usually consists of three layers which can be seen in the fruit of the peach (Figure 3-29). The outer layer (exocarp) forms the skin, the middle layer (mesocarp) is the juicy flesh, and the inner layer (endocarp) is the stony box or pit surrounding and protecting the seed. There is a tremendous amount of variation in the organization of the ovary wall; layers may be fused, dry, fleshy, or even absent at maturity. Nevertheless, the organization is sufficiently evident, at least during development, so that it is useful to classify fruits. It is of interest and importance to note that a particular fruit type is not restricted to one family. Berries, for example, are found in a number of evolutionarily distinct families, indicating that particular fruit types arose more than once in evolutionary history.

Fruit classification utilizes a number of different criteria depending on the interest of the person doing the classification, but over the years a taxonomy has developed that is generally accepted by botanists and horticulturists. (The taxonomy is given in the outline that follows.) The classification is, however, artificial since many transitional types are found and the sequences of develop-

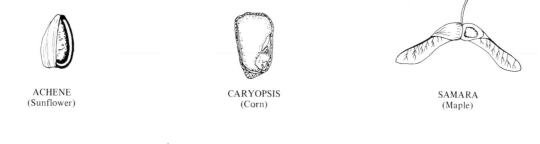

ACHENE
(Sunflower)

CARYOPSIS
(Corn)

SAMARA
(Maple)

NUT
(Oak)

SCHIZOCARP
(Cow Parsnip)

Figure 3-32   Simple indehiscent dry fruits.

ment even within a type may be different. Three major groups are recognized: simple fruits (Figures 3-30, 3-31, 3-32), aggregate fruits (Figure 3-33), and multiple fruits (Figure 3-34). Most fruits are derived from a single ovary and are called simple; fruits in which the flower receptacle becomes involved in fruit formation are called simple accessory fruits. Fruits that develop from flowers with more than one ovary are called aggregate fruits. Fruits that form from multiple ovaries that are fused into a single structure are termed multiple.

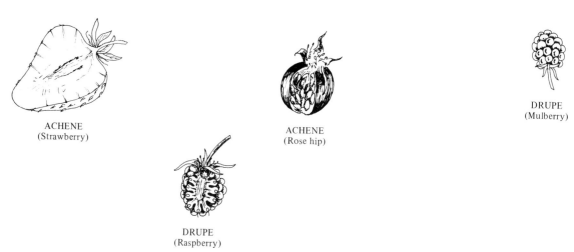

ACHENE
(Strawberry)

ACHENE
(Rose hip)

DRUPE
(Mulberry)

DRUPE
(Raspberry)

Figure 3-33   Aggregate fruits.

BERRY
(Pineapple)

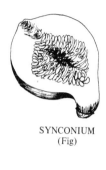

SYNCONIUM
(Fig)

Figure 3-34 Multiple fruits.

A Taxonomy of Fruits

I. Simple and simple accessory fruits

A. Fleshy fruits
1. Berry: pericarp fleshy, one or more carpels and seeds
   a. Typical berry: pericarp fleshy except for thin skin
      Tomato, grape, blueberry
   b. Pepo: pericarp fleshy, ovary wall leathery or hard
      Squash, watermelon, other cucurbits
   c. Hesperidium: rind separable and leathery, fruit segmented
      Orange, lemon, other citrus
2. Drupe: inner layer stony (pit), single seed
   Peach, cherry, olive, coconut, walnut
3. Pome: outer layer thin, core with seeds, flesh derived from flower receptacle
   Apple, pear, quince

B. Dry fruits
1. Dehiscent fruits (pods): open when ripe, one to many seeds
   a. Follicle: one carpel splitting along one side
      Columbine, larkspur

b. Legume: one carpel splitting along two sides
   Peas, beans, other members of pea family
c. Capsule: more than one carpel
   (1) Capsule (typical)
      Poppy, iris, azalea, lily, portulaca
   (2) Silique: elongate capsule, two carpels
      Mustard
2. Indehiscent fruits: do not open when ripe, one or more seeds
a. Achene: fruit small, one seed attached to pericarp
   Sunflower, buckwheat, dandelion
b. Caryopsis (grain): pericarp and seed coats fused
   All grasses including cereal grains
c. Samara: pericarp enlarged into wings
   Maple, ash, elm
d. Nut: large achene with stony ovary layers
   Oak, hazelnut
e. Schizocarp: two or more carpels
   Carrot, other members of umbel family

II. Aggregate fruits

A. Achene fruits
  1. Multiple achenes attached to enlarged, fleshy receptacle
    Strawberry
  2. Multiple achenes within enlarged, fleshy receptacle
    Rose hip

B. Drupe fruits
  Multiple drupes attached to enlarged, fleshy receptacle
  Raspberry, blackberry

III. Multiple fruits

A. Berry fruits
  Many seedless berries developed on fleshy receptacle
  Pineapple

B. Drupe fruits
  1. Many drupes borne on fleshy receptacle
    Mulberry
  2. Many drupes within fleshy receptacle (synconium)
    Fig

SEEDS

By definition, a seed is a fertilized, mature ovule containing an embryo capable, upon germination, of giving rise to a new plant. The embryo, plus its food supply in cotyledons or endosperm, is surrounded by seed coats derived from tissues of the parent plant's ovule. The seed coats are usually intact except for a pore (micropyle) at or near the point where the developing seed was attached to the ovary wall. The embryo is a complete plant, with a root (the radicle), one or two sets of leaves and a short stem (the epicotyl or plumule) which develops into the growing point of the stem.

Embryology

With rare exceptions, seed development is essentially the same for all flowering plants. Following fertilization of the ovule or egg and the simultaneous union of the second sperm nucleus with the double polar nuclei (the process called double fertilization) to give rise to the endosperm nucleus, the process of embryogenesis is initiated. The fertilized egg, now called a zygote, begins a series of cell divisions resulting in the formation of the embryo. All the stages in embryo development have been followed in detail in many plants and, while some differences are found, the pattern is essentially the same as seen diagrammatically in Figure 3-35.

Many plants have the ability to form viable seeds without fertilization. This phenomenon, called apomixis, can result from several different processes (Chapter 15). In one common process the embryo sac cells that remain diploid give rise directly to an embryo, bypassing the fertilization of an egg by a sperm nucleus. In other plants the egg cell itself does not form a haploid gamete and develops directly into an embryo and then into a seed. Basically, then, a seed produced apomictically has the genetic potential of the female parent plant. Such seeds give rise to clones of the parent plant and the offspring plants can be considered equivalent to vegetatively produced plants. Blackberries and raspberries *(Rubus),* hawthorns *(Crataegus),* and dandelion *(Taraxacum)* are notable for producing seeds apomictally. The important 'Kentucky' bluegrasses *(Poa pratensis)* produce apomictic seeds, so seeds from plants produced in different environments may allow the development of clones that are well adapted to different environmental situations.

Apomictic plants such as citrus may be polyembryonic, showing the development of more than one seed in a single embryo sac. For this reason, some seeds in a citrus fruit may be identical twins and may be utilized to produce clonal stocks. However, since citrus also produces seeds through normal fertiliza-

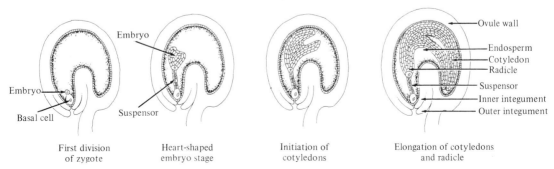

First division   Heart-shaped   Initiation of   Elongation of cotyledons
of zygote   embryo stage   cotyledons   and radicle

Figure 3-35 Stages in the development of an embryo.

tion, it is usually more efficient to increase populations of desirable trees by classical grafting procedures (Chapter 15).

Structure

One important difference among plants is whether the endosperm, which provides food to the developing embryo, is entirely used up or whether it persists in the mature seed. In many cultivated plants the major food storage tissue is the cotyledon and the endosperm is not found at maturity, but in some plants, the castor bean *(Ricinus communis)* being a typical example, the endosperm remains intact and is seen as a thin, leaflike structure. The endosperm in cereal grains is also present at maturity and, as in corn, forms the bulk of the edible portion of the kernel. The endosperm of field corn *(Zea Mays)* tends to have a hard portion with relatively large amounts of protein plus a softer part containing mostly starch (see Chapter 21). Sweet corn on the other hand, stores relatively little protein or hard starch, but contains large quantities of sugar. Sweet corn picked for the market has a milky endosperm with a high sugar content. The milk and meat of the coconut, a major source of plant fats, are endosperm tissue. The three major seed types are illustrated in Figure 3-36. Remember that the corn kernel and the grains of other grasses are one-seeded fruits with a seed enclosed in the tightly appressed fruit walls.

The taxonomic separation of the two major groups of angiosperms into monocots and dicots is based on the number of cotyledons present as part of the embryo, with the monocots (including grasses, lilies, palms, and orchids) having only one cotyledon and the dicots having two. Gymnosperms, on the other hand, may have a number of cotyledons seen as a circle of needles at the top of the young seedling. The size, thickness, and amount of food (carbohydrate, protein, and lipid) stored in cotyledons also varies with the plant species. In legumes the bulk of the seed is composed of cotyledon which is a major source of human food. The cotyledons of many seedlings become green and, in addition to providing food that was stored in them, can photosynthesize until, as their food reserves become exhausted, they shrivel and drop off. By then, the plant has

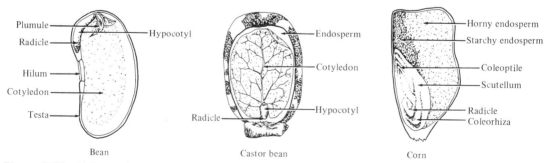

Figure 3-36   Major seed types.

formed several sets of true leaves and is usually capable of an independent existence.

The seed coats have important protective and regulatory functions. They are somewhat impervious to water and can prevent the drying out of the delicate embryo, although they must allow water to enter the seed for its hydration and germination. In many plants seed coats contain water-soluble substances that prevent germination which must be leached away by rain before the seed can germinate. In some plants substances leached from seed coats can prevent the germination of seeds of other species, giving the seedling a selective advantage by reducing competition with other plants. In morning glory *(Ipomoea purpurea)* the seed coats are thick and woody which provides protection, but prevents water uptake and germination until the seed coats either rot or are mechanically disrupted by scarification with a file or knife. This seems to be advantageous in extending seed longevity and preventing the seeds from germinating at the wrong time of year. Other seeds may also require disruption of the seed coats to allow oxygen to penetrate.

Dispersal and Harvesting

Plants have, over evolutionary time, developed many mechanisms for dispersing their seeds. Having the new plants develop at a distance from its parent plant is, in many cases, ecologically advantageous and it also serves to broaden the range of sites in which the plant can develop. Wind, water, and animals are major carriers of seeds, and plants have developed structures that facilitate dispersal. Many plants have wind-borne seeds or fruits (Figure 3-37). The dandelion *(Taraxacum officinale)* fruit, a one-seeded achene, has a stalk to which are attached a number of fine hairs which keep the fruit airborne for long periods of time. Similar hairs are found on seeds of milkweed *(Asclepias),* the cottonwood tree *(Populus deltoides),* and other plants. Other seeds, being very small, can be carried short distances by even gentle breezes. This is true of some orchids and tobacco *(Nicotiana* spp.). The winged fruits and seeds of the maples, elms, and ashes can whirl like propellers for some distance from the parent plant, and western tumbleweed *(Amaranthus albus)* is uprooted and blown by winds for long distances, scattering its seeds as it rolls across the prairies. The forcible

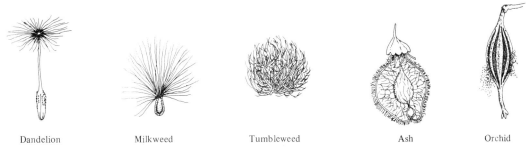

Dandelion   Milkweed   Tumbleweed   Ash   Orchid

Figure 3-37 Wind-dispersed seeds.

ejection of seeds by plants such as the wild geranium *(Geranium maculatum),* vetches *(Vicia)* (Figure 3-38), and jewelweed or touch-me-not *(Impatiens* spp.) is another mechanism for dispersal.

Relatively few horticulturally important plants have seeds dispersed by water. The coconut *(Cocos nucifera)* is probably the outstanding example of water dispersal, although the seeds of other palms also have this ability.

Animal distribution is common (Figure 3-39); squirrels planting nuts is so well-known as to be part of our language. Fleshy fruits may have evolved as an adaptation that ensures animal dispersal, and the commercial and home horti-culturists know that cherries and other crops have to be protected from birds. Although few economic plants have spurs or hooks which catch in animal fur, the beggar tick *(Bidens),* cocklebur *(Xanthium),* burdock *(Arctium),* and other weeds are difficult to remove from dogs and from our own clothing.

The quality of a batch or lot of seeds is affected by many factors including adverse conditions during their development and conditions of harvesting and storage. The presence of pathogenic microorganisms in or on the seed can also affect their utility. An international seed testing association develops standard methods for testing the quality of seeds of commercial value and to ensure the active support and cooperation of national organizations throughout the world. Assay items of interest include the percentage of contaminating weed seeds, cleanliness, freedom from disease (a difficult series of analyses), and the viability of the seeds as judged by chemical and germination tests. Compliance in North America and Europe is excellent, assuring the consumer of seeds that can be expected to perform as advertised, assuming that conditions of storage have been met (Chapter 14).

Figure 3-38 Self-propelled seed of vetch *(Vicia).*

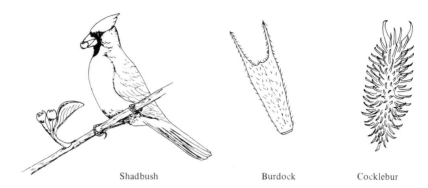

| Shadbush | Burdock | Cocklebur |

Figure 3-39 Animal-dispersed seeds.

SUPPLEMENTARY READINGS

Berrie, A. M. M. 1977. *An Introduction to the Botany of the Major Crop Plants.* Heydon, London.

Dale, J. E. 1982. *The Growth of Leaves.* Edward Arnold, London.

Esau, K. 1977. *Anatomy of Seed Plants.* Wiley, New York.

Fahn, A. 1982. *Plant Anatomy.* 3rd ed. Pergamon Press, Elmsford, N.Y.

Hall, J. L., T. J. Flowers, and R. M. Roberts. 1982. *Plant Cell Structure and Function.* 2nd ed. Longman, London.

Heyward, H. E. 1938. *The Structure of Economic Plants.* Macmillan, New York.

Langer, R. H. M., and G. D. Hall. 1982. *Agricultural Plants.* Cambridge University Press, New York.

Pijl, L., van den. 1982. *Principles of Dispersal in Higher Plants.* Springer-Verlag, Berlin.

Raven, P. H., R. F. Evert, and H. Curtis. 1976. *Biology of Plants.* 2nd ed. Worth, New York.

Rost, T. L., M. G. Barbour, R. M. Thornton, T. E. Weier, and C. R. Stocking. 1979. *Botany: A Brief Introduction.* Wiley, New York.

Steeves, T. A., and Sussex, I. M. 1972. *Patterns in Plant Development.* Prentice-Hall, Englewood Cliffs, N.J.

C H A P T E R 4

ANATOMY OF CULTIVATED PLANTS

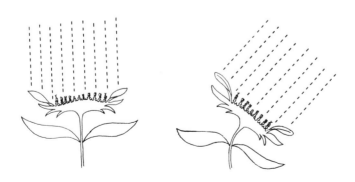

MICROSCOPIC STRUCTURE OF CELLS

Plant Cells

The plant cell consists of a nonliving wall containing cellulose surrounding the living protoplast (Figure 4-1). One major difference between plant and animal cells is that animal cells do not have a cell wall. The protoplast is bounded by a cell membrane; within the membrane are the gel-like cytoplasm and organelles (Figure 4-2). Cytology is the study of the structure of cells, and cell biology is the parallel study of cell function.

The primary plant cell wall is initiated when the cell is completing its division. It consists of a number of bundles of cellulose fibrils synthesized from sugar and excreted from the protoplasm. The cellulose fibrils are composed of microfibrils, and these, in turn, are composed of cellulose—an extended chain of glucose (a six-carbon sugar) molecules linked together much like beads on a string. Cellulose comprises less than half of the total plant cell wall; water, pectins, hemicelluloses, protein, and inorganic compounds (calcium, phosphorus) make up the rest of the wall. The pectins form a jellylike layer, the middle

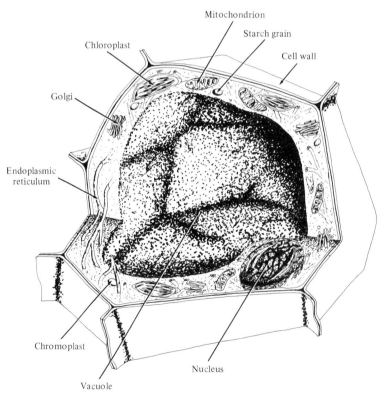

Figure 4-1 A typical plant cell.

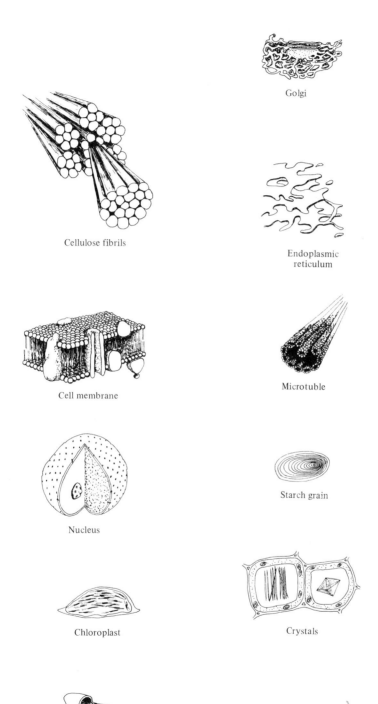

Golgi

Cellulose fibrils

Endoplasmic
reticulum

Cell membrane

Microtuble

Nucleus

Starch grain

Chloroplast

Crystals

Mitochondrion

Figure 4-2 Cell organelles and inclusions.

lamella, which binds adjacent cells together. As plant cells age, or when the wall thickens, additional cellulose fibrils are deposited in overlapping layers on the inside of the wall adjacent to the cell membrane. The mature wall may be impregnated with strengthening compounds such as lignin or with waterproofing substances such as suberin. Wood consists of dead cells whose walls were, prior to death, strengthened with additional cellulose and lignin. Paper is made from the wood from many tree species or from the stems of other plants. In the manufacture of paper the lignin is removed by chemical treatment of the wood pulp. Since lignin is highly resistant to decay, its disposal by the paper industry presents large environmental problems.

Protoplasm is a gel-like emulsion of water and a large number of organic (carbon-containing) substances. Many of these are proteins, most of which are enzymes, including those involved in energy metabolism and in the synthesis of a variety of chemicals. There are also a number of inorganic molecules and ions that serve as nutrients and as parts of enzymes and other molecules. The protoplasm is best described as looking like the white of an egg (itself a protein emulsion containing inorganic and organic molecules).

The cell membrane bounding the protoplasm is a typical bilayer membrane. Two layers of lipid form the major portion of this plasma membrane, or plasmalemma. In addition, there is an array of globular protein molecules that may be on the upper and lower surfaces of the lipid layers or may penetrate through both lipid layers (see Figure 4-2). Some of these protein molecules are hollow and others appear to be solid. The membrane is involved in the movement of water and dissolved substances in and out of the cell. Depending upon the function of the cell and upon environmental conditions, the membrane may facilitate or impede the passage of substances. Any loss of structural or functional integrity of the cell membrane, caused by toxins, high or low temperatures, or other unusual conditions, may result in loss of membrane function and the death of the cell. At least part of freezing injury is loss of membrane integrity; the mushy texture of frozen fruits and vegetables is due to the movement of water from the cells into the spaces between the cells. An impairment of the respiration process, resulting in a decrease in the availability of energy compounds, can also result in loss of membrane function.

A number of structurally organized bodies are found in the protoplasm. These are known as organelles (see Figure 4-2). The most prominent of the organelles is the nucleus (see Figure 4-2C). It is usually the largest organelle and, particularly in young cells, occupies a large portion of the cell volume. Most cells of flowering plants contain only one nucleus, although some algae contain several to many nuclei. The nucleus is usually a spherical to ovoid organelle, surrounded by inner and outer membranes. Its primary role is the storage and transmittal of genetic information. The nucleus contains the chromosomes—large, complex molecules of protein complexed with the hereditary material itself, deoxyribonucleic acid (DNA). One to several smaller bodies are imbedded within the nucleus. These nucleoli are the structures in which the other type of genetic molecule, ribonucleic acid (RNA), is synthesized, moving out through the pores in the nuclear envelope to activate and control protein synthesis that occurs on the endoplasmic reticulum in RNA-containing ribosomes.

Chloroplasts are not found in all living cells. Cells may have only one chloroplast, although most chlorophyll-containing cells have many; the cells of the leaves of spinach *(Spinacia oleracea)* may contain up to 100 chloroplasts, accounting for the deep green color of these leaves. Like other cell organelles, the chloroplast is bounded by an outer and an inner membrane. Since the chloroplast is the photosynthetic organelle, these membranes must be permeable to carbon dioxide, oxygen, water, and organic and inorganic compounds including sugars, acids, and amino acids. The chloroplast has within it a complex membranous structure imbedded in a proteinaceous, gel-like matrix, or stroma, which contains the enzymes that participate in fixing carbon dioxide during photosynthesis (Chapter 11).

Similar in shape and smaller than chloroplasts are the mitochondria. They are surrounded by a bilayer membrane inside of which is a deeply folded inner membrane. The enzymes on this inner membrane are involved in the respiratory process (Chapter 12). The number of mitochondria varies; cells that are actively respiring contain more than cells that are metabolically quiescent. The cells of a seed, for example, contain few mitochondria until the seed has absorbed water and begins germination at which time the mitochondria begin to divide and greatly increase in number.

The Golgi bodies, or dictyosomes, are membranous organelles with the capacity to bud off parts of the organelle to form new ones. The roles of Golgi bodies in the activities of plant cells are not thoroughly known, although they appear to be involved in the formation of new cell wall materials and probably serve as centers for the synthesis and secretion of regulatory chemicals.

Ramifying throughout the protoplasm is the diffuse organelle known as the endoplasmic reticulum (ER). Like the Golgi, it is membranous, forming long tubes or flattened, hollow plates. The ER seems to form connections continuous with the pores in the nuclear envelope and perhaps with other organelles. There are two kinds of ER, smooth and rough. Rough ER contains small round to dumbbell-shaped bodies, the ribosomes, composed of RNA and protein in which the information from the nucleus is used to code for the synthesis of specific protein molecules. Those that lack ribosomes are called smooth ER.

Microtubules are hollow tubes made up of long chains of protein molecules arranged in a series of spirals or helices. They, like the Golgi, are involved in cell wall formation and in the process of cell division.

Depending on internal and external environmental conditions and on the cell type, starch grains may be found floating freely in the protoplasm or embedded in the chloroplast. As needed, they are transformed back into sugars to be used in respiration. Some cells, those of the potato tuber and other storage organs, are genetically programmed to store starch; indeed, potatoes have been bred for this characteristic and are excellent carbohydrate sources.

Not all plant cells contain crystals, but they are sufficiently common to warrant inclusion in this survey of the constituents of cells. Crystal form is a function of the chemical composition of the inorganic or organic substance that constitutes the crystal. Some plant species accumulate specific chemicals as crystals in their vacuoles; examples are the calcium oxalate in leaves of rhubarb *(Rheum Rhabarbarum)* and dumb cane *(Dieffenbachia* spp.), which makes their leaves irritating when eaten and the crystals of silica found in cell walls of many grasses.

Another major difference between plant and animal cells, in addition to the presence of cell walls in plants, is the presence of vacuoles in green plant cells. If the criterion for an organelle is that it is bounded by a membrane, the vacuole certainly qualifies. Essentially, the vacuole of a mature plant cell is a membrane-bound bubble of water containing a variety of chemicals. When first formed, the cell does not contain a vacuole and the protoplasm fills the volume inside the cell membrane and cell wall. Water accumulates within a series of small vacuoles during cell enlargement, and these usually coalesce into one large vacuole that occupies much of the volume of the cell (see Chapter 13). Growth in the size of the cell occurs through the uptake of water into the vacuole. Because of this high volume of water, the plant cell is under considerable hydrostatic pressure. Cells having a vacuolar water pressure equal to that of the cell wall are said to be fully turgid. The internal water pressure of turgid cells tends to keep the tissues and organs containing the cells erect. When the vacuole loses water, and the cells become flaccid, the plant may wilt or even die.

Another function of the vacuole, in addition to growth and support, is the control of the water relations of plant cells (Chapter 6). It also serves as a reservoir for many substances. The sugar extracted from sugar cane and sugar beet, the red and blue compounds of flower petals and fruit skins, and the acids that confer specific tastes and odors to oranges, apples, tomatoes, and other fruits are found dissolved in vacuolar water.

The typical plant cell is structurally complex and its multiple roles are equally complex. Not surprisingly, the major organelles show the same structure and perform the same functions in all plant cells in which organelles are found (the prokaryotic bacteria and blue-green algae lack major organelles). In fact, with the exception of chloroplasts, vacuoles, and cellulosic cell walls, the structure and function of organelles of animal cells are the same as those of plants.

Cell Types

Cells of flowering plants are characterized both structurally and functionally; essentially, the structure of a cell reflects its function, and function depends on structure. When categorizing cell types (Figure 4-3), primary attention is focused on the development of the cell wall.

Structurally and functionally, the primary or fundamental plant cell type is parenchyma. Cells formed by division are always considered to be parenchyma, although their structural and functional fates and roles may eventually be quite different. Most parenchyma cells at maturity are roughly spherical, although the planes of contact with other cells makes them multifaceted. The cell is thin-walled, has a prominent nucleus, lacks a vacuole as a young cell, and has a prominent vacuole or vacuoles when mature. Parenchyma cells, as components of all living tissues, conduct many of the functions associated with plants; those containing chloroplasts carry on photosynthesis, all conduct energy transforma-

Parenchyma

Epidermis

Collenchyma

Sclerenchyma

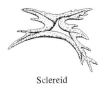

Sclereid

Phloem
sieve tube cell and
companion
cell

Fiber

Primary
xylem
elements

Secondary
xylem
tracheid

Secondary
xylem
vessel

Figure 4-3   Cell types.

tions, and all participate in maintaining plant turgor. Almost all other cell types are derived directly or indirectly by differentiation of parenchyma cells.

Epidermal cells are the outermost layer or sheet of cells of all plant organs. They are rarely photosynthetic, but may appear to be blue or red because of the accumulation of colored compounds in their vacuoles. Most epidermal cells of young stems and leaves secrete a waterproof substance, cutin, as a thin layer on the outside of the cell. This cuticle reduces water loss from the organ. Leaf and fruit epidermal cells may also secrete true waxes outside the cutin layer; the shine on an apple is due to these waxes. The epicuticular waxes of some fruits are used commercially; familiar examples include bayberry *(Myrica cerifera)* waxes used to make candles and the carnauba waxes, from the carnauba palm *(Copernicia cerifera),* used in shoe polish, plastics, and cosmetics. Young root epidermal cells are not coated with cutins or waxes; older roots are surrounded by suberin.

A common derivative of parenchyma is collenchyma. Collenchyma cells are alive and contain nuclei, but they differ from the parent cell in that they have cellulosic thickenings of the cell wall, usually at the corners or angles of the cell. Collenchyma cells serve as supports for organs, both because of the thickenings and because of vacuolar water pressure. The "strings" of celery stalks are collenchyma.

With additional thickening of the cell wall, and usually the subsequent death of the cell, sclerenchyma is formed. In addition to cellulose, the walls of sclerenchyma cells contain large amounts of lignin which further stiffens the wall. Some sclerenchyma cells are elongated to form fibers which strengthen the organ in which they are found. The long sclerenchyma fibers in hemp *(Cannabis)* or flax *(Linum)* are used to make rope or linen, respectively. Others, much less elongated and sometimes branched or irregular in outline, are called sclereids, or stone cells. The gritty texture of a pear is due to the presence of stone cells in the flesh of the fruit. When mature, sclerenchyma cells have lost their cell contents and are dead, but the thick walls continue to act as strengthening components. Because of the organization of the secondary thickenings of the walls, sclerenchyma cells provide resistance to both compression and shear. One obvious role of these cells is a protective function, as in the shells of nuts which consist of layers of sclerenchyma cells.

The vascular or "plumbing" system of plants is composed of several cell types organized into two major complex tissue systems: phloem and xylem. The phloem tissue, involved in the movement of materials from leaves to the rest of the plant, consists of parenchyma and sclerenchyma fibers plus sieve tube cells and their constant partner, companion cells. Phloem sieve tube cells are elongated derivatives of parenchyma cells whose end walls have become perforated like a sieve to allow the movement of dissolved substances. At functional maturity the sieve tube is alive since it contains protoplasm, but its nucleus has disappeared. Companion cells, on the other hand, are nucleated and play an important, but poorly understood role in the process of movement of materials from the leaves to the rest of the plant (see Chapter 6).

The other major tissue of the vascular system, the xylem, is also composed of several cell types. Fibers, parenchyma, and other living cell types are usually present in addition to the xylem cells that are primary pipelines for the movement of water and dissolved substances from the root to the rest of the plant. All functional xylem cells are dead at maturity; the cell contents have disappeared and the lumen of the cells is hollow. Xylem cells have extensive secondary thickening of their walls with deposition of many layers of cellulose, usually impregnated with lignin and other compounds, that provide additional strength and waterproofing. Based on their derivation, xylem cells are categorized as being primary or secondary. Primary xylem cells are formed by the direct differentiation of parenchyma cells in the young root or stem, while secondary xylem cells are formed by the division of special cells called cambium. The two categories are structurally distinguishable. The secondary thickenings of primary xylem cell walls do not cover the entire wall, but form rings, spirals, or incomplete sheets about the cell. The secondary xylem cells are usually completely covered by thickened walls with openings in the form of small pits in the walls.

Secondary xylem cells are further subdivided into two major types. Those in which the end walls remain closed are called tracheids, and those in which the end walls dissolve are called vessels. Both are capable of carrying water, although plants with a high proportion of vessels may carry water more efficiently since there is less resistance to flow in an open pipe than in a semiclosed pipe in which water must move through the pitted areas of the cells. Both vessels and tracheids, because of extensive secondary thickening, are effective strengthening elements. In woody perennials the woody bulk of the trunk and root is composed of xylem. In conifers, these are always tracheids, while the flowering plants may have both or, more usually, only vessels.

A number of other plant cell types occur in some species of plants. Several types of modified parenchyma cells are secretion cells such as those that synthesize rubber, resins, and nectar. Leaves possess modified epidermal parenchyma cells with walls that can bend as the water pressure within the cells is changed. As discussed in Chapter 6, these guard cells regulate the movement of water vapor and carbon dioxide into and out of the leaves. There are many other structural modifications, but for the most part, such specialized cells are found in only a few species.

ANATOMY OF PRIMARY ORGANS

Organization of cells into tissues and tissues into organs bears directly on how plants are put together and how and where desirable modifications can be made by breeding, selection, and manipulation of the plant's environment. The anatomical arrangement of organs is fairly constant and the plants of horticultural and agronomic importance have much the same microscopic structure. There may be species or even cultivar alterations in the proportions of various cells and tissues. The proportion of starch-containing parenchyma cells in the potato tuber is higher than in the aerial part of the stem system, but the cell types of these two stems are the same and all tissues systems are present in both. The edible leaf stalk (petiole) of celery is organized in virtually the same way as the petiole of spinach or tomato, although these plants are in different families. When studying a particular cultivated species, variations of the basic anatomical plan become important, but the organization will very likely be the same.

Roots and stems of many plants have one kind of anatomy when young (primary structure) and a more complex organization as they mature (secondary structure). It is convenient to look at primary structure before studying secondary structure.

Structure of Primary Roots

A diagrammatic representation of a typical young root is presented as Figure 4-4. A primary root, whether a tap root, lateral root, or adventitious root, can be subdivided into four areas or zones that represent the major stages in root development. The meristematic zone, also called the base or root tip zone, consists of two portions, the lower called the root cap and the area just behind the cap called the root apical meristem. The word meristem refers to a group of cells which tend to be small, lack cell vacuoles, and are in the process of rapid cell division without much subsequent cell enlargement. In the primary root, most of the cells that will initiate growth in length (but not the girth) of the root are formed in the meristem, which is also called the zone of division. The root cap at the tip of the meristem is composed of loosely arranged cells which, as the root grows through the soil, are rubbed off by frictional contact with soil particles and are replaced by the division of cells at the base of the meristem.

As older cells of the meristem are supplanted by the division of cells closer to the root apical meristem, these former meristem cells become organized into columns or files and begin to elongate. This area of the primary root is known as the elongation zone. Not only is cell elongation occurring, but the central cylinder of the root, composed of parenchyma cells, is beginning to show changes that indicate that it will become the vascular cylinder. The cells of the outer ring of the vascular cylinder, the endodermis, develop a band of waterproof material in the cell wall that effectively prevents water from entering the vascular cylinder without passing through these endodermal cells. Outside the endodermal ring is a region of thin-walled parenchyma cells, the root cortex, through which water can flow. The importance of a freely flowing intercellular path for water movement in the cortex and a water-impervious endodermal wall is discussed in Chapter 6.

The third growth zone of primary root structure is called the maturation zone, because it is in this zone that the vascular tissues, the xylem and phloem, assume their mature, functional form. These cells do not look different from primary vascular cells of the stem discussed below, but they are arranged in a different pattern. The epidermis covering the root at the zone of maturation may develop long outgrowths, root hairs, that extend out into the soil and greatly increase the root surface area available for the uptake of water and minerals from the soil solution.

The fourth root growth zone, the region of secondary thickening that results in increases in the cross-sectional area of the root, is discussed below in the section on secondary structure.

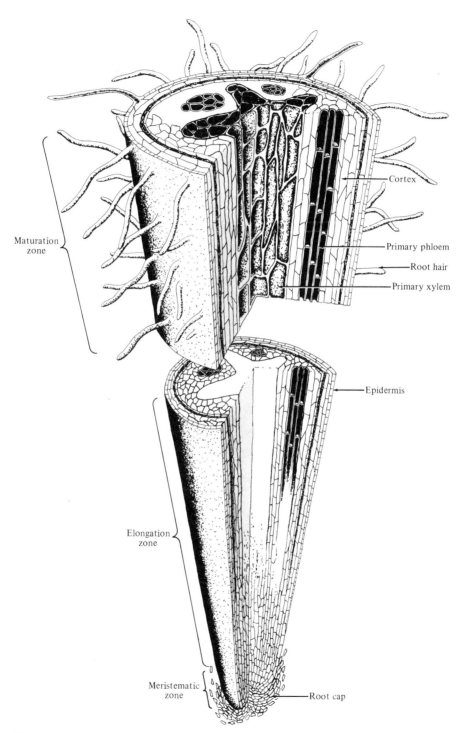

Figure 4-4 Anatomy of a primary root.

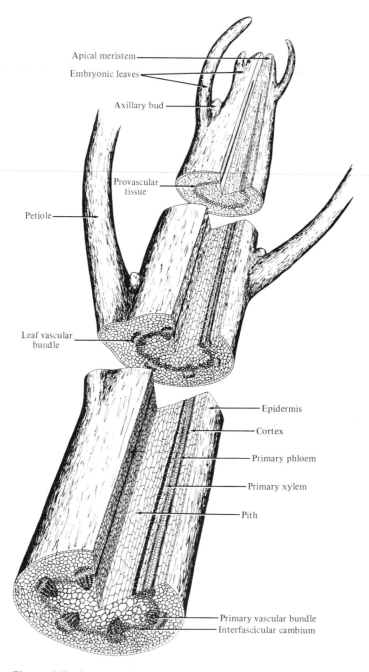

Figure 4-5 Anatomy of a young shoot.

Structure of Primary Stems

It is easiest to visualize stem anatomy as we did for roots in terms of four developmental zones or regions, three in the primary structure (Figure 4-5) and a fourth in the secondary structure. The tip of the stem, the apical meristem, is the zone of active cell division and also the zone of the initiation of the rest of the stem and of the leaves. In most plants the apical meristem is a dome-shaped structure surrounded by or covered by young leaves; this can be seen by cutting a cabbage head lengthwise.

As the apical meristem, through cell division, increases the length of the stem, those cells that had been meristematic and are now at the base of the meristem begin to elongate by water uptake. This is the elongation zone. Some of the elongating cells begin to mature. Cells in the core of the developing stem increase the density of their cell contents and some changes in the organization of their cell walls occur. These changes are the prelude to the conversion of the provascular cells into the primary vascular stele or cylinder.

The alteration of these stelar parenchyma cells into xylem and phloem occurs in the third zone, the zone of differentiation or maturation. Some of the altered parenchyma cells begin to develop secondary wall thickenings, and as their cell contents degenerate and finally disappear, they become functional primary xylem, capable of permitting the flow of water and minerals from the roots to the leaves and to the apical meristem. Other cells mature into phloem sieve cells and their companion cells and can carry sugars and other substances from the leaves to the rest of the plant. The stem xylem and phloem connect with their cell types of the root (and eventually to the vascular strands in the leaves) so that there is a continuous vascular tissue system throughout the plant.

The formation and spatial arrangement of the primary vascular system is precisely organized. The pattern of primary vascularization is genetically fixed and, while there is not much difference among the steles of dicots, the difference between dicots and monocots is striking. In the dicots the vascular tissues form a ring of discrete bundles, each bundle containing both primary xylem and primary phloem (Figure 4-6). In monocots, on the other hand, the vascular bundles appear to be scattered almost at random throughout the parenchymal cortical tissues of the stem. This difference is fundamental, because plants with scattered vascular bundles are unable to initiate the special cells involved in increasing the girth of the stem. The stems of monocots do not increase in diameter beyond that due to cell expansion. In monocots like corn, the stem can also thicken by the accumulation of clasping leaf bases.

The fourth zone, that of the increase in girth of the stem, is called the zone of secondary thickening and occurs in most dicots, although some short-lived herbaceous annuals develop very little secondary thickening. Secondary thickening of stems is covered later in this chapter.

Structure of Leaves

Leaves originate as small bumps of cells on the sides, or flanks, of the apical stem meristem (see Figure 4-5). At first the leaf consists only of a single layer of

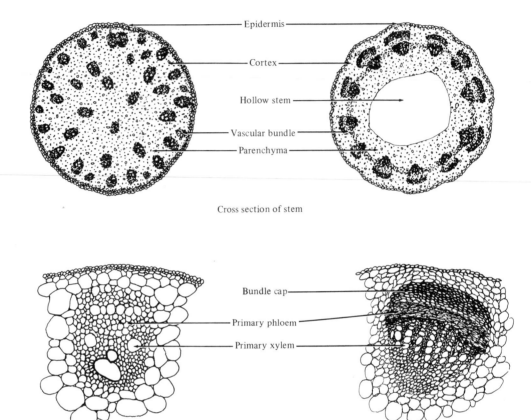

Epidermis

Cortex

Hollow stem

Vascular bundle

Parenchyma

Cross section of stem

Bundle cap

Primary phloem

Primary xylem

Cross section of vascular bundle

Monocot

Dicot

Figure 4-6 Comparison of monocot and dicot stems.

epidermal cells and a small mass of parenchyma cells. The parenchyma cells divide rapidly, and a young leaf may elongate or enlarge many times during a few days or even a few hours. New leaves are formed at appropriate positions on the apical meristem above the enlarging leaf. As the stem elongates, the vertical separation of one leaf from the leaf above it results in the formation of an internode, with the site of the leaf becoming the node. As the leaf develops, cell divisions, enlargements, and differentiations occur (Figure 4-7). The epidermal cells divide regularly as the area of leaf surface increases, and some epidermal cells undergo differentiation to form the guard cells that enclose the gas-exchange pores, the stomata (little mouths). The central parenchyma tissue undergoes a variety of changes leading to the structural differentiation of vascular strands or bundles—the veins. In a typical leaf parenchyma on the upward-facing portion of the leaf develops into columnar rows of palisade cells and those at the lower part of the leaf develop into the loosely attached and aptly named spongy mesophyll. Hairs, glands, and other structures may develop from the epidermis

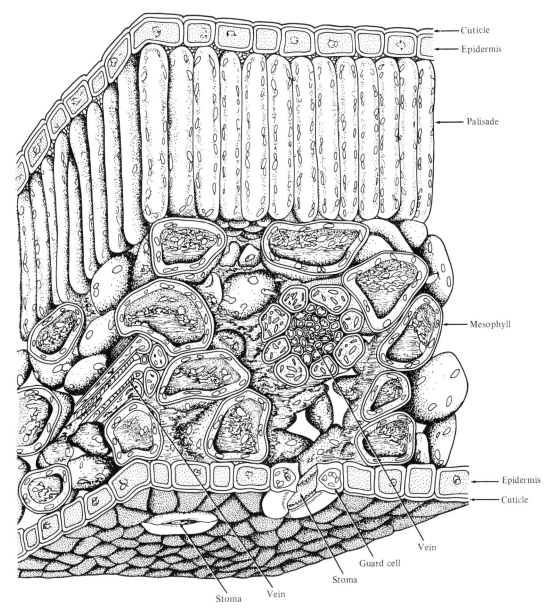

Figure 4-7   Internal structure of a leaf.

during leaf maturation. Leaf structure can be modified by environmental conditions, including water, light, mineral supply, and temperature singly or in combination.

During the early development of the leaf, some parenchyma cells will, as in the stem, differentiate into vascular cells and tissues to form the vein system. The leaf stalk or petiole also differentiates one or more vascular strands which become connected to the vascular system of the stem.

SECONDARY GROWTH

Enlargement of Roots and Stems

Stems and roots, but not leaves or flowers, increase in diameter primarily through the addition of new cells formed by division of a special cell type, the cambium cell. In mature primary stems of dicots, vascular xylem and phloem are separated from each other by layers of undifferentiated parenchyma cells. One of these layers changes into a layer or ring of cambium cells, giving rise to a fascicular cambium. Almost simultaneously, parenchyma cells between adjacent vascular bundles develop into interfascicular cambium so that there is an uninterrupted ring of cambium cells in the stem (see Figure 4-7 and Figure 4-8). The events leading to the formation of the cambial ring in roots are the same, except that interfascicular cambium does not need to be formed.

Stem and root cambia have the ability to divide in such a way that one of the two resulting cells remains a cambium cell within the ring and the other forms on the outside of the ring if it is to develop into a phloem cell or on the inside of the ring if it is to become xylem (Figure 4-9). The potential phloem or xylem cell may divide again or may start its maturation almost immediately. The oldest secondary xylem and phloem cells are those furthest from the cambium.

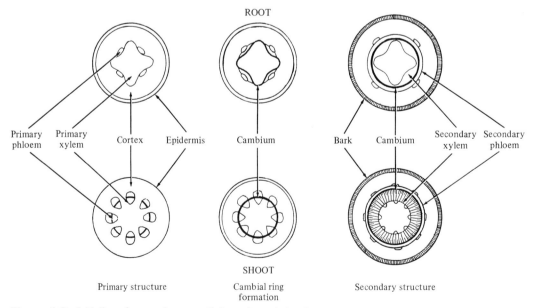

Figure 4-8 Initiation of secondary growth in roots and shoots.

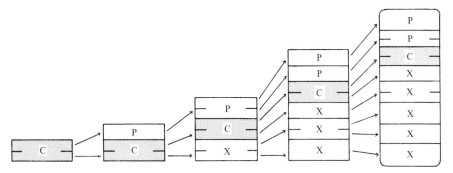

Figure 4-9 Formation of secondary xylem and phloem by division of the cambium.

The center of the thickened stem may consist entirely of secondary xylem with the primary xylem crushed out of existence, or it may be parenchymal pith.

Secondary phloem is structurally almost identical to primary phloem, but secondary xylem differs from primary xylem. The walls of primary xylem cells are strengthened only with spirals or rings (see Figure 4-3). The cellulosic walls of mature secondary xylem are thickened uniformly with openings or pits to allow water to move laterally. During the maturation of xylem vessels the end walls between adjacent xylem cells in a vertical column dissolve, leaving a continuous vertical pipe. The end walls of xylem tracheids do not dissolve, so the vertical movement of water occurs through the pits in the walls.

In perennials the cambium is not active throughout the year. Cambial activity is controlled by seasonal temperature in the temperate zones and by the yearly rhythm of water availability in arid climates. It ceases during the cold or dry seasons. Cambia are most active during the early part of the growing season, and the xylem cells formed at this time tend to be larger, with thinner walls, than those formed later. As the season advances, smaller cells with thicker walls are formed until in autumn or at the start of the dry season the cambium ceases activity, to resume again the following spring or wet season. This yearly rhythm of xylem cell formation with big cells preceeding small cells results in the appearance of annual rings.

As woody perennials age, the deposition of lignin and other chemicals in xylem cell walls results in the formation of darker-colored wood in the older, more central region of the stem or root. This is the heartwood. The lighter-colored sapwood consists of xylem formed in the previous three to five years. Only sapwood serves as the conduit for water movement. After a number of years of growth it becomes difficult to distinguish between the structure of large roots and stems, since the cambial activity and heartwood formation are essentially identical.

A cambium forms more rings of xylem in a year than rings of phloem. The phloem layer may be only 5 to 10 cells deep compared with 20 or more rings of xylem cells. The proportion of xylem to phloem cells formed in a growing season is regulated by the amounts of and ratios among growth substances. In contrast to secondary xylem, which accumulates as wood over the years, the previous year's phloem is lost or converted into bark. Functional phloem is only the current year's growth. If the phloem is injured, the cambium will begin to form phloem cells. A girdling cut around a stem must remove all of the phloem and the cambium. If the cambium is not removed, it will regenerate a new layer of phloem.

Other Secondary Growth Processes

Both stems and roots possess another generative layer, the cork cambium, the phellogen. As these organs increase in girth, the epidermal layer cannot grow fast enough or offer sufficient protection to the tissue layers beneath it. When epidermal cells die, parenchyma cells of the cortex or the phloem are changed into cambial cells. These differ from those of the vascular cambium in that new cork cells are formed (by cell division) only to the outside of the phellogen layer, with the inner cell of the dividing pair remaining a cork cambium cell. The new cells develop walls impregnated with waxy, waterproofing substances, and as they mature and die, they become cork cells (Figure 4-10). The potato skin is structurally a stem bark or cork. When potatoes are cut for planting, the cells just beneath the cut are activated by substances released from the cut cells and develop into a cork cambium. Formation of the cambium occurs in a day, and a new protective bark or skin is formed within a few more days, so that the potato surface has a barrier to both desiccation and infection.

In woody perennials the cork cambium is initiated from epidermal cells or from underlying cortical or phloem cells. As the stem or root increases in diameter through the formation of secondary xylem, expansion results in cracking of the bark into furrows characteristic of the species. Many trees and shrubs can be readily identified in winter by their bark. Cells in the base of the new furrow or crack become cork cambium cells that form new cork cells by cell division to fill in the protective bark layers. In the cork oak *(Quercus Suber)* selection over several centuries has resulted in a tree with the ability to make thick and economically valuable bark. Injury to young bark of woody perennials caused by wrapping the stem to prevent sun scald or insect damage can severely

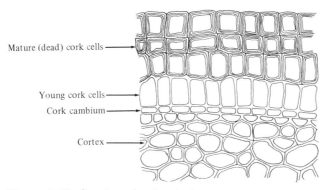

Mature (dead) cork cells

Young cork cells

Cork cambium

Cortex

Figure 4-10   Structure of cork or bark.

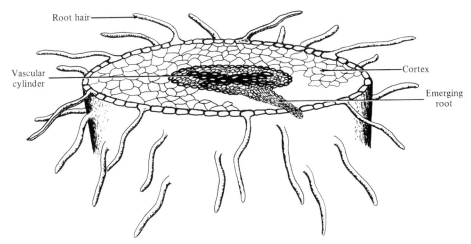

Figure 4-11 Initiation of a lateral root.

repress normal cork cambium activity and should be done carefully, if at all. Breaks in bark, if not healed by cork cambium formation, can allow microorganisms to enter and cause disease. Painting of pruning cuts (Chapter 14), which had been thought to decrease the chance for disease initiation, is now rarely done because the treatment represses cork cambium activity. Some trees, however, will develop heart rot if not treated; black oak *(Quercus nigra)* is an example.

Secondary or lateral roots are initiated in the cell type called the root pericycle. These roots are formed by division of pericyclic cells into a nest of small cells that becomes organized into a root meristem. Growing by cell division and cell enlargement, the new lateral root forces its way through the root cortex and epidermis to reach the soil (Figure 4-11).

SUPPLEMENTARY READINGS

Cutter, E. G. 1978. *Plant Anatomy.* Part I. *Cells and Tissues.* 2nd ed. Edward Arnold, London.
Fahn, A. 1982. *Plant Anatomy.* 3rd ed. Pergamon Press, Elmsford, N.Y.
Ray, P. M., T. A. Steeves, and S. A. Fulz. 1983. *Botany.* Saunders, Philadelphia.

PART TWO

THE
PLANT
ENVIRONMENT

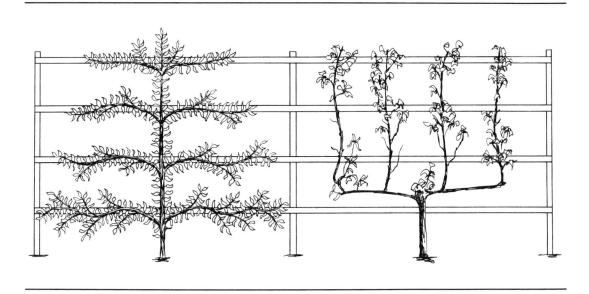

C H A P T E R 5

SOILS

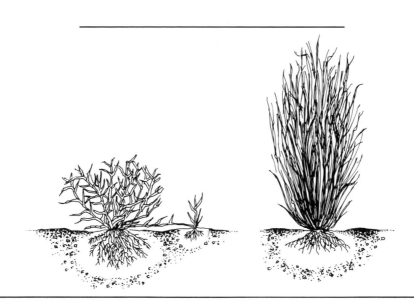

INTRODUCTION TO SOILS

Definition of Soils

Our word *soil* comes from the Latin *solum,* the "floor" or "ground." In spite of over a hundred years of critical research, a precise description eludes the soil scientist, in part because of the tremendous diversity of soils. Geologists might speak of mixtures of pulverized rock and organic matter, botanists and horticulturists might describe it as the substance on the earth's surface capable of supporting plant growth, and engineers might define it as the firm land that serves as the foundation for structures such as bridges, buildings, and roads. All these views are useful, but the idea of soil as the substratum in which plants grow will be a major focus of attention, as it has been for many centuries. Soils are basic components of the planet and how a culture attends to its soils affects its perpetuation.

Soils can be considered a three-phase system of solids, liquids, and gases. The solid phase consists of mineral and organic particles separated by a network of pores, some filled with gases—air with its carbon dioxide and oxygen being most important—and others filled with water. The proportions of each phase vary with the type of soil and are further modified by time, environment, and human, plant, and animal activities.

Genesis of Soils

The lithosphere, the solidified crust of the earth, currently is exposed over a quarter of the surface of the earth, with the remaining three quarters covered by water or ice. Oxygen, silicon, aluminum, calcium, sodium, potassium, and magnesium are the most abundant elements in the crust, accounting for about 90 percent of the lithosphere, although over 80 elements combined into 2000 compounds are present. The rocky crust, the parent rock for soil formation, is slowly fragmented into smaller pieces and into individual minerals by the action of wind, water, ice, and temperature changes. These fragments are altered by mechanical and chemical processes, mixed with organic materials, and changed by biological processes to form the extremely variable substance we call soil. Rates of soil formation from rock vary not only with the nature of the parent rock, but also with time. Many soils are, on a geological scale, very young and are still being developed. Depending on climatic conditions, the nature of the parent rocks, and a host of biotic factors, soil formation may be measured in eons, in centuries, or in decades. The establishment of a new home garden can be an example of soil formation within a few years.

Soils may not remain where their development has taken place. They may be moved by water (alluvial deposition), wind (loess deposition), ice (till or moraine deposition), or volcanic action (ash deposition). Topography, too, is important in soil movement and formation. The quantity of precipitation, exposure to wind, and temperature range and change all vary with elevation, slope angle, and aspect of the land (the direction the land faces), with consequent modifications in the rates of weathering of rock and erosion. Soils on upper slopes tend to be thinner and to contain fewer nutrients than those in valleys; hill farmers have a harder life than farmers who till valley soils.

The type of parent rock is of major importance in the type of soils developed in a particular location. Sedimentary rocks produce soils that tend to be neutral or slightly alkaline, while soils formed above igneous granites are usually more acidic. The soils of the southeastern United States are generally deposited by runoff from the Appalachian Mountains, are sandy or clayey, and tend to be acidic, while those of the Mississippi River basin are water deposited, are rich in nutrients, deep, and neutral in reaction. There are, of course, many exceptions to these generalizations. A good deal of effort has been made by geologists, geographers, and soil scientists to follow in detail the genesis of soils throughout the world.

The climate prevailing at the time a soil is formed is an important factor in the nature of that soil. In arid regions wind erosion and alluvial deposition is more important than water and many of these soils have high salt concentrations and tend to be alkaline. They may be highly productive soils if adequate water is supplied. In contrast, in the Pacific northwest, where rainfall exceeds 200 cm (78 in) per year, extensive leaching results in soils that have had alkali-forming materials removed. Similar evaluations of climatic influence have been made on many of the world's soils.

How people use or misuse the land affects soil formation. The construction of highways, dams, and parking lots, the development of irrigation systems, the modification of drainage patterns, and the type and extent of plant coverage can, in just a few years, cause dramatic changes in soils. Some of these have proved to be harmful. Continued plowing of areas in Oklahoma and Texas permitted the land to deteriorate and blow away during the 1930s dust storms. After the Dust Bowl disaster, land improvement practices instituted by U.S. Department of Agriculture's soil scientists permitted some of these areas to become productive lands.

Concept of Productivity

Soil productivity, like beauty, tends to be in the eye of the beholder. Productivity is the capability of a soil to permit development of a specific crop. Obviously, a productive soil is a fertile soil, but a fertile soil may not be productive. An acidic, organic soil may be optimum for acid-requiring azaleas or blueberries, but a totally unsuitable environment for the growth of soybeans. A heavy, peaty, muck soil in Indiana is nearly ideal for mint, but cannot be used for wheat or watermelons. Every soil is productive for some plant; permanently bare soils are rarely seen under natural conditions. Many soils in the West are fertile, but are not productive because they lack water. Other soils may be unproductive because they lack essential nutrients, show chemical imbalances, or contain excessive quantities of toxic substances. Soil productivity is relative and, in many cases, is capable of being altered. Essentially, decisions on soil modification to meet chosen needs for productivity of a given crop involve both short-term and long-term cost-benefit assessments that include financial as well as subjective factors such as desire, esthetics, and confidence.

PHYSICAL PROPERTIES

Texture

Many of the horticultural characteristics of soils depend upon the relative size of the mineral particles, termed texture. Texture is determined by the proportions of sand, silt, and clay that make up the soil. Sand is composed of compounds of silicon, primarily silicon oxides or quartz. Sand particles are comparatively large with a low surface-to-volume ratio (Table 5-1). Because particles may be large and irregularly shaped, there can be a large volume of space between the grains. Water enters easily, but passes out just as easily, so sand has little water-holding capacity. The large space between particles also means that sand has low cohesiveness. Sand tends to hold low amounts of plant nutrients.

Silt is chemically heterogeneous, composed of particles of whatever the parent rock was. Being smaller in particle size than sand, water-holding capacity is higher because the space between the individual particles is smaller. Silts have moderate to high levels of nutrients with low to moderate cohesiveness.

Clay particles are very small, with a high surface-to-volume ratio. Water-holding capacity is high, space between the particles may be almost nonexistent, and there is great cohesiveness of the particles. Many clays are composed of aluminum compounds, although other minerals are involved. Clays may be rich in nutrients. The minerals bound to clay may not always be available to plants because they may be tightly bound by electrostatic charges to the surface of the particles (see the section on chemical properties later in this chapter). Clays are separated into two major groups, those that swell when wet (and shrink when dry) and those that rarely swell. Swelling clays are usually composed of finer particles that play important roles in nutrient retention and soil cohesiveness.

Table 5-1 SIZE CLASSIFICATION OF MINERAL SOIL PARTICLES ACCORDING TO THE U.S. DEPARTMENT OF AGRICULTURE SYSTEM

Particle name	Diameter (mm)	Particles per gram	Surface area (cm²/g)
Boulder	Over 250		
Cobble	250–60		
Pebble	60–4		
Gravel	4–2		
Fine gravel	2–1	100	10
Coarse sand	1.0–0.5	700	25
Medium sand	0.50–0.25	6,000	50
Fine sand	0.25–0.10	50,000	100
Very fine sand	0.10–0.05	700,000	200
Silt	0.050–0.002	6,000,000	500
Clay	Less than 0.002	90,000,000,000	8,000,000

Few soils are composed of only one particle type, but are mixtures of all three plus organic matter. Several methods are available for determining the ratios among particle groups and when the proportions are plotted on a textural triangle (Figure 5-1), mineral soils can be classified in horticultural terms. Textural analyses refer to the soils in the upper meter (39 in.) of the soil, that region in which most plant roots grow.

Horticultural soils can also be classified simply by their feel. A handful of soil is mixed with water to the consistency of putty and squeezed into a ribbon between thumb and fingers. The ribbon that forms is related primarily to the clay content of the soil. If clay makes up more than 45 to 50 percent of the soil, the ribbon will be long and flexible due to the high cohesiveness of clay. Failure to form a ribbon indicates a soil with a high proportion of silt, and a gritty feel suggests that the sand content is high. Ribbons that start to form but then break are indicative of silty loams.

The formal designation of soil textures indicates the coarseness or fineness of soils, but not whether they are, in common terminology, heavy or light. These terms refer more to the ease of working or tilling soils than to texture, although heavy soils are almost always high in clay (when they aren't excessively stony).

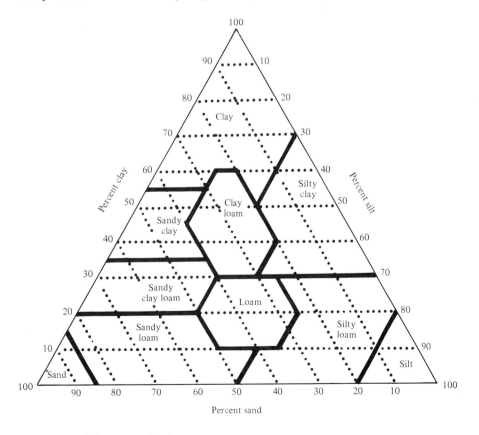

Figure 5-1 Soil texture triangle.

Ideal soils for horticulture or gardening are those with roughly 30 percent each of sand, silt, and clay plus 5–10 percent organic matter on a dry weight basis. These are indicated on Figure 5-1 as clay loams. Loam soils with lower percentages of silt and clay are also excellent, but show lower water retention. Those with above 50 percent clay tend to become waterlogged and warm up slowly in the spring. Ideal soils are rare, and appropriate management practices must be instituted (discussed later in this chapter).

Several textural classes of soil are not routinely included in this classification. Coarse-textured soils with over 20 percent organic matter and fine-textured soils with over 30 percent organic matter exhibit properties controlled by the organic fraction. These are called peat or muck soils. They are separated on the basis of the degree of decomposition of the organic matter; plant parts are structurally apparent in peats, while organic matter is more thoroughly decomposed in mucks. Intergradations are common. When peat soils are drained and the organic matter is more completely decomposed, they become mucks.

The texture of soils, although important, may not solely determine those soil properties—permeability, water-holding capacity, fertility, productivity, and ease of tilling—which are important for growing plants. Tilling and soil management practices may alter these characteristics greatly, and the growth of crops may be modified by cultural practices. Knowing textural characteristics is useful in selecting appropriate crop plants; corn will grow well on clay soils, while potatoes will not, and an irrigated sandy soil may yield as well or better than a loam that is not well watered.

Structure

Soil texture is the term that describes the size of soil particles, but it does not say how these particles are arranged. Particle arrangement is termed structure. With any ratio among sand, silt, and clay particles, their arrangement varies considerably depending on the amount and kind of organic matter present and cultivation practices. Environmental conditions, including availability of water, freezing and thawing, amount and kind of plant cover, and the temperature regime also affect structure. Basically, soil structure defines the aggregation or clumping of mineral particles into compound clusters. The aggregates are held together (flocculated) by electrostatic cohesion of mineral particles plus the binding capacity of organic matter, calcium ions, and oxides of iron and aluminum that form coatings on the particles.

Soil aggregates, frequently called peds, are classified on the basis of shape which ranges from granular and crumblike through a variety of plates, blocks, prisms, and columns. A well-tilled soil is usually granular or crumblike, with aggregates 2 to 5 mm ($\frac{1}{4}$ to $\frac{1}{2}$ in.) in diameter. The other aggregate types (blocks, columns, etc.) are more characteristic of regions below the topsoil (more than 1 m deep). Aggregation is only partly understood, but all theories include the idea that the charges on the particles, on inorganic ions, and on water molecules attract or repel each other, binding the particles and water molecules together. Hydration or dehydration and alkalinizing or acidifying materials and of organic matter can alter structure. Ice crystals fracture large aggregates into smaller ones, tilling further fractures large clods, and the activities of soil microorganisms alter adhesive forces. A well-managed, healthy soil will develop the desirable granular structure needed for good productivity.

In addition to a horticultural soil having a structure that permits development of a good root system, the organization is such that the aggregates are separated from each other by spaces, usually called pores (Figure 5-2). Depending on their size and on environmental conditions, pores contain air or water needed for plant growth. A good granular soil has two major pore-size classes. The larger, or aeration, pores are air filled; the smaller, or capillary, pores are water filled. Water held in the small pores is bound by capillary forces and so does not drain away. Nutrients in the soil dissolve in this water and it is called the soil solution.

Sandy soils usually have large numbers of large pores since the particles do not fit together tightly. Clays, composed of small particles, have few aeration pores, water is held tightly, and both water uptake (infiltration) and water movement (percolation) are slow. The diffusion of air through the pore space of soils is directly related to the volume, not the number of large pores. Sandy soils show excellent gas movement, and clays have poor exchange of gases. Clay soils, particularly when wet, may contain so little air that plant roots may be injured. Few cultivated plants can continue vigorous growth when the soil oxygen level drops below about 12 percent, which occurs frequently in wet clay soils.

Silty and particularly clayey soils are subject to compaction, which can eliminate both capillary and aeration pores. Foot traffic and the movement of tractors or similar heavy equipment across a garden plot, lawn, or field may in a short time reduce pore space by half, resulting in poor growth of plants caused by poor root aeration and restricted water supplies. Recreational areas and areas around hiking trails and campsites are always at risk of compaction. Compaction is particularly severe in wet soils; even walking on wet clay soils will severely reduce pore space. Cultivation or tilling wet, clayey soils will reduce pore space and may cause puddling, a complete elimination of pore space.

Pore space is usually determined by measuring the bulk density of the soil. Commonly expressed as the weight of oven-dry soil divided by the volume of

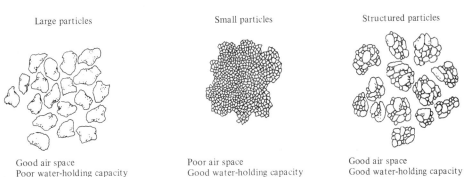

Large particles	Small particles	Structured particles
Good air space Poor water-holding capacity	Poor air space Good water-holding capacity	Good air space Good water-holding capacity

Figure 5-2 Soil structure.

oven-dry soil, or grams per cubic centimeter (g/cm³), soils with low bulk densities have large pore space volumes. A good horticultural soil will have a bulk density of 1.0 to 1.5 g/cm³ and a pore space fraction of 0.4 to 0.6 (i.e., close to one-half of the total soil volume is pore space). The bulk density of heavy clay soils ranges from 1.0 to 3.0 g/cm³, and tillable silty loams range from 1.6 to 1.9 g/cm³.

Soil Profile

Although plant science is primarily concerned with the topsoil (the uppermost meter), plant productivity is related to the entire vertical distribution of soils and subsoils. Water flow and retention, gas exchange, and soil temperature involve more than the topsoil fraction. A soil profile consists of a characterization of each layer of soil (a horizon) from the surface down to the parent bedrock. This vertical distribution of horizons is laid down during the genesis of undisturbed soils and is most easily seen when a road is cut through a hillside. Cultivation alters the uppermost horizons, but is rarely sufficiently deep to disturb the lower horizons.

The major soil horizons of a soil profile are designated by letters and/or numbers (Figure 5-3). In undisturbed field or forest soil, the solum or mineral soil is covered by an O horizon of organic matter. The O1 region consists of undecayed plant debris in which the original structure of leaves and twigs is seen. Beneath the O1 horizon is an O2 region of older plant debris undergoing decomposition. The structure of the plant parts slowly disappears into a semihumus called duff. Immediately below the duff is a third or O3 zone of humus, defined as totally decayed organic matter in which plant structure is no longer visible. In some soil profile schemes the O horizons are called L, F, and H.

The uppermost region of the soil, the topsoil, is called the A horizon. It is usually divided into three subhorizons. The A1 subhorizon is the zone of maximum humus content in which the mineral soil is well mixed with organic matter; it is frequently dark brown to black in color. Large numbers of roots and many soil microorganisms and animals are found in A1. Its depth varies from a few millimeters to a meter or more depending on the mode of soil genesis, the climate, plant cover, and the use to which the soil has been put. The A2 subhorizon contains less organic matter, a smaller number of plant roots, and fewer microorganisms and soil animals. The mineral nutrient supply is still fairly high, but water supply and air availability are less than in A1. Both A1 and A2 subhorizons are subject to leaching of minerals by precipitation and water percolation, particularly when there is no plant cover or layer of plant debris. An A3 horizon, an intergrade between the A and B horizons, is sometimes absent.

The three B horizon profiles represent the subsoil. They may contain fine organic matter particles that have been carried or sifted from the A horizon soils. They tend to be nutrient-rich, having received minerals leached from the A horizon. Because their depth limits the diffusion of oxygen and because they may contain high concentrations of leached iron and aluminum, few roots penetrate deeply into the B horizon. When A horizon soils are thin, cultivation tends to mix B and A soils. Mixing the soils may result in a topsoil with high organic

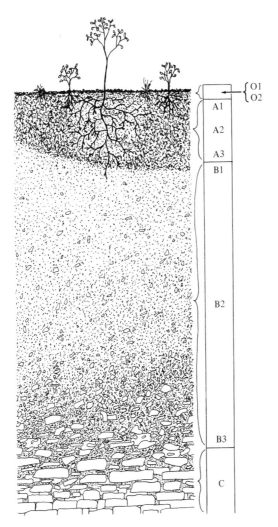

Figure 5-3 Soil profile.

matter, excellent structure, and high nutrient content, but attempts to prepare a topsoil with both A and B horizon soils should be done over a period of several growing seasons to permit the development of good soil structure.

The C horizon consists almost entirely of mineral rock in the process of being fragmented. It contains particles of various sizes plus some leached minerals from the upper horizons. Underneath it all is the parent bedrock, the R horizon.

Temperature

Temperature regimes are important for the growth and development of plants (see Chapter 8). Root development and function, the activities of soil microorganisms, and the structure of soils depend upon soil temperatures. Because of the chemical and physical composition of soil and its water content, soils have a high specific heat (the quantity of heat required to raise the temperature of 1 g of soil 1° C), and therefore they have the ability to prevent rapid changes in their temperatures. Soils warm up more slowly in the spring and cool off more slowly in the fall and also show a much smaller diurnal temperature fluctuation than does the air. The greater large pore space (less water) of sandy soils compared to clayey soils is reflected in their lower specific heat; clayey soils warm up much more slowly in the spring and rarely can be tilled or planted as early as lighter soils.

Radiation regimes also affect soil temperatures. A compacted soil radiates less heat than a more friable, porous, well-drained soil, and a granular soil tends to be warmer than one with clod-aggregate structure. Compacted, bare soil absorbs more heat than cultivated soils or soils with plant cover. The color of the topsoil, too, is a factor to be considered. A dark soil with considerable organic matter content absorbs more solar heat than a lighter soil and also releases the heat faster. The presence of a plant cover on soil also modifies the temperature regime. Since there is less direct water evaporation from soils with plant cover, they do not cool as rapidly.

Water Relations

From a plant's point of view, the soil in which it grows provides anchorage for its roots, a supply of air, and is the source of water and nutrients. The role of nutrients and of water in plant development is discussed later, but it is useful here to examine some of the water relations of soils. Water can exist in soils in all three physical phases, solid (ice), liquid, and vapor. Ice plays an important role in

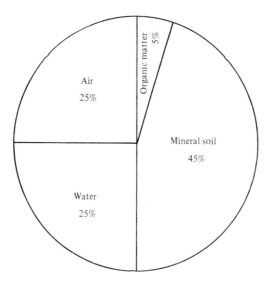

Figure 5-4   Proportions of soil constituents.

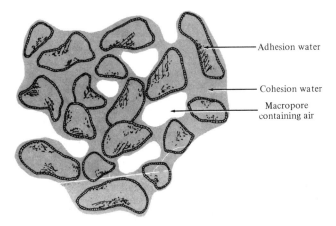

Adhesion water

Cohesion water

Macropore
containing air

Figure 5-5   Relationship of adhesion and cohesion water to pores and soil particles.

fragmenting rocks during soil genesis, and liquid and gaseous water are both involved in water retention, water movement through soil, and water uptake by plants. It should be remembered that soil water always contains dissolved minerals and gases. This soil solution is taken up by plants and is the source of minerals required by plants.

As noted previously, the solid portion of soils, composed of mineral particles and organic matter, does not occupy the entire volume of the soil, but is arranged with pore spaces that, in a good soil, can constitute close to half of the total soil volume (Figure 5-4). In saturated soils the pore space may be entirely filled with liquid water; in fully dry soil the space is occupied by air. Under conditions of adequate moisture, roughly half of the pore space, or a quarter of the total soil volume, is water filled.

Soil water is present in several forms (Figure 5-5). Some of it, the adhesion, or hygroscopic, water is bound tightly to soil particles by molecular attraction and can be removed only by heating the soil to over 100° C (212° F); this water is never available to plants. A larger fraction, the cohesion water, fills the small pores and is held there by capillary forces. Some, although not all, of these capillary forces are overcome by roots so that much of this water is available to plants. Once the pores have been filled, any excess water cannot be held by the soil. It is pulled down by gravitational forces and removed from the topsoil. This gravitational water collects at the water table and can move away into streams or aquifers. Depending on climatic conditions and on soil organization, the water table may be close to the soil surface or many meters below the surface. Impermeable layers in B or C horizons prevent free drainage of gravitational water and may lead to high water tables, saturated soils, and possible damage to plant roots.

The amount of capillary water available for plant uptake depends upon soil texture and structure (Figure 5-6). Sandy soils, composed of large, irregular particles, have many large aeration pores, but few small capillary pores. Water drains easily and quickly through such "droughty" soils. Silty soils can hold

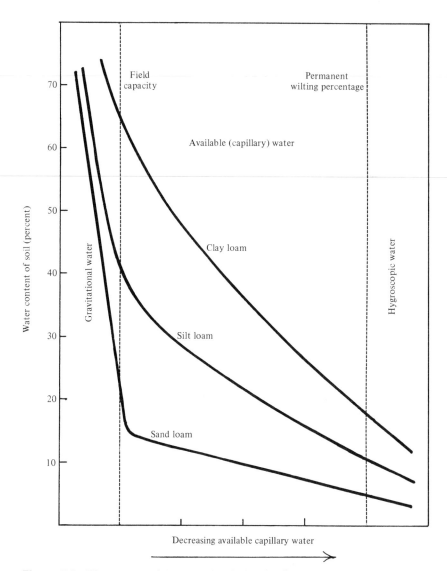

Figure 5-6 Water status of the major horticultural soil types.

more water, and clay soils hold the most water. Organic matter increases water-holding capacity both by its capacity to hold water and by improving structure and hence pore space volume. Sand can hold a quarter of its weight of water, clay can hold half its weight, and humus can hold almost twice its weight.

The terms field capacity and wilting point are frequently used in plant sciences. Field capacity refers to the water content of soils after the removal of almost all of the gravitational water (Figure 5-7). Soils at field capacity are holding all the water that they are able to hold in their capillary pores. This can easily be seen in potted plants that have been watered to the point where the soil

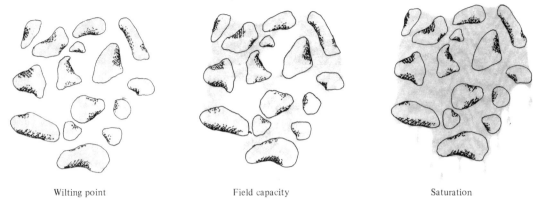

Wilting point   Field capacity   Saturation

Figure 5-7 Soil water conditions.

is saturated and pores are filled with water. The gravitational water drains from the pot for a period of time leaving the remainder of the soil at field capacity. As water continues to be removed by evaporation and by being taken up by plants, capillary pores hold less and less water and become filled with air until, at some point, the soil becomes dry to the touch. Hygroscopic or bound water is still present, but since it is unavailable, the plant begins to wilt. Unless additional water is supplied, the plant cannot recover. The amount of water in the soil when the plant wilts is termed the permanent wilting point (PWP). The permanent wilting point varies with soil texture. A sandy soil ceases to supply water to plants when it has reached about 10 percent water, while a clay loam has reached the permanent wilting point when the water has fallen to about 20 percent (see Figure 5-6).

The ability of water to enter and move through soils is called its infiltration capacity. Unless infiltration occurs, precipitation will run off the surface and can cause serious erosion. The amount of infiltration depends on soil texture, structure, and how close to field capacity the soil is at the time of precipitation. Surface crusts on dry clayey soils reduce infiltration as does compaction and the dispersion of aggregates caused by alkaline or saline conditions. Infiltration capacity is usually higher in sandy soils than clayey soils. Good tillage, the presence of plant cover, and channels formed by burrowing animals and decayed roots increase infiltration. Terracing, control of slope, and other practices are designed to hold water until it can infiltrate instead of running off (Figure 5-8).

The movement of water through horticultural soils is usually slow and follows the gradient of soil moisture from regions of high water content to low water content. Some movement of water vapor occurs along the same gradient, particularly when capillary pores are not completely filled, but vapor movement is not important in most soils.

The quality of soil solutions depends on many factors including the type and quantity of dissolved salts and the presence of potentially toxic quantities of inorganic and organic substances. Much attention has been given to controlling the amounts of salt in irrigation waters. Concern about environmental pollution

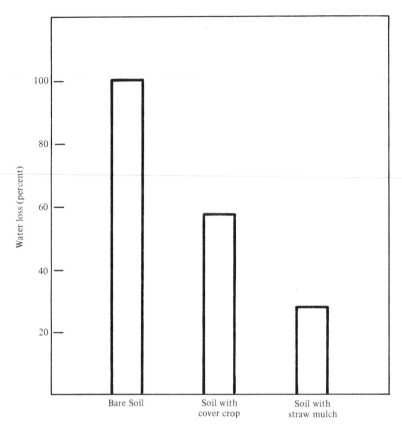

Figure 5-8 Water loss as a function of soil surface conditions.

has focused attention on the problems associated with toxic materials produced by human activity. Many pesticides (Chapter 10) can enter groundwater and be carried far from their point of application. Air-borne metals and acids derived from combustion of fossil fuels and from smelting and refining activities accumulate in soils, soil water, and water courses. These have been demonstrated to have serious effects on aquatic life and plants on land.

CHEMICAL PROPERTIES

pH

Water, H_2O or HOH, dissociates into two electrically charged particles or ions, one hydrogen ion (H^+) and one hydroxide ion (OH^-). In pure water the number of ions is very small relative to the number of undissociated molecules. One water molecule in over 500 million is dissociated; 1.0 mole of pure water (18 g) contains only 0.0000001 moles of each ion, a number conveniently expressed as an exponential, 1×10^{-7}.

Because of the difficulty of dealing with extremely small numbers, the concentration or activity of the hydrogen ions is given on a pH scale defined as:

$$pH = -\log [H^+]$$

For pure water, the pH can be calculated as follows:

$$pH = \log \frac{1}{0.0000001} = \log 10,000,000 = 7$$

Since a log scale is used, a full unit change in pH is a 10-fold change in the concentration of a hydrogen ion (Table 5-2).

Water in soils is not pure, but contains many inorganic and organic chemicals that supply hydrogen or hydroxide ions which contribute to the total concentration of these ions in solution. The addition of hydrochloric acid (H^+Cl^-), for example, supplies additional hydrogen ions; the pH of the solution decreases as the concentration of H^+ increases. When an alkali such as sodium hydroxide (Na^+OH^-) is added, some of the OH^- combines with H^+ present in the solution to form water, and the pH increases as the number of H^+ ions decreases. Soils at pH 7 are neutral in reaction (having an equal number of H^+ and OH^- ions); soils with pH values below 7 are acidic and those with pH values above 7 are alkaline. In plant science, soils with pH values from about 6.5 to 7.5 are considered neutral. Acid soils range from pH 6.5 to 4.0 and alkaline soils from 7.5 to 8.5. Soils with values below 3.5 or above 8.5 very rarely show good productivity.

The pH reaction of soils depends on many factors. Soils in areas of high rainfall tend to be more acidic than those of dry areas because alkaline components—sodium, potassium, calcium, and magnesium—are relatively easily leached. Soils with a high aluminum content or those formed from granitic parent rock are acidic, while those formed from limestone with a high calcium

Table 5-2   HYDROGEN ION CONCENTRATION AND pH

H^+ (moles/l)[a]	pH	Soil reaction	Substance with given pH	Soil types
10	0		Battery acid	
10^{-1}	1			
10^{-2}	2		Vinegar	
10^{-3}	3	Acid toxicity	Lemon juice	Acid peats
10^{-4}	4	Very acidic	Orange juice	
10^{-5}	5	Strongly acidic	Boric acid	Rainy region
10^{-6}	6	Mildly acidic	Milk	Agricultural Horticultural
10^{-7}	7	Neutral	Pure water	
10^{-8}	8	Mildly alkaline	Sea water	
10^{-9}	9	Strongly alkaline	Laundry soap	Arid region
10^{-10}	10	Alkali toxicity	Laundry bleach	
10^{-11}	11			
10^{-12}	12		Ammonia	
10^{-13}	13		Lye solution	
10^{-14}				

[a] 1 mole of H^+ = 1.0 gram/liter

content are alkaline. The accumulation of organic matter in soils results in the release of H^+ and consequent decreases in the pH. Fertilization, especially with the common nitrogen source, ammonium nitrate, also alters soil pH. However, soil pH does not usually change rapidly unless deliberate efforts are made (see the section on soil management later in this chapter) because soils have the ability to buffer or resist abrupt changes in H^+ concentration.

Soil pH profoundly affects the growth of plants. Bacterial and algal populations are greater and more varied in neutral soils than in acid soils; fungal populations predominate in acid soils. This can modify the rates of decomposition of organic matter or nitrogen fixation. The roots of plants are sensitive to pH and, depending on the species, may be restricted to certain pH ranges. It is sometimes possible to control weeds by modifying soil pH, and the susceptibility of plants to disease may be altered by soil pH.

Soil pH is an important factor in the availability of mineral nutrients (Chapter 7). It is also important in regulating the solubility of compounds that may be toxic to plants. While aluminum is not usually required by plants, it is a common soil constituent and is toxic to plant roots. When soil pH is below 4.5, aluminum is solubilized (mineralized) and may be taken up with other minerals present in the soil solution. Sensitive species or cultivars may fail to develop under such conditions.

Over the years knowledge of the pH requirements of many species has accumulated by direct experimentation and by trial and error. Horticultural and agricultural soils have been divided into four groups, based primarily on the pH of the topsoil (Table 5-3). Many cultivated and some wild plants have been shown to grow best in one of these soil groups, but such categorization is far from precise. Most plants will do quite well in soils as much as half a pH unit above or below their optimum pH range.

Few cultivated plants have optimum pH requirements above 7.5, although sugar beet *(Beta vulgaris),* sugar cane *(Saccharum officinarum),* asparagus *(Asparagus officinalis),* and some clovers will grow well at pH 8.0. "Acid-loving" plants include members of the heath family (rhododendron, azalea, blueberry, cranberry, heather), hydrangea *(Hydrangea* spp.), many orchids and camellia *(Camellia*

Table 5-3 HORTICULTURAL SOILS GROUPED BY pH

Group	pH range	Type	Optimum for representative plants
Medacid	4.0–5.5	Very low calcium— swamplands	Orchids, beets, heath family, swamp and mountain plants
Subacid	5.5–6.0	Low calcium— abandoned fields, uplands	Cereal grains, maples, woodland flowers
Minacid	6.0–7.0	Moderate calcium— garden loams, meadowlands	Most vegetables and ornamentals, lawn grasses
Circumneutral	6.5–8.0	High calcium— semitropical	Most fruit and nut trees, food and forage legumes, asparagus

japonica), all of which do best in soils with pH values between 4 and 5. Many ornamental trees, both conifers and broad-leaved species, grow well at pH's under 5. Not surprisingly, many persistent weeds can flourish at acidic or alkaline pH values beyond the range of cultivated plants.

Ion Exchange Capacity

Clay and organic matter particles, being very small, have large surface-to-volume ratios. Because of chemical and physical forces, the surfaces are electrically charged, usually with negative (anionic) charges. These attract and hold positively (cationic) charged particles, including positively charged ions such as hydrogen (H^+), calcium (Ca^{+2}), magnesium (Mg^{+2}), potassium (K^+), ammonium (NH_4^+), and sodium (Na^+). These ions can be removed from the negatively charged surfaces by being exchanged for positively charged cations with a greater affinity for the negative charge. Exchanges are not random. A soil particle binding hydrogen ions will, upon the addition of lime, release the hydrogen and become high in calcium; the released hydrogen ions move away from the soil particle and are capable of being leached. In this way, the acidity of the soil is reduced.

The number and distribution of the negative charges on soil particles and the chemical nature of the bound, positively charged ion determines the cation exchange capacity (CEC) of that soil. The finer the texture of a soil, the more clay and organic matter it will contain, and this usually means that its CEC will be greater. The CEC of a soil also depends on its pH; with soils of similar textures, the more acid ones will have altered CEC's, since the soil particles will be almost saturated with hydrogen ions.

CEC is usually expressed in terms of the weight in milligrams of H^+ that will combine with 100 grams of dry soil. A soil high in clay may have a CEC of 50 to 60, and an organic soil's CEC may exceed 100. Sandy soils have low CEC values, usually below 5, while silty soils are intermediate with values of 15 to 30.

The acidity of soils involves both the amount of H^+ in the soil water and the amount of exchangeable H^+ bound to soil particles. If lime is added to acidic soils, some of it will neutralize the free H^+ in the solution, and the calcium ions will also exchange with bound H^+ so that they can be neutralized. Many positively charged nutrients are bound to soil particles, are protected from being leached away, and will be slowly exchanged to become available for plant uptake. As exchange sites become available, they are filled from the reserves in the mineral components of the soil.

Another measure of exchangeable cations is the base saturation percentage, the extent to which the soil particle charges are saturated, that is, fully occupied by cations. If half are filled, the base saturation is 50 percent.

There is an equivalent anion exchange capacity (AEC), but it receives less attention than cation exchange because the quantity of ions exchanged is small. In clay minerals there may be relatively large numbers of hydroxide anions (OH^-) that can be exchanged for other anions including nitrate (NO_3^-), sulfate (SO_4^{-2}), phosphate (PO_4^{-3}), and chloride (Cl^-) which may be released slowly into the soil solution for uptake by plants.

Salinity and Sodicity

Independent of the chemical nature of the compounds involved, soils that contain high concentrations of salts present problems to the grower. By definition, soils in which more than 15 percent of the total cation exchange sites are occupied by sodium ions are considered to be sodic (sometimes called alkali soils), and those in which the sites are occupied by other cations in sufficiently high concentrations to impair plant growth are considered to be saline. Saline soils may result from the accumulation of almost any ionic substance, although those in which the excess salts are from sodium, potassium, or lithium usually have the additional problem of disruption of soil structure by deflocculation of soil colloids and loss of adequate pore space. Occasionally, soils are found which are both saline and sodic.

Saline and sodic soils are found primarily in arid or semiarid regions where rainfall is limited and where extensive leaching does not occur. Even in regions with adequate precipitation, poor drainage conditions can lead to the accumulation of salts. Lands irrigated with water containing salts may, over a period of years, become saline or sodic. Soils near marine waters may become sodic as the fresh water is removed, allowing the infiltration of sea water.

Under conditions of sodicity and salinity, water and mineral uptake from the soil solution is reduced (Chapter 7) with consequent reductions in growth and yield. Plants on sodic or saline soils tend to show wilting symptoms under conditions of adequate soil moisture and their leaves tend to develop a bluish tinge. A few crop plants benefit from salt; applications of 100 kg/ha of sodium chloride greatly increases the vigor of sugar beets, celery, swiss chard, table beets, turnips, and asparagus. Care must be exercised when adding salt; if soils already have adequate amounts of salt, additions may have no effect or may reduce crop growth.

Lands in western and southwestern United States have been irrigated for many years, and the crops are showing adverse growth responses to the now saline and sodic soils. Many ways of ameliorating the condition have been tried, but none has been particularly effective. To date, the only remedies are to provide adequate drainage to allow the leaching of the salts; to supply additional organic matter to alter the total soil CEC; and to reduce soil pH from the alkaline state to more neutral pH values by addition of sulfur, gypsum, or other acidifying material. Choosing crop plant species or cultivars that are relatively resistant to salt damage is still the method of choice to deal with existing conditions, but even this has limited applicability.

SOIL ORGANIC MATTER

Life in the Soil

So far we have considered only the inorganic characteristics of soils, although we have mentioned how the presence of organic matter affects some of these characteristics. Many plants can grow satisfactorily under experimental condi-

109

tions or in hydroponic culture in the complete absence of organic substances, but few plants do well in soils lacking organic matter. Microorganisms, plants, and animals all play roles in determining soil characteristics and productivity. For our purposes, we can separate organic soil constituents into two groups, those that are alive and those that are dead.

The numbers of living organisms in soil are staggering. In a gram of a good horticultural soil, there may be over 2 billion bacteria, 400,000 fungi, 50,000 algae, and 30,000 invertebrates, plus roots and other plant parts (Table 5-4). There are also uncountable numbers of virus particles. Soil organisms are not uniformly distributed since soils are themselves not homogeneous. They are concentrated in films on the surface of soil particles and congregate on fragments of decaying biotic debris. The species and numbers of soil organisms vary with the season and with environmental conditions; fewer are found during droughts and in the winter than in periods of optimum moisture and temperature. Changes in plant cover also affect the organisms in the soil. Conversion of a forest to an agricultural pasture results in alterations in the flora and fauna of the soils. Modifications of soils by fertilization, tilling, liming, and irrigation also alter the composition of the biota.

The roles played by soil organisms are as varied as the kinds of organisms present. Although most of the processes of soil formation are nonbiological, microbial processes are also involved. As microorganisms carry on their life processes, they produce acids that dissolve minerals from parent rocks; when they die, their remains become part of the nonliving fraction of the organic matter. In mature soils organisms contribute to the release of nutrients from soil particles through acid formation and through alterations in electrical charges on soil particles. Certain bacteria obtain energy by converting inorganic substances from one state to another (chemolithotrophic bacteria) and the end products —iron, sulfur, and nitrogen compounds—become part of the inorganic fraction of the soil. Soil microorganisms are important components in the various mineral cycles in soils.

Soil animals, too, contribute to soil formation and can alter productivity of soils. Charles Darwin recognized that earthworms not only increase soil aeration, but contribute to humus formation. Indeed the presence of earthworms has,

Table 5-4 KINDS AND AMOUNTS OF ORGANISMS AND ORGANIC MATTER TYPICAL OF A HORTICULTURAL LOAM SOIL IN THE NORTH TEMPERATE ZONE

Organisms	Dry weight	
	Percent	kg/ha
Bacteria	0.1–0.2	2,000–3,000
Fungi	0.1–0.2	2,000–3,000
Algae	0.0001–0.0005	5–10
Invertebrates	0.001–0.005	10–50
Vertebrates	0.0001–0.0005	1–5
Plant roots	0.5–5.0	5,000–50,000
Organic matter	4.0–8.0	75,000–150,000

for centuries, been an indication of a fertile, productive soil. There may be 1000 kg of earthworms in a hectare of soil. Mites and springtails, along with various bacteria and fungi, are involved in the conversion of dead plant parts (litter) into humus. The role of large animals in the life of soils is not well understood. Their waste products and eventually their bodies contribute to the organic fraction of soil.

The soil biota is not completely beneficial. Many organisms can cause infestations and infections of plant roots (Chapter 10). Others may eat or parasitize useful organisms in the soil. Soil microorganisms metabolize and utilize nutrients in competition with plants. Their nutrient demands may, under some conditions, be sufficiently large to deprive plants of needed minerals, and when fertilizer is added, the microorganism population can expand so rapidly that the deficiency is not relieved. Solubilization of aluminum by metabolic acids may also be a limitation in some soils. Metabolic waste products may be toxic to plants and to other organisms in the soil. The production of hydrogen sulfide by bacteria, the synthesis of antibiotics by bacteria and fungi, and the formation of specific toxins by a wide range of organisms must also be considered.

Decomposition and Cycling

In any ecosystem energy and nutrients are continually cycling, being built into plant substance by mineral uptake from the soil, photosynthesis, and a variety of biosynthetic processes and being released by respiration and decomposition. The minerals, organic substances, and energy in the living plant are immobilized during the life of the plant and are not available for other plants. When a plant dies, its substance again becomes available, through decomposition processes, for uptake and utilization by other plants. This freeing of nutrients is called mobilization and, in the case of inorganic compounds, is considered to be mineralization. Through nutrient cycling, the supply of minerals made available to a natural plant population is conserved.

Organisms that are involved in the mobilization of nutrients and energy can conveniently be divided into two groups, consumers and decomposers, linked together in food chains of considerable complexity. Soil animals are both consumers and decomposers since they consume plant material and in the process decompose it. The classic example is the earthworm; arthropods such as mites, centipedes, and springtails and insects also have both roles.

Dead animals or dead plant parts consist of a large variety of substances. To be recycled, they must be decomposed into constituent compounds through their incorporation into decomposer organisms which then decompose. During the utilization of plant and animal residues as food by decomposing organisms, some of the carbon, energy, and nutritive substances are immobilized for a time. As decomposition proceeds, carbon is lost as carbon dioxide and hydrogen and oxygen are lost as water through respiration (Chapter 12) with the loss of some of the total energy of the ecosystem. The lost energy, carbon, and water are restored to the ecosystem by photosynthesis, maintaining the cycle's integrity.

Formation of Soil Organic Matter

Decomposition processes, in addition to permitting the cycling of nutrients, also contribute to the accumulation of organic matter in the soil. Soil scientists, horticulturists, and botanists agree that there is no one factor that makes or breaks the productivity of soils as much as does the quantity and quality of soil organic matter. Few natural soils have adequate levels of satisfactory organic matter for all crop plants, although some of the nearly black soils of the Midwest come close to this ideal. Optimum levels depend upon soil texture, climate, management, and desired use. It is a rule of thumb that the percentage of organic matter for a good cultivated soil should be between 5 and 15 percent by weight of the top soil. Climate, particularly precipitation and temperature, regulates the amount of organic matter in soils (Figure 5-9). Tropical and subtropical soils can lose organic matter rapidly since the rate of decomposition is greater in warmer, more moist soils than in colder, drier soils. Northern temperate zone soils may also have low amounts of organic matter since rate of decomposition of plant residues slows as temperature drops. Radiocarbon dating shows that in cold, subarctic soils the organic fraction is over 1000 years old.

A major factor in the loss of soil productivity through erosion is the loss of humus and other organic matter. Even on lands not subject to water or wind erosion, cultivation results in a progressive loss of organic matter. Unless additional organic matter is incorporated into the soil, the new equilibrium level

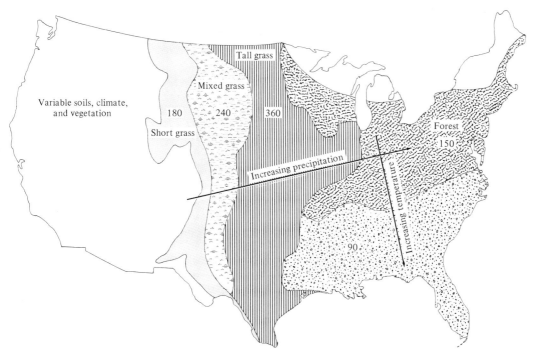

Figure 5-9 Organic matter in soils as related to vegetation and climate. Values are kilograms per hectare to 100 cm depth.

reached is frequently too low for optimum plant growth and soil structure. This new equilibrium level is usually less than 20 percent of the original level and is reached in 10 to 20 years. On the other hand, the cultivation and irrigation of soils in dry regions, which are normally low in organic matter, may result in a significant increase in organic matter.

For organic matter to play its roles in soil composition and function, it must be converted into humus (Figure 5-10). There is as much disagreement about the precise definition of humus as there is about the definition of soils. Humus is chemically and physically exceedingly complex. In general, it is dark in color and colloidal and is a complex of many organic substances that are somewhat resistant to the decomposing action of microorganisms. The humus fraction has lost its original structure and is not recognizable as leaves, twigs, bones, or the bodies of microorganisms. Humus is continually being altered, disappearing through slow degradation processes and being formed from dead organisms.

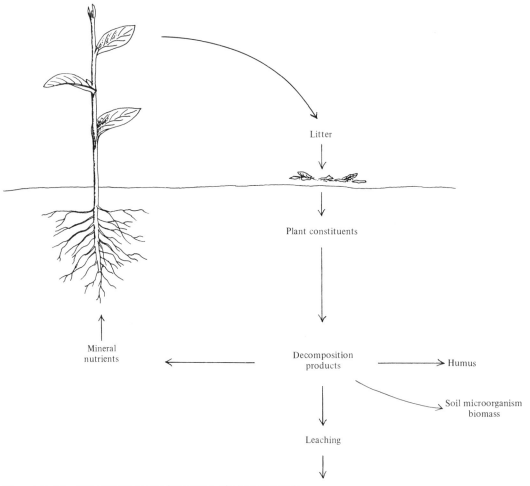

Figure 5-10 Generalized model for cycling of plant materials.

As litter accumulates, some of it is consumed by animals, bacteria, and fungi which start the decomposition processes. Some components of plant and animal residues are readily incorporated into these primary decomposers. Carbohydrates (sugar and starch), organic acids, and many inorganic constituents are quickly utilized, with fats and soluble proteins disappearing soon thereafter. Many cellular proteins and other nitrogen-containing substances are incorporated into decomposer organisms, leaving the more resistant components of cell walls, particularly lignins and waxes.

The types of decomposer microorganisms vary with environmental and soil factors. In general, bacteria dominate the degradation flora in soils with neutral or near neutral pH values, while fungi are most prominent at acidic values of pH 5.0 and below. The source, nature, and composition of the litter also determine the microorganism spectrum and the rates of litter decomposition. Conifer needles and twigs, for example, are more resistant to degradation than are leaves and nonwoody stems. Temperature, moisture, and soil conditions affect the rates of decomposition.

A critical feature of humus or other decomposed organic matter is the proportion of carbon (C) to nitrogen (N), usually given as the carbon-to-nitrogen or C:N ratio (Table 5-5). In fresh leaves or herbaceous stems this ratio may be as high as 80:1, while the ratio in mature humus may range from 12:1 to 20:1. Much of the reduction in the ratio comes from the liberation of carbon as carbon dioxide from sugars and cellulose during the metabolism of the primary decomposers. As these die and are decomposed, their nitrogen content (usually as protein) tends to increase the nitrogen portion of the C:N ratio.

Although humus is usually considered in relation to the organization of the soil particulate matrix and in water relations of soil, it does supply small amounts of phosphorus and sulfur. The water-holding capacity of humus is great since the material can swell as does a sponge. Clay soils with adequate amounts of organic matter do not bake or crust readily. Pore space is increased with consequent benefit to both plants and microorganisms. The cation exchange capacity (CEC) is much greater than that of the undegraded organic material;

Table 5-5   CARBON-TO-NITROGEN RATIO OF COMMON MULCHING MATERIALS

	Percent carbon (C)	Percent nitrogen (N)	C:N ratio
Green cover crops			
Alfalfa	40	2.0	20:1
Clovers	40	3.0	13:1
Grasses	40	1.0	40:1
Buckwheat	38	2.0	19:1
Mulches			
Peat moss	48	0.8	58:1
Fresh grass clippings	40	2.0	20:1
Dry leaves	40	1.0	40:1
Mixed mature compost	15	1.0	15:1
Straw	40	0.5	80:1
Sawdust	200	0.5	400:1
Rotted manures	30	1.5	20:1

humus possesses more cation exchange sites than clay and can maintain cations in forms that are available to plant roots. This enhanced exchange capacity favors the adsorption of nitrogen so that increased levels of organic matter are accompanied by increased amounts of some nutrients in the soil. Humus is important in determining the level of soil aggregation and hence soil structure. There is a correlation between clay content of soils and the amount of organic matter present. The higher water-holding capacity of clay compared with sand favors the accumulation of organic matter and the adsorption of organic compounds on clay particles appears to protect them from attack by decomposing microflora.

Rhizosphere

Plant roots greatly modify the soil in which the plants are growing. As they grow through the soil, structure is modified. As they die, pore space is increased with alterations in water relations and soil aeration. The dead roots are degraded to humus. The uptake of nutrients and of substances that may be toxic will also alter the chemical composition of soils.

Soil scientists and plant physiologists have started to recognize that the soil-plant interface is quite narrow and is essentially the surface of the root plus a thin film of water containing dissolved chemicals and a unique microbiological flora. This region, usually less than 3 mm in thickness, is called the rhizoplane and the relatively small volume of soil solution surrounding each root is called the rhizosphere. The rhizosphere is different in chemical composition, structure, and texture from the bulk soil. There is no doubt that study of rhizospheres, involving microbiologists, soil scientists, and botanists, will become increasingly important in both theoretical and applied plant science.

Plant roots are "leaky," with efflux of many organic substances into the rhizoplane and rhizosphere. These substances support unique microfloras that, in turn, influence the growth and development of the root. Many nitrogen-fixing bacteria are active in the rhizoplane and contribute nitrogen directly to the soil solution and the plant. Alterations in pH in the rhizoplane can increase or decrease the soluble and available concentrations of nutrients available to the plant (Chapter 7). In addition, the transport of gaseous oxygen from the aerial to the subterranean portion of the plant and its movement into the rhizoplane affect the oxidative potential of the rhizosphere. It is not unusual to find a brown coating of iron oxides on the epidermis or bark of roots, and the oxidation products of other inorganic substances have also been found.

SOIL CLASSIFICATION

Taxonomy of Soils

The grouping of similar soils allows predictions of productivity and potential in precisely the same way as does the classification (taxonomy) of plants. There are several classification schemes, the first developed by V. V. Dokuchaev in Russia about 1880, which attempt to integrate soil form and structure, chemistry, profiles, and underlying rocks. These classifications have been modified many times. The most recent system was published in 1975 by the U.S. Department of Agriculture and the land-grant colleges. The classification is hierarchical, like that of plants, with categories from order (the most comprehensive group) through suborder, great group, subgroup, family, and series in decreasing rank. The names are derived from classical languages and, again like plant taxonomy, are designed to indicate some characteristic of the taxon.

All soils are separated into ten orders (Figure 5-11 and Table 5-6) distinguished primarily by differences in the quality and quantity of organic matter in the surface horizons, moisture availability, and base saturation. These reflect the degree of horizon development and a consideration of climatic conditions. Suborders separate soils on the basis of soil moisture, temperature regimes, and variations in horizon composition. There are 47 suborders (Table 5-7). The great groups narrow the ranges of these characteristics and the subgroups account for intergradations and atypical soils. Family categories are defined primarily on the basis of the mineralogical composition, texture, and temperature that are important in soil productivity. The most restrictive category, the series, is based on horizons, parentages, and physical and chemical properties. Series soils are, like plant species, individual soils with which the soil scientist, engineer, and botanist deals directly. Series are named for some natural feature or specific

Table 5-6   THE 10 SOIL ORDERS AND THEIR SIGNIFICANCE THROUGHOUT THE WORLD

Order name	Meaning of name	Older names	Diagnostic characteristics	Percent of world total[a]	Rank
Entisol	Recent soils	Alluvial, humic gley	Limited development, little profile form	12.5	4
Inceptisol	Young soils	Brown forest, tundra	Moderate development, cambic horizons	15.8	2
Aridisol	Dry soils	Desert, sierozem	Arid regions, little development	19.2	1
Mollisol	Soft soils	Chernozem, prairie	Thick A1 horizon productive, friable	9.0	6
Spodosol	Ashy soils	Podzol, groundwater	B horizons with free iron and aluminum	5.4	8
Alfisol	Artificial soils	Noncalcic, planosol	Forest soils, high in clays	14.7	3
Utisol	Ultimate soils	Red-brown, lateric	Humid climates, moderate in clays	8.5	7
Oxisol	Oxidized soils	Latisol, laterite	Highly weathered, iron oxides	9.2	5
Vertisol	Inverted soils	Grumusol, smonitza	Subhumid climates, self-mulching	2.1	9
Histosol	Organic soils	Bog, swamp	Wet, poorly drained, mainly acidic	0.8	10

[a]Ice fields, mountains, and unclassified land comprise 2.8 percent of total land area.

116

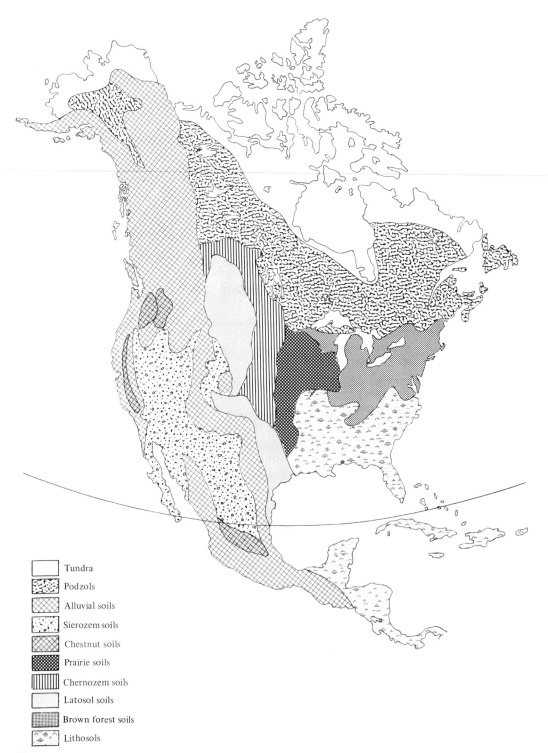

Tundra

Podzols

Alluvial soils

Sierozem soils

Chestnut soils

Prairie soils

Chernozem soils

Latosol soils

Brown forest soils

Lithosols

Figure 5-11 Soil orders in North America.

Table 5-7 FORMATIVE ELEMENTS IN THE NAMES OF SOIL SUBORDERS

Formative element	Derivation of formative element	Connotation of formative element
alb	L. *albus,* "white"	Presence of albic horizon (a bleached eluvial horizon)
and	Modified from Ando	Andolike
aqu	L. *aqua,* "water"	Characteristics associated with wetness
ar	L. *arare,* "to plow"	Mixed horizons
arg	Modified from argillic horizon; L. *argilla,* "white clay"	Presence of argillic horizon (a horizon with illuvial clay)
bor	Gk. *boreas,* "northern"	Cool
ferr	L. *ferrum,* "iron"	Presence of iron
fibr	L. *fibra,* "fiber"	Least decomposed stage
fluv	L. *fluvius,* "river"	Flood plains
hem	Gk. *hemi,* "half"	Intermediate stage of decomposition
hum	L. *humus,* "earth"	Presence of organic matter
lept	Gk. *leptos,* "thin"	Thin horizon
ochr	Gk. base of *ochros,* "pale"	Presence of ochric epipedon (a light surface)
orth	Gk. *orthos,* "true"	The common ones
plag	Modified from Ger. *plaggen,* "sod"	Presence of plaggen epipedon
psamm	Gk. *psammos,* "sand"	Sand textures
rend	Modified from Rendzina	Rendzina-like
sapr	Gk. *sapros,* "rotten"	Most decomposed stage
torr	L. *torridus,* "hot and dry"	Usually dry
trop	Modified from Gk. *tropikos,* "of the solstice"	Continually warm
ud	L. *udus,* "humid"	Of humid climates
umbr	L. *umbra,* "shade"	Presence of umbric epipedon (a dark surface)
ust	L. *ustus,* "burnt"	Of dry climates, usually hot in summer
xer	Gk. *xeros,* "dry"	Annual dry season

location where the soil was first recognized. There are close to 12,000 soil series in the United States. Series tend to be familiar names, for example, Cabot refers to a town in Vermont and Carlsbad to the cave region in New Mexico. Changes in series may occur abruptly over distances of less than a meter; a survey and agricultural or engineering recommendations prepared for one plot of land may be useless for a neighboring plot.

Soil Surveys

A large proportion of the activities of federal and state soils agencies are devoted to conducting soil surveys. To be of value for various people that use the land, surveys must classify soils down to series, accurately map the soils, and correlate and predict the potential behavior and productivity of the soil. Soil surveys provide necessary information for agriculture and horticulture, land-use planning (suitability for housing, roads, location of pipelines), as well as for determining the presence of flood plains, hardpans, and other features. General soils maps embracing a county or a state and detailed maps covering less than 100 hectares are made using aerial reconnaissance and direct soil determinations. Anyone planning any kind of soil use should obtain from the Soil Conservation Service the detailed soils map for the area being considered. The maps are usually accompanied by a resume of the soil series types and recommendations and evaluations for use; they are invaluable.

SOIL MANAGEMENT

Although most soils can support some plant development, high productivity requires that the soil be properly managed. Inadequate management of intensively cultivated soils will lead to soil degradation and eventual inability to sustain plant growth. Management involves both preparation of the soil and continued maintenance. Depending on circumstances, it may involve leveling, modifying physical and chemical properties, control of unwanted plants and animals, and developing good tilth. Tilth is a word not usually used by soil scientists, but commonly employed to refer to physical conditions of the soil that facilitate the growth of a desired crop. It includes aspects of soil structure, particularly the granular or crumb feel of a well-managed soil, as well as its color, odor, and water-holding capacity. For most crops the uppermost 20 to 40 cm (8 to 16 in.)—the topsoil—is the most important since this region will contain the majority of plant roots. Several aspects of soil management are considered here. Fertilization, also an important aspect, is discussed in Chapter 7.

Tilth and Topsoil

Obtaining satisfactory tilth almost invariably involves some tillage, the mechanical manipulation of the soil. From a crude pointed stick to scratch the soil to the wide array of instruments and techniques now available, tillage tools have both eased the burden of cultivation and have contributed greatly to plant production. Tillage may modify soil structure, remove undesirable plants, and incorporate soil-amending materials. Proper tilling will loosen the soil to promote aeration, porosity, and water-holding capacity. Plowing inverts soils, disking breaks up large aggregates, and harrowing further disrupts clods to produce smooth and level soils. Rototillers can do all three of these tasks simultaneously. Weed removal to reduce competition for space, water, and nutrients (Chapter 10) can be accomplished by mechanical control. Wild plants or crop residues can contribute valuable organic matter by being turned into the soil.

Depth of tilling depends on the soil profile, moisture conditions, and the crop to be grown. It may be deep, as much as a meter (39 in.) in the western part of the United States where irrigation is practiced and soil tends to be dry or where a hardpan exists. Most tilling, however, is much shallower. Tap root crops, for example, are usually grown in soil tilled to slightly more than half a meter (20 in.). In some areas it may be desirable gradually to incorporate some of the less productive subsoil into the topsoil layer by deep tilling over a period of several years.

Time of tilling is a factor in obtaining a soil with good tilth. Wet or frozen soils should never be cultivated since aggregate structure will be damaged. Clay soils, particularly those low in organic matter, may be destroyed, and the soil may puddle. Any disruption of such soils when they are wet, even walking on them, may cause damage. Lighter sandy soils, because they do not clump as readily, can be tilled when wet and rarely require deep tilling. Fall tilling of gardens may be useful since the alternate freezing and thawing of clods promotes granulation and allows water to percolate more easily through the soil. This practice is particularly useful in southern climates.

Growing crops on the same land for a number of years may cause changes in the physical characteristics of the soil that require correction. There is usually a decrease in soil aggregation with consequent compaction. This reduces total pore space, increases bulk density, and reduces the average volume of pores. As pore volume decreases, more of these small pores are water-filled and fewer are available for air.

In recent years some attention has been given to no-till techniques in which the soil is not cultivated between successive crops. To some extent, this developed as agricultural machinery became larger and heavier and soil compaction became more of a problem. No-till or minimum till techniques have proved to be useful for some, but not all crops. For agricultural production, no-till techniques may be a financial trade-off. Labor, fuel, and machinery costs are reduced, but there is increased reliance on pesticides to control weeds, insects, and disease organisms. For the gardener the no-till techniques have little to recommend them.

Acidification and Alkalinization

Tolerance of plants to pH is fairly wide, ranging from about pH 4 (fairly acidic) to pH 8 (moderately alkaline). Many cultivated plants have a much narrower range. It is necessary to modify soil pH to ensure nutrient availability, reduction of metal toxicities, growth of desirable microorganisms, and conditions for increased crop productivity. The pH optimum for horticultural plants is species-dependent, but most will thrive at pH values between 5.5 and 7.0 and alteration of pH of soils within this range may not be necessary. Some alteration may be desirable to obtain the optimum for a specific crop, and alteration will be necessary for acid-loving plants since their optimum values range from 4.0 to 5.5. Decisions on modifying soil pH should always be made on the basis of a soil analysis.

Acidification of soils can be done by several methods. Organic materials that provide hydrogen ions, such as conifer needles, bark mulches, sawdust mulches, cottonseed meal, oak leaves, and peat (sphagnum moss) are frequently used. Their acidifying potential is high and long lasting, but they are slow acting since they must break down before releasing hydrogen ions. Much quicker, but

Table 5-8   SOME CHARACTERISTICS OF COMMON SOIL-ACIDIFYING MATERIALS

	Sulfur S	Ferrous sulfate $FeSO_4 \cdot 7H_2O$	Aluminum sulfate $Al_2(SO_4)_3$	Ammonium nitrate NH_4NO_3
Solubility	Low	Moderate	High	High
Effect on pH	Slow	Moderate	High	High
Corrosivity	None	None	None	None
Effective time	Long	Moderate	Moderate	Moderate

not as long lasting, are a variety of inorganic chemicals (Table 5-8). Among the least expensive is elemental sulfur, also called flowers of sulfur. Its use in poorly drained or heavy soils is questionable since the sulfur may be converted by microorganisms into toxic compounds. Ammonium sulfate [$(NH_4)_2SO_4$], ammonium nitrate (NH_4NO_3), and ferrous sulfate ($FeSO_4$) are used for small areas, and urea or liquid ammonia are used for agricultural lands. It is difficult to predict the effects of these chemicals and the amounts to be applied since soil depth, organic matter content, cation exchange capacity, and other factors are involved; soil tests are vital.

Many crop plants do best at pH values near neutrality. Soils that are subject to leaching of basic cations or that have been cropped for many years may require upward adjustment of pH. With few exceptions, lime is the substance of choice to reduce acidity. It is inexpensive, readily available, easy to handle, and very effective. Lime is a generic term covering ground limestone or calcium carbonate ($CaCO_3$), slaked lime or calcium oxide (CaO), hydrated lime or calcium hydroxide [$Ca(OH)_2$], and dolomitic limestone, which is a mixture of calcium carbonate and magnesium carbonate ($MgCO_3$). Other liming substances include marl, ground oyster shells, hardwood ash, basic slag, and egg shells. All of these act similarly by increasing the base saturation level of the soil and converting the exchangeable hydrogen ions into water. In order to determine the amount to be applied, a soil test is conducted. The liming substances have different neutralization capacities based on weight, but similar capacities based on the calcium content (Tables 5-9 and 5-10).

Limestone has a more immediate effect if it is finely ground, although this increases the chance of its being blown away during and after spreading. A

Table 5-9   FIELD ESTIMATION OF CALCIUM CARBONATE ($CaCO_3$) CONTENT OF SOIL

Percent $CaCO_3$	Sound	Effervescence
0.1	None	None
0.5	Faint	None
1.0	Faint–low	None
2.0	Distinct	Visible bubbles
3.0	Quite distinct	Small bubbles
5.0	Very distinct	Moderate bubbling
8.0	Very distinct	Vigorous bubbling

Note: To estimate $CaCO_3$ content place 2 tablespoons of soil in a glass container, mix well, and flood with 10 percent (volume/volume) HCl. Examine for effervescence and listen for sound.

Table 5-10 AMOUNT OF ACIDIFYING SULFUR OR ALKALINIZING LIMESTONE NEEDED TO ALTER SOIL pH

To change upper 20 cm		Sandy Loam		Silty Loam		Clay Loam	
From pH	To pH	Lime[a]	Sulfur	Lime[a]	Sulfur	Lime[a]	Sulfur
4.0	5.6	250	—	400	—	500	—
5.0	6.5	170	—	280	—	325	—
6.0	6.5	70	—	110	—	120	—
7.0	6.5	—	5	—	8	—	15
8.0	6.5	—	60	—	75	—	100

[a]Amounts for lime are given in kg/100m^2 (to approximate lb/1000 ft^2, divide by 2). For quicklime (CaO) multiply amount by 0.67; for hydrated lime [Ca(OH)$_2$] multiply by 0.83.

compromise grind of 90 percent capable of passing a 20-mm screen and 25 percent passing a 0.15-mm screen is usually used. Coarser grinds are also available and are less expensive. Lime does not move horizontally in soils to any extent and its vertical movement is limited even when it has dissolved in soil water. A critical factor is the mixing of the lime with the soil. While this is more easily accomplished by supplying the lime during cultivation, it can be spread at any time of year. Applications to lawns, pastures, and hay fields, where tilling is impractical, may not show significant changes in pH or plant growth for several months or even several years in heavier soils.

Mulches and Composts

The optimum percentage of organic matter in a productive soil varies somewhat with climate, soil type, and the nature of the crop, but generally it is about 5 to 15 percent. As soils are tilled, as microorganisms gradually utilize the humus and other organic matter, and as leaching or erosion occurs, the amount and quality of the organic fraction decreases. Among the many consequences of this are (1) decreased soil porosity, (2) disruption of soil aggregates and loss of granularity, (3) decreased water-holding capacity, (4) decreased aeration, (5) increased erosion potential, (6) increased water evaporation, (7) decreased pH buffering capacity, (8) increased leaching of nutrients, (9) alteration in favorable microorganism populations, (10) increased temperature variations. These changes are more rapid in soils of tropical areas where temperatures and rainfall are high, but occur fairly rapidly even in temperate zones. For good productivity the lost organic matter should be replaced.

Amending soils with plant materials which, through microbial action, are converted to humus can involve a variety of materials and methods. In agricultural fields and in some horticultural plots, green manures or cover crops may be used. Fall-planted cover crops will retain snow cover. Green manuring involves growing selected plants on the land and then tilling the crop into the soil before it matures so that the cover species does not become a weed. Useful characteristics for cover crops include rapid top and root growth and, where possible, the ability of the plant to fix nitrogen which will then become available to the next planting. Members of the legume family, especially the clovers *(Trifolium* spp.), alfalfa *(Medicago* spp.), and vetch *(Vicia* spp.) are excellent cover crops in cool climates as are annual rye *(Secale cereale),* buckwheat *(Fagopyrum esculentum),* and Sudan grass *(Sorghum vulgare* cv. Sudanese). In warmer climates legumes, such as cowpea *(Vigna unguiculata),* lespedeza *(Lespe-deza* spp.), and soybean *(Glycine max),* are used along with nonlegumes including pearl millet *(Pennisetum glaucum),* the sorghums, and rape *(Brassica napus).*

Many nonliving plant and animal materials can be used to improve the organic content of soils. Cottonseed meal, fruit residues, and dried blood are also good sources of nutrients, while others are introduced primarily as potential humus. The animal manures are among the best. Poultry manures are highest in nutrients and decompose most rapidly, but tend to induce injury to plants because of their high concentrations of inorganic compounds. When boron compounds are used for fly control in poultry houses, the manure cannot be used for plants because of the possibility of boron toxicity (see Chapter 7). The manures of domestic mammals are fairly close in composition and can be used interchangeably (Table 5-11). Cow and horse manures may contain considerable bedding material, usually straw or hay, which is an excellent source of organic matter. Fresh manures are bulky and odoriferous, contain weed seeds, and tend to damage delicate plants, particularly those at the seedling stage. Curing or composting reduces weight and odor, but the resulting "well-rotted" manure does not contain much nitrogen since ammonia is quickly volatilized. Dried manures are available to the home gardener, and although they are not adequate sources of nitrogen, they are excellent organic additives with reasonable concentrations of phosphorus and potassium. Dried blood from slaughterhouses, bird manures (guano), fish meals, and sewage sludges are other animal end products that can be purchased. Some of these, particularly sewage sludges, may contain toxic concentrations of heavy metals or other industrial wastes and caution is indicated in their use.

A variety of plant materials are used as soil additives to increase soil

Table 5-11   APPROXIMATE COMPOSITION OF COMMON MULCHING MATERIALS

| | Nutrients (as percent of dry weight)[a] | | | |
	Nitrogen	Phosphorus	Potassium	Percent dry weight[b]
Cow manure	1.5	0.4	0.8	20–30
Horse manure	2.0	0.3	2.0	20–30
Sheep manure	4.0	0.6	3.0	25–40
Poultry manure	4.0	2.0	2.0	30–40
Bone meal	0.1	10.0	0	100
Dried blood	13.0	1.0	1.0	100
Hay and straw	2.0	0.3	2.0	90
Cottonseed meal	6.0	1.0	2.0	100
Peanut hulls	2.0	0.1	0.7	100
Dried kelp	0.6	0	1.0	100
Wood ash	0.0	2.0	6.0	100
Hardwood sawdust	0.2	0.1	0.2	100
Softwood sawdust	0.1	0.1	0.1	100

[a]Percent of nutrient in the dry portion of the mulch.
[b]Proportion of dry material to water content in total mulch.

Table 5-12 CHEMICAL COMPOSITION OF PLANT-DERIVED SOIL ORGANIC MATTER COMPARED WITH THE COMPOSITION OF PLANT TISSUE

Compounds	Percent dry weight	
	Soil organic matter	Living plant tissues
Cellulose	30–60	2–8
Hemicelluloses	15–30	0–2
Lignins	15–30	30–50
Proteins	2–12	1–5
Fats and waxes	1–5	1–4

organic matter. Dried marine algae have been used by peoples living near the sea. Sawdust, wood and bark chips, peanut and cocoa hulls, and grass and grain stems (hay and straw) have been used for centuries. These materials may, however, compete with the crop for soil nitrogen and may offer protection for rodents. Peats have been used for a long time. The peat moss of commerce (Canadian peat) is derived from sphagnum, a moss that grows in acidic bogs, which is collected, dried, and sometimes ground into a coarse powder. Michigan peat or reed peat is obtained from bogs or swamps; in addition to sphagnum, it contains grasses, reeds, and sedges. The water-holding capacity of sphagnum peat is higher than that of reed peat. The nutrient content of plant materials used as soil additives is lower in nitrogen than the animal residues, although their phosphorus and potassium contents are as high or higher (see Table 5–11). Some animal and plant residues are low in available nitrogen and their degradation into soil organic matter is limited by the nitrogen available to the decomposition microorganisms. Unless supplemented with available nitrogen at 15 to 30 kg/1000 m^2, decomposition will be slow. Peats, being acidic, should be mixed with lime, if necessary, as determined by a lime-requirement analysis.

Composts, properly prepared, are excellent sources of organic matter for horticultural soils because the conversion to humus is usually well advanced and the carbon-to-nitrogen ratio has decreased to close to optimum value before the composts are added to soil. Composting also has the virtue of recycling of organic matter. Claims that composts are the cure for all soil ills are greatly exaggerated, and statements that the inorganic nutrients obtained from organic sources are somehow better than the same compounds derived from commercial fertilizers have no experimental foundation. Nor is there any evidence that plants can absorb and utilize the organic compounds in humus or compost. The value of composted organic matter lies in its ability to form disease-free humus quickly.

In general, composting can utilize almost all plant debris, with the obvious exception of diseased or infested plant parts (Table 5-12). In order to facilitate the microbiological activities that result in degradation, reduction of the C:N ratio, and formation of humuslike material, a well-designed compost pile allows adequate aeration, has sufficient moisture, is constructed to obtain necessary temperature levels, and is composed of the proper mix of materials. There are many techniques for constructing and caring for compost heaps, but all were developed with these same ends in mind.

A compost pile usually consists of layers of the organic matter to be decomposed alternating with layers of soil or manure which are the sources of the decomposition microorganisms. A useful ratio is 15- to 20-cm layers of organic material separated by 5-cm layers of soil or manure. A freshly constructed pile can be 1.5 m tall and about the same width and depth. These, and similar size and depth ratios, facilitate aeration and the necessary accumulation of heat. It may be contained inside wire, wooden, or cement block barriers. Heavy twigs or brush are not usually included unless they have been shredded. Since grass clippings and leaves tend to mat down, they are usually dried and mixed before being added to the pile. The pile is firmed, but not compressed, so that aeration is not reduced. To preserve adequate moisture content, the pile may be shaped like a catch basin to capture rainfall, covered to reduce evaporation, and watered when necessary.

During the early stages of decomposition, metabolism of the microorganisms raises the temperature of the pile to 40° to 50° C (100° to 120° F), temperatures sufficiently high to kill many weed seeds and the vegetative stages of some disease-causing fungi. These temperatures also repress many bacteria and fungi except those that are thermophilic (heat-loving). After the initial stages, within about a week, the heat level drops to close to ambient temperature and nonthermophilic microorganisms continue the decomposition processes.

The rate of decomposition depends on the activity of the soil microorganisms which is frequently limited by the available nitrogen and phosphorus in the plant material. Additions of fertilizers usually increase the rate of heating up and the subsequent slower breakdown. Since the active microorganisms are most efficient at neutral or near-neutral pH values, the decomposition of acidic leaves or needles is aided by incorporating lime or wood ashes. Aeration is promoted by turning over the pile several times during the first month and once or twice more during the year. The rate of decomposition and reduction of the C:N ratio to 15:1 depends on ambient temperatures. Compost piles in northern regions may not mature in a full year, while those in the south may be ready in a few months. Mature compost is usually recognized by a dark brown color, freedom from odor, and granular structure without visible sign of undecomposed plant structure.

Composts are widely used in the nursery production of container-grown plants, both conifers and broad-leaved species. Composts made from layered organic material, as described above, are frequently mixed with good potting soil to improve drainage and enhance root growth. Composts of southern pine bark or milled and composted hardwood barks are often used alone or with other substances for specific plants, in home garden plots, and for field crops of high value.

In addition to organic matter, there are a number of useful inorganic materials that can be used to amend the soil. Vermiculite and perlite can lighten heavy clay or silt soils and increase water-holding capacity. Vermiculite is a mica mineral which exfoliates when heated to high temperatures to form a lightweight substance. Perlite is a volcanic mineral which is similarly treated. Because of cost, these substances are used for small areas like seed beds or in potting mixtures for indoor plants. For larger areas sandy soils may be amended with bentonite clay or montmorillonite clay (hydrous silicates) to enhance exchange capacity, increase surface area, and change pore-size distribution. Zeolites (hydrated aluminosilicates) are used interchangeably with these clays to amend heavy soils.

Soil Sterilization

It is occasionally considered desirable to prevent the growth of plants in areas such as driveways. The compounds used for this purpose are phytotoxic inorganic or organic substances. The inorganics include arsenic, boron compounds, sodium chlorate, and, more recently, an array of organic substances. The inorganics tend to be persistent, lasting up to 10 years, while the organics are slowly decomposed by soil organisms and cannot be expected to remain effective for more than a year or two. These materials should be used with caution; in addition to their being phytotoxic, most are effective animal (including human) poisons and can be transported into groundwater sources.

Freeing soil of unwanted microorganisms is a difficult task except for relatively small batches of soils used for potting plants or for seedbeds. The least dangerous procedure is pasteurization, in which the soil is exposed to live steam to reach a center temperature of 70° to 80° C (160° to 175° F) for 30 minutes to an hour. A variety of fumigation agents, especially methyl bromide gas or the less toxic chloropicrin, are used on seed beds covered with plastic sheets to hold in the fumigant. Dichloroprogene is a volatile fumigant used under carefully controlled conditions. It is now economically feasible to fumigate soils used to grow fruit and vegetable crops of high commercial value, berries and asparagus, for example. These compounds are nonselective, killing disease organisms but also killing useful bacteria, fungi, algae, and soil animals. Recolonization of the soil will occur, bacteria entering first, followed by fungi and algae and then soil animals. The proportions of organisms and their speciation will frequently be different than before sterilization.

Erosion Control

Erosion of arable land is a worldwide, major problem. However, at the garden or horticultural level, soil erosion need not be a large problem if common sense is used. Horticultural or crop plants should not be placed on slopes greater than about 5 percent without water bars, retaining walls, or terracing. Management practices that increase drainage can reduce the problem in areas that under conditions of heavy precipitation show sheet erosion or form gullies. Orchards are particularly prone to rill erosion, that is, the formation of small gullies between rows on downhill slopes. Maintaining plant cover on the soil slows water movement and allows more time for percolation. Where possible, tilling should be done at right angles to a slope, the concept of contour cultivation. Wind erosion is not usually a serious matter in small areas, but in locations known to be both windy and arid permanent plantings of sheltering trees or shrubs can break the force of the wind and, not incidentally, enhance the beauty of an area.

Steep banks, such as road cuts and shoulders or small cliffs, present difficult erosion-control problems. Terracing or retaining walls are often impractical or expensive. For such areas, the only practical erosion control is permanent plantings. Steep slopes frequently have poor soils or no soil to speak of. As soon as possible, a plant cover should be developed; annual rye or common grasses *(Poa* spp.) should be sown and covered with a straw mulch to protect the area until the plants are established. Permanent plantings should be done when practicable. Among the best are the members of the legume family which, because of their ability to fix nitrogen, can establish quickly on poor mineral soils. Trefoils *(Lotus corniculatus* or *Medicago lupulina)* and vetches or indigo bush *(Amorpha fruticosa)* are excellent cover plants for difficult areas. Once established, their remains contribute to the organic fraction of the soil, and as their roots decay, humus is formed in the soil. A few trees are also excellent cover plants. The sumacs *(Rhus glabra* or *R. typhina)* and black locust *(Robinia pseudoacacia)* grow quickly and have spreading root systems that can withstand adverse water conditions and become established on poor soils.

SOIL MIXES FOR HOMES AND GREENHOUSES

Few house or greenhouse plants do well in soil dug out of the garden. Garden soils are usually too heavy and have variable composition. To standardize and

Table 5-13 POTTING MIXES FOR HOUSE PLANT, GREENHOUSE, AND GARDEN TRANSPLANT USE

Ingredient[a]	Cornell Peat-Lite	University of California C	John Innes	Humus mix	Succulent and cacti mix	Epiphyte mix #1	Epiphyte mix #2	General house plant mix	Perennial container mix	Cornell seed starting mix	John Innes seed compost	Rooting cuttings mix #1	Rooting cuttings mix #2	Coniferous bonsai mix
Major ingredients														
Sphagnum peat (shredded)	2	1	3	1	1	1	1	1	1	1	1	1	1	1
Sharp sand (0.5–1.0 mm)		1	2	1	1			1	1		1	1	1	1
Bark (shredded)						1				1				
Leaf mold or humus				1	1	1	1	½	1					1
Sandy loam soil			7					1	2		2	1		1
Vermiculite	1				1				1	1				
Perlite	1			1		1							1	
Additives														
Dolomitic lime (ground)	20	300	250		75		150	100	50	50	100			
20 percent superphosphate	50	50	50				50		75	25	100			25
Chelated iron	5	5					5		5	5				5
Fritted trace elements	1								1					

[a]Major ingredients given as proportional volumes. Additives are given as grams per bushel (38 l, 40 qt, 1.3 ft³).

control the substrate, potting mixes have been developed, some containing soils and some soilless. A variety of all-purpose and specialty mixes are commercially available, but for general use and volume production they are not cost efficient, and some contain sewage sludges contaminated with household and industrial wastes.

Potting mixes, also called growing mixtures or soil mixes, have advantages over topsoil. They can be reproduced and are stable, have excellent porosity, water-holding capacities, cation exchange capacity, and are pest-free. Because they are light in weight, large plants may topple or be pulled from the pot, but the advantages outweigh the disadvantages.

Most potting mixes contain both plant-derived and inorganic materials with high water-holding capacity, resistance to compaction and high cation exchanges (Table 5-13). Milled peat moss, leaf mold, shredded bark, humus, well-rotted manure, and wood chips are used. Inorganic constituents, such as sharp builder's sand, vermiculite, perlite, scoria (ground lava rock), and ground granite, improve drainage and increase pore volume. Small amounts of other substances are added to regulate pH and supply trace elements or nutrients.

Since bulk densities of soil mixes are low, ingredients are blended by volume rather than by weight. The mixture is dampened slightly to reduce dusting while blending. Commercial greenhouses have mechanized the mixing. Potting mixes are sterilized to free them of pests and disease organisms. Greenhouses use medium-pressure steam for several hours. Small batches can be oven heated to 80° C (175° F) in a foil-covered pan.

Few potting substrates contain adequate levels of required nutrients, and some contain virtually none. This is usually an advantage, since nutrients can be added as necessary to meet the requirements of different species at different stages in development. The appropriate nutrients are supplied by regular feedings with soluble fertilizer formulations and/or the incorporation of slow-release fertilizers.

Starting seeds for greenhouse production or for transplanting into the garden is frequently best done with one of the soilless potting mixes. Several have been developed for this purpose and are commercially available at reasonable cost. The Cornell Peat-Lite formulation (see Table 5-13) is satisfactory.

Nursery production of container-grown perennial plants has also been converted to modified potting mixes. They provide excellent conditions for root and top development for ease and success in transplantation. Mixes containing shredded or chunk bark are used for both conifers and hardwoods.

SUPPLEMENTARY READINGS

Barber, S. A. 1984. *Soil Nutrient Bioavailability: A Mechanistic Approach.* Wiley, New York.
Bohn, H., B. McNeal, and G. O'Connor. 1985. *Soil Chemistry.* 2nd ed. Wiley, New York.
Brady, N. C. 1984. *The Nature and Properties of Soils.* 9th ed. Macmillan, New York.
Bresler, E., and B. L. McNeal. 1982. *Saline and Sodic Soils: Principles, Dynamics, Modelling.* Springer-Verlag, New York.

Bunt, A. C. 1976. *Modern Potting Composts.* Pennsylvania State University Press, University Park.

Donahue, R. L., R. W. Miller, and J. C. Shickluna. 1983. *Soils: An Introduction to Soils and Plant Growth.* 5th ed. Prentice-Hall, Englewood Cliffs, N.J.

Flagman, A. W., and R. A. I. George. 1977. *Soils and Other Growth Media.* Avi Books, Westport, Conn.

Foth, H. D. 1984. *Fundamentals of Soil Science.* 7th ed. Wiley, New York.

Gasser, J. K. R. 1985. *Composting of Agricultural and other Wastes.* Elsevier, London.

Glinski, J., and W. Stepniewski. 1985. *Soil Aeration and Its Role for Plants.* CRC Press, Boca Raton, Fla.

Greenland, D. J., and H. B. Hayes. 1980. *The Chemistry of Soil Processes.* Wiley, New York.

Hanks, R. J., and G. L. Ashcroft. 1983. *Applied Soil Physics: Soil, Water and Temperature Applications.* Springer-Verlag, New York.

Hillel, D. 1982. *Introduction to Soil Physics.* Academic Press, New York.

Jenny, H. 1980. *The Soil Resource: Origin and Behavior.* Springer-Verlag, New York.

Jones, J. B. 1985. *A Guide for the Hydroponic and Soilless Culture Grower.* ISBS/Timber Press, Beaverton, Ore.

Kilmer, V. J. (ed.). 1982. *CRC Handbook of Soils and Climate in Agriculture.* CRC Press, Boca Raton, Fla.

Phillips, R. E., and S. H. Phillips. 1984. *No-tillage Agriculture: Principles and Practices.* Van Nostrand Reinhold, New York.

Richards, B. N. 1974. *Introduction to the Soil Ecosystem.* Longman, London.

Stevenson, F. J. 1986. *Cycles of Soil, Carbon, Nitrogen, Phosphorus, Sulfur, Micronutrients.* Wiley, New York.

Tisdale, S. 1975. *Soil Fertility and Fertilizers.* 3rd ed. Macmillan, New York.

C H A P T E R 6

WATER

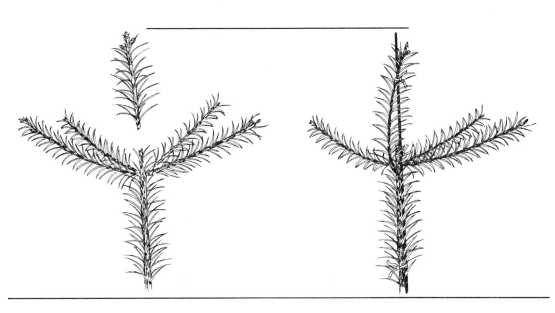

CHARACTERISTICS OF WATER

Water is the most abundant single chemical compound on earth and is the most prominent constituent of living matter. With the exception of seeds, most plant protoplasm is between 75 and 85 percent water; the watermelon, tomato fruits, and lettuce leaves are over 90 percent water. A decrease in the water content of protoplasm, by even a few percent, drastically alters growth and physiological activites of plants and animals. In the broad sense water plays three major roles in the economy of plants. It is a solvent in which gases, inorganic compounds and ions, and organic substances are dissolved and the medium in which they enter and leave cells. It is an obligatory constituent in many cellular reactions and processes. It is a structural component; its presence in plant cells maintains their turgor and thus it maintains the form of the soft tissues of leaves, stems, and

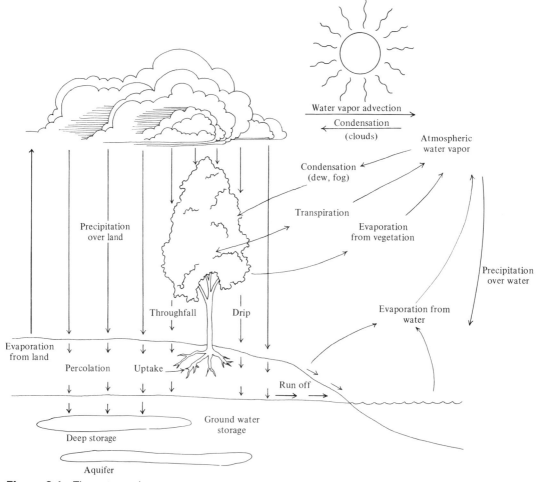

Figure 6-1 The water cycle.

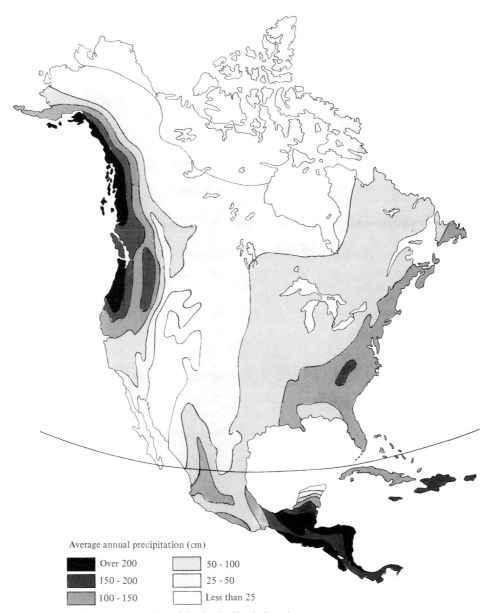

Figure 6-2 Average annual precipitation in North America.

Average annual precipitation (cm)

Over 200	50 - 100
150 - 200	25 - 50
100 - 150	Less than 25

flowers and is primarily responsible for the enlargement of plant cells. Water is also present in plant cell walls.

The supply of water on earth is stable and has been so since the planet cooled, some 5 billion years ago. This indicates that water is recycled over and over again. Of the earth's water, 97 percent is found in bodies of water, 2 percent as ice and snow packs, and less than 1 percent in soils, plants, and animals and as water vapor. Most of the water that reaches the earth's surface reaches it by precipitation or condensation. Not all of this is available to plants. Most precipitation falls on oceans and other bodies of water. Precipitation that falls on land evaporates from soil and plant surfaces, runs off into bodies of water, or infiltrates into soils where it percolates into the water table and underground aquifers (Figure 6-1). A good deal of horticultural and agricultural practice is directly concerned with modifying the hydrological cycle to increase the availability of water to plants and people. In North America few regions are truly arid, defined as receiving less than 25 cm (10 in.) of precipitation a year, but substantial parts of the west are semiarid, with 25 to 50 cm a year (Figure 6-2).

Properties of Water

The biological importance of water is due to its chemical and physical properties. Water is transparent to visible radiation, permitting the penetration of light through cells and down to 3 to 5 m (10 to 17 ft) in lakes and oceans where photosynthetic algae can grow. Since it absorbs heat (infrared radiations), it is a reasonably good heat filter. Water is only slightly ionized. The hydrogens and oxygen are bonded together asymmetrically (the molecule exhibits polarity); thus water has a high dielectric constant (it is a poor conductor of electricity) which accounts for its ability to allow substances to dissolve in it. Water is cohesive; because of the great internal attractive forces between adjacent water molecules, the molecules resist being separated from one another. Because of this cohesion, water has an unusually high surface tension, a viscosity (resistance to flow) much greater than would be expected, and great tensile strength in thin strands of water. Water is also adhesive, having the ability to stick closely to surfaces such as soil particles and plant cell walls. Cohesional and adhesional properties also account for the ability of water to move by capillary action through soil pores and through the vascular system of plants.

Several other physical properties of water relate to its varied roles in organisms. The resistance to separation of molecules is reflected in its high boiling point, 100° C (212° F), and its high heat of vaporization. When water vaporizes (evaporates) from a leaf or other surface, heat is removed from the surface and its temperature is reduced. Water has the ability to absorb considerable heat energy without much alteration in its temperature. It thus prevents rapid changes in the temperature of cells, soils, and bodies of water and they cool off or warm up much more slowly than the air temperature.

Water Potential

Water has a tendency to move spontaneously (that is, with no external energy needed) from one place to another, the direction of flow depending on several factors. This tendency is usually expressed as the water potential, Ψ (Greek psi). Water potential is measured as energy per unit volume (equivalent to pressure) and is calculated as bars (1 bar = 10^6 dynes/cm^2), atmospheres (1 atm = 14.7 lb/in^2; 0.98 atm = 1 bar), or megapascals (1 Mpa = 10 bars). When there is a difference in the water potential of two regions, water will move from the region of higher potential to the region of lower potential. The movement can be seen as the spontaneous flow of water down a slope from a greater to a lesser height or movement down a gradient. Water will stop moving when the potential difference becomes zero. Thus a glass of water sitting on a table will have a water potential of zero. Water that contains dissolved minerals has a lower (more negative) potential than pure water; a more concentrated solution of substances dissolved in water has a lower (more negative) potential than a less concentrated solution. Water at a lower temperature has a lower potential than water at a higher temperature. Water not under pressure has a lower potential than water under pressure.

The key thing to remember is that water will flow only from a region of higher potential to a region of lower potential and that it will, therefore, move from sites of negative to sites of a more positive potential, even if this potential is still negative. Put another way, water will move toward a more concentrated (more negative potential) from a less concentrated (less negative potential) solution.

In considering the movement of water from soil into and through a plant, three major types of water potential are involved. The first is the solute pressure, that of the water plus dissolved substances, designated as Ψ_s; pure water has a potential of 0, and solutions have a negative value. The second is the pressure potential, Ψ_p, which is usually positive in living cells and is the force exerted by cytoplasm on cell walls. The third is the osmotic potential, Ψ_τ, which is always negative. The importance of these three potentials and their positive or negative signs will become clear as we examine the movement of water through cells and through whole plants.

MOVEMENT OF WATER

Uptake of Water

A living plant cell, bounded by its plasma membrane and its cell wall, will, if placed in pure water, begin to take up water since the water potential of the cell is lower (more negative) than the zero water potential of the surrounding water. As water continues to enter the cell, it accumulates in the cell vacuole and builds up water pressure within the cell. This turgor pressure can build up only as far as the equal and opposite pressure of the rigid wall (Figure 6-3). When the cell has taken up water to the point where the osmotic potential of the cell, Ψ_c, plus the pressure potential of the wall, Ψ_p, equals the water potential, water uptake stops and the cell is said to be fully turgid—holding all the water it possibly can. Expressed in water potential notation

$$\Psi_p = \Psi_\tau \; \boxed{2} \text{ and } \boxed{2} \; \Psi_c = 0$$

If water moves out of a cell into a solution with a more negative potential, a concentrated salt solution, for example, its vacuole will shrink and the cell may

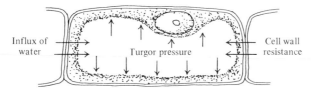

Figure 6-3 Development of turgidity.

become plasmolyzed (Figure 6-4). If many of the cells in a leaf or a herbaceous stem become even partly plasmolyzed (less than fully turgid) the plant may wilt.

The soil solution in which a root is growing has a negative potential because minerals are dissolved in the water. The potential of the root epidermal cell, through which this water must move to enter the root, also has a negative potential (its osmotic potential) due to the substances dissolved in cell water. The potential of root cells is usually more negative (its osmotic potential is greater) than that of the soil solution so that soil water will move into the cell from the higher (less negative) potential of the soil solution to the lower (more negative) potential of the cell. If the soil solution is more negative than the cell potential, water will move out of the root cells into the soil. This occurs all too frequently when de-icing salt or fertilizer is concentrated in one place in the soil; the "burning" is due to plasmolysis and dehydration of root cells, leading to injury or death.

As roots age, the epidermis is replaced by water-resistant cork or bark which greatly reduces the ability of water to enter living cells inside the bark. Therefore, most water uptake by roots occurs through young roots, sometimes called feeder roots. The root hair projections of the epidermal cells of these young roots greatly increase the water-absorptive surfaces. Water and mineral uptake may also be enhanced by the presence of mycorrhiza, a symbiotic (mutually beneficial) association between roots and specific fungi. The presence of the fungus facilitates the uptake of the soil solution (water and minerals, particularly phosphates) and may prevent root infections, and the fungus

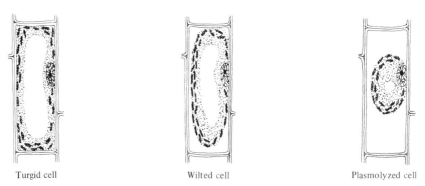

Turgid cell   Wilted cell   Plasmolyzed cell

Figure 6-4 Water status of cells.

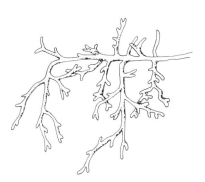

Distorted roots of a conifer
infected with mycorrhizal fungi

Cross section of young root
with fungus mycelium growing
between cortical cells (Hartig net)

Figure 6-5 Ectotrophic mycorrhizae.

receives sugars and other metabolites from the plant. It was formerly thought that such associations occur only in tree species, but it is now known that many field and garden plants have mycorrhizae. Two types of association have been found. Ectomycorrhizae, or ectotrophic mycorrhizae, form a network of hyphae between the cells and sometimes can be seen external to the root (Figure 6-5). The fungal partner is usually a basidiomycete. Endomycorrhizal associations, involving herbaceous or woody angiosperms and ascomycetes, do not show a network of hyphae between cells, but the fungus penetrates into the plant cells and may also appear external to the root surface.

Once water has entered the root epidermal cells, it is moved to the vascular tissue both by apoplastic flow, movement from cell to cell in the cortex through cortical cell walls, and by intercellular flow, movement between the cortical cells. Prior to entering the vascular tissues, however, water must pass through the endodermis. Because there are no intercellular spaces in the endodermis (the Casparian strip prevents such water flow as shown in Figure 6-6), water must enter an endodermal cell from the cortex and move out of the endodermal cell into the vascular tissue (Figure 6-7). This movement causes the water to enter the vascular tissues under about 5 bars of pressure, accounting for most of the root pressure observed when a plant is cut off just above the soil line and "bleeds." Although this pressure would theoretically be adequate to move water vertically about 4 m (1 bar is sufficient to move water about 745 cm), the resistance of

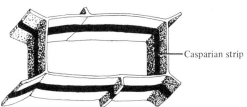

Casparian strip

Figure 6-6 Structure of an endodermal cell.

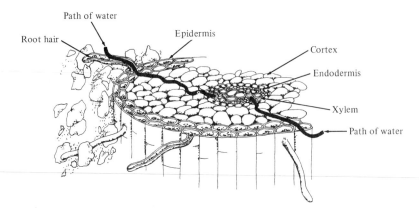

Figure 6-7 Pathways of water from soil solution to root vascular tissue.

water to flow due to its viscosity and its adhesive properties mean that root pressure cannot move water up a plant taller than about 0.2 to 0.5 m. Yet it is obvious that water ascends plants like redwood trees that are taller than 100 m with root lengths that add another 20 to 30 m.

Movement Through Stems

Once water has entered the xylem tissues of the root vascular system, it must move up into the stem vascular system to be distributed through the rest of the plant. The xylem is structurally well designed for water flow, consisting of vessel cells (open pipes) arranged in a continuous series or of interconnected tracheids (closed cells with perforated walls; Figure 6-8). Many studies have demonstrated that water is not pumped up from below and that water movement occurs through dead tissues, so that upward movement must occur by the water being pulled up by physical forces. The most comprehensive theory on how water is raised through the xylem pipe system is called the Dixon-Joly cohesion theory after the plant physiologists who first proposed it. The available evidence strongly indicates that water is pulled up as fine threads or strands in the xylem cells by the strong negative pressures developed as water evaporates from the leaves. The focus of attention on upward water transport thus is on the evaporation of water from leaves.

If water is to be pulled up long distances from the vascular xylem of the root to the upper leaves of a plant, several requirements must be fulfilled. The water must be in its liquid state; it must be in a continuous, unbroken, and very thin column; and the columns must be under tension so that they do not break and so that they can be pulled up. Additionally, the suction force or negative water potential to be exerted on the column must be large, not only to lift a long column of water against gravity, but also to overcome water's tendency to resist flow (its viscosity) and to overcome the adhesion of water to surfaces such as the walls of the xylem vessels and tracheids. Direct and indirect measurements have

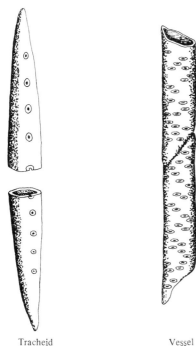

Tracheid   Vessel   **Figure 6-8** Xylem tracheid and vessel showing pits.

shown that water in functional (dead with no cellular contents) xylem is liquid and in unbroken columns and, since the lumen, or hollow center, of a xylem cell is small, the columns are thin. The cohesive property of water molecules (their resistance to being separated from each other) is such that the tensile strength of a microscopically thin strand of water in xylem is greater than a steel strand of the same diameter. Thus, if the negative pressure is great enough to lift a long column of water against its weight and the resistances encountered in its path, water can be pulled vertically for long distances. The suction force needed is developed in the leaves by the process called transpiration—the evaporation of water from a leaf.

Transpiration

The epidermal surface of a leaf is covered by a thin, water-impermeable cutin layer that prevents evaporation from the surface. Both epidermal surfaces may, however, have stomata—pores—through which water can evaporate, moving from the leaf interior into the outside air. There are usually more stomata on the lower than on the upper surface (Table 6-1). The pore opening is surrounded by guard cells; interior to the pore is a hemispherical open area, called the substomatal cavity, which is bounded by thin-walled mesophyll cells (Figure 6-9).

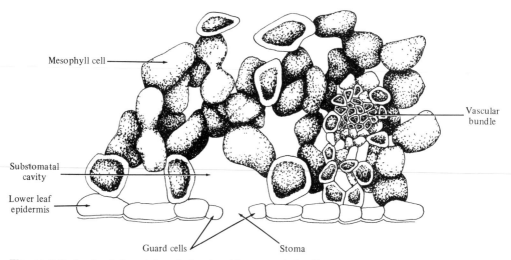

Figure 6-9   Leaf substomatal cavity bordered by mesophyll cells.

   Water in the mesophyll cell moves out of the cell, wetting its cell wall. This water evaporates into the substomatal area and then diffuses out through the stoma into the atmosphere. Since the mesophyll cell has lost water, its negative potential is increased and water from the leaf-vein xylem will move into the cell. Essentially, the whole water column from the root to the end of the leaf vein is pulled up. This leaf potential in the mesophyll cells can reach −50 bars, enough to pull water to a height of close to 20 m.

   An even larger suction force or negative potential develops as the water evaporates into the outside air (Figure 6-10). When water evaporates into dry air

Table 6-1   **AVERAGE NUMBER OF STOMATA PER SQUARE CENTIMETER OF LEAF SURFACE**

Species	Upper epidermis	Lower epidermis
Red oak	0	100,000
Black walnut	0	40,000
Apple	0	30,000
Pines	12,000	12,000
Larch	1,400	1,500
Linden	0	35,000
Sedum	2,800	3,500
Cucumber	5,000	60,000
Onion	17,000	17,000
Sunflower	12,000	17,500
Bean	2,800	3,500
Alfalfa	17,000	14,000
Oat	2,500	2,500
Corn	7,500	10,500
Bluegrass	16,000	10,000

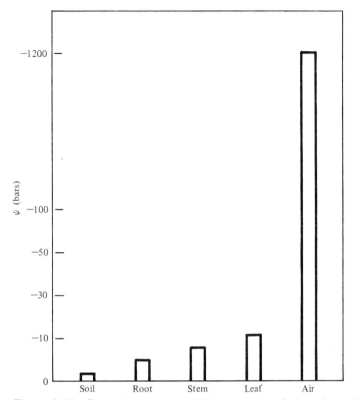

Figure 6-10 Change in water potential through the soil-plant-air continuum.

blowing across the leaf, the potential can reach −1000 bars, more than enough to pull water up 200 m (over 600 ft), greater than the height of any living tree.

The rate of transpirational water loss is controlled by many factors, including the number of stomata per leaf. This number is usually species- or even cultivar-dependent (see Table 6-1) and tends to be related to the water status of the habitat in which the species evolved. Even in plants with many fully open stomata, the pore area rarely exceeds 2 to 3 percent of leaf surface. Experimental evaluation of pore areas has shown that the transpirational evaporation of water through open stomata is close to 50 percent of the rate of evaporation from an open water surface, an indication that the rate of transpirational water loss from leaves may be very high.

More important than number of openings as a rate-controlling factor is the degree to which the stomata are open or closed. Plants must regulate water movement to keep outgo in balance with uptake. If transpiration exceeds uptake, cells and tissues lose turgidity, metabolic processes begin to shut down, and, if water stress is severe, cells plasmolyze and may die. The main regulatory mechanism at a plant's disposal is its ability to open and shut the stomatal opening by altering the shape of the two guard cells that surround it. The guard

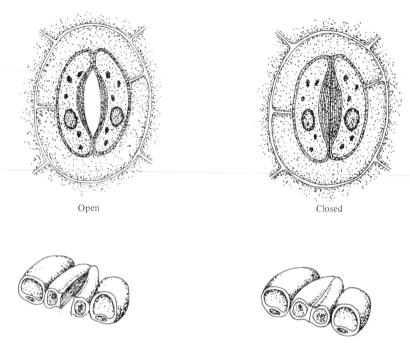

Open   Closed

Figure 6-11   Views of open and closed stomata.

cell's cell wall consists of areas of different thickness. Because of these differences, as the guard cell takes up water from adjacent cells, its shape changes, and adjacent guard cells pull apart to create the open stomatal pore (Figure 6-11). This water movement is regulated by the differences in water potential between adjacent epidermal cells and the guard cells, with the differences in cellular osmotic potential regulated by movement of potassium ion (K^+) and hydrogen ion (H^+). When potassium ion moves out of guard cells back into the adjacent cells, there is a reversal of the potential difference between these cells, water flows out of the guard cells and the stomatal pore closes. Closing or opening is not an all-or-none process; all gradations between fully open and fully closed can be found.

The question of what regulates the movement of ions into and out of guard cells is, at this time, difficult to answer, primarily because there are so many known and suspected factors involved. The water status of the guard cells and adjacent cells is a factor, since as the water available to the leaf decreases, the guard cells close and lessen the possibility of severe dehydration of the leaf. Leaf temperature is also involved, since when the temperature rises to the level where the leaf could be damaged, stomata open and the evaporation of leaf water can reduce cell temperature by almost 10° C. Since the stomata are also the sole entry points for the carbon dioxide needed in photosynthesis, they tend to open in light and close in darkness. As carbon dioxide is fixed in photosynthesis, its concentration within the leaf falls and stomata open. This may occur even when water supplies are limited and is observed as a midday wilting of a plant even when the

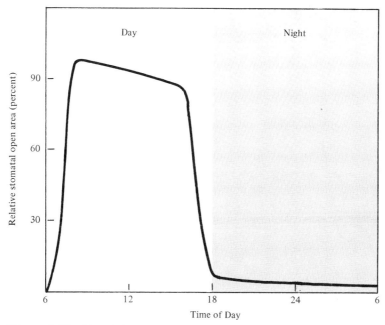

Figure 6-12 Diurnal rhythm of stomatal opening.

soil is moist. A still incomplete list of cell metabolites, including photosynthate and growth-regulating compounds are also involved.

Because of the interaction among these internal and external regulating factors, transpiration exhibits a daily periodicity primarily, but not exclusively related to temperature and light (Figure 6-12). At night stomata close (with the exception of CAM plants; see Chapter 11) and transpiration is minimal. Temperature rises in the morning, reaching a maximum in early afternoon, and gradually decreases to reach its minimum after dark. If water is a limiting factor in midday, there may be a dip in the transpiration rate as stomata are partly closed by the loss of turgidity of the guard cells (Figure 6-13).

The rates of diffusion of water vapor from a leaf can vary greatly even with open stomata. Since this process is directly related to temperature, evaporation occurs much faster from a leaf exposed to the sun than from a shaded leaf. A change of even 2° C in the difference between leaf and air temperature will permit a large difference in transpiration rates. The rate of diffusion of water vapor also depends on the difference in internal and external saturation of air with water vapor. Transpiration is lowered by high air humidities and greatly increased by low humidities. Wind blowing across a leaf sweeps away the water-saturated air, increasing the differential between internal and external vapor concentrations and increasing transpiration. Thus transpiration is maximized on a warm, sunny, dry, and windy day and minimized on a cool, cloudy, humid, and windless day. These atmospheric factors must be considered when the water requirements of potted plants or irrigated fields are to be determined.

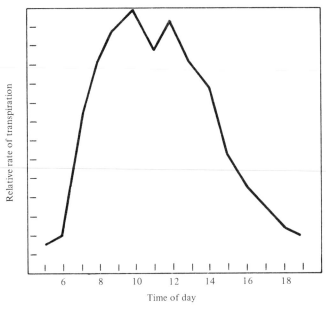

Figure 6-13 Transpiration through daylight hours.

Conditions Affecting Water Availability and Movement

Under certain conditions a large positive root pressure may develop in herbaceous plants and force liquid water out of a plant, a process called guttation. Familiar plants like cabbage *(Brassica oleracea)* and strawberry *(Fragaria* spp.) form droplets of water along their leaf margins, particularly in early morning when root pressures are highest (Figure 6-14). In these plants special water channels, called hydathodes, connect the leaf veins to the leaf margins. Guttation fluid is an excellent growth medium for fungi and bacteria and is a factor in infection.

Plants can take up water directly through their leaves, just as they have the capacity to take up minerals through foliar feeding (Chapter 7). The ecological significance of this phenomenon and its relation to uptake of dew, intercepted fog, and light showers is not known. It may also be of importance for maintenance of cell water levels in cuttings being rooted under mists (Chapter 15).

Water availability is a major factor in regulating the world's vegetation. Desert regions may have fertile, potentially productive soils, but remain almost barren because of lack of water. Over evolutionary time plants have adapted, both structurally and functionally, to various water regimes. Xerophytes are plants that can cope with dry habitats, mesophytes are adapted to habitats with adequate water, and hydrophytes occupy wet sites or grow in water. This classification does not mean that a xerophyte cannot be grown in a mesophytic environment. The adaptations mean that a plant can survive in a particular habitat and not necessarily that that habitat is optimum or even required. Thus,

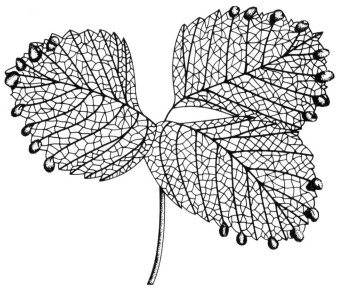

Figure 6-14 Guttation droplets on strawberry (*Fragaria*) foliage.

many conifers show xerophytic characteristics, although they grow luxuriantly in a well-watered environment. Similarly, some hydrophytes can gradually be physiologically adapted to grow well under conditions of reduced water supply. Thus, the horticulturist is not necessarily limited in choosing plants for home and landscaping.

A common structural adaptation to different water regimes is the organization of the stomatal apparatus. Xerophyte leaves tend to have fewer stomata and they are frequently depressed below the surface of the leaf or are covered with hairs, both of which impede diffusion of water vapor from the leaf. Other dry-habitat plants, such as the cacti and some members of the Euphorbiaceae, have dispensed entirely with leaves, and a number of the Crassulaceae have thick, leathery leaves.

Under certain conditions, it becomes useful to reduce the rate and extent of transpiration. Newly planted ornamentals and plants transplanted into the field frequently require several weeks to develop an adequate root system at a time when top growth may be vigorous. Evergreen plantings, both coniferous and broad-leaved, can transpire in winter when water is unavailable because the ground is frozen. Mature cut flowers to be shipped long distances will continue to transpire through stomata in their petals. Two types of antitranspirants are currently available. One operates by causing partial closure of guard cells, and the second physically blocks the stomatal pore. For plants in which it is desirable to maintain photosynthesis, the antitranspirant chemicals that regulate stomatal opening are preferred since some carbon dioxide can enter the leaf. For winter protection of evergreens, the plastic or wax coating type of antitranspirant works well.

The amount of available soil water at any time depends on a large number of factors including the water status of the soil in which the plants are growing. Soil surfaces are capable of evaporating water as a function of temperature, wind, their composition, structure, and texture, and the type and amount of cover of the surface. In evaluating losses of water from the soil surface, it is necessary to consider both transpiration and evaporation (evapotranspiration) since both involve basically the same processes. Overall, one-quarter of all precipitation on land surfaces is collected in streams and aquifers and of the remaining three-quarters, close to half is lost as soil evaporation. Even greater evaporative losses are found in hot, dry regions where crop cover tends to be sparse. Removal of plant cover may greatly increase evaporation, an important consideration in the management of watersheds or timing of harvests where such removal is contraindicated because of both evapotranspiration and the increased potential for erosion. In horticultural plantings evaporative water loss can be reduced by mulching between crop rows with natural mulches or plastic sheeting or by frequent mowing of permanent cover crops in orchards during hot, dry periods. These soil covers also assist in reducing weeds that deplete nutrient supplies.

WATER STRESS

Water Deficits

Plants are rarely in the situation where adequate amounts of water are always available to them. Recently watered potted plants or field plantings shortly after a soaking rain are likely to be in soil that is at field capacity, where soil holds its maximum amount of water against the force of gravity. Assuming that the soil solution is relatively dilute so that the water potential gradient between the solution and the root epidermal cell is sufficiently large and that the rate of transpiration is not greater than the rate of supply of water from the roots, it is likely that all cells of the plant are fully turgid and that no water deficit exists. Clearly, this situation is rare, and most plants at most times have at least some cells with less than their full complement of water. No matter how small or large the deficit, the plant is undergoing some degree of water stress measurable as a water deficit of cells, tissues, or organs. Even in well-watered plants, midday temperatures cause the rate of transpiration to exceed the rate of uptake, and plants may lose turgidity and exhibit internal responses to stress (Figure 6-15).

At the whole plant level water stress is manifested as a reduction in growth which, depending on the severity and the duration of the deficit, may be so small as to be of no importance or so great as to reduce the productivity or the viability of the plant. Because of the economic consequences of water deficits, there has been a good deal of research to establish the extent of water deficits under different conditions and with different plants and to determine the structural and biochemical effects of water deficits.

As the severity of water stress increases, there is a progressive sequence of reduction in a number of cellular activities. Cell growth by enlargement appears

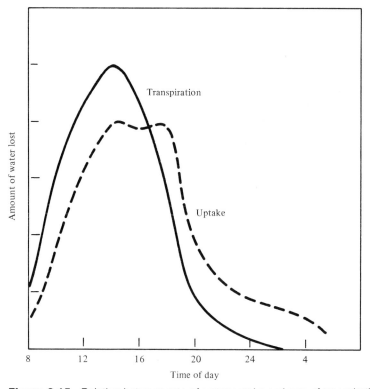

Figure 6-15 Relation between rate of water uptake and rate of transpiration through a day.

to be the most sensitive process, followed by cell wall synthesis, protein and chlorophyll synthesis, the formation of plant growth-regulating substances, and photosynthesis in that order. As stress becomes more severe, respiration and other vital processes begin to decrease. The cells usually do not show plasmolysis until respiration has been reduced, although the plant may show incipient or extensive wilting before this level has been reached. For most plants water stress may develop prior to the soil's reaching its permanent wilting point, a value usually set at −15 bars where plants will remain wilted unless water is supplied. When the potential of the soil water remains at or below the permanent wilting point for extended periods of time, death of cells, tissues, and organs can be expected. There are species differences in the sensitivity of cultivated plants to extended periods of severe water stress. Many of the vegetable crops and a number of ornamentals are particularly sensitive, while most cereal grains, cucurbits, and annuals native to naturally arid regions have higher survival.

The age and stage of development of a plant are critical in its response to water stress. Seedlings and young plants often die at stress levels that can be withstood by older plants. Flower, fruit, and seed formation are sensitive stages in the life cycle. Prolonged drought during the heading-up (anthesis) of cereal grains may have a devastating effect on crop yields.

The health and vigor of a plant is also a factor in the degree of stress response. Plants with poor, injured, or diseased root systems cannot absorb and transmit enough water to the top and, as uptake and outgo become more and more unbalanced, stresses may be severe. It is common to observe wilting and other visual manifestations of water stress in newly transplanted plants where root systems have been injured. Reduction in leaf area by selective pruning may be necessary to restore a balanced shoot-root ratio. Nutrient imbalances, the presence in soil solutions of toxic substances, metabolic inhibitors or even high concentrations of required nutrients alter water relations and may be seen first in transient wilting of the planting and, unless corrected, will lead to more severe stress and plant death.

Where the possibility for water deficits is great, as in droughty soils, during dry and windy periods, or when the soil water potential is very negative, water can be supplied to potted plants or to gardens, but only with irrigation can this be done for most agricultural crop areas. Antitranspirants can be used for valuable plantings, but their use is limited because of costs.

Drought Tolerance

Few cultivated plants exhibit true drought tolerance in the sense that they can continue active development under conditions of low water availability. Most plants that withstand water stress do so by avoidance mechanisms. Some plants, particularly those that evolved in xerophytic environments where the possibility of water stress is high, have developed structural and functional characteristics that reduce water loss. Plants native to arid regions tend to have root systems that either spread laterally to take up water from a large area or have roots that grow vertically to tap deep water tables or aquifers. Some, such as the ocotillo (Fouquieria splendens), can drop their leaves when stressed and can regrow a new canopy within a few days after adequate soil moisture is available. The thick, fleshy leaves of members of the Crassulaceae, the complete absence of leaves from members of the Cactaceae, and the sparse leaf formation in members of the Euphorbiaceae are adaptations to an arid environment where water stress is the rule.

A variety of other water conservation measures have been evolved by plants. In many of the grain and forage grasses, stomata are found almost exclusively on the lower surface of the leaf. Such leaves have special cells, bulliform cells, that tend to collapse when they lose turgidity so that the entire leaf curls inward to prevent transpiration (Figure 6-16). Plants that possess crassulacean acid metabolism (Chapter 11) keep their stomata closed during the day, when because of high levels of light and temperature, transpiration would be high, and open them only at night.

In some plants relatively mild water stress may be beneficial, even though it may reduce vegetative growth. The maturation of fruits, such as apple and peach, is promoted by low water stress, and it has been known for many years that the content of medicinal substances in drug plants is enhanced by water stress. The same may be true for the formation of essential oils in mint and the lipids of oil

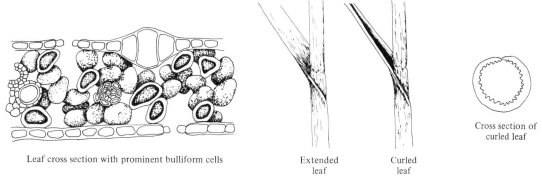

Leaf cross section with prominent bulliform cells   Extended   Curled
                                                                      leaf   leaf

Cross section of
curled leaf

Figure 6-16   Anatomy of corn (*Zea Mays*) leaf showing curling mechanism.

crops. For perennial plants that form winter buds, mild water stress is required both for bud formation and for the hardening necessary to withstand cold periods; heavy watering of woody perennials in late autumn can reduce resistance to cold.

Flood Tolerance

Hydrophytic species normally develop in water or in water-saturated soils and have evolved structures that allow them to survive under these conditions. Floating and submerged water plants (*Elodea* and others) rarely have either stomata or epidermal cuticles so that uptake of nutrients and carbon dioxide occurs directly through the epidermis. Water lilies *(Nymphea* spp.) have large air channels in their long petioles that channel air to the root system. Terrestrial plants vary greatly in their ability to grow well in or at least withstand wet sites for extended periods of time. Table 6-2 lists some plants adapted to wet soils, and Table 6-3 lists some ornamental woody plants capable of withstanding flooding.

The physiological effects of flooding are not completely understood, but it is believed that most, if not all, of the failure of plants to develop well under

Table 6-2   PLANTS FOR VERY MOIST OR WET SOILS

Trees	Shrubs
Acer rubrum	*Calluna vulgaris*
Alnus spp.	*Chionanthus virginicus*
Ilex spp.	*Clethra alnifolia*
Larix laricina	*Cornus alba*
Liquidambar styraciflua	*Euonymus japonica*
Magnolia virginiana	*Ilex verticillata*
Nyssa sylvatica	*Juniperus communis*
Quercus bicolor	*J. conferta*
Quercus palustris	*J. horizontalis*
Salix spp.	*Rhododendron nudiflorum*
Taxodium distichum	*Rosa rugosa*
Thuja occidentalis	*Rubus* spp.
Tsuga canadensis	*Viburnum* spp.

Table 6-3   PLANTS THAT CAN WITHSTAND UP TO HALF YEAR OF FLOODING

Latin name	Common name
Acer negundo	Box elder
A. rubrum	Red maple
A. saccharinum	Silver maple
Carya spp.	Hickory
Cornus stolonifera	Red-osier dogwood
Crataegus mollis	Downy hawthorn
Eucalyptus camaldulensis	Red gum
Fraxinus pennsylvanica	Green ash
Gleditsia aquatica	Water locust
G. tricanthos	Honey locust
Liquidambar styraciflua	Liquidambar (sweet gum)
Nyssa aquatica	Tupelo
Platanus Xacerifolia	London plane
P. occidentalis	Sycamore
Populus deltoides	Eastern cottonwood
Quercus bicolor	Swamp white oak
Q. macrocarpa	Bur oak
Q. palustris	Pin oak
Salix spp.	Willow
Taxodium distichum	Bald cypress
Ulmus americana	American elm

conditions of soil saturation with water is due to lack of adequate aeration of the root system. Roots, like all other cells of flowering plants, have an absolute requirement for oxygen needed in the respiratory process (Chapter 12). Some of the energy derived from respiration is used to maintain the integrity of cell membranes through which all water and dissolved substances enter the plant, and some is used to maintain the health of cell organelles. Injured roots are incapable of taking up enough water to supply the tops, and it is not unusual to see fully wilted plants standing in water. Waterlogged soils are notably oxygen-deficient since the air in the pore space has been replaced by water, which holds relatively little oxygen. This anaerobic condition of the soil also suppresses the activities of soil microorganisms involved in mineralization and conversion of organic matter into humus and available inorganic substances. The development of muck soils is due, in large part, to years of flooded conditions resulting from high water tables.

The structural and functional basis for flood tolerance has been examined for many horticultural and agricultural species. Rice, which is normally grown in flooded paddies, and the cranberry which is very flood-resistant, have developed the ability to provide energy by the fermentative, anaerobic respiratory pathway. Other flood-tolerant species have organs with large, air-storing spaces between their cells that can maintain aerobic conditions for short periods of time (Figure 6-17). Some plants, such as tomato and sunflower, quickly form adventitious roots at or near the surface of the waterlogged zone that can take up air and transfer it to other root tissues. Dormant plants (those still in winter rest or lacking leaves) appear more capable of withstanding prolonged flooding than those in vigorous growth. Even dormant plants, however, can be injured when

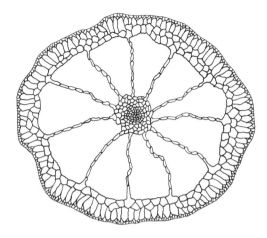

Figure 6-17 Cross section of a hydrophyte stem showing air
chambers.

flooding is accompanied by high temperatures because more oxygen is required
by plants as temperature rises. High temperatures accelerate the respiratory
process and therefore increase the demand for oxygen. Recent research has
indicated that some of the observed effects of flooding on growth may be due to
imbalances among the various growth-regulating substances formed by plant
cells.

Soils that are in a location subject to flooding, such as on floodplains or
above water-impermeable hardpans, present severe problems when they are used
for cultivation. In general, the situation can be alleviated by providing drainage
and by adding substances like sand that promote freer infiltration and percolation of excess water. Selection of flood-tolerant species or cultivars is also
important.

IRRIGATION

Growing Plants on Semiarid Land

Close to three-fourths of the earth's land area is arid, receiving less than 25 cm
(10 in.) of precipitation a year, or semiarid, receiving less than 50 cm (20 in.).
These figures are misleading, since they represent averages taken over many
years. Semiarid lands may in any given year receive much less rain than the
average. The plants native and adapted to dry lands are rarely suitable for human
needs, and major food and ornamental plants are rarely adapted to such
conditions. Since the need for water by plants is absolute, irrigation is necessary
if such areas are to be utilized.

People have known for thousands of years that many arid and semiarid soils
tend to be nutrient-rich and potentially highly productive. The biblical injunc-
tion that the desert shall bloom like the rose has a good physiological basis. The
ancient civilizations of North Africa, the Middle East, and the Far East all
developed irrigation techniques. Primitive irrigation systems consisted of little

more than a manually operated apparatus, such as a treadmill or a simple screw device, to lift buckets of water from a stream and empty them into furrows between rows of cultivated plants. More advanced systems of extensive piping and mechanized pumping are simply variations of the same fundamental techniques for flowing water across the land.

Agriculture is the biggest single consumer of water in the United States. Over 300 billion gallons per day are withdrawn from ground or surface sources, including 100 billion gallons per day used solely for irrigation. A proportion of this water is returned directly to surface waters, frequently to be used many times before emptying into the sea.

Types of Irrigation Systems

There are three basic techniques of supplying water to plants. The simplest is the furrow or flood technique in which water carried in open culverts or in pipes is transferred to furrows between rows of plants or simply floods the fields periodically. Less than half of this water is actually taken up by plants, most of it being lost by percolation and evaporation. Because of runoff problems, this method is restricted to fairly level areas. Such a system is the least expensive to construct, but where water is scarce and a high water loss through rapid evaporation of soil water is to be expected, as in the western United States, it may be wasteful. The second technique supplies water to the plants as a spray. This can be as simple as the hose used to water a flower or vegetable garden or a lawn or as complex as the highly mechanized center pivot irrigation systems developed in 1949 and now widely used on the Great Plains. In this technique underground aquifers are tapped, and the water is carried out on long booms to irrigate as much as 160 acres with a single pivot. As in furrow irrigation, losses from evaporation and evapotranspiration are high and the initial and maintenance costs are considerable. A single center pivot system can pump over 1000

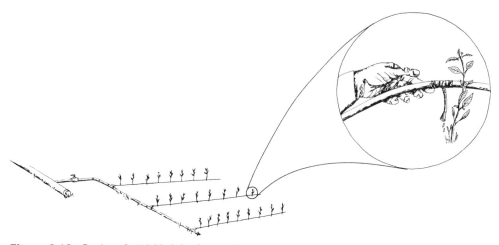

Figure 6-18 Design of a trickle irrigation system.

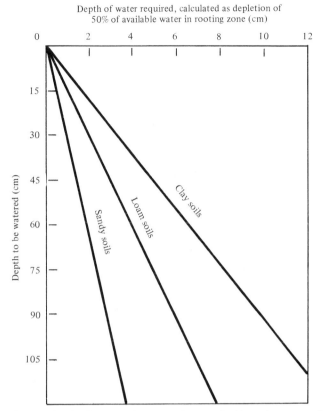

Depth of water required, calculated as depletion of
50% of available water in rooting zone (cm)

Figure 6-19 Amount of water to be supplied in order to wet different depths of soil.

gallons a minute, and reductions of aquifer levels and lowered water tables have
been reported.

A third irrigation system, also recently developed, is the drip or trickle
method. A single, small-diameter tube is tapped at each plant or at several places
along a row through a small hole or special emitter (Figure 6-18). The rate of
water trickle is adjusted according to species needs and plant stage of development so that the soil immediately around the plant is maintained at the desired
level of available moisture. It is moderately expensive to install, but conserves
water and, as most tests show, permits better plant growth and yield. One variant
of the trickle method, used in home gardens, is the flexible plastic or fiber hose
(soaker) that exudes small amounts of water over a long period of time. Trickle
irrigation can be combined with liquid fertilization of the plants with little loss of
nutrients and virtually no runoff.

Decisions on the amount of water to be supplied must take into account a
number of factors including species-specific demands, the rooting depth of the
plants, the level of evapotranspiration, soil characteristics, temperature, wind,
crop cover, and the stage of development of the plants. A rough field determination of soil moisture is useful in many horticultural situations (Table 6-4). Figure
6-19 is a chart indicating the amount of water necessary to saturate the desired

Table 6-4   FIELD DETERMINATION OF SOIL MOISTURE

Moisture condition	Percent field capacity (0.5 bar)	Sandy loam	Silty loam	Clayey loam
Dry	0–5	Powder dry (0–3%)	Crumbles (0–5%)	Dry clods (0–8%)
Low	5–15	Crumbly	Loose crumbs	Pliable, no ball
Moderate	25–50	No ball	Forms weak ball	Balls with pressure
High	75–95	Forms weak ball (10–15%)	Forms durable ball (15–20%)	Easily forms ball
Wet	Waterlogged	Free water released	Free water released	Free water released

A handful of soil is squeezed with moderate pressure, the hand is opened, and the soil is shaken around in the hand. Numbers in parentheses are average percentages of available water.

depth of soil when the soil is 50 percent depleted. Estimates of required amounts may be given as depths of water supplied, such as 2 cm or 1 in., or as volumes, that is, depths of water per unit of area, such as acre feet or hectare centimeters. Computer programs that can integrate all the factors involved have permitted considerable conservation of water.

As water evaporates from a soil surface, salts that were in solution are left behind. Over periods of time the resulting increase in salinity or sodicity of the soil may reduce plant growth. This may occur in agricultural irrigation and in garden plantings and even in pot culture. Although some plants are more or less tolerant or resistant to salts (either as the ions *per se* or as solutes that decrease the water potential of the soil solution), many important food and ornamental crops are sensitive to them. To date, no economically practical method has been developed to reduce salt buildup in soils and soil solutions. Attention has been focused on breeding and genetic engineering of salt-tolerant species or cultivars and the use of special planting techniques. Research is also being done to determine whether salt-requiring plants, halophytes, can be used in rotation with other crops to absorb some of the salt. When potted plants are fertilized frequently, it is important to flush out the excess salts periodically by one or more applications of water alone.

TRANSLOCATION

Translocation Tissue System

In 1679 the Italian scientist, Marcello Malpighi, concluded that ascending "raw sap" from the soil was modified by leaves and converted into "elaborated sap" that fed other parts of plants. Malpighi girdled trees and observed that upward movement of sap through the wood was unaffected, but that the bark region above the girdle enlarged (hypertrophied) as food materials accumulated (Figure 6-20). It was 150 years before the translocation tissue system in the bark region was identified as the phloem. Radioactive (^{14}C) substances are now used to allow

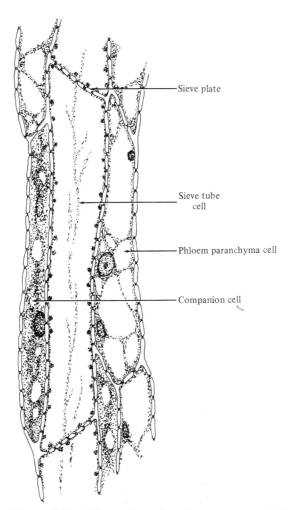

Sieve plate

Sieve tube
cell

Phloem paranchyma cell

Companion cell

**Figure
6-20** Hyper-
trophic effect of
girdling on a
tree.

Figure 6-21   Phloem sieve tube cell and associated phloem cells.

detailed studies on the translocation of photosynthate from the leaves to the rest
of the plant.

    The phloem consists of several cell types (Chapter 4) which may be primary
(differentiated from parenchyma cells) or secondary (initiated from cambium).
The functional cells in translocation are phloem sieve tubes and their adjacent
companion cells (Figure 6-21). A sieve tube at functional maturity lacks a
nucleus, although it is metabolically active, and its lumen is filled with slimy
materials called callose and P-protein. Intercellular plasmodesmata (protoplas-
mic connections between cells) between sieve tubes and their companion cells
are believed to play a role in translocation. Phloem translocation moves sugars,
primarily sucrose, formed in photosynthesis (Chapter 11) plus amino acids and
other substances rapidly from the leaves and hence is a basic process in the

economy of plants. Accumulation of these substances in fruits, seeds, roots, tubers, and rhizomes is critical to development of many food plants and to the survival of perennial plants.

Mechanisms of Phloem Translocation

Any comprehensive theory must account for the movement of photosynthate and other products from leaf cells into the phloem of leaf vascular bundles, their rapid movement over long distances, and their final transfer out of the phloem into other cells. The mechanisms of translocation are not fully understood. There are at least five major hypotheses, none of which is capable of accounting for all of the facts, although each can account for some that others do not. In all these theories it is recognized that metabolic energy (Chapter 12) is required, since part of the translocation process requires moving solutes against a concentration gradient.

Basic to understanding translocation is the concept of the source-sink relationships. The final storage site is referred to as the sink or consumer. The sites at which the substances are produced are called sources. Photosynthesizing leaves are sources, capable of exporting considerable quantities of sugars, but young leaves are sinks since they do not produce enough sugars for their own development. Young leaves at the apex of a shoot are consumers of sugar and removal or injury of lower, more mature leaves on that shoot will depress the development of the young leaves. In spring the starch stored in roots or tubers is transformed to sugars that move upward to sinks in growing parts of young shoots. The development of new shoots by herbaceous and woody perennials the following year depends upon adequate supplies of sugar having been deposited in these organs. Similarly, the starch in seed cotyledons is a source for the young shoot. The initiation of flowers and of fruit transforms the altered apex into a sink requiring large quantities of sugars and other metabolites supplied by leaf, stem, and root sources. Although the bulk of translocation occurs via the phloem, some upward translocation occurs in the xylem.

It is known that the process is influenced by a variety of environmental and internal factors independent of the mechanism involved in translocation. The concentrations in source and sink of inorganic ions such as potassium and phosphate, the availability of several plant growth-regulating substances, temperature, light, and the metabolic requirements of source and sink cells are certainly involved. The movement or loading of sugars into phloem from a source such as photosynthesizing leaves requires metabolic energy provided by respiration of the cells. If, during maturation of vegetable seeds or root crops, it is desirable to increase the rate and extent of translocation, these factors can be manipulated separately or in combination. However, the most practical way of increasing the accumulation of starch or sugar in sink tissues is to increase the photosynthetic accumulation of sugars (see Chapter 11).

Although inadequate in some respects, the most acceptable hypothesis of translocation is called the mass flow theory (it is also known as the Münch pressure flow hypothesis). Sugar formed by photosynthesis in leaf cells is, with

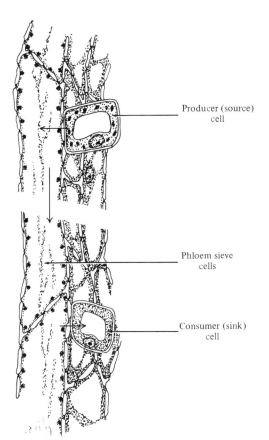

Producer (source) cell

Phloem sieve cells

Consumer (sink) cell

Figure 6-22 Model of the Munch pressure flow hypothesis for phloem translocations.

the use of metabolic energy, "pumped" into sieve tubes of leaf veins, the process called phloem loading (Figure 6-22). The increase in the osmotic potential (decreased water potential) causes water to flow into the sieve tubes with the result that the total water pressure in the phloem increases. This forces the sugar solution down the sieve tube system. At the sink end, the sucrose is unloaded, again with the use of metabolic energy, into recipient cells, and the water pressure in the sieve tubes is reduced as water moves back into the xylem. The system can be recharged at the source. In most plants the sugar in sink cells is transformed into insoluble starch grains for long-term storage. When this starch is required by a new sink, it is converted back into sugars.

Efficient operation of the translocation mechanism requires that adequate water be available to the plant. Plants under water stress do not translocate actively. When plants are under water stress during the time of seed maturation, seeds do not accumulate enough stored food for the subsequent development of the embryo. This is a factor in the viability of a seed lot and in the use of seeds as human or animal food. Water stress in late summer may also reduce the accumulation of starch in roots and rhizomes and thus depress the development of the next year's shoots. The recommendation that faded flowers or fruits be removed to promote the growth of the vegetative parts of the plant is due partly to the conservation of source supplies.

SUPPLEMENTARY READINGS

Baker, D. A. 1978. *Transport Phenomena in Plants.* Chapman & Hall, New York.
Billings, W. D., F. Holley, O. L. Lange, and J. S. Olson. 1976. *Water and Plant Life.* Springer-Verlag, New York.
Crafts, A. S., and C. E. Crisp. 1971. *Phloem Transport in Plants.* Freeman, San Francisco.
Curl, E. A., and B. Truelove. 1986. *The Rhizosphere.* Springer-Verlag, New York.
Elving, D. C. 1982. Crop response to trickle irrigation. *Hort. Rev. 4.*
Frenkel, H. and A. Heiri (eds.). 1985. *Soil Salinity: Two Decades of Research in Irrigated Agriculture.* Reinhold, New York.
Gale, J., and R. M. Hazen. 1966. Plant antitranspirants. *Annu. Rev. Plant Physiol.* 17:269–282.
Hansen, V. E., G. E. Stringham, and O. W. Israelson. 1980. *Irrigation Principles and Practice.* Wiley, New York.
Jackson, R. M. 1983. *Mycorrhizas.* Studies in Biology No. 159. University Park Press, Baltimore, Md.
James, D. W., R. J. Hanks, and J. J. Jurinak. 1982. *Modern Irrigated Soils.* Wiley, New York.
Kozlowski, T. T. (ed.). 1968–1983. *Water Deficits and Plant Growth.* Vols. 1–8. Academic Press, New York.
Kramer, P. J. 1983. *Water Relations of Plants.* Academic Press, New York.
Martin, E. S., M. E. Donkin, and R. A. Stevens. 1983. *Stomata.* Studies in Biology No. 155. University Park Press, Baltimore, Md.
Meidner, H. 1976. *Water and Plants.* Halsted Press, New York.
Milburn, J. A. 1979. *Water Flow in Plants.* Longman, London.
Moorby, J. 1981. *Transport Systems in Plants.* Longman, London.
Mussell, H., and R. C. Staples (eds.). *Stress Physiology of Crop Plants.* Wiley, New York.
Paleg, L. G., and D. Aspinall. 1982. *Physiology and Biochemistry of Drought Resistance in Plants.* Academic Press, New York.
Raschke, K. 1975. Stomatal action. *Annu. Rev. Plant Physiol.* 26:309–340.
Russell, R. S. 1977. *Plant Root Systems: Their Function and Interaction with the Soil.* McGraw-Hill, New York.
Salter, P. J., and J. E. Goode. 1967. *Crop Responses to Water at Different Stages of Growth.* Commonwealth Agricultural Bureau, London.
Simpson, G. M. 1981. *Water Stress on Plants.* Praeger, New York.
Steward, F. C. (ed.). 1986. *Plant Physiology: A Treatise.* Vol. 9. *Water and Solutes in Plants.* Academic Press, Orlando, Fla.
Winter, E. J. 1974. *Water, Soil and the Plant.* Macmillan, New York.

C H A P T E R 7

MINERAL NUTRITION

INORGANIC REQUIREMENTS OF PLANTS

Source of Mineral Nutrients

Research on mineral nutrition of plants has waxed and waned in importance over several centuries. The experimental approach to its study started in the sixteenth century when it was recognized that plants take up elements from the soil which function as nutrients. During the early nineteenth century, a time of marked advancement in chemistry, a modern experimental approach to mineral nutrition was developed. Plants were grown in distilled water containing various inorganic salts—early hydroponics—and were found to absorb both beneficial and toxic compounds. By the middle of the nineteenth century all of the macroelements, that is, elements required in relatively high concentration, were identified. As these studies continued, mineral elements required in small amounts, referred to as minor or trace elements or microelements, were also identified.

It became apparent that inorganic compounds—fertilizers—could be applied to soil in order to supplement minerals naturally present in too low a concentration to permit maximum plant growth. The use of fertilizers today has produced an estimated 25 percent increase in the yield of crop plants on a worldwide basis; in the United States commercial application has increased almost 10-fold since 1940. But the cost of fertilizers has risen dramatically, a serious economic problem for less developed countries. Excessive fertilizer application can lead to environmental problems. Not the least of these problems is that a considerable amount of fertilizer is not absorbed by root systems, but rather is lost by leaching into the ground water, contributing to the pollution of water supplies.

Given adequate water and light for photosynthesis and respiration, plants need only certain inorganic compounds to fulfill their total nutrient requirements for growth, development, and reproduction (Table 7-1). The specific mineral elements (ions) required by plants are derived, with the exception of

Table 7-1   ELEMENTS IN THE NUTRITION OF HIGHER PLANTS

Essential macronutrients	Essential trace nutrients	Beneficial or required by some plants	Essentiality not established
Metals			
Potassium	Iron	Sodium	Gallium
Magnesium	Manganese	Cobalt	Vanadium
Calcuim	Zinc		Strontium
	Molybdenum		Rubidium
	Copper		Aluminum
			Nickel
Nonmetals			
Nitrogen	Boron	Selenium	Iodine
Phosphorus	Chlorine	Silicon	Fluorine
Sulfur			Bromine
Carbon			
Hydrogen			
Oxygen			

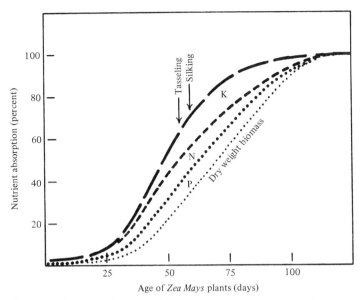

Figure 7-1 Loss of macronutrients from soil by crop removal

some of the nitrogen, from the various inorganic compounds that make up the rocky layers (bedrock) underlying the several horizons of soil (Chapter 5). These compounds become part of the mineral soil in which plant roots grow. There must be an array of compounds of potential nutrient value. These must be in a soluble form so that the specific elements (ions), as part of the soil solution, are available for uptake by the root system. A variety of environmental factors can affect the processes by which these mineral nutrients can be solubilized as well as absorbed by the roots (Chapters 5 and 6).

Inorganic compounds containing nitrogen are present in soils as mineral complexes, through the nitrogen-fixing and nitrogen-decomposing activities of various soil microorganisms and through the application of nitrogenous fertilizers. Several inorganic nitrogen compounds in soils contain the nitrate ion (NO_3^-) which is highly soluble and rapidly taken up by roots, but easily leached down through the soil below the root zone. Ammonium ion (NH_4^+), on the other hand, is strongly absorbed to negatively charged soil particles and consequently does not move as rapidly as does the nitrate ion. Ammonium ion is converted to nitrate ion by bacterial activity (nitrification). In addition to leaching and plant uptake, nitrogen is lost from the soil by crop removal, up to 50 lb per acre during a single growing season (Figure 7-1). Bacteria also contribute to nitrogen loss when they convert nitrate ion to gaseous forms which diffuse into the atmosphere.

Complex organic nitrogen compounds (dead organisms, manures) are not absorbed by plant roots, but must first be decomposed to inorganic forms, the process of mineralization and ammonification. Amino acids, the organic products of protein breakdown, can be taken up by plant roots, but they are a negligible contribution to the total nitrogen requirements. Urea, a simple

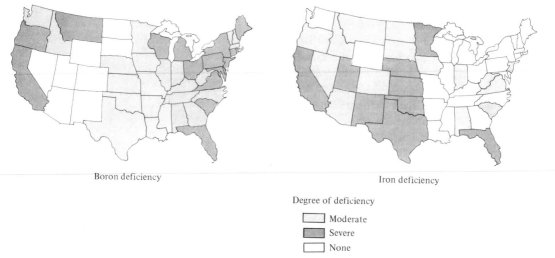

Boron deficiency   Iron deficiency

Degree of deficiency

☐ Moderate
■ Severe
☐ None

Figure 7-2   Examples of trace nutrient deficiencies in the United States.

organic, nitrogen-containing compound, may also occur in soil, but it, too, is not of major consequence. Urea is, however, extensively used as a fertilizer in the form of a spray since it can be directly absorbed by soil and leaves. Combined urea (ureaform—see Chapter 10) is a major slow-release form of nitrogen used on lawns and some ornamental plants.

Phosphate ions become unavailable to plants in very acid or very alkaline soils forming insoluble complexes with calcium, iron, or aluminum. Phosphorus and potassium in soluble forms are not easily leached through the soil. On the other hand, soluble compounds containing calcium, magnesium, or sulfate ions are rapidly leached.

Iron, in the ferric form, is usually in plentiful supply except in alkaline soils where it becomes combined into insoluble compounds, a relatively common situation in the western United States and in Florida (Figure 7-2). Acidification of the soil or use of chelated iron (discussed later in this chapter) overcomes this deficiency.

Several groups of inorganic compounds become insoluble at an alkaline pH, so their specific ions are unavailable for absorption by plant roots. These include compounds of manganese, zinc, and copper. When the soil is very acid, these ions may become too readily available and reach toxic levels. Boron, however, is frequently deficient in acidic soils, common east of the Mississippi River (Figure 7-2). Molybdenum-containing compounds are more soluble in alkaline soils, and in very alkaline soils toxic concentrations are easily reached.

Macroelements

Table 7-2 lists the macroelements essential for plant growth; these are nitrogen, phosphorus, potassium, calcium, magnesium, and sulfur. The first three are

Table 7-2 ESSENTIAL MACRONUTRIENT ELEMENTS IN PLANT NUTRITION

Element	Form in which available to plants	Average percent in plant tissues (dry wt)	Natural source	Compounds used as fertilizer
Nitrogen (N)	NO_3^- NH_4^+	1.0–2.0	Nitrogen-fixing and nitrogen cycle activities of various bacteria and blue-green algae	Organic: dried blood, aged manures, cottonseed meal, bone meal Inorganic: ammonium sulfate, ammonium nitrate, ammonium phosphate, magnesium-ammonium phosphate, urea
Phosphorus (P)	$H_2PO_4^-$ HPO_4^{-2}	0.2	Apatite (calcium phosphate)	Superphosphate: calcium hydrogen phosphate Triple superphosphate: ammonium phosphate, calcium metaphosphate, bone meal
Potassium (K)	K^+	1.0	Micas Feldspars	Potassium chloride Potash (potassium carbonate) Wood ashes (potassium carbonate) Potassium sulfate Cow manure
Calcium (Ca)	Ca^{+2}	0.2–0.5	Limestones (calcite, dolomite)	Limestones (calcium-magnesium carbonates) Gypsum (calcium sulfate)
Magnesium (Mg)	Mg^{+2}	0.2	Numerous minerals	Dolomitic limestone (magnesium carbonate) Epsom salts (magnesium sulfate) Magnesium nitrate Magnesium chloride
Sulfur (S)	SO_4^{-2}	0.1–0.2	Rocks with iron sulfides	Ammonium sulfate Calcium sulfate
Hydrogen (H)	H_2O	6.0	Water	Water
Carbon (C)	CO_2	45.0	Air	—
Oxygen (O)	O_2 H_2O	45.0	Air	—

referred to as primary macronutrients and the second three as secondary macronutrients. The elements carbon, hydrogen, and oxygen are nutrients only in their combined form, that is, as molecules of water, carbon dioxide, and oxygen.

Root systems will tend to absorb from the soil solution all of the minerals that are present. A large volume of information is available on the mineral composition of important crop plants. It must be remembered, however, that the chemical composition of plant tissue reflects, in general, the mineral composition and the fertility of the soil in which the plant was grown. A deficiency of a particular nutrient can have harmful effects on general growth and on productivity of all crops. An overabundance of a nutrient (luxury concentration) may also have negative effects; it may be toxic to the plant, depress production, or result in poor root formation. The old adage "If a pinch is good, a pound is better" should be disregarded as far as mineral nutrition is concerned.

Plant roots, while tending to absorb from the soil all the available nutrient ions, show species variation and a degree of selectivity that may result in lower or higher concentrations of certain ions in specific tissues or organs. Chloroplasts are rich in magnesium as well as in the microelements manganese, copper, and iron. Mitochondria have high levels of calcium but low levels of the microelement boron.

Ion interactions in the soil that promote or inhibit uptake also have a regulatory role in nutrient concentration. Potassium ions are rapidly taken up by roots and toxic levels could be reached in plant tissues; however, if even trace levels of calcium are present, the excessive uptake of potassium is inhibited, and a toxic accumulation is prevented. Calcium thus inhibits, or antagonizes, the absorption of potassium. Calcium also antagonizes sodium uptake and the reverse is also true; low levels of potassium or sodium antagonize calcium uptake.

Other ion antagonisms have been documented such as between magnesium and calcium and between magnesium and potassium. Work with fruit trees has indicated that excess application of one nutrient results in decreased absorption of the other leading to an induced deficiency. For reasons not completely understood, there is also an ion antagonism between calcium and boron. Boron deficiency of the plants is sometimes observed in fields or garden plots that are heavily limed to raise soil pH. Death and discoloration of apical meristems and young leaves appearing shortly after lime application is characteristic of this interaction; it is relieved by small, carefully regulated applications of commercial borax.

Nitrogen   Plant roots absorb nitrogen as the nitrate ion or ammonium ion. Once in the plant the nitrate ion is enzymatically reduced to ammonium ion which is rapidly incorporated into various nitrogen-containing molecules synthesized by the plant: protein, nucleoprotein, enzymes, vitamins, alkaloids, and chlorophyll. Nitrogen is able to move, in its ionic form and as organic compounds, from older leaves to the apical meristem regions, a phenomenon referred to as ion mobility. Symptoms of a deficiency are chlorosis, or yellowing, of older leaves and the presence of red anthocyanin pigments along veins.

Phosphorus   Phosphorus is a constituent of many organic compounds, including nucleic acids, phospholipids, and coenzymes; it functions in protein metabolism and in energy metabolism (Chapter 12). It is stored in seeds as a complex molecule called phytin and is important in the early maturation of various crops as well as for good root and seed development. Deficiency symptoms, occurring first in older leaves, include darker green color of leaves and an accumulation of red or purple pigmentation. A general reduction in growth, slow maturation of fruit, and reduced yield of fruit and seed are characteristic. Oranges from phosphorus-deficient trees have a poor, sour flavor.

Potassium   Potassium is not a part of any organic molecule in plants, but it has several important functions. It is an ionic regulator in such processes as opening of stomata and an activator of many enzymes including those involved in protein metabolism and carbohydrate synthesis. It promotes growth of meristematic tissues, enhances root and stem development and flavor and color of some fruits. It seems to be involved in cold hardiness. It is mobile in the plant. Crops that synthesize large quantities of carbohydrate have a high requirement for potassium. A deficiency leads to a mottled chlorosis, which occurs in older leaves first. It results in reduced productivity, lowered disease resistance, and weakened roots and stems. Lodging of weak stems (being knocked over by wind and rain) is common in cereals.

Calcium   Calcium is required for normal membrane function, cell division processes, and the formation of the middle lamella between cells. It is not readily translocated from older parts of the plant and the first sign of deficiency is in the youngest regions where leaves and meristems die. Root growth and fruit formation are inhibited. There may also be a general interveinal chlorosis. Blossom-end rot of tomatoes is due to a calcium deficiency. Calcium oxalate crystals (Chapter 4) are commonly found in cell vacuoles.

Magnesium   Magnesium is the central element in the chlorophyll molecule (Chapter 11). It functions as an enzyme activator for the synthesis of amino acids and vitamins, in energy metabolism, and in the translocation of phosphorus. Deficiency symptoms occur usually in older leaves; these include dying of leaf tips and interveinal chlorosis resulting in a striped effect in monocots such as corn.

Sulfur   Sulfur is a component of essential amino acids and plays a role in protein metabolism. It is generally not deficient in soils for two reasons: it is a contaminant in potassium and other fertilizers and a product of industrial combustion. The presence in plants of sulfur-containing compounds contributes to the characteristic pungent flavor of cole plants such as cabbage and broccoli and of onions and garlic. Deficiency of sulfur leads to a marked chlorosis in younger leaves which may become white in color. Weak stems and reduced growth are other symptoms.

Microelements and Other Elements

The trace elements that have been established as essential for the growth of flowering plants are iron, boron, manganese, zinc, molybdenum, copper, and

Table 7-3 ESSENTIAL TRACE ELEMENTS IN PLANT NUTRITION

Element	Form in which available to plants	Average percent in plant tissues (dry wt)	Natural source of element	Compounds used as fertilizer or technique to increase availability
Iron (Fe)	Fe^{+2} (ous) Fe^{+3} (ic) (rarely)	0.01–0.1	Hornblende and other minerals	Reducing soil pH to below 7.0 Iron chelates
Boron (B)	BO_3^{-3}	0.002	Various minerals	Borax (hydrated sodium borate) Calmanite (calcium borate) Common contaminant in commercial fertilizers
Manganese (Mn)	Mn^{+2}	0.005	Various minerals	Reducing soil pH to below 7.0 Manganous sulfate Manganous chelates
Zinc (Zn)	Zn^{+2}	0.002	Same minerals as iron	Zinc sulfate Zinc chelates Galvanized nails hammered into tree trunks
Molybdenum (Mo)	MoO_4^{-2}	0.00001	A few minerals	Increasing soil pH to above 7.0 Sodium molybdate
Copper (Cu)	Cu^{+2}	0.0005	Various minerals	Copper sulfate Copper chelates
Chlorine (Cl)	Cl^-	0.01	Ubiquitous distribution in air, water, soil	(Never required)

chlorine (Table 7-3). With the exception of boron and chlorine, they are ionic forms of metals. The availability to the plant of the metal ions depends upon their solubility which, in turn, is a function of the pH of the soil solution. In soils with an acid pH, these metals, with the exception of molybdenum, become much more soluble and, therefore, more available for absorption by the root system (Figure 7-3). In very acid soils toxic soluble levels of these metals may exist, but modification of soil pH decreases the available concentration permitting normal plant growth.

The ions of heavy metals (cadmium, cobalt, nickel, chromium, manganese, copper, and zinc) are quite toxic to plants, even in low concentrations, as is the aluminum ion, because they interfere with various aspects of plant metabolism. Toxicities are increased when calcium is in too low a concentration. Many plants tolerate and even accumulate high concentrations of these metals (see Table 7-4). In general, metal toxicities are not common except where mine tailings are spread or unique geological formations exist. Roots, however, may show selectivity since some of these elements accumulate to high levels in tissues, while others are excluded or taken up to a limited extent. Roots tend to retain metals such as cobalt, copper, lead, nickel, and chromium.

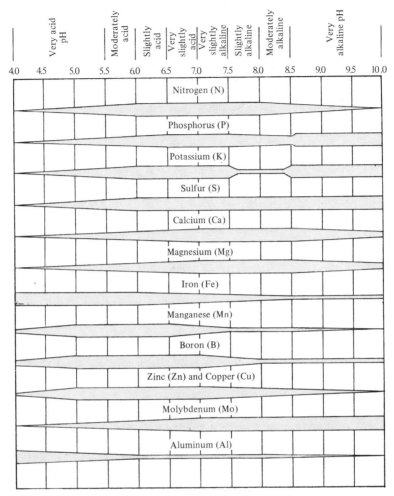

Figure 7-3 Effect of pH on solubility of mineral nutrients and aluminum.

Iron Iron is important in the proper functioning of enzymes that participate in oxidation-reduction reactions such as occur in the light-requiring reactions of photosynthesis (Chapter 11) and the electron transport chain of aerobic respiration (Chapter 12). It is also required for the synthesis of chlorophyll, some proteins, and various membranes within cells. A deficiency of this nutrient shows up first in younger leaves as lighter green color in the interveinal regions. Leaves may become yellow or chlorotic and even white although the veins remain green. Growth is retarded.

Boron Boron is required for flowering and fruit formation, cell division, pollen germination, salt absorption, and translocation of hormones, but its precise role is unknown. The leaves of boron-deficient plants thicken and become darker, meristems die, and flowers and fruits may abscise (fall) prematurely. Blueberry

(Vaccinium corymbosum) is particularly susceptible to this deficiency. Asparagus *(Asparagus officinalis)* has a higher requirement than many crop plants.

Manganese Manganese is an activator for enzymes involved in respiration, nitrogen metabolism, and the oxygen-yielding reactions of photosynthesis. A deficiency shows up as necrotic spots on leaves and interveinal areas becoming lighter green than veins, similar to magnesium and iron deficiencies. In the case of manganese, younger leaves are affected first. Manganese may become toxic in acid soils.

Zinc Zinc is required for the synthesis of the hormone indoleacetic acid (Chapter 13) and in protein synthesis. Its deficiency results in short, stunted plants because internodes do not elongate normally (the condition called rosetting). Chlorosis occurs in older leaves.

Molybdenum Plants become nitrogen-deficient if they lack sufficient levels of molybdenum. It is required as an enzyme activator for nitrogen assimilation and fixation reactions and for proper development of nodules on legume roots. Leaves of molybdenum-deficient plants are mottled, the margins wilt, and older leaves become pale green and then chlorotic. Seeds may not develop properly.

Copper Copper is a required constituent of a variety of enzyme molecules. Leaves of copper-deficient plants become dark and withered, and the leaf tips die.

Chlorine This element established as essential in 1954, is required in the oxygen-yielding reactions of photosynthesis. Chlorine is ubiquitously distributed and a deficiency is never seen under natural conditions. Deficient plants wilt, roots are stunted, and fruiting is reduced. Tomato *(Lycopersicon esculentum)* is especially sensitive to this deficiency.

Other Elements The essentiality of sodium for some, but not all plants, was established in 1960. It is required by those plants that possess the C_4 photosynthetic pathway for the fixation of carbon dioxide (Chapter 11). It is also required by some halophytes (salt-loving) such as saltbush *(Atriplex)* and asparagus *(Asparagus officinalis)*.

Aluminum and silicon may be found in high concentration in plants, but they have no known essential function. Aluminum interferes with the absorption of iron and calcium when it forms insoluble compounds around roots. Silicon is found in the leaves of horsetails, many grasses, and many tropical plants where it gives added strength. Rice and corn grow better in its presence. Cobalt is found in higher plants but has no known function, although it is required by symbiotic bacteria that fix nitrogen. The essentiality of vanadium, selenium, and nickel has not been firmly established. Iodine, fluorine, and gallium are found in higher plant tissue but no function has been discovered; they are, however, required by some microorganisms and by higher animals.

Table 7-4 SOME ACCUMULATOR AND BIOGEOCHEMICAL INDICATOR PLANTS

Element	Plant species	Comments
Gold	*Typha latifolia*	
Mercury	*Holosteum umbellatum*	Sterile seed capsules contain elemental mercury
	Arenaria setacea	
Lead	*Tussilago farfara*	
Selenium	*Astragalus racemosus, A. pattersonii, A. bisulcatus, A. pectinatus*	Restricted to seleniferous soils
	Aster spp., *Atriplex canescens*	Accumulates selenium; not confined to seleniferous soils
Aluminum	*Camellia sinensis*	Accumulates and may require aluminum
	Hydrangea macrophylla	Accumulates aluminum which determines blue flower color
	Symplocos tinctoria	
Zinc	*Thlaspi calaminare*	Calamine flora; may be restricted to zinc-rich soils
	Viola tricolor	
Copper	Caryophyllaceae	
Manganese	*Digitalis purpurea*	
Nickel	*Betula alba, Alyssum bertolonii*	Serpentine soil indicator
Silver	*Eriogonum ovalifolium*	Indicator plant

Accumulator and Biogeochemical Indicator Plants

Some higher plants have the ability to take up unusually large quantities of certain elements and to tolerate high tissue levels. Some species seem to grow only where the soil contains specific minerals. Accumulation of unusual heavy metals in specific plants has been used in identifying likely areas for prospecting for these compounds. These plants are called accumulator and biogeochemical indicators (Table 7-4). An example is milk vetch *(Astragalus)* which grows only in seleniferous soils and specifically accumulates selenium in high concentrations. This was not realized until range cattle, feeding on these plants, died of selenium poisoning (blind staggers). The plants are totally unaffected. It now seems that selenium may play a role in sulfur metabolism.

FERTILIZERS

Macronutrients: NPK

We have already indicated that when a soil is deficient in one or more mineral elements, the usual practice is to add a fertilizer that will increase the concentration of those nutrients in the soil solution for absorption by the plant's root system. The aim of fertilization is to provide soil nutrients in concentrations required by the specific plant to maximize its productivity.

It is necessary to add fertilizer not only to overcome any natural deficiencies, but also to replace nutrients that are in low concentration due to absorption during plant growth and to removal of plant parts at harvest. Plants lose minerals during their period of active growth. As cotyledons and leaves are shed, less mobile ions, such as calcium and sulfur, may remain with the dead plant parts. During growth roots excrete many compounds including potassium, some nitrogen compounds, and sodium. Leaching of essential minerals from leaves by rain may, if precipitation is extensive or is acidic, be large. Cuttings under misting conditions (Chapter 15) may become nutrient deficient and foliar feeding is used to prevent deficiency when the time for root formation is measured in months as in hard-to-root cuttings.

Fertilizers to be incorporated into soil may be various natural organic or chemical inorganic materials. The organic materials include well-rotted animal manures, crop residues, dried blood, and many others. These tend to be low in available nitrogen (N), phosphorus (P), and potassium (K), but positive effects on soil texture, tilth, and structure make their use quite beneficial. Complex organic nitrogen must be converted by microorganisms to the mineral or inorganic form, the process of mineralization. Chemical fertilizers, being soluble inorganic compounds, are more readily and rapidly available for uptake. The usual method is to add a dry granular or powder material to the soil, although fertilizers may be applied as a liquid suspension or an aqueous solution. Nitrogenous fertilizer in the form of a gas (gaseous ammonia) is sometimes used for field crops.

The only sure way to determine how much of what elements should be added is to do a soil analysis of pH and concentrations of mineral elements in the soil are determined. These analyses are done for a small fee by laboratories associated with the U.S. Department of Agriculture Extension Service associated with state agricultural experiments stations or by private laboratories. Soil analysis kits, designed for the home gardener, are also available. Plant tissue analysis is a reliable but expensive method of determining plant nutritional requirements.

The macronutrients nitrogen, phosphorus, and potassium are needed in higher concentrations than the other required nutrients and are the ones combined in the usual commercial fertilizer that is called a complete formula. The nitrogen, phosphorus, and potassium content of commercial fertilizers, referred to as NPK, is given as a sequence of three numbers, for example, 5–10–5, 10–10–10, 8–32–16. These are the percents by weight of the three elements. The first number is the percentage of nitrogen as elemental nitrogen; the second is the percentage of phosphorus pentoxide (P_2O_5) as some form of phosphate compound; and the third is the percentage of potassium oxide (K_2O) as some form of potassium compound. These formulations may include other ingredients such as various salts, which are impurities in nutrient compounds, and inert material called ballast. The ballast may also be gypsum (calcium sulfate).

Certain formulations of commercial fertilizer contain nitrogen in a relatively insoluble form, ureaform. Ureaform slowly goes into solution only under certain conditions, thus slowly releasing a continuous supply of available nitrogen. It is an insoluble product of urea and formaldehyde and its solubilization is temperature-dependent. Its solubility is minimal at 25° C (77° F) and increases as the temperature rises. It is used extensively as a single annual application for turfgrass, ornamental shrubs, and greenhouse plants. The amount of ureaform in a formulation can be varied according to the desired length of time during which the ureaform is solubilized and thus available to the root system. NPK formulas of 10–6–4 may have 25 or 50 percent of the nitrogen as ureaform for fast or slow effect, 20–12–8 may have 25 percent, or 5–10–5 may have 40 percent.

Micronutrients

Other nutrients may be incorporated, as varying percentages, into regular NKP formulas; magnesium 1.8 percent, sulfur 5.0 percent, boron 0.02 percent, and zinc, 0.07 percent is one example. But as pointed out earlier, zinc and boron are required in very low concentrations and easily reach toxic levels under certain soil conditions as well as through overfertilization.

An efficient and effective method for applying essential metal ions of iron, zinc, manganese, and copper is to use the chelated form. A chelating, or sequestering, agent is an organic compound that binds to the metal ion to prevent its reaction with other ions and thereby to prevent it from becoming insoluble. The chelated metal remains soluble and available to the plant. Examples of chelating agents are Versene or EDTA (ethylenediaminetetraacetic acid) and EDDHA [ethylenediamine di(o-hydroxyphenyl) acetic acid]; EDDHA forms a better chelate with iron for application on calcareous (calcium-containing) soils. They are not toxic to plants and are eventually broken down by microorganisms. A number of organic substances in soil also act as chelating agents, including some root exudates.

Adjusting Acidity

Soil acidity or alkalinity is a prime factor determining whether various macro- and micronutrients will be soluble in the soil solution and available for uptake by roots (see Figure 7-3); soil pH also affects the growth and the nitrogen-fixing and decomposing activities of microorganisms that are normal inhabitants of soil. Bacteria which fix nitrogen or participate in the decomposition of organic residues grow poorly or not at all in acidic soils, although many soil fungi will tolerate a low pH. Most crop plants and ornamentals grow and reproduce optimally at a soil pH between 6.0 and 7.0. A few, such as sweet potato and white potato, have a lower pH optimum of around 5.5; and acid-loving plants such as blueberries and other members of the heath family (Ericaceae), and hydrangea and gardenia do best between 4.5 and 5.5.

The importance of determining soil pH must again be emphasized. A soil with a too-acid reaction can be made more alkaline by adding basic ions such as calcium, magnesium, or potassium as their nitrate salts. The positively charged sodium ion, or other basic ion, binds to negatively charged sites on soil particles; hydrogen ions slowly replace the sodium ions, which, together with negatively charged hydroxyl ions in the soil water, create weakly alkaline solutions. Sodium nitrate is a useful supplement to a complete fertilizer for beets, asparagus, and corn as these plants respond favorably to a slightly alkaline pH. The more usual and least expensive procedure is liming, the addition of calcium compounds such as calcium magnesium carbonates. Calcium sulfate (gypsum) is applied to sodic soils and improves the structure of saline soils. The application of superphosphate fertilizers has little effect on soil pH; other substances are added to adjust the acidity level as required for maximum productivity.

A soil with too high a pH can be modified by the addition of compounds that increase the acidity. Some nitrogen fertilizers have this effect; these include ammonium nitrate, diammonium phosphate, ammonium sulfate, and urea. Organic residues such as dried blood, cottonseed meal, animal manures, and peat moss also have an acidifying effect. Aluminum sulfate is commonly applied to blueberry plantings, but care must be exercised to prevent an accumulation of aluminum. The use of elemental sulfur, flowers of sulfur, is a good way of acidifying soil as it is rapidly converted to sulfuric acid through bacterial activity.

Fertilization Practices

Excessive amounts of nitrogen fertilizers promote exuberant shoot growth, although root systems tend to be poorly developed. High, but not excessive nitrogen, may be desirable for plants grown solely for their attractive foliage. For plants grown for flowers or fruit, too high a level of nitrogen application can depress flowering and delay the coloring and maturation of fruit. Tomato fruit tend to split as they ripen and potato tubers are small. Too much nitrogen applied to hyacinth, daffodil, and tulip bulbs and iris roots promotes leaf growth rather than flower formation. Rose fertilizers typically have a low percentage of nitrogen.

Other deleterious effects on plant growth of too much nitrogen include weak, succulent stems, lowered resistance to low temperature damage, and delayed formation of winter buds. If outdoor ornamentals are given any fertilizer four to six weeks before the time of the usual first frost, the plants may not be sufficiently dormant to withstand even barely freezing temperatures.

The choice of fertilizer and the method of application for use on vegetable and flower gardens, house plants, trees, and field crops depend upon the type of plant, the stage of growth at the time of application, the type of soil, and the soil analysis. For example, young plants being transplanted in the spring into a well-prepared soil are usually watered with a dilute solution of soluble complete fertilizer to aid the plants in becoming established rapidly and in overcoming transplantation shock. Once established, young vegetable plants may be side-dressed with a dry, granular complete fertilizer, that is, fertilizer is placed in bands a few inches away from the stems. Care must be exercised when using dry fertilizer to prevent its getting too close to the stems or on leaf surfaces, since it will burn the plant—cause plasmolysis of the living cells (Chapter 6). Annual flowers benefit from additional soluble fertilizer during the growing season. Perennial flowers are side-dressed with granular fertilizer in the spring, when their leaves are just emerging. Bone meal, as a supplement, aids in promoting good root growth. Watering with soluble fertilizer in midsummer tends to perk up these plants.

Solutions of soluble complete fertilizer, urea nitrogen, and chelated metal ions can be applied to plants as foliar sprays. The nutrients are quickly taken in through the leaf surfaces. The plant response is rapid, but it is also brief since the nutrients are quickly utilized. The convenience factor is considerable and this may be the method of choice for alleviating metal ion deficiencies.

A number of types of complete fertilizers are available for use on ornamental house plants. Granular formulas are dissolved in water and are added directly to the soil or may be sprayed on the foliage, although spraying may leave unsightly white deposits on the leaves which should be washed off. NPK ratios will vary, 15–30–15 or 20–20–20, and some formulations also contain chelates of trace metals. Fertilizers with an NPK ratio of 30–10–10 are often used for plants that need an acidic fertilizer.

A type of slow-release fertilizer for potted plants is composed of granules of dry nutrients encapsulated within multiple layers of polymeric resin. When water penetrates the permeable shell, the nutrient core dissolves and slowly leaches through the coating into the surrounding soil. An application of this type of material lasts three to four months at a soil temperature of 70° F (21° C) or longer at lower temperatures. NPK ratios may be 14–14–14 or higher. The granules should always be evenly distributed over the soil surface of potted plants and covered by a half inch of soil. When scattered directly on the soil surface, they tend to wash or float out of the pot when the plants are watered. Other types of slow-release fertilizer dissolve slowly.

The proper fertilization of forage and field crops is a specialized science where information on soil fertility as well as how much nutrient the crop may be expected to take from the soil is required. When to fertilize to achieve the maximum productivity is also an important consideration. Some crops (corn, tomato, potato) are "heavy feeders" and high nitrogen levels given at the proper time in their growth cycle enhance yields. Legumes, which fix part of their required nitrogen, need less nitrogen fertilizer, although other nutrient requirements are not decreased. In fact, yields of certain leguminous crops (soybeans and peanuts) are not increased by the application of nitrogen compounds because nitrogen fixation is depressed when these crops receive nitrogen fertilizers.

A variety of application methods are used to fertilize large acreages. Slurries broadcast by tank trucks result in a more even application than spreading dry materials. Liquid fertilizers may be sprayed directly onto crops from long arms or booms mounted on trucks. Anhydrous ammonia, a gas, is injected directly into the soil to precise depths. Fertilizer may be applied at the time seeds are planted by drill application where dry fertilizer is pushed into the soil to a level below and to the side of the seed. Fertilizers may be added to irrigation water. And aerial application is successfully used for large areas that are not easily accessible by truck.

Fertilization of trees where the root system is close to the soil surface and

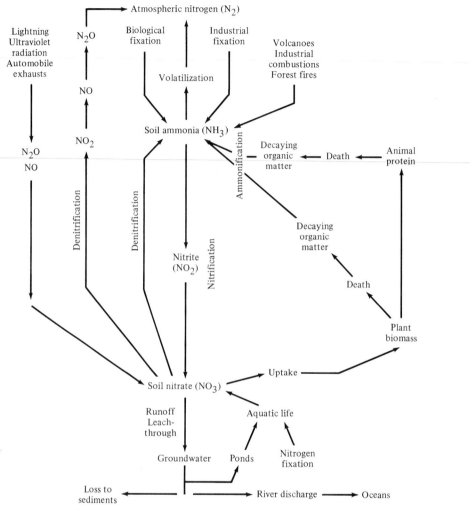

Figure 7-4 Nitrogen cycle.

there is not much lateral spread, such as in young fruit orchards or Christmas tree plantations, is done by side-dressing the plants or by foliar sprays. A different technique is required for large ornamental trees, since the roots have penetrated into the soil and have spread laterally to about the edge of the growth of the crown of the tree, the drip line. Narrow holes are bored at the drip line and filled with fertilizer, the choice depending upon the type of tree.

Nitrogen Cycle

Dinitrogen, N_2, constitutes 78 percent by volume of the earth's atmosphere which is the major reservoir for the gas. Dinitrogen is odorless, colorless, and a biologically inert gas that cannot be used by organisms except for a few prokaryotic bacteria and blue-green algae (see Chapter 10). For their nutrition most plants require a combined form of nitrogen (nitrate or ammonium ion, ammonia, amino nitrogen) that is relatively scarce in soil and water and is frequently the ecological limiting factor for plant growth. The present yearly application for agricultural purposes, worldwide, is estimated at 40 million metric tons of nitrogen fertilizer.

The transformation of elemental nitrogen into utilizable forms, that is, its fixation, occurs in both nonbiological and biological ways (Figure 7-4). The nonbiological ways include natural events and human technology. The energy of lightning discharges and of solar ultraviolet light is sufficient to combine nitrogen and oxygen to form nitrogen oxides that are washed out of the atmosphere into the soil by rain. The internal combustion engine also forms nitrogen oxides. Ammonium ion, formed during volcanic activity, industrial combustions, and forest fires, enters the soil during rainstorms. Nitrogen is also fixed in the manufacture of anhydrous ammonia for fertilizers (the Haber-Bosch process) in which nitrogen is combined with hydrogen. The process requires large amounts of energy and natural gas (as the hydrogen source), both derived from fossil fuels, and has become very expensive. The Haber-Bosch process accounts for at least 15 percent of the nitrogen fixed, worldwide.

The bulk of nitrogen fixation—70 to 80 percent—is of biological origin, with an estimated 60 percent of that occurring in terrestrial habitats. Agricultural nitrogen-fixing crops contribute about half of that 60 percent. Intensive research is currently focused on genetic engineering techniques (see Chapter 15) to include nitrogen-fixing ability in cereal grains and other nonleguminous crops in

Table 7-5   FREE-LIVING NITROGEN-FIXING ORGANISMS

Organism	Natural habitat
Nonphotosynthetic bacteria	
Azotobacter vinelandii	Aerobic soils
Bacillus polymyxa	Aerobic soils
Beijerinckia spp.	Aerobic soils
Clostridium pasteurianum	Anaerobic soils
Klebsiella pneumoniae	Aerobic and anaerobic soils; water
Photosynthetic bacteria	
Rhodospirillum rubrum	Surface of polluted ponds
Chromatium spp.	Anaerobic moist mud, stagnant ponds,
Chlorobium spp.	fresh and salt water
Blue-green algae (at least 20 genera)	
Heterocystous nitrogen-fixers	
Anabaena	Freshwater, salt water, soil
Calothrix	Soil, freshwater
Fischerella	Soil, freshwater
Nostoc	Soil, freshwater
Scytonema	Soil, freshwater
Nonheterocystous nitrogen-fixers	
Oscillatoria	Soil, freshwater
Plectonema	Soil, freshwater
Gloeocapsa	Soil, freshwater

Table 7-6   SPECIES OF RHIZOBIUM THAT FORM NODULES ON THEIR LEGUMINOUS HOST PLANTS

Species	Host
Group I	
R. leguminosarum	*Pisum* spp., *Vicia* spp. *Lens* spp.
R. phaseoli	*Phaseolus vulgaris, P. anguistifolius, P. multiflorus*
R. trifolii	*Trifolium* spp.
R. meliloti	*Melilotus* spp., *Medicago* spp., *Trigonella* spp.
Group II	
R. japonicum	*Glycine* spp., *Lupinus* spp., cowpea miscellany
R. lupini	*Lupinus* spp., *Ornithopus* spp., limited infectivity for *Glycine* spp., and cowpea miscellany

order to decrease the dependence on expensive fertilizers and to look to a future when fossil fuels, required for the Haber-Bosch process, will be in short supply. Enhancing the nitrogen-fixing ability of legumes is also being explored.

The organisms that can fix elemental nitrogen are of two kinds, free living and symbiotic. The free-living microorganisms, including a number of blue-green algae, a few aerobic bacteria, and several species of anaerobic bacteria, live in soil, damp places, rice paddy soils, swamps, and sediments of lakes (Table 7-5, p. 173). Symbiotic organisms, including a few species of blue-green algae and several species of bacteria, live in association with a variety of host plants (Tables 7-6, 7-7, 7-8).

The symbiotic bacteria invade root hairs of leguminous and certain nonleguminous plants and stimulate the root to form overgrowths called nodules in which the bacteria, now called bacteroids, live and fix nitrogen (Figure 7-5). Symbiotic nitrogen fixers do so only in association with their plant host although they can survive as free-living organisms. The symbiotic blue-green algae and certain symbiotic bacteria do not induce the formation of nodules, but rather live within organs or associate in other noncomplex ways (see Table 7-8). The symbiotic process contributes much more fixed nitrogen to the soil than does the

Table 7-7   NORTH AMERICAN NONLEGUMINOUS PLANTS THAT FORM NODULES IN ASSOCIATION WITH SYMBIOTIC NITROGEN-FIXING BACTERIA

Family	Genus	Bacterium
Betulaceae (birch)	*Alnus* spp.	*Frankia alni*
Elaeagnaceae (oleaster)	*Elaeagnus* spp.	*F. elaeagni*
	Shepherdia spp.	*F. elaeagni*
Myricaceae (bayberry or wax myrtle)	*Myrica gale* and other species	*F. brunchorstii*
Rhamnaceae (buckthorn)	*Ceanothus greggii* and other species	*F. ceanothi*
Rosaceae (rose)	*Dryas drummondii*	*F. dryadis*
	Purshia tridentata	*F. purshiae*
	Chamaebatia tuliolosa	Unidentified

Table 7-8 SYMBIOTIC NITROGEN-FIXING ORGANISMS THAT DO NOT FORM NODULES ON THEIR NONLEGUMINOUS HOSTS

Organism	Host	Site of Fixation
Bacteria		
Spirillum lipoferum	*Digitaria decumbens*	Root cortex between cells
Unidentified actinomycete	Various member of grass family	Rhizosphere
Blue-green algae		
Anabaena azollae	*Azolla* (tropical water fern)	Leaf cavities
Nostoc muscorum	*Gunnera macrophylla*	Leaf glands and stems

nonsymbiotic (Table 7-9). It is estimated that there are about 12,000 different species of higher plants that have symbiotic associations with nitrogen-fixing bacteria and about 200 of these are legumes grown as crop and ornamental plants.

There is increasing evidence that, in addition, a loose or casual symbiotic nitrogen fixation occurs in some members of the grass family (Gramineae) including Bahiagrass, guineagrass, millet, forage grasses, and sugar cane, as well as in the cereal grains such as rice and corn. This has also been documented for certain freshwater and marine angiosperms. In these plants the bacteria are found in the rhizoplane, the transition zone between the root surface and the soil.

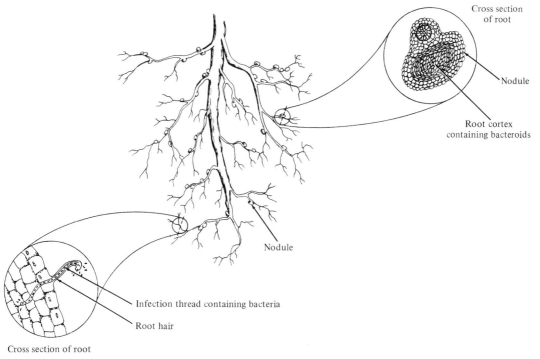

Figure 7-5 Legume root with nodules.

Table 7-9 AMOUNT OF NITROGEN FIXED BY SOME PROKARYOTIC ORGANISMS

Organism	Average nitrogen fixed (kg/acre/yr)
Symbiotic association (plant host: bacterium)	
Alfalfa: *Rhizobium*	119
Clover: *Rhizobium*	99
Lupine: *Rhizobium*	60
Nonsymbiotic organisms	
Blue-green algae	10
Bacteria	
Azotobacter	0.1
Clostridium pasteurianum	0.1

The fixed nitrogen is taken up by the root which, in turn, releases carbohydrates utilized by the bacteria for their nutrition. In other grasses the bacteria are found within the root, usually between root cortical cells.

Rice fields in Southeast Asia often remain productive without the addition of fertilizers due in large part to the simultaneous growth of rice and the small, floating water fern, *Azolla,* which harbors a nitrogen-fixing blue-green alga (see Table 7-8). Free-living nitrogen fixers, especially anaerobic bacteria living in the mud, also contribute nitrogen to this crop. A common aerobic free-living nitrogen fixer, *Azotobacter,* has been inoculated into soil in an effort to increase the amount of fixed nitrogen, but this procedure has proven to be of little merit.

Biological nitrogen fixation is an energy-requiring reaction, the energy coming from photosynthesis in photosynthetic organisms or from respiration in nonphotosynthetic ones. Dinitrogen and water, in the presence of the enzyme nitrogenase and energy, interact to yield ammonia, the first inorganic product of nitrogen fixation. Nitrogenase, which seems to be the same molecular complex in both blue-green algae and bacteria, requires molydenum and iron as specific activators. Cobalt is required by the bacteria in symbiotic associations. Amino acids, the first organic products of nitrogen fixation, are synthesized from chains of carbon atoms plus ammonium ion.

Nitrogenase is oxygen-labile, that is, its activity is destroyed in the presence of oxygen. For this reason, the nitrogen-fixing reaction proceeds only in an anaerobic environment. Within the legume root nodule a reddish-pink protein, leghemoglobin, is synthesized by the plant, binds to oxygen, and maintains an anaerobic milieu in which the enzyme functions. In fact, these nodules, when young, are quite obviously pink. In those blue-green algae where the fixation process occurs in the heterocyst, the oxygen-yielding reaction of photosynthesis does not occur; thus, an anaerobic environment is maintained. It is assumed that nitrogen fixation occurs in a free-living organism only when the organism is in an anaerobic environment, which may occur as a discrete pocket even in an aerobic soil.

Nitrogen-fixing organisms are quite sensitive to a variety of environmental conditions. Most aerobic soil organisms will fix nitrogen only at a pH between 6.0 and 7.5, while the anaerobic ones, which are less exacting, can fix nitrogen below pH 6.0. An excess of ammonium ions in the soil results in a marked

Table 7-10 BACTERIA OF THE NITROGEN CYCLE

Process	Bacteria
Denitrification	
From nitrate to nitrite: NO_3^- to NO_2^-	*Bacillus* (many species)
From nitrate to ammonia: NO_3^- to NH_3	*Nocardia*
	Staphylococcus
	Vibrio
From nitrate to dinitrogen: NO_3^- to N_2	*Pseudomonas stutzeri*
	Thiobacillus denitrificans
	Paracoccus denitrificans
	Bacillus (a few species)
Nitrification	
Nitrosofying: NH_3 to NO_2^-	*Nitrosomonas*
	Nitrosococcus
Nitrifying: NO_2^- to NO_3^-	*Nitrobacter*
	Nitrococcus

decrease in the total nitrogen fixed, and high nitrate ion concentrations may inhibit nodule formation.

Nitrogen fixation is a critical step in the nitrogen cycle since without it denitrifying reactions, in which nitrate ion is converted to gaseous oxide forms of nitrogen and dinitrogen, would rapidly deplete the level of available soil nitrogen below the requirements for plant growth. Denitrification, occurring in anaerobic soils, is a multistep series of reactions, the major end products being either ammonia or dinitrogen. The formation of ammonia from nitrate (ammonification) can be carried on by many anaerobic soil bacteria in anaerobic (water-logged) soils (Table 7-10). The ammonia is volatile and some may be lost from the soil. The sequence of reactions leading to elemental nitrogen is: nitrate (NO_3) → nitrite (NO_2) → nitric oxide (NO) → nitrous oxide (N_2O) → dinitrogen (N_2). The last three compounds are gases which diffuse out of the soil. The main product of this type of denitrification is dinitrogen in an anaerobic soil and nitrous oxide in acidic and slightly aerobic soil.

Nitrification is a rapid process in aerobic soils with a neutral pH, but the nitrifying bacteria are inhibited in anaerobic, highly acidic soils. There are two steps in this process (see Table 7-10). In the first step ammonium is oxidized to nitrite by the nitrosofying bacteria. The nitrite ion, which may accumulate under mild acidic conditions, is quite toxic. This reaction can be inhibited by application to the soil of certain compounds that act against these specific bacteria, thus conserving fertilizer nitrogen. In the second step nitrite is oxidized to nitrate by the nitrifying bacteria. Nitrate ion is rapidly taken up by plant roots.

HYDROPONICS

Hydroponics, growing plants in water solutions of required mineral nutrients, was first attempted in the middle of the nineteenth century. It was developed as a means of assessing the requirements of individual minerals. Sophisticated chemical techniques for the purification of the water and chemicals used allowed the eventual determination of the essential macronutrients as well as those trace elements required in exceedingly low concentrations. Hydroponics is a powerful tool for research in plant nutrition since all aspects of the plant's environment can be controlled. It has also become a cultural method. A large number of annual and perennial ornamentals as well as many crop plants, including root crops, have been successfully grown in hydroponic culture. It is invaluable where good soil and water are in limited supply as in some desert areas.

There are four general methods for raising plants in solution culture. The first is to immerse plant roots in a nutrient solution held in some sort of container. The containers have a large surface area to permit adequate root aeration, and the solution is further aerated by some sort of bubbler system. Containers made of Pyrex glass are avoided because they leach boron, but most plastics are suitable. A second method is to spray the roots at intervals with a mist of nutrient solution. The third is to grow the plants in rigorously purified sand or gravel which is flooded at intervals with the nutrient solution and allowed to drain out. Air enters the sand as the containers dry out. A fourth is to grow plants in a flowing nutrient solution. In all methods the containers are made of opaque material, painted with aluminum paint, or covered with aluminum foil. Keeping the roots darkened has two benefits: root growth is inhibited by light and the contaminating growth of algae is depressed or eliminated. Sand or gravel cultures have become the method of choice for greenhouse-grown flowering and vegetable plants. The plants do not need to be held up artificially since they grow as they would naturally in a soil substrate.

The nutrient solutions must be prepared and changed frequently to take into account the selective removal of ions from solution by plant roots, which results in an unbalanced solution. Plant roots also secrete into the solution compounds such as amino acids, carbohydrates, and others which may eventually reach toxic levels. Nutrient solutions are a suitable growth medium for a large number of microorganisms and any solution which becomes cloudy or filmy should be discarded.

The essential macronutrients can be supplied using three salts, potassium nitrate, calcium phosphate, and magnesium sulfate. A fourth salt, which adds the ammonium ion, results in a better buffered solution, that is, the pH does not change rapidly. A pH between 5.0 and 7.0 is appropriate for most crop plants. The four-salt nutrient solution, devised by Hoagland and Arnon in 1938 and usually referred to as Hoagland solution, has become a standard (Table 7-11). Trace element solutions, with iron in the chelated form, must be added to whichever macronutrient solution is used (Table 7-12).

Table 7-11 TWO USEFUL MACRONUTRIENT SOLUTIONS FOR HYDROPONIC CULTURE

| Compound | Knop | | Hoagland & Arnon | |
	g/liter	mM[a]	g/liter	mM
KNO_3	0.2	2.0	0.66	6.0
$Ca(NO_3)_2$	0.8	5.0	0.66	4.0
$NH_4H_2PO_4$	—	—	0.115	1.0
$MgSO_4 \cdot 7H_2O$	0.2	0.8	0.49	2.0
KH_2PO_4	0.2	1.5	—	—

[a]A 1 millimolar (mM) solution contains the molecular weight in milligrams dissolved in distilled water and made to a final volume of 1 liter.

Table 7-12 MICROELEMENT STOCK SOLUTIONS FOR ADDITION TO ANY MACRONUTRIENT SOLUTION

Trace (micro) elements

Compound	g/liter	mM
H_3BO_3	0.72	12.00
$CuCl_2 \cdot 2H_2O$	0.02	0.12
$MnCl_2 \cdot 4H_2O$	0.45	2.30
$ZnCl_2$	0.06	0.40
$H_2MoO_4 \cdot H_2O$	0.01	0.06

Add each compound in order to 500 ml distilled water. Be sure each compound is dissolved before the next compound is added. Add distilled water to make a final volume of 1 liter. Use 2 ml of this solution in 1 liter of macronutrient solution.

Iron EDTA

Dissolve 1340 mg disodium EDTA in 500 ml hot distilled water. Add 990 mg $FeSO_4 \cdot 7H_2O$, stirring vigorously. Use 2 ml of this solution to 1 liter of macronutrient solution.

SUPPLEMENTARY READINGS

Aubert, H. 1980. *Trace Elements in Soil.* Elsevier, Amsterdam.

Charles-Edwards, D. A. 1982. *Physiological Determinants of Crop Growth.* Academic Press, New York.

Delwiche, C. C. 1978. Legumes—past, present and future. *BioScience* 28:565–570.

Epstein, E. 1972. *Mineral Nutrition of Plants: Principles and Perspectives.* Wiley, New York.

Follett, R. H., L. S. Murphy, and R. L. Donahue. 1981. *Fertilizers and Soil Amendments.* Prentice-Hall, Englewood Cliffs, N.J.

Hewitt, E. J., and T. A. Smith. 1975. *Plant Mineral Nutrition.* Wiley, New York.

Hignett, T. P. 1985. *Fertilizer Manual.* Kluwer, Hingham, Mass.

Klein, R. M., and D. T. Klein. 1970. *Research Methods in Plant Science.* Natural History Press, Garden City, N.Y.

Mengel, K., and E. A. Kirby. 1982. *Principles of Plant Nutrition.* 3rd ed. International Potash Institute, Bern, Switzerland.

Nicholls, R. E. 1977. *Beginning Hydroponics.* Running Press, Philadelphia.

Olsen, R. A., R. B. Clark, and J. H. Bennett. 1981. The enhancement of soil fertility by plant roots. *Amer. Sci.* 69:378–384.

Pendias, A. K., and H. K. Pendias (eds.). *Trace Elements in Soils and Plants.* CRC Press, Boca Raton, Fla.

Peters, G. A. 1978. Blue-green algae and algal associations. *BioScience* 28:580–585.

Postgate, J. 1978. *Nitrogen Fixation.* Studies in Biology No. 92. University Park Press, Baltimore, Md.

Pratt, C. J. 1965. Chemical fertilizers. *Sci. Amer.* 212 (6):62–72.

Schwartz, M. 1968. *Guide to Commercial Hydroponics.* Israel University Press, Jerusalem.

Sutcliffe, J. F., and D. A. Baker. 1974. *Plants and Mineral Salts.* Studies in Biology No. 48. University Park Press, Baltimore, Md.

Swietlik, D., and M. Faust. 1984. Foliar nutrition of fruit crops. *Hort. Rev.* 6.

Thompson, L. M., and F. R. Troeh. *Soils and Soil Fertility.* McGraw-Hill, New York.

Torrey, J. G. 1978. Nitrogen fixation by actinomycete-nodulated angiosperms. *BioScience* 28:586–592.

C H A P T E R   8

TEMPERATURE

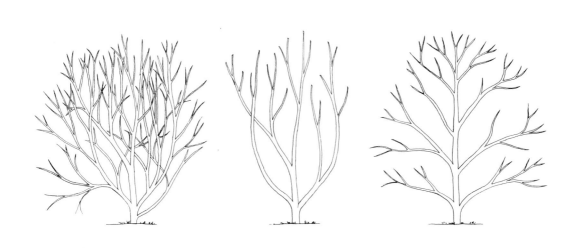

BIOLOGICAL TEMPERATURE RANGE

In the temperature range from absolute zero (0° Kelvin), where molecular motion stops, to about 5,000° K, where molecules dissociate, biological activity can occur only within narrow limits. Although many organisms remain alive below freezing (0° C, 32° F, 273° K), their metabolism virtually stops. Protein integrity and function are destroyed at temperatures above about 50° C (121° F). Some bacteria, blue-green algae, and fungi—those that live in hot springs or in compost piles—develop best at temperatures of 55° C (130° F) or above, but these thermophiles are exceptional. Few flowering plants can maintain structure or function above 45° C (112° F). Specifying an optimum temperature range for any complex biological process such as growth must take time into consideration; temperatures of 0° C or 50° C for a second or even for a few minutes will rarely cause plant damage.

TEMPERATURE REGULATION IN PLANTS

Thermal Balance

Although all living organisms produce heat as a by-product of metabolism (Chapter 12). The low heat production of plants relative to their mass and their large, poorly insulated surface area mean that the temperature of plants is dependent upon the temperature of their environment. There are some important exceptions to this generalization. The intense respiration of germinating seeds will significantly raise their temperature, and the temperature inside flowers of skunk cabbage *(Symplocarpus foetidus),* other members of the Arum family, and digitalis *(Digitalis purpurea)* may be considerably higher than the ambient air. The ability of snowdrops *(Galanthus nivalis)* and other early spring-flowering plants to grow through snow is due to heat production by their flower buds.

A plant's temperature at any given time is determined by its total internal and external environment. Three major physical factors are involved in thermal balance of plants: radiation, convection, and transpiration (Figure 8-1). Thermal radiation is received from the sun and from soils and other plants or objects that are warmer than the plant. In midsummer the earth receives close to 1.3 cal/cm^2/min as direct solar radiation, solar radiation reflected from clouds, and solar radiation scattered by the atmosphere. While solar sources are available only during daylight, convective thermal radiation from soils and other sources is available at all times.

If a plant absorbs more thermal energy than it gives up, its temperature rises, and the reverse is true. Thermal balance requires that uptake and loss of heat are equal. As discussed in Chapter 6, the loss of heat by the cooling of leaves during transpiration, which can be regulated by the opening and closing of stomata, is a major heat-control mechanism. The surfaces of leaves and stems can also radiate and convect heat, particularly at night when air temperatures tend to be lower than those of the plant. Roots, too, can absorb or lose heat to soils, but temperature changes are slower and usually not as wide. The ability of

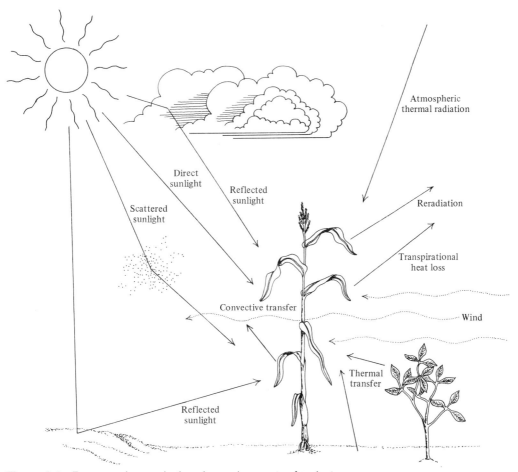

Figure 8-1 Energy exchanges in the microenvironments of a plant.

water to absorb energy with little change in temperature (due to the high specific heat of water) also serves to prevent wide and potentially destructive swings in the thermal balance of plants. These regulatory mechanisms are vital to the survival of plants; in the absence of convective and transpirational heat loss, a single leaf can reach a temperature close to 60° C (140° F) at which cell death can occur within 10 to 20 minutes.

Temperature is a controlling influence on many processes involving plants. The solubility of nutrients in the soil solution and the solubility of oxygen and carbon dioxide in cellular fluids are temperature-dependent. Chemical reactions are speeded up by increases in temperature, with a doubling of the rate for every 10° C rise in temperature. This is referred to as the Q_{10} of a reaction. In plant systems the Q_{10} rule operates only within a limited temperature range, the range between 2° C (34° F) and 45° C (112° F) where enzymes function (Figure 8-2). Generally, Q_{10} values are calculated in the temperature range from 10° C (50° F) to 25° C (77° F). The growth, development, and metabolism of plants involve

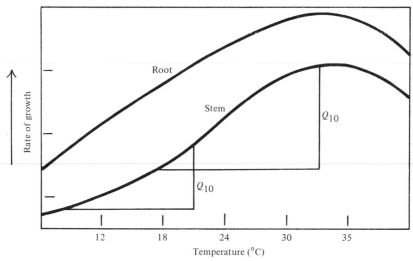

Figure 8-2 Growth rate of stems and roots as a function of temperature.

many separate processes, each mediated by one or, more commonly, many enzymes. Since each enzyme reaction has a minimum, optimum, and limiting temperature range, the overall effect of temperature on plants is a composite interaction of individual reactions which vary with the cells, tissues, and organs concerned, with the particular process being considered, with time, and with the developmental stage of the plant. There is no "right" temperature for plants.

Factors Affecting Thermal Balance

Weather and Climate   The short-term interaction of temperature, precipitation, radiation, wind, and humidity is considered to be weather, while the long-term pattern of these and other meteorological factors is climate. Record temperatures on earth extend from a high of about 60° C (140° F) in Libya to a frigid −70° C (−90° F) in Siberia. Mean annual temperatures range from 30° C (86° F) in Ethiopia to −30° C (−22° F) at the South Pole. At the soil-plant interphase, these values are undoubtedly conservative.

The climate in an area or region is controlled by a variety of factors including seasonal changes in solar radiation, elevation and topography, precipitation, the ameliorating effects of bodies of water, wind patterns, soil characteristics, and the results of human activity. Few of these are under our control, although a number of practices are used to modulate the stresses on plants caused by temperature, just as we have learned to relieve stresses caused by unsatisfactory water status of plants. In some plants even small differences in temperature can significantly alter growth and yields.

Under natural conditions plants are adapted to the climatic conditions in which they are found, although they may actually grow better under different conditions. Selection and genetic engineering have provided the grower with cultivars that do well under conditions far different from those in the natural habitat. Nevertheless, knowledge of the climate in the native habitat is a guide to successful cultivation.

Soil Soil temperature, like plant temperature, is a product of thermal gains and losses. Dark-colored soils absorb more solar radiation than do light-colored soils. Because of the amount of water that highly organic soils hold, they change temperature more slowly than do more mineral soils. Soils with large amounts of water (clayey or muck soils) warm up more slowly in the spring and cool down more slowly in the fall. The aspect and degree of a slope is also important; those with a southern exposure receive more solar radiation than those facing north. Valleys tend to be warmer in summer than the slopes surrounding them, although they collect frosty air more readily in other seasons.

Cover may modify soil temperatures a good deal. Snow is an excellent insulating blanket, serving to lessen the depth to which frost will penetrate. Mulches or plant cover can serve the same purpose. Light-colored organic mulches (hay, straw) reflect solar radiation and keep soils cooler in summer. Dark mulches, including black plastic sheeting, increase heat absorption and keep soils warmer. These are particularly useful for short-season plants and those, like melons, that have high thermal requirements for maturation.

Air Movement In addition to serving as the bearer of weather changes, wind can directly affect the thermal balance of plants and soils. This is due partly to the ability of wind to increase evapotranspiration with a consequent decrease in soil and plant temperatures. Wind also increases convective thermal transfer. The temperature of the moving air mass itself will modify the temperature of plants. A shelterbelt of tall plants or trees on the prevailing windward side of fields or garden plots can deflect or break up wind flow patterns that can cause rapid changes in temperature (Figure 8-3). Shelterbelts also reduce evapotranspiration and water stress.

Another consideration is the tendency for heavier, lower-temperature air

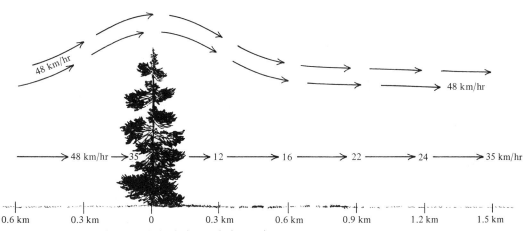

Figure 8-3 Effect of a tree shelterbelt on wind speed.

masses to settle through warmer, lighter air to accumulate near the ground. The settling of cold air near the ground is an important consideration in growing plants that are sensitive to low-temperature damage. It is a matter of economic importance in citrus groves in Florida as well as in chosing species or cultivars for horticultural or garden plantings. Moving air may protect crops from cold injury by preventing cold air from settling. Large fans are turned on in citrus orchards to sweep away cold air.

TEMPERATURE AND PLANT GROWTH

Climatic Classification

The natural distribution of plants is determined by the interaction of their genetic potential with their environment. Temperature and water are the two major limiting environmental factors in determining the success of a species. Several schemes have been developed to classify various climatic regimes in which integration of climatic factors can be expressed. They have considerable value in predicting the probability of survival and productivity in cultivation for many native and introduced species. In North America, where irrigation is economically possible, the temperature factor can be dominant. Common sense tells us that sugar cane will not grow in Minnesota and that plants that require a

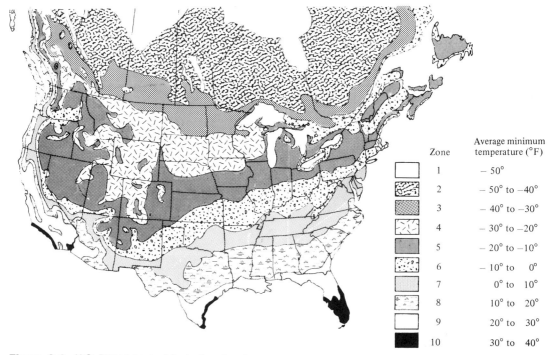

Zone	Average minimum temperature (°F)
1	− 50°
2	− 50° to −40°
3	− 40° to −30°
4	− 30° to −20°
5	− 20° to −10°
6	− 10° to 0°
7	0° to 10°
8	10° to 20°
9	20° to 30°
10	30° to 40°

Figure 8-4 U.S. Department of Agriculture hardiness zone map.

period of chilling will not develop normally in southern Florida. However, plants are capable of growing under temperature conditions quite different from their natural environment or their optimal range, and it has become clear that it is the extremes, particularly the low-temperature extreme, that serve as a major limiting factor on growth. For this reason, a good deal of attention has been given to maps designating hardiness zones.

One such map, developed by the U.S. Department of Agriculture, is shown in Figure 8-4. North America is divided into 10 hardiness zones based on the average or expected annual minimum temperature in degrees Fahrenheit. Most states and provinces have prepared more detailed zonal maps that indicate regional and local variations in average temperature. Zonal classification is no guarantee of successful plant growth. Not only may an area experience temperatures below an average minimum, but even within a zone local conditions can alter the rating of an area by one or even two zones. A north-facing slope, a deep valley, the presence of a large body of water, the soil type, and other factors must be considered. Nevertheless, hardiness zone maps are invaluable for the agriculturist and horticulturist.

In recent years responsible nurseries and seed companies have included hardiness zone information in their catalogues. It is usual to indicate the lowest zone in which a plant may be expected to develop normally. A designation of Zone 6 for a peach cultivar indicates that it will grow in Zone 6 and in several zones warmer than 6. Nurseries and seed companies do have a tendency to

Figure 8-5 Average number of days in the frost-free season.

overstate the hardiness of plants, and a conservative approach to zonal classifications is wise. Also, hardiness of the plant may not guarantee productivity. For example, a cultivar of a tender fruit tree may grow reasonably well in a zone, but temperatures that do not harm leaf buds may kill flower buds. On the other hand, appropriate cultural practices such as winter protection, increased planting depth, or fall lifting may permit the grower to maintain plantings in one hardiness zone colder than designated.

Several other meteorological compilations are useful in determining the suitability of a particular plant for a specific growing area. The average dates of the last killing frost in spring and the first killing frost in autumn determine the average length of the frost-free growing season (Figure 8-5), so the grower can tell if there is enough time in the area for a plant to reach maturity. In general, the days to maturity given in seed catalogs is determined in regions with reasonably equitable weather patterns. Tomato, a warm-season crop plant, may require almost double the designated time to maturity where summer temperatures are lower than the optimum for vegetative and reproductive development.

In addition to the length of the frost-free season, the depth to which soils are frozen (Figure 8-6) will determine how early seeds or plants may be put into the soil. This depends on many complex factors; soil types, cover (including snow), and soil moisture levels are all involved.

Figure 8-6 Depth of frost penetration in soil in regions of the United States.

Growing Degree Days

Growing degree days, also called heat unit accumulations, are an arithmetic sum of daily average temperatures above a threshold or base value of either 5° C (40° F) for cool-season plants or 10° C (50° F) for warm-season plants (see below). A degree day is determined by subtracting the threshold value from the average daily temperature. Thus, for a crop like peas, whose threshold temperature is 5° C, if the day temperature is 18° C (65° F) and the night temperature is 14° C (55° F), the degree day would be calculated as: (18 + 14)/2 − 5 = 11° C [(65 + 55)/2 − 40 = 20° F]. Growing degree days are cumulative over the growing season (negative values are ignored). For each tested species, development is proportional to the heat unit accumulation, and maturity is expected when the growing degree days have added up to a value determined for each plant. Peas require close to 1500 Fahrenheit degree days and tomatoes require more than twice as many. Although the growing degree day system oversimplifies the relationship between temperature and plant growth and ignores the fact that the temperature at the plant-soil interface is different from that measured at weather stations, there is a reasonably good correlation between degree day accumulations and the ability of a plant to complete its growth and reproductive cycle.

Temperature Classification

Temperate-zone vegetables can be divided into three broad groups, designated as cool-season, moderate-season, and warm-season crops (Table 8-1). Cool-season plants develop best when the average daily temperatures are between 10° and 20° C (45° and 68° F) with a minimum night temperature of 4° C (40° F) and a day maximum of 30° C (86° F). They usually are planted in early spring to mature by midsummer or are planted in midsummer for fall maturation. Most cool-season vegetables are cold-tolerant, their seeds germinate at low soil temperatures, and maturation is repressed by high temperatures. Warm-season crops develop best in midsummer conditions and are rarely tolerant of cold or frost conditions; they are called tender. Their optimum temperature range is 10° C higher than that for cool-season crops. A third group of plants, the moderate-season crops, has intermediate temperature tolerances.

Some of these growth requirements can be modified or satisfied by cultivation techniques. In regions where the frost-free season is short, where soils warm up slowly, or where there are too few days in the optimum range, seedlings and young plants may be grown indoors or in hot or cold frames. In cooler climates it is frequently necessary to harden off these plants by exposing them to outdoor temperatures for a few days before transplanting them into the field. For tender plants, additional field protection is afforded by the use of hot caps or clear plastic tunnels (see Chapter 16). Hot caps are usually constructed of domes of translucent paper or plastic placed over each plant and are removed after danger of late frost has passed. Clear plastic tunnels can, with appropriate framing, cover an entire row. They may be lifted on warm days to avoid overheating the plants. Either will conserve heat and prevent freeze damage at

Table 8-1   **TEMPERATURE RANGES (°C) FOR SEED GERMINATION, GROWTH, AND DEVELOPMENT OF COOL-SEASON, MODERATE-SEASON, AND WARM-SEASON VEGETABLE CROPS**

Seed Germination[a]			Development[b]			
Minimum	Optimum	Maximum	Minimum	Optimum	Maximum	Species
Cool-season crops						
2	10–20	35	4	13–24	30	Beet, broad bean, broccoli, Brussels sprouts, cabbage, chard, chives, collards, garlic, kale, leek, onion, parsnip, peas, radish, rutabaga, shallot, spinach
Moderate-season crops						
4	13–28	35	7	15–26	32	Artichoke, carrot, cauliflower, celery, Chinese cabbages, endive, lettuce, lima bean, mustard greens, parsley, potato, snap beans, sweet corn, southern peas
Warm-season crops						
15	20–30	40	15	18–25	37	Cucumber, eggplant, melons, okra, peppers (sweet and hot), pumpkin, squash, sweet potato, tomato, watermelon

[a]Range of soil temperature.
[b]Range of air temperature.

temperatures down to −3° to −5° C, thus allowing the grower to field—plant a week or two earlier than would otherwise be possible and to extend the season for a short period in the fall.

Temperature and Dormancy

Colder regions of the temperate zone have an annual cycle of temperature change that includes a winter period when temperatures are below that necessary for most physiological activities of plants. Annuals are usually killed by these temperatures, but biennials and perennials are not. Not only do they survive, but it is known that if some of these plants, including most northern woody and herbaceous perennials, do not receive a period of low temperature, their development the following spring is poor. Thus, the cessation of growth and development is not merely a protective mechanism against unfavorable temperatures, but it is a requirement for normal development. The plant's life is thus synchronized with the flow of the seasons.

A dormant plant is incapable of growth and development even if all external environmental conditions such as water, temperature, light, and nutrition are adequate. In some of the horticultural literature this condition is called physiological rest. When a plant fails to grow because one or more of these environmental requirements are not fulfilled, the condition is usually called quiescence. In some of the literature the term dormancy is used in place of quiescence, which tends to create some confusion. Dormancy requirements exist in some seeds (see below) as well as in other parts of plants. Dormancy is induced by a progression of changes in light (Chapter 9) and temperature with a corresponding sequence of changes in the structure and function of cells and tissues. The dormant state is initiated and frequently attained prior to the onset of winter temperatures. Low temperatures do not, by themselves, induce dormancy, but a period of low temperatures is required to break or reverse the dormant state. The dormancy of winter buds on woody perennials, underground stems (rhizomes, bulbs, and corms), and meristems like the vascular cambium all involve a temperature-dependent period. Many spring-flowering bulbs, whose flower buds are already initiated, will not produce flowers without a cold-induced dormant or rest period. Indoor forcing of narcissus, hyacynths, and tulips involves chilling the bulbs for a period of time to complete the dormancy requirement (Chapter 17).

The low-temperature requirement to break winter dormancy (sometimes called winter rest), has both a time and a temperature component. Once cold hardiness and the dormant state is achieved, the required time-temperature relations are usually expressed in chill units, with each hour at a given temperature equal to 1 chill unit. The number of chill units per hour is determined as a function of temperature and varies with the plant under consideration. (For example, for apple, 1 hr at 7° C (45° F) is equal to 1 chill unit; 1 hr at 10° C (50° F) is equal to 0.7 chill unit.) A chill unit curve for apple, which has a threshhold temperature of 5° C (41° F) and a ceiling of 18° C (65° F), is given in Figure 8-7. At 7° C (45° F), close to 1500 chill units are needed before the dormancy requirement is fulfilled. Different plants have chill-unit requirements as low as 250 hours or as high as 2500 hours. Many rhizomes and corms require close to 500 hours at 5° C (41° F). Temperatures below freezing do not appear to be necessary to fulfill chill requirements.

Chill requirements appear to be under genetic control. Plant geneticists are attempting to obtain cultivars with lower chill-unit requirements so that plants can be grown in warmer climates. They are also breeding plants with longer dormancy requirements so that plants growing in colder climates will not lose their hardiness too early in the spring.

No completely successful procedures have been developed to initiate dormancy, but treatments with plant growth-regulating compounds, such as the gibberellins, can substitute for chill-unit requirements. This work has led to a better understanding of the physiology and biochemistry of dormancy. Techniques are being developed to allow the cultivation of plants in warmer parts of the temperate zone by reducing the time or increasing the temperature needed to fulfill chill-unit requirements.

Once chill-unit requirements have been fulfilled, vegetative growth can

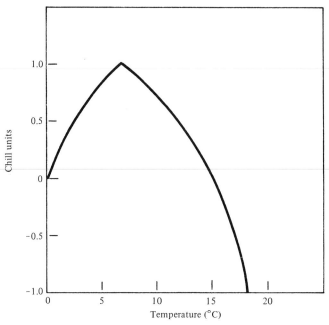

Figure 8-7   Chill unit curve for completion of dormancy in apple. Each hour at 7° C is 1.0 chill units.

resume when environmental conditions permit. In regions colder than Hardiness Zone 6 or 7, requirements have usually been met by the end of February, but since these Zones are still experiencing winter conditions, the plants cannot initiate growth and remain quiescent until spring. The late winter or early spring forcing of cut flowering twigs of forsythia, lilac, or pussy willows can be done because the dormancy requirements have already been fulfilled and the plant is in the quiescent period awaiting a change in environmental conditions. Placing the shoots in water at 30° to 35° C (86° to 95° F) for 8 to 10 hours, wounding them or applying growth-regulating substances will start bud development.

Quiescence can be a period of some danger; if a warm spell permits growth to start, a subsequent return of severe weather may result in freezing injury to the young and tender growth. Flower buds are particularly vulnerable, and spring damage is a problem with many fruit trees (Chapter 20).

Seed Germination

Although many seeds can start germinating as soon as they are shed from the plant, and some germinate even while still on the parent plant, seeds of many species have dormancy requirements. There are a variety of reasons for the failure of seeds to germinate immediately, not all related to a requirement for low temperature. Light requirements (Chapter 9), lack of the ability to take up water or oxygen, embryo immaturity, and other causes have been described. Many temperate-zone plants have an absolute requirement for a chilling period before the seeds can germinate, while others show increased germination percentages or more rapid germination. It is not unusual for species to have multiple germination requirements with temperature, light, and other environmental factors each playing a role that supplements or modifies the internal dormancy requirement.

Not unexpectedly, absolute chill requirements are most common in plants from the cooler portions of the temperate zone. When seeds of these plants germinate without completing their dormant period, the seedlings are stunted (physiological dwarfing) with abnormal leaves and short internodes; such plants are occasionally used as potted or garden ornamental plants. It is sometimes possible to reverse this by subjecting the seedlings to a chill period.

Seed dormancy may, depending on the plant, be short or may be prolonged for a year or more, particularly in seeds where the embryo may not be physiologically ripe and matures slowly at low temperatures (after-ripening). A few species are rendered dormant by low temperatures and some, such as heather *(Calluna)*, have dormancy broken by alternations of cold and warm temperatures. Other species may require only a few minutes of elevated temperature to break dormancy.

Low-temperature requirements can be satisfied by one of several standard practices. Many seeds are simply planted in late summer or fall and are chilled naturally during the winter. For many of the rosaceous fruit trees, conifers, and northern deciduous trees, the technique called stratification is used. Seeds are sown in a moist substratum (sand, peat, or vermiculite) and stored at low temperatures for several months (Figure 8-8), usually a minimum of 10 to 12

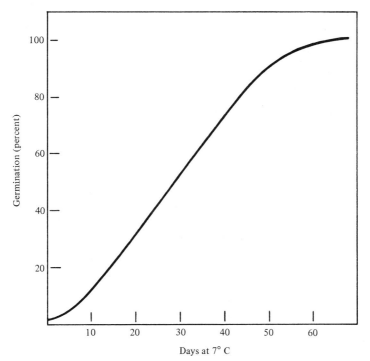

Figure 8-8 Effect of stratification on germination of apple seeds.

weeks at 3° to 6° C (37° to 43° F). Temperatures below freezing are rarely required. Alternatively, dampened seeds may be stored at appropriate low temperature in plastic bags or jars, but some provision for aeration must be made.

Differential Temperature Effects

Not all cells, tissues, or organs of a plant have the same temperature optimum or even temperature range for growth. It is assumed that this is the consequence of the integration of many temperature-sensitive metabolic processes that are in different balances in plant parts at various times during growth and development, but the topic requires considerably more investigation. However, some general conclusions have been reached over the years that have importance for horticultural and agricultural practice.

For most plants, roots, situated in soil, have a temperature optimum below that of the above-ground parts of the plant. The roots of lawn grasses, for example, can grow at 2° to 3° C (34° to 36° F) and stop growing at 18° to 22° C (64° to 72° F); however, the stems and leaves cannot grow below 6° to 8° C (43° to 46° F) and show no heat injury until 25° to 30° C (77° to 86° F) or even higher, if properly maintained. This difference explains why lawn fertilization (Chapter 18) is most effective either in early spring or in late fall; it is desirable to have the nutrients available during the periods of most active root growth. Maintaining adequate soil moisture to provide water for evaporation and hence cooling of soil will keep soils cooler and facilitate root growth. Differential effects have been observed in other plant parts also. For example, cambial and other meristematic activity as well as bud break will occur in early spring when leaf growth and many metabolic processes are at low ebb.

Thermoperiod

Although ambient night temperature is usually lower than day temperature, the significance of this to plant growth was not discovered until 1957. Frits Went, using tomato, found that growth and development were markedly improved by diurnal cycling of temperatures. This phenomenon was termed thermoperiodism. Stem elongation, leaf development, flower initiation, and fruit maturation are affected. Not all plants are thermoperiodic. Wheat, sugar beets, peas, and beans develop well at constant temperatures, but most plants benefit from thermoperiodic cycling. While this is rarely a matter of concern under field conditions, plants grown in greenhouses, those started indoors for transplanting, and house plants should receive a thermoperiodic cycle. With some exceptions the optimum day-night differential should be a drop of 3° to 5° C (5° to 8° F) during the dark period.

Under field conditions only a few plants have been evaluated for thermoperiodicity. The most thoroughly investigated plant is the potato *(Solanum tuberosum)*. The optimum daytime air temperature for vegetative growth is close to 25° C (77° F), but tuberization will not proceed normally unless the ambient night temperature is close to 12° C (53° F). Since it is the air temperature that is involved, the thermoperiodic signal must be perceived by the stems and leaves rather than the stolons from which the tubers develop. A light signal is also involved. This suggests that the transmission of the light and temperature signals involves plant growth substances. In Wedgewood iris, for example, initiation of the flower primordium requires a low temperature, with more elevated temperatures required for flower formation.

VERNALIZATION

In the late nineteenth century curious results of experiments were reported which only later were recognized for their importance to plant reproduction. It was

Table 8-2 SOME PLANTS THAT REQUIRE VERNALIZATION

Winter annuals
    Cereal grains
    Forget-me-not (*Myosotis* spp.)
    Field speedwell (*Veronica agrestis*)

Biennials
  Ornamentals
    Canterbury bells (*Campanula medium*)
    Foxglove (*Digitalis purpurea*)
    Hollyhock (*Alcea rosea*)
    Sweet William (*Dianthus barbatus*)
    Honesty (*Lunaria annua*)
    Stock (*Matthiola incana* cv. Annua)
    Mullein (*Verbascum* spp.)
    Black henbane (*Hyoscyamus niger*)

  Vegetable crops
    Beet (*Beta vulgaris*)
    Cabbage (*Brassica oleracea*)
    Brussels sprouts (*Brassica oleracea*)
    Carrot (*Daucus carota*)
    Parsnip (*Pastinaca sativa*)
    Celery (*Apium graveolens*)
    Onion (*Allium cepa*)

Herbaceous perennials
    Primrose (*Primula vulgaris*)
    Violets (*Viola* spp.)
    Wallflower (*Cheiranthus cheirii*)
    Chrysanthemum (*Chrysanthemum,* cvs.)
    Rye grass (*Lolium perenne*)
    Michaelmas daisy (*Aster* spp.)

Woody perennials
    Peach (*Prunus persica*)

Earlier flower promotion
    Winter cereal grains
    Lettuce (*Lactuca sativa*)
    Radish (*Raphanus sativus*)
    Pea (*Pisum sativum*)
    Spinach (*Spinacia oleracea*)
    Tomato (*Lycopersicon esculentum*)

found that winter rye, barley, and wheat, normally planted in the fall of the year, could be "converted" to spring rye, barley, or wheat, normally planted in the spring for summer harvest, by storing the moistened grains at temperatures close to freezing. When the stored grains were planted in the early spring, the plants flowered and set seed at about the same time as did spring-planted cereals. When the winter varieties were planted in the spring without the cold treatment, they did not flower until autumn, which meant that an early frost could kill the fruiting heads and ruin the harvest. These results showed that winter cereal grains could be grown in more northern, colder environments than was formerly possible. Since the winter types possess certain valuable qualities not found in spring types, extending their range of growth was commercially important. Other plants, such as winter annuals, biennials, and some herbaceous and woody perennials, were found to require an overwintering period (a cold period) to permit flowers to form during their second year's growth or to promote early flowering during the following growing season (Table 8-2).

The term vernalization, to make springlike, was coined to refer to the exposure of flowering plants to a period of cold temperatures in order for flowering to be initiated when the plant is again in a condition of growth or in order to promote earlier flowering. Plants that can be vernalized—in effect, made ready to flower—vary in their temperature requirements and in the length of time at that temperature (Figure 8-9). The average time of vernalization required to induce flower initiation is 8 to 10 weeks. A few plants are promoted with as little as 4 days, and some require as much as 12 weeks. To be most effective vernalization temperature must be between −3° and 13° C (27° and 56° F) with an optimum temperature of 3° to 5° C (36° to 41° F). A temperature above 15° C (59° F) does not induce vernalization in most plants.

Winter annual seeds, germinating in the fall, grow into seedlings or young plants which overwinter and, hence, are vernalized. These plants flower in the

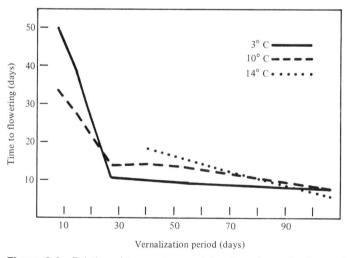

Figure 8-9 Relation of temperature and duration of vernalization to time of flowering.

Rosette of
leaves of a typical biennial
during first year of
growth

Flowering (bolting) response during
second year after overwintering

Figure 8-10 Vernalization of biennials.

early spring. A few herbaceous perennials have a chilling requirement and must be revernalized every winter (see Table 8-2).

Biennials form a rosette of leaves during their first year's growth; at the beginning of their second year's growth after overwintering, they form a few leaves and then the flower stalk rapidly elongates above the leaves, a condition called bolting (Figure 8-10) as seen in mullein, Canterbury bells, and foxglove. Many biennials will not flower, following vernalization, until the plant is exposed to the appropriate day length, that is, to a photoperiodic induction (Chapter 9).

A few vegetable crops are biennials and must be exposed to a cold period to induce flowering. As food crops these vegetables are harvested during their first year's growth, but commercial nurseries induce flowering to obtain seeds. A number of vegetable crops will flower earlier following vernalization (see Table 8-2). Tomato is an interesting example. The first flower bud forms, depending on the cultivar, at node 12 to node 17; this can be shifted to an older node, earlier than node 12, if the young seedlings are exposed to low temperatures. A two-week exposure to a temperature between 10° and 15° C (50° and 59° F) may lower the first flower bud from node 14 to node 9.

Vernalization can be reversed, called devernalization, by exposing the plant to an elevated temperature, usually 35° C (95° F) for a day. This has important practical applications. Flowering in onion, which retards or prevents edible bulb formation, can be controlled. Onion sets, the small bulbs formed during the first year's growth from seed, are usually stored at temperatures close to freezing to retard spoilage. Since onion is a biennial, this vernalization normally promotes flowering during the next year's growing season. In order to prevent flowering and thus to enhance bulb formation, onion sets are devernalized by holding them at 27° C (80° F) for two to three weeks before planting.

The moistened seeds of a few crops can be vernalized (winter cereal grains, beet, kohlrabi), but most plants that require a cold treatment before initiating flowers are sensitive only after a certain amount of vegetative growth has taken place. Honesty *(Lunaria annua)* becomes sensitive to a cold treatment after 7 weeks growth. Celery plants *(Apium graveolens)* that are 25 days old at the start of vernalization, a period of 4 weeks at 8° C (46° F), do not initiate flowers until 5 months after the end of the cold treatment, but celery plants that are 50 days old at the start of vernalization initiate flowers about 2 months after chilling. Actively dividing meristem cells, in which a number of events are presumed to take place, have been shown to perceive the low temperature stimulus. These events are, in part, hormonally regulated since the hormone gibberellic acid can substitute for or satisfy the cold-temperature requirement for some plants.

It must be emphasized here that not all cold-temperature responses are vernalization; this term is restricted to flower initiation and the promotion of earlier flowering. Many tree species (poplar, maple, linden), some fruit trees (apple, pear), some flowering shrubs, and grapevine have a winter temperature requirement of 0° C (32° F) for three or more weeks in order to break dormancy and permit normal vegetative and flower bud growth to proceed the following growing season. Perennials that form corms or tubers also require a chilling period. In the case of flowering bulbs (hyacinths, narcissus, tulips, and Easter lily) the cold-temperature requirement promotes normal development of the flower bud which is already present in the bulb. The temperature need not go below freezing since 2° to 5° C (35° to 41° F) will satisfy the cold requirement. This is also true for some flowering shrubs (azalea, hydrangea).

TEMPERATURE STRESS

High- and Low-Temperature Injury

Although most attention has been paid to damaging effects of low temperatures, elevated temperatures can also cause severe stresses. In many plants high-temperature injury is directly related to concomitant water stress. Thin leaves heat up more rapidly than do thick or leathery leaves, but thick leaves can reach much higher temperatures and cool off more slowly. Heat stress is usually controlled by ensuring adequate soil moisture during hot periods, but even turgid leaves will be injured at cell temperatures above 45° C (112° F) for two to four hours. Heat injury is usually manifested by loss of chlorophyll (usually called scorch, tip burn, or sun scald) starting at leaf margins. In addition to leaves, young stems and fruits may exhibit cell and tissue death.

High-temperature injury is a matter of concern in cool-season crops where temperatures above the maximum lead to cessation of growth and reproduction. It is difficult to grow some cool-season plants in Hardiness Zone 9 or 10, although crossbreeding may provide less sensitive cultivars. Even in moderate- or warm-season crops, elevated night temperatures may alter growth patterns. Tomato flowers will abscise when night temperatures do not fall, and many garden plants stop growing.

Alpine ornamental plants, particularly conifers and heaths, can rarely be grown successfully in semitropical areas. These plants have photosynthetic systems with temperature maxima close to 25° C (77° F) and are permanently injured above 30° C (86° F). In addition, their dark respiration (Chapter 11) increases with rising temperature and photosynthetically produced sugars may be used at rates that limit their availability for growth. Death rarely occurs, but reduced growth and increased sensitivity are common.

Many temperate-zone plants can acclimate or adapt to high temperatures, and some strains or clones within a species can be genetically programmed to withstand high temperatures for at least short periods of time. Adaptation appears to be primarily a matter of alteration in the heat sensitivity of photosynthetic and respiratory components and modifications in membranes. Adaptation can occur in less than eight hours.

Low-temperature injury is divided into two categories: chill injury, in which temperatures do not fall below freezing, and freezing injury. Chill injury is seen in tropical and subtropical plants that are not physiologically or genetically capable of adapting to temperatures of 3° to 5° C (36° to 41° F). Seedlings of plants originally from semitropical regions are frequently injured by nonfreezing temperatures. Freeze injury may occur in temperate or arctic plants that have not been adequately adapted to low temperatures.

Among the economically important crops subject to chill injury are citrus, cotton, and coffee, which are at risk of chill injury when a temperature of 5° C (41° F) occurs for several hours. Tropical fruits—bananas, citrus, avocado, and pineapple—are injured within six to eight hours at 5° to 8° C. In general, succulent plant tissues are most susceptible to chill injury. Young seedlings, especially those grown indoors for transplanting, can be chill injured at temperatures that do not affect older, established plants. Such seedlings are hardened off (adapted to harsher conditions) before transplanting by being placed outside first for a few hours and then for successively longer periods over a week. Chill injury is believed to result from damage to cell membranes. Leaf margins may brown and shrivel, and succulent stems may develop soft, translucent spots that later die or become infected.

Freeze injury requires temperatures below −3° to −5° C (26° to 23° F) for a period of at least several hours, temperatures at which ice can crystallize in cells. The length of time at subfreezing temperatures and the rate of temperature reduction are important factors in determining the extent of injury. If the rate of temperature decline is slow, water moves out of cells into intercellular spaces, the solute potential of cell water is reduced, and intracellular ice crystals will not form. The increased intercellular water contains fewer particles about which ice can form, and the plant shows a small but significant hardening adaptation. Abrupt and prolonged exposure to freezing conditions is the more severe condition since crystallization of water can occur within protoplasts, cytoplasm is disrupted, proteins are inactivated, and cell membranes are punctured by the ice crystals. Affected cells invariably die. Cells that do not contain extensive ice crystals may be injured by a subsequent rapid thaw. Water is rapidly redistributed and abrupt turgor changes damage cell membranes with consequent cell death.

Cold Hardiness

Many plants have the genetic capacity to avoid freeze injury by an adaptation called cold hardiness. Once fully hardened, plants can withstand temperatures well below $-40°$ C ($-40°$ F). The sequence of changes in the environment that initiate hardiness are fairly well known, but there are still a number of open questions concerning the alterations that occur in cells and tissues.

Hardiness is initiated in the northern temperate zone by the decrease in day length that occurs in late summer, before there is any perceptible alteration in temperature regimes. The second signal is the decrease in night temperature that occurs later in summer and in early fall. The next signal is one or more nights during which the temperature is close to freezing. By the middle or end of September, the plants are entering their dormant state and are capable of withstanding early fall frosts. A critical signal is the occurrence of one or more hard frosts with temperatures below $-3°$ to $-5°$ C (26° to 23° F), temperatures at which nonhardened plants are injured. Full hardiness develops slowly; the ability to resist very low temperatures is acquired over a period of a month or more, although hardiness increases steadily during this period as determined by the plant's ability to remain uninjured at successively lower temperatures.

Not all organs or even tissues harden at the same rate or to the same extent. Depending on species, roots may achieve the same, a lower, or a higher level of hardiness than shoots. Different root or stem tissue systems may also exhibit different degrees of hardiness.

The most obvious result of the cold-hardening process is the decrease in the amount of free water within living cells. This is accomplished by movement of water into intercellular spaces and by reductions in the amount of free (unbound) water within cells. The freezing point of cell sap is reduced by the increase in solutes (the "anti-freeze" effect), although this lowers the cell's freezing point by only a few degrees. Additional water becomes bound to cell constituents and cannot freeze. There are a number of alterations in the concentration and physical state of proteins, lipids (fats and oils), and other constituents and increases in the viscosity of the protoplasm. These changes are accompanied by changes in cell membranes and cell organelles.

Not only do the cells become cold hardy, but they also may enter dormant or rest states. Dormancy is initiated and controlled by the same environmental factors as bring about hardiness, but the two states are different. Dormancy requirements may be fulfilled while the plants are still winter hardy. Dehardening occurs independently of the completion of dormancy and is controlled by increases in day length and the concomitant changes in day and night temperatures that occur in early spring. Dehardening occurs slowly and a partly dehardened plant can be rehardened by cold weather that may follow a thaw. A major problem may occur with alternate freezing and thawing because quiescent cells may be activated and the new growth from early leaf or flower bud break may not possess any cold hardiness. There is no protection currently available to prevent such damage, which, in spring-flowering plants, is a matter of economic concern.

It is conservatively estimated that worldwide agricultural losses to frost exceed $10 billion a year. A great deal of research is being directed toward breeding economic plants that show enhanced resistance to chilling and freezing. In many cases wild species from severe climates are used as parents to be crossed with known cultivars of plants having only limited resistance to cold damage. Plants from mountainous regions, Siberia, upper Canada, or other places where low temperatures can be expected are tested for both cold resistance and the ability to cross with important cultivars of economic plants. Classical selection techniques are sometimes used in which a population of plants is grown in a cold environment and then the survivors are grown in even harsher conditions. Special attention has been paid to members of the tomato family (tomato, peppers, eggplant) that were originally from warm climates and frequently lack resistance to chilling or freezing. Cotton, peanuts, millets, and sweet potatoes, plants usually associated with southern climates, can now be grown in more temperate regions of the world. Efforts to develop fruit and nut trees with reduced winter chill requirements have resulted in apples adapted to Florida, peaches capable of yielding fruit in northern climates, and strawberries that mature in northern Canada. Micropropagation and genetic engineering techniques (Chapter 15) are also being used for this work. Studies are also underway to evaluate the possibility that certain common bacteria applied to foliage can prevent ice formation during periods of frost.

HOUSE PLANTS

Where plants grow successfully in nature is a reflection of the myriad of environmental factors that impinge upon them. Those grown as house plants are no exception. Some house plants seem to survive in spite of constant neglect, while others rapidly expire in spite of tender loving care.

Air temperature is one aspect of the home environment that is relatively easily controlled. In general, a daytime temperature of 18° to 25° C (65° to 77° F) and a nighttime temperature about 5° to 10° C (8° to 18° F) lower will be satisfactory for growing most house plants. This temperature reduction lowers the rate of respiration which, in turn, decreases the rate at which carbohydrate reserves are used up. Most potted plants will adapt to a regime in which the nighttime temperature drops to 15° C (59° F) or slightly lower. Growth will be slower and other environmental factors may need to be modified such as decreasing fertilization and watering. High nighttime temperatures are to be avoided, particularly when the daytime light level is low, to prevent excessive rates of respiration. Very high daytime temperatures lead to increased transpiration that may cause wilting and even death of plants. High temperatures require an increase in watering and humidity to permit the plants to survive.

Foliage and flowering potted plants have different temperature optima, particularly the nighttime minimum (Table 8-3). Most ornamental foliage plants are of tropical origin where nighttime temperatures rarely go below 15° C (59° F), and serious chill injury results if the temperature drops to 2° to 4° C (35° to 40° F) (Table 8-4). Too cool a nighttime temperature is not conducive to active growth

Table 8-3 NIGHTTIME TEMPERATURE REQUIREMENTS OF SOME POPULAR HOUSE PLANTS

Latin name	Common name	Temperature[a]
Aeschynanthus pulchera	Lipstick plant	M
Asparagus densiflorus	Sprenger fern	M
Several species	Bromeliads	M–C
Calathea spp.	Peacock plant	W
Cissus spp.	Grape ivy	M
Crassula arborescens	Chinese jade plant	M
Cyclamen persicum	Florist's cyclamen	C
Fatsia japonica	Japanese false aralia	M
Gynura aurantiaca	Velvet plant	M
Soleirolia soleirollii	Baby's tears	C
Howea spp.	Sentry palm	C
Pelargonium Xhortorum	House geranium	C
Saintpaulia ionantha	African violet	W
Schlumbergera bridgesii	Christmas cactus	C
Senecio mikanioides	German ivy	C
Sinningia speciosa	Gloxinia	W
Tolmiea menziesii	Piggyback plant	C
Tradescantia fluminensis	Wandering jew	W
Zebrina pendula	Inch plant	W

[a]C = cool, 10° to 15° C (50° to 59° F); M = moderate, 15° to 18° C (59° to 64° F); W = warm, 18° to 23° C (64° to 73° F).

of foliage potted plants which will continue active growth if the nighttime minimum is about 20° C (68° F). Some house plants can tolerate low nighttime temperatures (Table 8-5). Flowering house plants in general form more flowers when the nighttime temperature drops to about 16° C (60° F) with the exception of African violets *(Saintpaulia ionantha)* and a few others, for which the optimum is about 20° to 21° C (68° to 70° F). A number of house plants are tolerant of elevated daytime temperatures (Table 8-6).

Plants that can be grown successfully as house plants but have fairly stringent requirements for temperature, light, and water include bromeliads and

Table 8-4 HOUSE PLANTS THAT ARE INJURED BY NIGHTTIME TEMPERATURES BELOW 7° C (45° F)

Latin name	Common name
Aglaonema commutatum	Chinese evergreen
Aphelandra squarrosa	Zebra plant
Coleus Xhybridus	Coleus
Codiaeum spp.	Croton
Dieffenbachia spp.	Dumb cane
Epipremnum aureum	Pothos
Fittonia verschaffeltii	Nerve plant
Maranta leuconeura	Prayer plant
Several species	Palms
Monstera deliciosa	Split-leaf philodendron
Philodendron scandens	Heart-leaf philodendron
Plectranthus spp.	Swedish ivy
Sansevieria spp.	Bowstring hemp

Table 8-5 HOUSE PLANTS THAT ARE TOLERANT OF LOW NIGHTTIME TEMPERATURES, 7° TO 10° C (45° TO 50° F)

Latin name	Common name
Araucaria heterophylla[a]	Norfolk Island pine
Ardisia crenata	Coralberry
Aspidistra elatior	Iron plant
Beaucarnea recurvata	Ponytail
Brassaia actinophylla	Schefflera
Chlorophytum comosum	Spider plant
Hedera helix	English ivy
Hoya carnosa	Wax plant
Pilea cadierei	Aluminum plant
Pittosporum tobira	Mock orange
Podocarpus macrophylla[a]	Southern yew
Saxifraga spp.	Rockfoil
Syngonium podophyllum	Arrowhead vine
Yucca elephantipes	Spineless yucca

[a]Gymnosperm; popular house plants.

orchids. Orchids can be divided into three temperature categories in terms of nighttime temperature optima: cool, 13° to 16° C (56° to 60° F); moderate, 16° to 18° C (60° to 65° F); and warm, 18° to 21° C (65° to 70° F). Most species of bromeliads are cool to moderate in their requirements and also need a 7° to 8° C (12° to 14° F) increase in the daytime temperature. Very few are heat-requiring tropical plants.

A relatively even temperature during the day and night is generally best for house plant growth. Sudden changes in temperature, particularly cold drafts, must be avoided. A rapid drop in temperature can cause flower bud and leaf drop

Table 8-6 HOUSE PLANTS THAT ARE TOLERANT OF ELEVATED DAYTIME TEMPERATURES, 23° TO 27° C (75° TO 80° F)

Latin name	Common name
Aglaonema commutatum	Chinese evergreen
Ananas comosus	Pineapple
Aphelandra squarrosa	Zebra plant
Aspidistra elatior	Iron plant
Beaucarnea recurvata	Ponytail
Brassaia actinophylla	Schefflera
Many species	Cactus
Chlorophytum comosum	Spider plant
Cordyline terminalis	Good luck plant
Dizygotheca elegantissima	False aralia
Dracaena spp.	Dracaena
Ficus spp.	Fig, rubber tree
Hedera helix	English ivy
Hoya carnosa	Wax plant
Several species	Palms
Peperomia argyreia	Watermelon peperomia
Several species	Succulents

in very sensitive plants (gardenia and poinsettia). Low, but above freezing temperatures can cause chill injury (leaf necrosis, wilting) to the foliage of many plants. Placing plants immediately next to windows can also be a problem both in summer and winter, although the low temperature next to the glass, common in cold climates, is the greater hazard. The temperature of the water used for watering should be approximately that of the room in which the plants are growing. Very cold water will chill the root system causing injury to the meristem regions.

SUPPLEMENTARY READINGS

Clutter, M. E. 1978. *Dormancy and Development Arrest.* Academic Press, New York.

Gates, D. M. 1972. *Man and His Environment.* Harper & Row, New York.

Graham, D., and B. D. Patterson. 1982. Proteins, metabolism and acclimation. *Annu. Rev. Plant Physiol.* 33:347–372.

Hill, L. 1982. *Successful Cold-Climate Gardening.* Stephen Greene Press, Brattleboro, Vt.

Jones, H. G. 1983. *Plant and Microclimate: A Quantitative Approach to Environmental Plant Physiology.* Cambridge University Press, Cambridge.

Levitt, J. 1980. Responses of Plants to Environmental Stress. Vol. 1. *Chilling, Freezing and High Temperature Responses.* 2nd ed. Academic Press, New York.

Li, P. H., and A. Sakai. 1982. *Plant Cold Hardiness and Freezing Stress.* 2 vols. Academic Press, New York.

Lyons, J. M. 1973. Chilling injury in plants. *Annu. Rev. Plant Physiol.* 24:445–466.

Olien, C. R., and M. N. Smith (eds.). 1981. *Analysis and Improvement of Plant Cold Hardiness.* CRC Press, Boca Raton, Fla.

Rosenberg, N. J., B. L. Blad, and S. B. Verma. 1983. *Microclimate: Biological Environment.* 2nd ed. Wiley, New York.

Smith, A. 1978. *The Seasons.* Penguin Books, London.

Sutcliffe, J. 1977. *Plants and Temperature.* Edward Arnold, London.

Thompson, P. D., and R. O'Brien. 1965. *Weather.* Time-Life Books, New York.

Trewartha, G. T. 1968. *An Introduction to Climate.* 4th ed. McGraw-Hill, New York.

Villiers, T. A. 1975. *Dormancy and Survival in Plants.* Studies in Biology No. 57. University Park Press, Baltimore, Md.

C H A P T E R 9

LIGHT

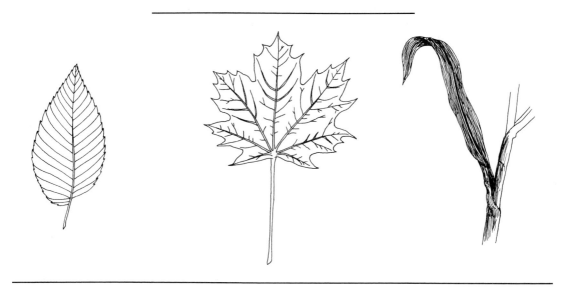

SUNLIGHT

Solar Radiation

With the exception of certain bacteria that obtain energy by purely chemical means, (Chapter 1), all plants and all animals are directly or indirectly dependent upon solar radiation. Although the earth intercepts only a small fraction of this energy, and only a fraction of this is absorbed by plants, solar radiation allows life to be maintained. Plants, although regulated by many environmental factors including temperature, water, and nutrients, are successful only to the extent that they can use sunlight efficiently.

Solar energy is derived by a series of high-temperature reactions in which hydrogen atoms are converted into helium atoms to produce, in accordance with Einstein's famous $E = mc^2$, a broad spectrum of radiant energy. The energy flows through space as electromagnetic radiation which, for convenience, is divided into wavelength bands (Figure 9-1).

A good deal of the radiation emitted toward the earth by the sun fails to reach the earth. It is reflected back into space by atmospheric dust or filtered out by gases in the upper atmosphere. Of the radiation that does penetrate, most of it is converted into heats of conduction or convection and is reradiated, leaving only part of the ultraviolet, much of the visible, and a fraction of the infrared to act upon plants and animals. Even here, there is considerable modification of the

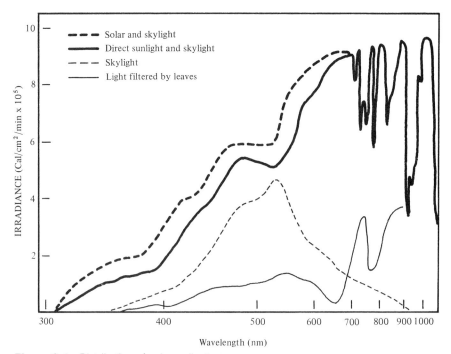

Figure 9-1 Distribution of solar radiant energy.

light. Cloud cover, diffusion and reflection by dust, the shading of plants by other plants, or solid objects, and the selective absorption of wavelengths by plant canopies are among the factors that must be considered in determining how much radiation finally reaches plants.

Light Quality and Intensity

Three major aspects of the physics of light must be examined in evaluating its effects upon plants: duration, quality, and intensity. (A fourth aspect is polarity, but its roles are poorly understood and, although some solar radiation is polarized, it is not usually considered.) Of the three, duration presents the fewest problems. The days and the seasons march inexorably on and, when artificial lighting is used, a time clock can be introduced; duration is best viewed in the context of photoperiod (discussed later in this chapter).

The quality of light is usually expressed in terms of its wavelength or wavelength band. Wavelength is the linear distance between two similar points on adjacent electromagnetic waves expressed in nanometers (1 nm = 10^{-9} m). Visible radiation—light—is defined as the wavelengths between 400 nm and 700 nm which, in color terms, include violet through red (Figure 9-2). Although the human eye is almost insensitive to wavelengths beyond 700 nm, the wavelength band called the far red (700 to 810 nm) is included as light because of its significance for plants. The 400 to 700 nm band includes half of the solar energy reaching the earth's surface and all of its wavelengths are capable of activating photosynthesis, although to different extents (Chapter 11). This wavelength band is called photosynthetically active radiation (PAR). Instruments ranging from hand spectroscopes through calibrated spectroradiometers are used to determine radiation quality.

Intensity is more difficult to define since there are several measurement systems, each based on a different characteristic of light. The easiest to use, but

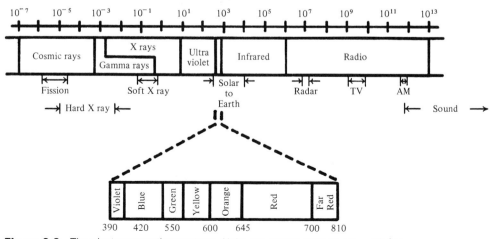

Figure 9-2 The electromagnetic spectrum. Units are nanometers (1 nm = 10^{-9}m).

the least useful in plant biology, is the foot-candle (fc) or its metric equivalent, the meter-candle or lux (1 lx = 10.76 fc). These are psychophysical measurements based on actual candles maintained at Bureaus of Standards throughout the world. Basically, they measure the intensity of green light which is what we see most efficiently. To compare different measures of intensity, we can use as an example the intensity of light at high noon in midsummer in an Iowa corn field at plant height; according to the foot-candle system, that intensity would be measured as 10,000 fc (930 lx). Many photographic meters, light meters, and photometers measure light in foot-candles or lux.

Since plants respond to light energy, there are a number of systems based on physical characteristics of the radiation. One is the amount of total radiant energy given as gram-calories per square centimeter per minute (g-cal/cm^2/min). The energy measured is primarily the thermal infrared and is of limited value in plant work, although it is used in meteorology and ecology. An Iowa corn field receives 1.2 g-cal/cm^2/min (1000 g-cal/cm^2/day) in midsummer. Special instrumentation is used for this measurement and data can be obtained from National Bureaus of Standards or weather bureaus.

Two other ways of expressing light energy have become the international standards. The first is in units of radiant power or flux per unit area. The intensity or irradiance is usually given as power units, or watts per square meter (W/m^2). When irradiation time becomes a factor, the joule (J), the number of watts per square meter × seconds, is used. There are 65 W/cm^2 or 3.5×10^6 J/day in the Iowa corn field in midsummer. Radiometers are used for these measurements. When the wavelength spectrum and the irradiance of a wavelength band is to be determined, spectroradiometers are used.

Radiation can also be expressed in terms of quantum mechanics where photons are involved; the unit used is the einstein (E) or microeinstein (μE; 10^{-6} E). Photon detectors used in plant light measurements are calibrated to determine the photon energy over the 400 to 700 nm wavelength band and are expressed in PAR units as microeinsteins per square meter per second (μE/m^2/sec). For virtually all light measurements in plant science, the PAR system is preferred since it can compare radiation used in photosynthesis and other light-regulated processes from different light sources (solar, fluorescent, incandescent). The Iowa corn field receives over 40,000 μE/cm^2/day in midsummer.

In this chapter light measurement values are given in PAR, lux, and foot-candles. Of these, the only one that has botanical utility is the PAR measurement since it measures a plant response (photosynthesis) and is not a measurement that is related to human vision; except for potato tubers, plants don't have eyes. In photobiology, a useful measure is the power unit expressed as watts per square meter (W/m^2). Instrumentation for this measurement is generally available. The lux (lx) and the foot-candle (fc) units can be used only where the light sources are specified with precision so that other investigators or growers can duplicate conditions exactly. Several commercially available plant-growth light meters measure light intensities in arbitrary units that correlate with plant requirements and others are calibrated in lux or foot-candle units.

Light Absorption and Photomorphogenesis

When light energy strikes a plant organ, some of it is reflected and some penetrates. The amount of reflection depends upon the wavelength and the receiving surface. Infrared is most strongly reflected, while only about 10 percent of the PAR wavelength band is reflected. Leaves with mats of hairs reflect more than do smooth leaves, and waxy-surfaced leaves reflect more than do those without such coatings. Cell walls absorb some wavelengths more strongly than others, and pigments in epidermal cell vacuoles may effectively filter out certain wavelengths. For example, the red anthocyanin pigments and certain flavones screen out deleterious ultraviolet wavelengths. There is a variable amount of light scattering within cell walls and tissues, and some light is transmitted through the organ.

If light energy is to affect metabolic processes, it must be absorbed by some compound within the cell. Such a compound is, by definition, a pigment. The most prominent pigments in plants are those of the photosynthetic system, chlorophylls and carotenoids, which absorb all the wavelengths in the 400 to 700 nm band, although with varying efficiency. The radiation energy is used directly in the light reactions of photosynthesis. With the development of precise lamp-filter systems to control the wavelength band width and sensitive instrumentation to measure the intensity or flux of radiations, almost all of the wavelengths of electromagnetic radiation reaching the earth have been examined for their effects on the development, physiology, and biochemistry of a wide range of plants including those of agronomic and horticultural importance.

Electromagnetic radiation includes highly energetic cosmic, X, and gamma radiations capable of ionizing matter and penetrating through many solid substances. The ability of X rays to penetrate through tissues is an invaluable medical consequence of the powerful nature of photons of ionizing radiation. Solar ionizing radiation reaches the earth's surface and is capable of causing mutations in plants.

Beyond the ionizing radiation are the ultraviolet, visible, heat (infrared), microwave, and radio wavelengths (see Figure 9-2). While infrared radiation plays an important role in temperature regulation and both ultraviolet and ionizing radiations may deleteriously affect plants, studies on the effects of light on plants have concentrated on that narrow band of wavelengths in the middle of the electromagnetic spectrum that, because the human eye can perceive them, we call visible light.

The most energetic ultraviolet radiation bands, the vacuum ultraviolet (100 to 200 nm), are screened out by gases in the upper atmosphere; they play no role in plant growth and development. The upper atmosphere also screens out the highly damaging UV-C radiations (200 to 290 nm) which are absorbed by nucleic acids and proteins and can so modify these macromolecules that mutations or cell death occurs. UV-C wavelengths can be generated by inexpensive lamps and are used in nucleic acid research and are occasionally used to induce potentially favorable mutations in plants.

Ozone in the stratosphere reduces the intensity of the UV-B wavelengths (290 to 320 nm), although significant radiation fluxes of UV-B penetrate to the earth's surface. The UV-B is responsible for vitamin D synthesis, skin cancer, and skin tanning in mammals. In plants UV-B can cause mutations and has been reported to affect several biochemical processes including photosynthesis, nucleic acids, and enzymes. Its role in other plant processes is suspected, but too little information is available to reach any conclusions. Research is underway to evaluate the possibility that decreases in the stratospheric ozone layer by human pollutions (especially by chlorinated hydrocarbons) may modify crop productivity. UV-B is not transmitted through glass so that the greenhouse light environment is deficient in UV-B wavelengths.

The UV-A radiation band (320 to 400 nm) is a significant factor in plant growth. Limited studies indicate that UV-A, which is emitted by most fluorescent lamps and can penetrate through glass, is a growth repressant and may also interfere with the flowering response of plants. Research has shown that the form of many alpine plants grown at high altitudes is different from the form of the same species grown at lower elevations, where UV-A is a smaller fraction of the solar radiation.

Visible radiation includes wavelengths from violet (400 nm) through indigo, blue, green, yellow, orange, and red (700 nm) wavelengths. Human visibility is conventionally assumed to end at about 700 nm, but people can see, albeit poorly, into the near infrared region which plant scientists call the far red (700 to 810 nm). Photosynthetic bacteria contain bacteriochlorophyll that can absorb and utilize wavelengths of 800 nm for photosynthesis.

Heat radiations, the infrared portion of the spectrum, affect plants primarily through their effects on the temperature balance of the plant and its environment and on the water relations of plants.

Many morphogenetic (development of plant form) and physiogenetic (development of function) processes are controlled by specific wavelengths of light. In contrast to photosynthesis, however, the absorbing pigment is altered by the photon energy; it becomes a trigger that starts a large number of processes in motion that result in alterations in patterns of growth and development. The intensity and duration of radiation necessary to activate and control these light-requiring morphogenetic and physiogenetic systems are both small, several orders of magnitude less than those required to activate and to maintain photosynthesis. We can think of macroradiations that supply the energy to make a process such as photosynthesis "go" and microradiations that serve as triggers for processes that utilize metabolic energy.

A number of photomorphogenic systems have been identified and are under intensive study because of their theoretical and practical importance. One of these, sometimes called the cryptochrome system, absorbs wavelengths in the UV-A and the blue regions of the spectrum. The absorbing pigment appears to be a flavin compound related to the vitamin riboflavin (vitamin B_2), although carotenoids may also be cryptochrome pigments. The cryptochrome system controls a variety of plant responses. Among these is the bending response of plants called phototropism. A plant responds to light coming from one direction by bending toward the light. This is a growth response in which those cells farthest from the light elongate more than do cells closest to the light. As a consequence, the stem or the petiole bends. The bending is actually caused by a differential distribution of plant growth substances in the tissues. A special type of phototropism is heliotropism in leaves or flower heads which move daily so that the plant part remains at right angles to the sun; this permits equalization of light intensity and maximizes light interception of photosynthetic organs (Figure 9-3). Roots may be negatively phototropic, bending away from the light; the ability of ivy (*Hedera helix*) to cling to walls is also a negative phototropic response of stems and adventitious roots. Where house plants are growing on window sills, it is standard practice to rotate the plants frequently so that they will grow in the upright position.

The UV-A and blue radiations play other important roles in plant development. These wavelengths activate many enzyme systems including those that synthesize the carotenoids of the photosynthetic apparatus (Chapter 11), anthocyanin synthesis, nitrate reduction (Chapter 7), stomatal opening (Chapter 6), and many others. The proper functioning of plant cell membranes seems also to be partly under photocontrol. It has not been determined whether these complex responses to UV-A and blue wavelengths are all mediated through a flavin pigment or by more than one photoreceptor.

Since green wavelengths (centered about 550 nm) form more than a quarter of the visible radiant energy from the sun that reaches the earth, it is surprising that so little is known about their effects on plants. They are relatively inefficient in photosynthesis since the chloroplast pigments absorb green light poorly (Chapter 11). It appears that they may repress growth of plants, but that there is another wavelength, in the orange-red region, that can negate the effects of green light.

In 1945 it was found that a number of morphogenetic reactions of plants involve the red end of the visible spectrum. The absorbing pigment, named phytochrome, was isolated in 1959. It is a complex bile-type (tetrapyrrole) compound attached to a specific cellular protein. At the same time it was also found that the positive developmental effects of red light at 660 nm could be negated by simultaneous or subsequent exposure to far red light at 720 to 740

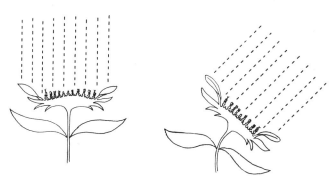

Figure 9-3 Heliotropic curvature of sunflower.

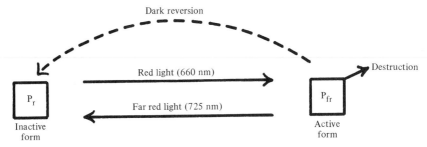

Figure 9-4 Intercoversion of the forms of phytochrome.

nm. Phytochrome occurs in two forms and conversion from one form to another is controlled by exposure to red or far red light. The light-controlled interconversions of phytochrome are given in Figure 9-4. It is believed that when all of the phytochrome is in its red-absorbing form (P_r), the systems controlled by phytochrome are inactive; when the phytochrome is converted to the far red-absorbing form (P_{fr}), the systems are activated. The extent to which a phytochrome-controlled system will react depends on the ratio of the two light-absorbing forms of the pigment, which in turn, depends on the ratio and photon activity of the two activating wavelength bands (Figure 9-5). In most

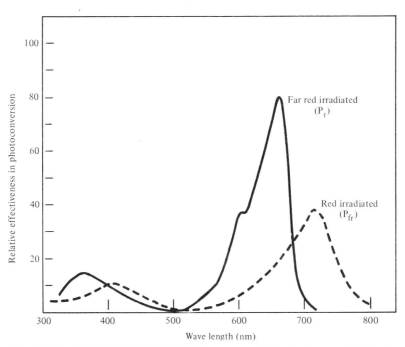

Figure 9-5 Action spectra for the interconversion of the two forms of phytochrome.

Table 9-1   PARTIAL LIST OF PHYTOCHROME-CONTROLLED RESPONSES IN PLANTS

Activation of growth processes	Activation of control processes
Seed germination	Bud dormancy induction
Rhizome formation	Winter hardiness induction
Bulb and tuber formation	Leaf abscission
Leaf primordia formation	Bud break
Grass leaf unfolding	Respiratory control
Vascular element formation	Succulence
Stomata differentiation	Etiolation
Stem and petiole elongation	Growth substances metabolism
Leaf enlargement and differentiation	Membrane regulation
Root development	Protein synthesis
Hypocotyl hook opening	Leaf movement
Epinasty	Cotyledon expansion
Flower induction	Plastid morphology
Activation of biochemical processes	
Chlorophyll synthesis	
Anthocyanin synthesis	
Enzyme formation	
Lipid and protein metabolism	

Note: Not all of these responses occur in all tested plants.

cases the intensities of red and far red light needed for phytochrome interconversion are several orders of magnitude lower than for photosynthesis and the time required to shift the phytochrome from one molecular form to the other is measured in seconds or minutes.

The list of phytochrome-regulated processes in plants is large and still growing (Table 9-1). It includes seed germination (both stimulation and repression), cell division, enlargement and differentiation, flowering, dormancy, enzyme activation, biosynthesis of pigments and chloroplasts, and many other processes.

A third photomorphogenetic system is known as the high-intensity response (HIR). Both blue and far red wavelengths participate in this group of photomorphogenetic reactions. They differ from phytochrome reactions in that higher light intensities and longer periods of time are required to active HIR systems. It is not known whether the HIR functions through the phytochrome system or whether other pigment and control systems are involved. It is known, however, that parallels between phytochrome-controlled response and the HIR are far from exact. The synthesis of some pigments, some seed germination processes, and other growth responses involve the HIR.

Photoperiodism
Daily and Seasonal Cycles

All organisms living on earth are exposed to daily periods of light and dark due to the rotation of the earth on its axis (Figure 9-6). Because the axis is tilted (about 23.5° from the vertical), the duration of the periods varies on different parts of

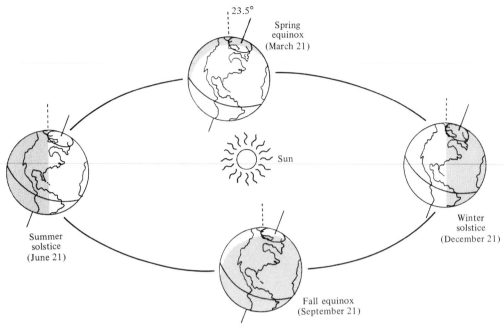

Figure 9-6 Annual revolution of the earth around the sun.

the globe at different times of year. Daylength, that is, the number of hours of light in each 24-hour cycle, is 12 hours at the equator essentially year-round (Table 9-2). Daylength at the North Pole is 24 hours on June 21, but is zero hours on December 21. These are the dates of the summer and winter solstices in the Northern Hemisphere. On March 21 and September 21, the dates of the spring and fall equinoxes, daylength from the North Pole to the equator is 12 hours. Thus, daylength at any point in the Northern Hemisphere is increasing from

Table 9-2   EFFECT OF LATITUDE ON DAYLENGTH

Approximate latitude	Daylength on specific dates			
	March 21	June 21	September 21	December 21
0° Equator	12 hr	12 hr	12 hr	12 hr
10°N Caracas	12 hr	12 hr 35 min	12 hr	11 hr 25 min
20°N Hawaii	12 hr	13 hr 12 min	12 hr	10 hr 48 min
30°N New Orleans	12 hr	13 hr 56 min	12 hr	10 hr 04 min
40°N Denver	12 hr	14 hr 52 min	12 hr	9 hr 08 min
50°N Vancouver	12 hr	16 hr 18 min	12 hr	7 hr 42 min
60°N Anchorage	12 hr	18 hr 27 min	12 hr	5 hr 33 min
70°N Point Barrow	12 hr	24 hr[a]	12 hr	0 hr 00 min[a]
80°N Northern Greenland	12 hr	24 hr	12 hr	0 hr 00 min
90°N North Pole	12 hr	24 hr	12 hr	0 hr 00 min

[a]The period during which there are 24 hours of light lasts 2 months at 70°N, 4 months at 80°N, and 6 months at 90°N. The period during which there are 24 hours of darkness lasts 2 months at 70°N, 4 months at 80°N, and 6 months at 90°N.

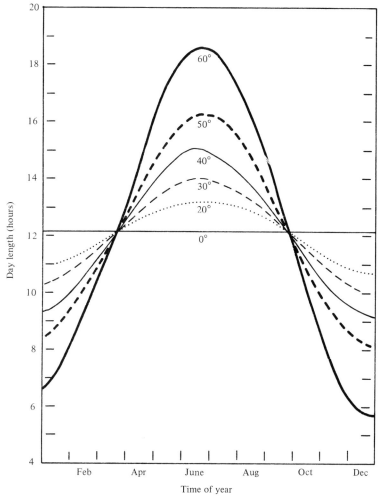

Figure 9-7 Relation of daylength and latitude.

December 21 to June 21 and decreasing from June 21 to December 21 (Figure 9-7).

As the earth spins on its axis, it is also revolving in its annual cycle around the sun giving rise to the seasons. The Northern Hemisphere is colder during the winter season because solar radiation strikes it at an oblique angle and is therefore less intense than during the summer season when the radiation reaches the Northern Hemisphere almost vertically. Also the duration of exposure to the radiation is shorter. The summer season is the period when temperature in the Northern Hemisphere is higher as the earth's tilt is toward the sun, radiation is nearly vertical, and the duration of light and heat is increasing. The changes in the duration of light on a daily basis and the changes in temperature on a seasonal basis are responsible for a large number of modifications in plant development.

Photoperiodic Responses

The response of flowering plants to daylength is termed photoperiodism and an explanation of this concept includes how the plant is able to perceive and measure time in terms of daily alternating periods of light and dark.

The first good experimental evidence supporting the concept of photoperiodism was presented in the early twentieth century, but the real breakthrough came when Garner and Allard of the U.S. Department of Agriculture presented their findings in the 1920s. They were working with a large-leaf tobacco, *Nicotiana tabacum* cv. Maryland Mammoth, which would form flowers only when exposed to short periods of light during each 24-hour cycle, that is, a short daylength or photoperiod. This tobacco cultivar is called a short-day plant (SDP) because it will form flowers only when the photoperiod is less than a certain critical length, specifically 14 hours (Figure 9-8). When there are more than 14 hours of light, the plant remains in the vegetative condition. Long-day plants (LDP) were also discovered which form flowers only when photoperiods are longer than a critical number of hours and remain vegetative when the photoperiods are shorter. Both types of plant may require a 13-hour photoperiod, but the short-day plant flowers only when the photoperiod is shorter than 13, and the LDP flowers only when the photoperiod is longer than 13.

Still a third type of photoperiodic response was described. A day-neutral plant (DNP) will flower on any photoperiod after it has reached a certain level of vegetative growth. Other categories of photoperiod sensitivity are now known; a few plants require an exposure to long days and then to short days (LSDP), and some require the opposite sequence of short then long days (SLDP). (The photoperiod requirements for flowering for some crop and ornamental plants are given in Tables 15-3 and 15-4.)

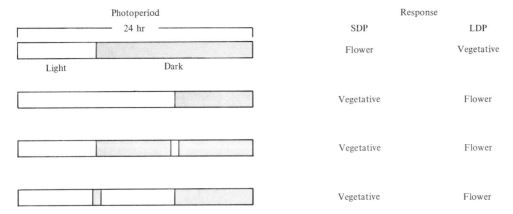

Figure 9-8 Response of flowering plants to light regimes: short day, long day, light interruption of long night, and dark interruption of long day.

For most plants exposure to the required daylength will not induce flowering if the plant has not attained a certain amount of vegetative growth; this species-specific level of growth is called "ripeness to flower." There are a few plants that can be induced to form flowers at the cotyledonary stage of growth, for example, Japanese morning glory (*Pharbitis nil* cv. Violet, now *Ipomoea nil*). But most are not sensitive to photoperiodic induction until a minimum number of leaves have formed, for example, 7 for some cereal grains and 12 for the apostle plant (*Neomarica northiana*). Many species of bamboo and the century plant (*Agave* spp.) do not flower until after many years of vegetative growth.

Numerous short-day and long-day plants initiate flowers in an all-or-nothing response; they will not form flower buds until exposed to the full required photoperiod. Other SDP and LDP show a quantitative response; the plant will flower increasingly rapidly as the photoperiod approaches the optimum number of hours, down to about 8 hours for the SDP and up to about 16 hours for the LDP. The quantitative SDP will not flower, however, when exposed to very long days, and the quantitative LDP will not flower when grown under very short-day conditions.

To complicate matters even further, temperature during photoperiodic induction can modify the photoperiod requirement of some plants. Poinsettia (*Euphorbia pulcherrima*) and common morning glory (*Ipomoea purpurea* cv. Heavenly Blue) are both short-day plants when grown at warm temperatures and long-day plants when grown at cool temperatures. Cosmos (*Cosmos sulphureus* cv. Orange Flare) is a short-day plant at cool temperatures and a day-neutral plant at warm temperatures. Differences in flowering time from year to year in many strongly photoperiod-sensitive plants are probably a reflection of the interaction of temperature with the photoperiodic response.

The term photoperiod implies that the number of hours of light that a plant receives in each 24-hour cycle is critical. Yet it has been shown that the number of hours of darkness in each cycle is the more important part of the signal by which plants are able to measure time to promote their flowering. Flowering plants should perhaps be called long-night or short-night plants. The definitive experiments were done in the 1930s with the cocklebur (*Xanthium strumarium*), a very sensitive SDP. It was found that flowering can be prevented when the plant is grown under the appropriate photoperiod by interrupting the dark period with a few minutes of white light at about the middle of the dark period (see Figure 9-8). A brief period of darkness during the middle of its short day has no effect on subsequent flowering. Long-day plants were also found to be responsive to the light break. When grown on a short-day noninductive photoperiod, interruption of the long night with a short period of white light promotes flowering.

The significance of the light break experiments was immediately apparent. If white light is effective, then an action spectrum could be determined with the possibility for identifying the pigment functioning in photoperiod. This was indeed the case. The wavelength of the visible spectrum that inhibits flowering in SDP is red light at 660 nm. Far red light at 730 nm, presented immediately following exposure to red light, negates the inhibitory effect of red light. LDP are also sensitive: the red light break promotes flowering and far red light negates the promotive effect of red light. The pigment eventually isolated was phytochrome.

In the discussion of vernalization it was indicated that meristems were the organs of perception of the cold period. The organ that perceives daylength is the leaf. The photoperiod influences the form and amount of the phytochrome pigment. The P_{fr} form is predominant in the leaf during the light period and the P_r form during the dark (see Figure 9-4). In the short-day plant the synthesis of flower-inducing hormones begins when the concentration of P_{fr} falls to a sufficiently low level. The hormones are translocated in the phloem to the shoot apex where the cells are transformed from vegetative to flower primordia. In the long-day plant the concentration of P_{fr} must remain sufficiently high in order to promote the synthesis of the flower-inducing hormones. When the dark period is too long, P_{fr} falls below the required threshold level.

It has been proposed and is now generally accepted that the flowering process in short-day plants also has as an underlying mechanism, a circadian clock, that is, a daily cycle of biological activities which once started persists for a time without cues from the environment (discussed below). The circadian rhythm appears to regulate the photoperiodic measurement of time by interaction with phytochrome. The rhythmic phasing is probably set by phytochrome, since the clock seems to be started by transfer of the SDP to darkness, but the transfer to light also phases the clock. The situation is less clear in LDP as photoperiodic induction occurs in some plants maintained in continuous light.

The flower-inducing hormone has been named florigen, but it is hypothetical in that no such single substance has been isolated from any plant tissue. It may be that more than one hormone or a combination of several compounds are synthesized or required to act as the flowering stimulus.

Most flowering plants require many successive exposures to a favorable photoperiod before flowers are initiated (Figure 9-9), but a few SDP and LDP will flower when exposed to only one appropriate inductive cycle. Examples include SDP such as Japanese morning glory (*Ipomoea nil*), cocklebur (*Xanthium strumarium*), and rice (*Oryza sativa* cv. Zuiho) and LDP such as spinach (*Spinacia oleracea*), common pimpernel (*Anagallis arvensis*), and chervil (*Anthriscus cerefolium*).

Applications Photoperiod can modify the morphology of the flower. In *Viola* (*V. fimbriatula* and other species) conspicuous flowers with showy petals form only during the shorter days of early spring; flowers without petals or with inconspicuous ones, which are self-pollinating, develop during the longer days of late spring and early summer.

The June-bearing type of strawberry is a short-day plant if the night temperature is above 19.5° C (67° F), but it can become a day-neutral plant, and therefore effectively everbearing, if the night temperature is below 19.5° C.

The photoperiod requirements of some important crop plants have been modified through conscious selection. Researchers select from the wild population plants with characteristics that enable them to be grown over a wider range of photoperiods. For example, soybean, an SDP, was limited to areas where the seed would mature before a killing frost. New cultivars, with early flowering and

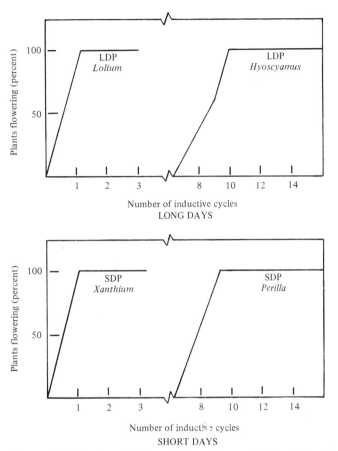

Figure 9-9   Number of photoperiodic cycles required to induce flowering.

hence early seed maturation, permit this plant to be grown in the more northern parts of North America. Rice, as a wild plant, is an SDP. The cultivars that are now most widely grown are usually DNP.

The flowering response of greenhouse and house plants can be promoted by supplying the correct inductive hours of light. The end result of artificially modifying photoperiod is seen when such SDP as poinsettia and chrysanthemums are commercially available considerably before or after their natural flowering time.

The situation is not so simple in the garden. Many cultivars of chrysanthemums, an SDP, particularly those with deeper bronze and maroon flowers, do not flower sufficiently early in the colder northern areas of the United States and Canada because the number of frost-free days is too small to permit full development of photoperiodically promoted flower buds. Vegetative growth may be quite vigorous and flower buds may form, but unless there is a considerable delay in the first hard frost, flowers will rarely develop fully.

Another problem is the presence of artificial light, such as street lamps or home security lamps, too close to photoperiodically sensitive plants. When exposed to too long periods of light, some trees retain their leaves due to failure of the abscission process, and some short-day plants do not flower. Light intensities of 0.1 to 5.0 fc are sufficient, when given throughout the night, to be the equivalent of extending the daylength. Tungsten-filament and sodium-vapor lamps, in particular, emit wavelengths that are photoperiodically effective; mercury-vapor lamps have less influence on photoperiodic responses.

Photoperiod affects a number of aspects of growth and vegetative reproduction; these will be discussed in Chapter 15.

Rhythms Regulated by Light

Most of the structural and functional activities of plants are regulated by environmental factors including temperature, water, nutrients, and light. There are, however, biological rhythms that, once started, will continue without any apparent environmental control. The most obvious of these are the sleep movements of leaves in which the leaves oscillate between a horizontal position during the day and a vertical position at night (Figure 9-10). Beans, peas, the prayer plant (*Maranta leuconeura*), and coleus show sleep movements. These nyctinastic (night closure) movements are caused by turgor pressure changes similar to those that cause opening and closing of stomata or the leaf movements of the sensitive plant (*Mimosa pudica*). In contrast to phototropic responses, sleep movements are not growth changes and therefore do not cause permanent changes in cell size or shape.

Many biological rhythms are diurnal, completing one full cycle in approximately 24 hours. These are termed circadian (about one day). Most are activated

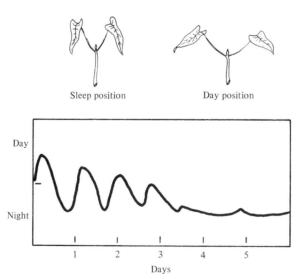

Sleep position   Day position

Day

Night

1   2   3   4   5

Days

Figure 9-10 Rhythmic leaf movements of a bean seedling, with damping cycle in the absence of entraining stimuli.

or the timing of the oscillation is changed (entrained) by one or several photoperiodic cycles, but once the control mechanisms are started, the rhythm persists for many cycles even though other environmental factors are altered. After a time, the rhythm damps off and will be lost unless the clock is restarted by another appropriate photoperiod stimulus (see Figure 9-10).

In addition to leaf movements, the opening and closing of flowers are photoperiodically initiated by endogenous clocks. The mechanism is unknown, but the cycle has been observed in kalanchoe, evening primrose (*Oenothera* spp.), portulaca, morning glory, and night-blooming flowers. It is known that the opening and closing of stomata in some plants, such as cacti and other succulents, are regulated by a light-driven clock. The synthesis and activity of enzymes, cell elongation and division, and many other processes are at least partly controlled by biological clocks. It has been suggested that nyctinastic leaf movements permit the plant more adequately to regulate the solar radiation falling on the leaves and to control carbon dioxide and water movement. It is thought that the phytochrome and the HIR systems are involved, but this is still under investigation.

There are several important plant science implications of this phenomenon. Alterations in photoperiod can entrain one biological clock so that it is out of phase with other rhythmic activities of the plant. If plants are under continuous artificial illumination, no clock can be entrained. With rare exceptions (African violets and other gesneriads), plants do not show normal growth and development under a 24-hour photoperiod and some, like tomato and other solanacean plants, may die. Abrupt changes in photoperiod, such as moving plants from one photoperiod to another can upset or stop biological clocks and resetting to the new rhythm may take several days.

SHADE

Types of Shade

There are three major types of shade situations to be considered in terms of plant growth and development. The first is neutral shade, in which there is no alteration in the ratio among the various wavelengths, but all are quantitatively reduced in intensity by the same amount. Neutral shade exists under stands of coniferous trees where the needles absorb all visible radiations equally, under shading cloth and dark plastic sheeting, and under greenhouse glass coated with shading paint.

A second type is selective shade, in which different wavelengths are reduced by varying amounts so that the radiation impinging on the plant is qualitatively as well as quantitatively different from unfiltered light. Selective shade exists under canopies of broad-leaved plants, both deciduous trees and the upper canopy of leaves in crop plants. Looking up into a deciduous canopy, it is obvious that the light transmitted through the leaves is greatly enriched in green wavelengths because the red and blue ends of the visible spectrum have been

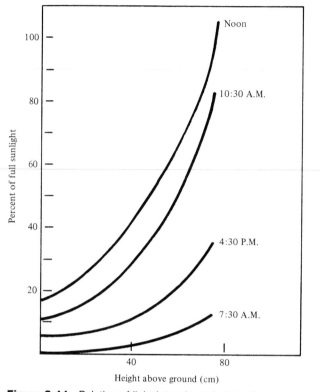

Figure 9-11 Relation of light intensity to height of plant crop and to time of day.

selectively absorbed by photosynthetic pigments in the chloroplasts (Chapter 11).

A third type of shade is usually called diffuse light or skylight and is found on the north sides of buildings and in valleys shadowed by hills in early morning and late evening. Because of scattering of sunlight by particles in the atmosphere, skylight is qualitatively and quantitatively different from direct sunlight. The intensity of radiation received by plants depends not only on the time of day, but also on the height of the plants (Figure 9-11).

In addition to qualitative and quantitative alterations in visible wavelengths under shade conditions, there are significant alterations in the thermal balances of the plants and the soils receiving the altered radiation. There is considerably less thermal radiation under shade conditions; soils and plants tend to be cooler, and the transpiration of shaded plants or plant parts is reduced. The shade environment usually has higher humidity, decreased wind speed, less air tubulence, and higher carbon dioxide concentrations than the sun environment. These characteristics modify several aspects of plant development. The analysis of the effects of shade independently of other components of the shade microenvironment is achieved only under controlled experimental conditions.

Sun and Shade Plants

It is well known that different plants grow better under different light conditions. Many seed and plant catalogues note that a particular species or cultivar should be grown in full sunlight, in partial shade (full sun for only part of a day), or in shade. Plants are sometimes referred to as "sun-loving" or "sun-hating," although it is more correct to speak of sun or shade tolerance.

Light requirements are genetically determined, but can be altered by selection and breeding of plants that have adapted under natural conditions to particular light regimes. Even within a species, some individuals grow best in full sun, while others will be present only in partly or fully shaded conditions. The ecologist recognizes that there are adaptations of clones to light; these are called ecotypes (ecologically adapted races). Transplantation to a light regime to which a plant is not adapted is usually unsuccessful. This accounts for the death of many wild plants when moved into a garden. In general, shade-requiring plants do poorly under full sun conditions, and, while many full-sun plants can be grown in partial or even full shade, they rarely attain their maximum potential.

The shade tolerance of a plant (whether positive or negative) varies with its developmental stage. A number of ornamental or forest trees are highly shade-tolerant at the seedling stage and become progressively less tolerant with age. Birches, several species of maple, and some conifers can be seeded in or planted as seedlings under the shade of larger trees to become replacements as the older trees die. The same is true of some herbaceous plants; those that are shade-tolerant can be planted among taller plants and, as the dominant ones die back during the season, the tolerant plants will mature in the garden plot.

There is, however, a limit to shade tolerance. Light intensities below 10 percent of full sunlight usually cause etiolation of even tolerant plants. The extreme is seen in plants grown in darkness. They are usually white or pale yellow, the internodes are elongated, the leaves are small, and the plants are very succulent. The etiolation syndrome is due to almost complete absence of red radiation (Figure 9-12). The word is from the French *etioler*, "to blanch," and accurately describes the condition. White hearts of celery (*Apium graveolens*) and Belgian endive (*Cichorium Endivia*) and white asparagus (*Asparagus officinalis*) are etiolated plants produced by hilling soil around the developing plants to prevent light from reaching them. Etiolation is not an all-or-nothing phenomenon; the pale, succulent, and elongated ("leggy") plants that grow indoors near north-facing windows are partly etiolated as are many seedlings grown indoors for subsequent transplanting. If an etiolated plant is exposed to adequate light, the development of chlorophyll and other pigments and subsequent growth may be essentially normal, but the elongated initial growth is permanent. Since red wavelengths are required to prevent etiolation, the inclusion of some natural sunlight or the use of incandescent light is valuable when starting seedlings or growing plants indoors (artificial illumination is discussed later in this chapter). Sun plants that have been grown under shade or partial shade conditions will adapt to full light. The adaptation is gradual, requiring a week or more.

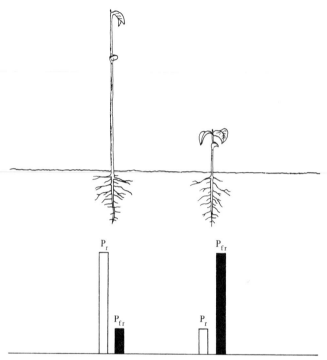

Figure 9-12 Etiolation of a bean seedling and the phytochrome ratios involved.

Immediate and prolonged exposure to full sun will usually result in wilting, bleaching of chlorophyll, and leaf and stem injury.

The consequences of reduced radiation on sun plants have been examined in many economically important plants. Many of the alterations are found in the leaves. Shaded leaves tend to be thinner, with poor palisade and mesophyll development and thin cell walls, but they have an increased surface area (Figure 9-13). Tobacco leaves are deliberately grown in shade because this structure makes them particularly suited to be used for cigar wrappers. Sun leaves require 2 to 10 times more light intensity (measured in PARs or $\mu E/m^2/sec$) to reach light saturation than shade leaves, contain more chlorophyll, and are considerably more active photosynthetically (Figure 9-14). The compensation point of sun leaves is up to 10 times higher than that of shade leaves. The compensation point is that radiation intensity where the utilization of sugars in respiration is just balanced by the photosynthetic formation of sugars (Chapters 11 and 12). This means that shade leaves may not have a net production of sugars for their metabolism and, unless sugars are imported from other parts of the plant, they cannot grow nor can they contribute to the metabolism of the plant as a whole. Plants such as corn, possessing the C_4 photosynthetic pathway (see Chapter 11), are severely retarded by low light conditions.

Low light also affects branch development. Trees grown in dense stands or exposed to reduced light are frequently self-pruning; lower branches drop since

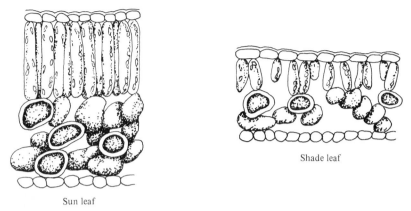

Figure 9-13 Structure of sun and shade leaves.

they cannot supply themselves with sugars. Trees in mature forests may have unbranched trunks for a considerable vertical distance, and ornamental trees shaded by buildings may lose their lower branches. Shading of sun-requiring shrubs by buildings or by trees is a frequent cause of poor growth. Internal branches may be lost and twigs may become elongated. Some house plants, too, will show poor development in low light.

The fact that shaded plants are more succulent than sun plants has relevance in terms of their response to alterations in other environmental conditions common in shade environments. Shaded plants are less able to tolerate water stress and may die at soil moisture levels that would scarcely cause wilting in adapted plants. This is important both for house plants and for partly etiolated plants grown for field transplantation. Shaded plants also appear to be

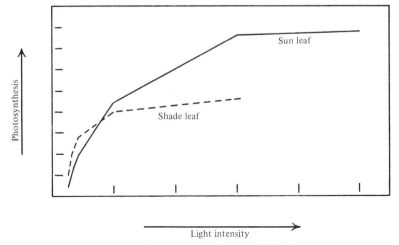

Figure 9-14 Photosynthetic responses of sun and shade leaves.

Figure 9-15 Light attenuation within a dense-foliaged plant, with darkest area receiving less than 15 percent of full solar radiation.

less disease-resistant than sun plants. They have narrower limits for nutrient deficiencies and for potential injury from salts.

These general statements on the effects on light intensity on the development and metabolism of different types of plants (sun and shade species) are equally appropriate for different parts of an individual plant. In dense-foliaged plants like soybean, corn, some garden flowers, and many ornamental trees and shrubs the leaves at the top of the canopy are typical sun leaves, while those within the canopy show many characteristics of shade leaves (Figure 9-15). Under conditions of attenuated light leaves are thinner and paler or more yellow, many leaves have fallen, and the branches are somewhat spindly. The severely shaded leaves are net importers of photosynthetically produced sugars and may divert sugars that would otherwise be used for vegetative or reproductive growth.

Aside from genetically altering the growth habit of the plant—something that is being studied for economically important plants—there are few procedures that can alleviate the condition. Of these, the most productive is to establish crop rows in such a direction that self-shading is minimized. In much of the Northern Hemisphere, closely spaced rows should be in an east-west direction rather than north-south. However, consideration must also be given to slope, soil types, and the presence of other sources of shade. The space between rows and between plants is also controllable; there is, however, a cost-benefit ratio to be considered between increased illumination and decreased number of plants per area. Ornamental woody perennials and fruit trees can be pruned to open up the canopy.

ARTIFICIAL ILLUMINATION

Types of Lamps

The ideal for artificial illumination of plants is a lamp system equivalent in intensity and quality to solar radiation. This ideal can almost be achieved with filtered, high-pressure xenon lamps, but such a system is expensive and suitable only for experimental purposes. The horticulturist, the gardener, and, indeed, almost all plant research scientists utilize three lamp types: fluorescent, incandescent, and mercury, sodium, or metal-halide lamps. None of these, alone or in combination, can fully simulate solar radiation.

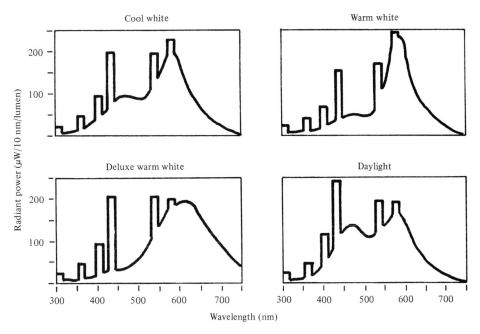

Figure 9-16 Spectral energy distribution curves for white fluorescent lamps.

Comparison of various white fluorescent lamps shows that their emission spectra are different (Figure 9-16), but none can substitute for the spectrum of sunlight. In all types there is a deficiency in the red–far red end of the spectrum, the intensity of green wavelengths is high and there is an excess of blue wavelengths. Combining different fluorescent lamps, particularly warm white and daylight lamps with cool white lamps, may improve the balance, but the red–far red end of the spectrum needed for phytochrome activation remains somewhat inadequate. The PAR intensity is, at best, a quarter to a fifth of sunlight. Fluorescent lamps have low initial and operating costs and relatively small heat production. The fluorescent lamps said to be designed for plant lighting are relatively expensive, are esthetically unsatisfactory, and provide no benefits for plant growth except for gesneriads, such as African violet.

The two types of incandescent lamp, standard and tungsten-halogen, have the same spectra, with low blue, moderate green, and high red–far red (Figure 9-17). Like fluorescent lamps, they have low initial and operating costs. However, they produce high heat levels, frequently high enough to damage plants. Incandescent lamps sold specifically for growing plants are usually standard lamps with a blue-tinted glass envelope to decrease the amount of yellow through far red radiation. They are esthetically satisfactory, and there is some reduction in heat production, but the radiation intensities are adequate only for low-light plants. Plants grown under these lamps may become pale and etiolated.

Mercury vapor lamps, extensively used for security lighting, are not suitable for horticultural or gardening purposes because their color balance is inadequate and they may emit potentially dangerous ultraviolet radiations unless properly

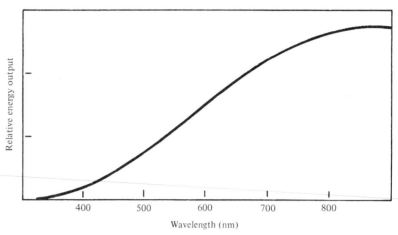

Figure 9-17   Spectral energy distribution curves for incandescent lamps.

filtered. Sodium lamps as the sole source of light are adequate for growing many plants and they are used to supplement the natural light entering greenhouses.

A luminaire (a complete lighting unit) constructed with cool white fluorescent and incandescent lamps on an equal watt input ratio provides reasonable wavelength balance without greatly increasing the heat load on the plants. A 3:1 ratio of fluorescent to incandescent can be used for many plants. To provide even distribution of the incandescent illumination and to reduce the heat load, several low wattage incandescent lamps are distributed along the length of the fluorescent lamp fixture. A luminaire can also be constructed using combinations of different types of fluorescent lamps.

In addition to wavelength balance and heat production, the geometry of radiation must be considered in constructing a lighting unit. The inverse square law (radiation intensity decreases as the square of the distance from the source) is applicable for a point radiation source such as the sun-earth, but not to artificial sources which have a broad emission pattern relative to the lamp-plant distance. The decrease in intensity more closely approximates a linear falloff in intensity; intensity doubles by decreasing the distance by one-half (Figure 9-18). Commercial fixtures for fluorescent lamps usually contain two or four lamps. These are satisfactory only for narrow installations since the pattern of light decrease is related to the form of the lamp tube. This is also true for incandescent lamps where there are a series of concentric rings of decreasing intensity (Figure 9-19). For more permanent installations, combination luminaires are best constructed with the fluorescent lamps placed as close together as possible. It is feasible to use a single luminaire for plants with different light requirements by appropriate positioning of the plants.

As can be seen in Table 9-3, no inexpensive lamp system can deliver more than 100 PAR even when placed close to the plants where there is the danger of thermal injury. This is only 10 percent of light saturation for photosynthesis in sun plants. To some extent, this deficiency can be relieved by lengthening the

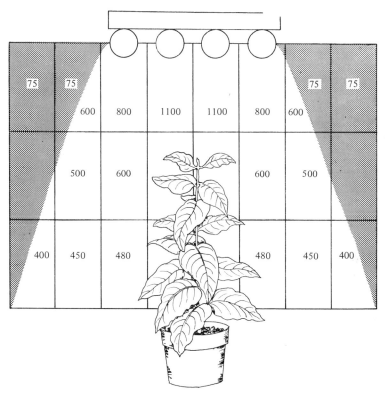

Figure 9-18 Decrease in light intensity from a fluorescent luminaire. Light values are measured in foot-candles.

photoperiod. In both photosynthesis and some of the photomorphogenetic responses, there is a relationship between intensity and duration of exposure to light. A low intensity for a long time may produce about the same response as a higher intensity for a shorter period of time. This is known as the reciprocity rule. In the Northern Hemisphere between 30° north and 50° north latitude, daylengths do not exceed 16 hours and many plants can be grown successfully with an 18-hour photoperiod. This increases the daily light received by the plant by 12 percent, an increase that is significant for plant growth. However, increases

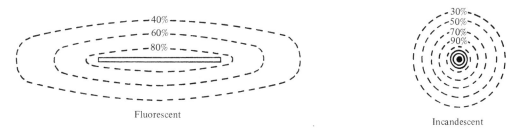

Figure 9-19 Flux density distribution patterns from fluorescent and incandescent lamps.

Table 9-3   LIGHT LEVELS FOR VARIOUS PLANT GROWTH SITUATIONS

	Irradiance (PAR, or μE/m²/sec)	Illuminance	
		lx	fc
Natural sources			
Summer sun	2,400	930	10,000
Summer cloud cover	1,000	465	5,000
Skylight	400	186	2,000
Artifical sources			
Incandescent (100 W at 1.5 m)	5	2	22
Fluorescent (40 W at 15 cm)[a]	60	26	280
Fluorescent (150 W at 1.5 cm)[b]	17	88	950
Adequate light levels for plants			
Sun plants	1,000	465	5,000
Shade plants	250	112	1,200
House plants			
Low-light requirement	50	16	175
Moderate-light requirement	70	34	370
High-light requirement	200	102	1,100
Growing vegetable and flower seedlings	150	84	900

[a]4-ft cool white lamp.
[b]9-ft cool white: Power Groove, VHO, 1500 ma; Power Twist

beyond an 18-hour photoperiod are usually not advisable because biological clocks are unfavorably reset. Few plants grow well under 20- to 24-hour photoperiods. It is also not possible to use an extended photoperiod when flowering of short-day plants is desired.

Where plants are grown under artificial lights with some exposure to natural radiation, obtaining adequate balance of red–far red radiation is less of a problem. Even skylight contains enough of these wavelengths to provide photomorphogenetic radiation for the phytochrome and the HIR systems. A few hours of direct or indirect solar radiation is usually all that is required for adequate plant development. During extended periods of gloomy weather, short-term supplementation of skylight with artificial light can be valuable. High pressure sodium lamps are being used in greenhouses to supplement natural light.

Growing Plants Under Artificial Lights

Plants can be grown to maturity without any source of natural solar radiation, although even under the best possible conditions, they may not be the equal of plants grown in sunlight. There are two frequent situations in which artificial sources must be relied upon partly or completely. The first is the cultivation of house plants in homes where no or only minimal natural light can be provided. The second is the need in northern climates to start plants indoors that are to be eventually transplanted outside. The problems faced in both situations are similar, but not identical.

Many house plants are of tropical or semitropical origin and in their natural habitats are found as part of the shaded understory beneath tree canopies. They are, therefore, primarily shade plants and many have low- to moderate-light requirements (Table 9-4). Most are grown as foliage plants and control of photoperiod is less important. Where there is a source of natural light for at least part of the day, supplementary illumination with either fluorescent or incandescent sources, singly or in combination, usually works well.

The direction of the natural source and the season of the year bear on the amount of natural light available to the plants. In the Northern Hemisphere

Table 9-4   LIGHT REQUIREMENTS OF SOME POPULAR HOUSE PLANTS

Low-light requirement

Aglaonema commutatum	Chinese evergreen	*Ficus elastica*	Rubber plant
Asparagus spp.	Asparagus fern	*Fittonia* spp.	Fittonia
Aucuba japonica	Goldust plant	*Ligularia* spp.	Leopard plant
Aspidistra elatior	Iron plant	*Nidularium* spp.	Bromeliad
Calceolaria spp.	Calceolaria	*Pandanus* spp.	Pandanus
Chamaedoria elegans	Parlor palm	*Philodendron* spp.	Philodendron
Cordyline terminalis	Hawaiian ti plant	*Epipremnum* spp.	Pothos
Dracaena spp.	Dracaena	*Sansevieria* spp.	Snake plant
Dieffenbachia spp.	Dumbcane	*Spathiphyllum* spp.	Spathe flower

Moderate-light requirement

Anthurium spp.	Flamingo flower	*Monstera* spp.	Monstera
Begonia spp.	Begonia cultivars	*Peperomia* spp.	Peperomia
Chlorophytum comosum	Spider plant	*Pilea cadeirei*	Aluminum plant
Cissus spp.	Grape ivy	*Plectranthus* spp.	Swedish ivy
Dizygotheca spp.	False aralia	*Rhoeo spathacea*	Moses-in-a-cradle
Episcia spp.	Episcia	*Saintpaulia ionantha*	African violet
Fatsia japonica	Fatsia	*Saxifraga* spp.	Strawberry geranium
Ferns	(many species)		
Ficus benjamina	Weeping fig	*Senecio cruentus*	Cineraria
Ficus lyrata	Fiddle-leaf fig	*Sinningia speciosa*	Gloxinia
Helxine soleirolii	Baby tears	*Syngonium* spp.	Nephthytis
Hoya carnosa	Wax plant	*Tolmiea menziesii*	Piggyback plant
Maranta leuconeura	Prayer plant	*Zebrina pendula*	Inch plant

High-light requirement

Abutilon spp.	Chinese lantern	*Fatshedera lizei*	Fatshedera
Acalypha hispida	Chenille plant	*Gynura aurantiaca*	Velvet plant
Achimenes spp.	Rainbow flower	*Hedera helix*	English ivy
Aeschynanthus pulchera	Lipstick vine	*Hippeastrum* spp.	Amaryllis
Agave spp.	Agave	*Iresine herbstii*	Bloodleaf
Bromeliads	(many species)		
Camellia spp.	Camellia	*Kalanchoe* spp.	Live-forever
Carissa grandiflora	Natal plum	*Pelargonium* ✕*hortorum*	Geranium
Citrus spp.	Orange, lemon	*Persea americana*	Avocado
Clerodendrum spp.	Bleeding heart	*Rosa* spp.	Rose
Codiaeum spp.	Croton	*Stephanotis* spp.	Stephanotis
Coleus spp.	Coleus	Succulents	(many species)
Euphorbia spp.	Poinsettia	Cacti	(many species)

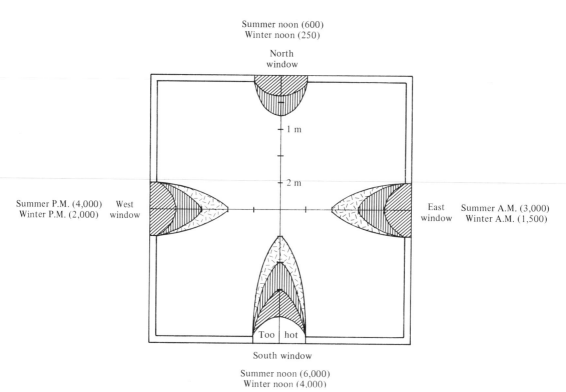

Summer noon (600)
Winter noon (250)

North
window

1 m

2 m

Summer P.M. (4,000)   West
Winter P.M. (2,000)   window

East   Summer A.M. (3,000)
window   Winter A.M. (1,500)

Too | hot

South window

Summer noon (6,000)
Winter noon (4,000)

Figure 9-20 Distances for growing high-, moderate-, and low-light house plants. Light values are measured in foot-candles.

high-light-requiring plants do best in south-facing windows and low-light-requiring plants do best in north-facing windows where they rarely receive direct sunlight (Figure 9-20). The distance from a window is a consideration since the inverse square rule of decreasing intensity tends to hold under this situation (Figure 9-21). Glass reflects close to 8 percent of solar radiation and filters out ultraviolet radiations, so that with changes in solar angle throughout a day, the total light impinging on a plant is rarely more than 40 to 50 percent of that received by a plant in a garden plot. Even though the light intensity is considerably reduced in any window, low-light-requiring plants are usually placed in north windows because they may be heat- or light-damaged by direct sunlight from south, east, or west windows.

Several other factors must be considered in house plant lighting. Not only is there a distance effect in light, there is also a distance effect in temperature. In summer, plants immediately adjacent to windows receive considerable heat; the resulting increase in evapotranspiration requires careful attention to watering. In winter in northern climates, there is a steep temperature gradient; the temperature on a window sill may actually be close to freezing, while the air temperature a meter away will be adequate.

Starting vegetable or flower seeds for transplantation presents the same

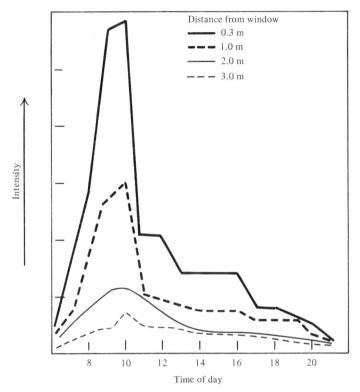

Figure 9-21 Light intensity through an east-facing window throughout a summer day.

problems of temperature and water control, but the need for adequate light is even more critical. Most vegetable and flower plants are sun plants, requiring high levels of balanced radiation for proper development into thrifty, dark green, compact plants. In order to obtain these desirable characteristics, light intensities and careful control of radiation balance are important. Failure to provide adequate red–far red balance results in semietiolated, succulent plants that either die upon transplanting or require some time to recover. To provide adequate light levels where fluorescent lighting is used, lamps should be placed as little as 5 to 10 cm (2 to 4 in.) above the plants, with this distance maintained as the plants elongate. To provide radiation balance incandescent lamps, which are high in red–far red, can be used in conjunction with fluorescent lamps or cool white and warm white florescent lamps can be combined. Even when some natural light is available, high red–far red is indicated. Since the plants are to be out-planted, maintaining relatively low temperatures during seedling development will reduce the time needed for hardening off, decrease etiolation and succulence and allow the transplants to start regrowth quickly. Small circulating fans can be used to control any temperature increase caused by the incandescent lamps.

SUPPLEMENTARY READINGS

Bickford, W. D., and S. Dunn. 1972. *Lighting for Plant Growth.* Kent State University Press, Bowling Green, Ohio.

Boardman, N. K. 1977. Comparative photosynthesis of sun and shade plants. *Annu. Rev. Plant Physiol.* 28:355–377.

Cathy, H. M., and L. F. Campbell. 1980. Light and lighting systems for horticultural plants. *Hort. Rev. 2.*

Evans, L. T. 1975. *Daylight and the Flowering of Plants.* W. A. Benjamin, Reading, Mass.

Hendricks, S. B. 1980. *Phytochrome and Plant Growth.* Carolina Biology Readers, Burlington, N.C.

Kendrick, R. E., and B. Frankland. 1976. *Phytochrome and Plant Growth.* Studies in Biology No. 68. University Park Press, Baltimore, Md.

Levitt, J. 1980. *Responses of Plants to Environmental Stress.* Vol. 2. *Water, Radiation, Salt and Other Stresses.* 2nd ed. Academic Press, New York.

McNair, J. K. 1975. *The Facts of Light About Indoor Gardening.* Ortho Books, San Francisco.

Manaker, G. H. 1981. *Interior Plantscapes.* Prentice-Hall, Englewood Cliffs, N.J.

Salisbury, F. B. 1982. Photoperiodism. *Hort. Rev. 4.*

Senger, H. (ed.). 1980. *The Blue Light Syndrome.* Springer-Verlag, Berlin.

Shropshire, W., Jr., and H. Mohr (eds.). 1983. Photomorphogenesis. *Encyclopedia of Plant Physiology.* New Series. Vol. 16A. Springer-Verlag, New York.

Smith, H. (ed.). 1981. *Plants and the Daylight Spectrum.* Academic Press, New York.

Vince-Prue, D. 1975. *Photoperiodism in Plants.* McGraw-Hill, New York.

Zeevaart, J. A. D. 1976. Physiology of flower formation. *Annu. Rev. Plant Physiol.* 27:321–348.

Note: A comprehensive listing of the light requirements of common ornamental plants is included in the seed catalog of the Geo. W. Park Seed Co., Greenwood, S.C. Useful information on light requirements is found in the catalogue of Thompson and Morgan, Jackson, N.J.

C H A P T E R   1 0

BIOLOGICAL INTERACTIONS

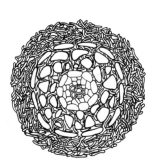
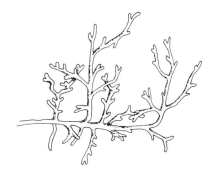

ENVIRONMENTAL FACTORS

Competition

The growth, development, and physiology of plants is frequently studied under controlled experimental conditions where the plant is not being influenced by other plants. This allows an accurate assessment of the ability of the plant to express fully its genetic potential. However, it is obvious that this does not occur under natural conditions. In the field, garden and in the home plants are exposed to an environment in which some plants are in the immediate vicinity of or in actual physical contact with other plants. Under these conditions plants interact in many ways that affect their development. A general term for these interactions is competition. Competition is not, as the name might suggest, the pitting of one plant against another nor is it usually an active opposition or struggle among the plants. There are, however, only finite amounts of water, mineral nutrients, and space in an area, and the success of a plant—determined by its ability to grow and to complete its life cycle—depends upon its capacity to obtain these materials from its environment. Success can also be measured in other terms. People grow plants for food, fiber, oil, and esthetic satisfaction, and competition among plants may either aid or detract from what we want of the planting.

We can illustrate some of the effects of competition by visualizing a test plot of $1m^2$ to be planted in radish (*Raphanus sativus*). If one plant is grown in that area, competition will be nonexistent, and it can be expected that the plant will express its full genetic potential. Suppose, however, that many hundreds of plants are placed in the same space. The total mass of the planting will increase greatly, but the weight of individual plants will decrease in a predictable, logarithmic fashion with a geometric increase in number (Figure 10-1). Even if the test planting receives optimum water and fertilizer, the growth of individual plants will decrease as the population increases. A planting of strawberry (*Fragaria* spp.) may not be limited by competing plants the first year, but in successive seasons, if the number of plants in the plot is allowed to increase, a point will be reached when the crowding and competition will limit the yields and thinning will be economically advisable (Figure 10-2).

There are a large number of factors that cause such alterations in growth potential. Some of them are obvious. In a population the individual plants are competing for available water, nutrients, and light. Those with larger or more efficient root systems possess a selective advantage for acquisition of the soil solution. Flowering plants may also compete with soil organisms for nutrients and water. In a mixed planting those species that have higher requirements for one or more mineral nutrients may be favored or may become nutrient-deficient. In general, competition among plants of the same species or cultivar is more severe than competition among plants of different species. Several reasons have been advanced to explain this finding. It is possible that the requirements of the different species are slightly different or that different species have different sensitivities to environmental hazards like disease, insect depredations, or

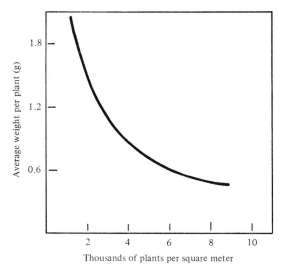

Figure 10-1 Effect of competition on development of radish plants.

pollutants. In a crowded planting the penetration of light is decreased, photosynthesis of shaded plants decreases, and therefore the amount of sugar synthesized for energy and growth decreases. Smaller plants may be completely shaded, while taller plants are favored. The amount of water and nutrients supplied can be controlled in garden plantings, but the amount of light supplied cannot be, and so light is frequently the limiting factor in crop growth and development.

In garden plantings there is also competition for root space, not only to obtain water and nutrients, but also simply for space. If genetically identical

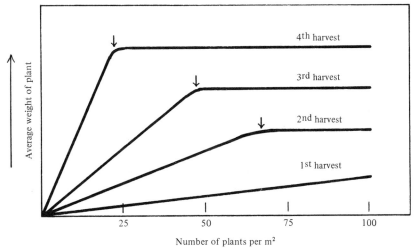

Figure 10-2 Relation between strawberry plant population and weight of individual plants. Arrow shows point where competition starts.

tomato plants are individually grown in a series of pots of increasing size and all receive adequate amounts of water and nutrients and equal light, those in the smaller pots do not develop as well. They flower more sparsely and fruits remain small and mature slowly. Similarly, if root space is limited, competition among the same or different species may significantly slow down development and maturity. The reasons for this are not fully understood, although it has been suggested that substances released from roots may affect the growth and function of other roots.

Dense stands of plants are growing in an environment where wind speed is greatly reduced. Stomatal function in transpiration and the uptake of carbon dioxide for photosynthesis are altered which, in turn, affects water and mineral uptake, leaf temperatures, and the rates of photosynthesis. Relative humidity remains elevated, further repressing transpiration. The high air, soil, and plant moisture levels tend to make the plants more susceptible to a number of bacterial and fungal diseases. There is also the danger of a particular disease sweeping through a planting since the spores of the pathogen have only a short distance to travel between susceptible plant hosts. These problems of dense planting are as important in a greenhouse or in a group of house plants as in garden and field plantings.

Plant spacing relative to competition is of considerable practical importance. Carrots (*Daucus carota*) may be planted with close spacing to obtain small, tender, and usually sweeter tap roots for table use or with less crowded spacing to obtain larger, longer, and firmer roots for cooking. Growth of other vegetables for home or market use can be similarly managed to develop smaller or larger products. Brussels sprouts, cauliflower, eggplant, bell peppers, and many other vegetables can be appropriately spaced depending on needs and the market. At wide spacing pea plants will continue to flower and fruit for a longer period of time than with close spacing and it may be possible to obtain more than one crop in a season. Where water, one or more mineral nutrients, or any other environmental factor is limiting, spacing must be carefully controlled. For example, in semiarid regions where soil moisture levels are quickly depleted, wide spacing facilitates development of large root systems and reduces the root competition for moisture that could be excessive in closely spaced rows.

Interplanting, the alternation of rows of one species with another, must also consider several aspects of competition. The possibility of utilizing a legume that fixes nitrogen between rows of a high-nitrogen-requiring plant like corn is of considerable interest because of the high cost of nitrogenous fertilizer. Row widths and the direction of rows become important because of competition for light; as the corn grows it can shade the smaller legume. Similarly, in flower or vegetable beds taller plants should not be placed in front of shorter ones.

Except for large-scale farming operations, spacing for species of horticultural interest has not usually been determined. In part this is because the experimentation and calculations are not usually cost effective, and the variability in growing conditions from place to place is too difficult to evaluate. Observation and trial and error seem to be the best available guide.

Weeds

A weed is usually defined as a plant growing where it is not wanted; a rose bush in a cabbage patch would be a weed. The unwanted species becomes a competitor with the desired crop for light, space, water, and nutrients. It is conservatively estimated that crop losses due to weeds are between 8 and 12 percent a year. As is true of other flowering plants, weeds are divided into annuals (pigweed, lambs-quarters) and biennials (wild carrot, burdock) that reproduce solely by seed and perennials that reproduce by seed and by division of roots (dandelion, plantain), stolons (chickweed, knotgrass), or rhizomes (bindweed, Johnsongrass). This reproductive classification bears directly on the choice of control methods. Since seedlings and young plants are most susceptible to control methods, identification of weeds at early stages of growth is important. Weeds are highly successful plants. They are called opportunistic plants, which means they are aggressive, highly adaptable, tolerant of wide variations in environmental conditions, and able to grow vigorously under conditions incapable of supporting the growth of vegetable or flower crops. A visit to a weed-choked vacant lot will illustrate this point. Many common weeds have astoundingly high reproductive capacities. An annual weed can produce up to 20,000 seeds and several common perennial weeds produce over 15,000 seeds each year. These seeds are easily disseminated; dandelion, milkweed, ragweed, and burdock are examples. In contrast to seeds of most fruits and vegetables, many weed seeds are very long-lived, capable of retaining viability in soil for decades. Of 100 seeds of weed species tested, half retained viability for over 20 years in soils.

Root growth of weed species is extensive. Bindweed (*Convolvulus* spp.) roots can spread laterally for 6 m (19.8 ft) and grow vertically for 5 m. Canada thistle (*Cirsium arvense*) roots will spread laterally for 3 m and penetrate 20 m (65 ft) under favorable conditions. Roots, rhizomes, and stolons are capable of regenerating the entire plant from segments less than 2 cm ($\frac{3}{4}$ in.) in length. Cutting off the stem of such plants or breaking up root stocks will not only not eradicate the plant, but will probably increase the number of plants.

In addition to the need to limit competition with the desired plantings, there are several other reasons for controlling weedy species. Some are health hazards. Ragweed (*Ambrosia* spp.) produces pollen to which sensitive people are allergic, and a large number of weeds contain substances capable of causing skin rashes, hallucinogenic states, or potentially fatal internal poisoning. Some species of weeds are hosts for disease organisms that can also infect crop species and others are food and shelter for insects that also attack desirable species.

Management of weeds involves several different strategies (Table 10-1). Among the mechanical methods, hand pulling is practical only in small garden plots, but is very effective when done consistently. Since many weed rootstocks are capable of regenerating the whole plant, weed pulling works best when the soil is wet and the entire rootstock can be removed. Hoeing is a traditional control method, dating back thousands of years. It, too, requires repeated attention, at least until the desired plants are large enough to compete successful-

Table 10-1   SUMMARY OF METHODS USED TO CONTROL WEEDS

Mechanical	Biological	Chemical
Hand pulling	Crop rotation	Selective herbicides
Hoeing	Parasitism	Nonselective herbicides
Cultivation	Competition with	
Tilling	vigorous plants	
Mowing		
Burning		
Smothering		

ly with the weed species. Cultivation methods (tilling and mowing) are designed to remove the tops of the weeds frequently to deplete food reserves in the rootstocks and to prevent the formation of seeds. Many annual and some perennial weeds can be controlled by cultivation, although these methods are usually only partly successful. Burning is rarely practiced, but may be useful when a weedy area is to be brought into cultivation. There is always a danger of fires getting out of control and many communities have stringent regulations on open fires.

Smothering techniques may, under some circumstances, prevent weeds in gardens from becoming established. This may be done by mulching plots with thick layers of organic materials such as well-rotted manure, compost, shredded bark, or hay. Organic mulches may contain weed seeds, but normal composting methods that raise the temperatures to 60° to 70° C (140° to 160° F) will heat-kill many common weed seeds. Synthetic mulches, such as plastic, are also used. Plastic sheeting with holes through which the crop plant grows prevents weed seeds from being deposited and stops their development. Appropriate mulching may also benefit the crop plants by conserving water and increasing the organic content of the soil. During periods when the soil is not covered by the plantings, weeds can develop quickly. The use of a cover crop in between plantings can be effective. Buckwheat, rye, or alfalfa are commonly planted.

Rotation of plantings is sometimes useful in reducing the weed population in soils, particularly for those weeds that accompany particular crop plants. It usually requires a three- to four-year cycle to be effective. Allowing a plot of ground to remain fallow without any crop can be effective if coupled with cultivation methods to prevent seed production.

Several successful weed control procedures are based on parasitism, the use of highly specific insects whose food supply is entirely the weed species. The introduction of moth borers almost completely eliminated cactus (*Opuntia* spp.) which had been brought into Australia, and St. Johnswort (*Hypericum per-foratum*) has been controlled with beetles. Extreme caution must be exercised before introducing a pathogen or parasite to control weeds since there is always the danger of discovering, too late, that the control has become a more serious problem than the weed.

In some situations vigorously growing plants can successfully compete with the weeds. No weed control method for lawns is as effective as a well-established turf.

Weeds may be planted inadvertently in mass plantings, such as plantings of grasses and grains. In recent years, governments have organized testing laboratories that determine the number of species and amounts of weed seed present in a seed lot and certify the seed for agricultural plantings. The percentage of weed seeds in lawn grass seed and in some cereal grains is usually given. Seed lot contamination is not usually a problem for plants used in horticulture or gardening.

Chemical weed control is undoubtedly the most extensively used method. Arsenic compounds, copper salts, and borax were used during the nineteenth and early twentieth centuries, but have almost entirely been superseded by organic chemicals. The history of organic weed control substances (herbicides) dates from the early 1940s when the first of these, 2,4-dichlorophenoxyacetic acid (2,4-D), was introduced. There are now more than 200 registered herbicides available under many trade names and others continue to appear. They are divided into those that will nonselectively kill or repress all plants and those that are more or less selective, killing only certain species. Some selectivity can also be achieved by regulating the concentration presented to the plants. Among herbicides in both categories, some are designed to be applied as foliage treatments, while others act following application to the soil and uptake by the plant roots. Some are local, affecting only the plant part to which they have been applied, while others are systemic, being transported throughout the plant. Herbicides can also be divided into those that are employed prior to the planting of the crop (preplanting treatment of soil), those that are applied before the seed germinates (preemergent application to soil), and those that are applied after plants develop (postemergent application to soil or plants).

Criteria used in the development of an herbicide include high phytotoxicity, low cost, convenience of application, selectivity (when desired), persistence (when desired), and low toxicity to other life forms. Toxicity to mammals is determined by laboratory tests with animals, usually mice. Results are reported in terms of the lethal dose that will kill 50 percent of the test population (LD_{50}). The LD_{50} is calculated as grams of test substance per kilogram of body weight of the test animals. The larger the amount of test compound needed to reach an LD_{50} number, the less toxic is the compound. Although there is always the question of whether mice are equivalent to Men, the LD_{50} is a reasonably good way of determining relative toxicity to mammals. It must, however, be remembered that some herbicides leave residues on the surface of the plant and internally, and caution is necessary before handling and eating plants that have been treated. Some herbicides contain contaminants that are extremely toxic to humans and other animals.

The extensive use of herbicides and insecticides has required development of detailed legal and social controls. Before marketing, all pesticides must be registered with the appropriate federal agency and the labels must meet stringent requirements. Labels must contain full information on the chemical composition of the herbicide and other ingredients. LD_{50} information, any necessary use precautions, antidotes and other health information, and, where applicable, the international skull and crossbones symbol for poisons, must appear on the label.

It cannot be overemphasized that directions for use of any herbicide or insecticide should be followed precisely.

Depending on the intended use, herbicides can be manufactured in a variety of formulations. Granular and powdered forms are applied to the soil and mixed with mulches. Many are sold as wettable powders (WP) or are already in solution. They may contain surfactants (surface-active agents) which include stabilizers, emulsifiers, wetting agents, adhesives and stickers, and dispersers.

Surfactants assist in allowing the herbicide to reach the absorptive surface and remain in place over a period of time. The most common mode of application is spraying. Aerial presentations should be done with extreme caution. Many of the formulations are volatile and should not be used during hot weather; such information is included on the label. Where the weed is in intimate contact with the desirable planting, it is necessary to apply the herbicide directly on the leaves of the plant to be killed. Spraying can also result in drift, with or without wind, and applications should never be made when it is windy. There have been many lawsuits resulting from damage done to plants on other people's property by drifting pesticides. Several common herbicides are lethal to useful insects such as honeybees, and most governmental agencies proscribe spraying during periods when orchards are being bee-pollinated. The laws regarding inadvertent introduction of herbicides into springs, streams, or other bodies of water are equally restrictive. Herbicides can also kill aquatic life and may be carried or leached to contaminate water supplies. Persistence in soil is a mixed blessing. Although it may prolong the effective life of the herbicide, it may also prevent crop plants from developing and any decision to use a persistent herbicide should be made with some forethought.

The mode of action of many herbicides is only incompletely known. Some appear to alter or interfere with one or another plant metabolic process. Others block a single step in a metabolic process, such as the synthesis of chlorophyll, steps in photosynthesis, respiration, or nucleic acid metabolism. A few seem to be general cell poisons, blocking cell growth or interfering with the metabolism of plant growth-controlling substances. A few kill the plant immediately, but others require up to two weeks to be effective. Killing noxious weeds may not inactivate their toxins; poison ivy (*Rhus Toxicodendron*) leaves, stems, and roots are still dangerous when dead and should not be handled or burned.

Under special circumstances it is cost-efficient to treat an area with one of the soil fumigants. Many of the formulations are actually biocides, killing all or most of the living organisms in soil. Since many soil microorganisms and soil animals are useful, fumigation must be done with caution and an awareness of possible consequences.

A comprehensive weed-control program usually involves a combination of methods. Chemical control combined with cultivation procedures is usually more effective than either method alone. Modern chemical technology has developed formulations of several pesticides that are supplied simultaneously to increase the spectrum of weeds controlled or to permit a single application of both herbicides and insecticides. The cautions that apply to the use of single herbicides apply with even more force to applications of multiple spectrum combinations.

Allelopathy

Flowering plants produce a variety of complex organic compounds that are excreted from living roots and leaves. Dead plant parts also leach these materials. Once in the soil some of these compounds inhibit seed germination or seedling growth of other plants, while some of these compounds can stimulate the growth of other plants. This interaction between plants has been named allelopathy. It must be distinguished from competition for water, minerals, or light.

The earliest report of this phenomenon seems to be a 300-year-old Japanese document which mentions the harmful effect of rain or dew washings from needles of Japanese red pine (*Pinus densiflora*) onto plants growing underneath the tree. This phenomenon was confirmed in the 1960s. Observant gardeners and greenhouse workers have long been aware of the deleterious and stimulating effects of certain plants on other plants. But the scientific validation of these casual observations was slow in coming. Many allelopathic effects have been demonstrated by making water extracts of various plant parts and testing these extracts for their effect on seed germination and seedling growth of numerous horticultural, agricultural, and wild plants.

A variety of plants are used as "smother crops"; they are planted expressly to suppress the growth of weeds presumably through competition, but allelopathy may also be involved. Such plants as barley (*Hordeum*), rye (*Secale*), and other cereals, as well as sweet clovers (*Melilotus*) and sunflower (*Helianthus annuus*) have long been used for such purposes. The roots of a number of smother crops produce water-soluble compounds that inhibit the growth of many plants.

Many weeds produce allelopathic compounds that have deleterious effects not only on other plants in nature, but also on crop plants. Extracts of leaves and fruits of piru (*Schinus molle*), a weedy plant in some areas of Mexico, strongly inhibit seed germination and seedling growth of cucumber (*Cucumis sativus*) and wheat (*Triticum*). Canada thistle (*Cirsium arvense*), a noxious and ubiquitous weed of cultivated and open areas, produces allelopathic compounds that inhibit seed germination and seedling growth of itself, perennial rye (*Lolium perenne*), and a forage crop (*Trifolium subterraneum*). Other examples are given in Table 10-2.

A number of crop plants, in addition to the smother crops mentioned above, have allelopathic effects on certain weeds. Kentucky-31 fescue (*Festuca elatior*), a forage grass, excretes compounds from its roots that inhibit the growth of black mustard (*Brassica nigra*) and birds-foot trefoil (*Lotus corniculatus*). This type of effect could be taken advantage of in breeding programs for the production of allelopathic compounds against specific weeds. Biological control of weeds certainly seems feasible. One extensive study with almost 600 cucumber cultivars showed that 25 of them formed allelopathic compounds that inhibited the growth of several weedy plants.

There are a few examples of crop or ornamental plants that inhibit other ornamentals. The seed coats (hulls) of sunflower, a seed commonly used in bird feeders, contain allelopathic compounds inhibitory to lawn grasses and many garden plants.

Table 10-2 SOME FLOWERING PLANTS THAT FORM ALLELOPATHIC COMPOUNDS

Plant Source		Deleterious Effects on	
Latin name	**Common name**	**Latin name**	**Common name**
Weeds			
Celosia argentea	Woolflower	*Pennisetum americanum*	Pearl millet
Lolium multiflorus	Italian ryegrass	*Lactuca sativa*	Lettuce
Agropyron repens	Quackgrass	*Triticum*	Wheat
Convolvulus spp.	Bindweed		Many test plants
Brassica spp.	Mustard		Many test plants
Cynodon dactylon	Bermudagrass		Many test plants
Asclepias syriaca	Common milkweed	*Raphanus sativus*	Radish
Chenopodium album	Lambs-quarters	*Zea Mays*	Corn
Setaria faberii	Giant foxtail	*Zea Mays*	Corn
Setaria glauca	Yellow foxtail	*Zea Mays*	Corn
Digitaria sanguinalis	Crabgrass	*Zea Mays*	Corn
Polygonum pensylvanicum	Pennsylvania smartweed	*Glycine max*	Soybean
Tree and shrub species			
Quercus stellata	Post oak		Numerous herbaceous and tree species
Q. marilandica	Blackjack oak		Numerous herbaceous and tree species
Q. rubra	Northern red oak		Numerous herbaceous and tree species
Juglans nigra	Black walnut	*Malus* spp.	Apple
		Pinus strobus	Eastern white pine
		Betula papyrifera	Paper birch
Acer pseudoplatanus	Sycamore apple	*Betula alleghaniensis*	Yellow birch
A. saccharum	Sugar maple	*Betula alleghaniensis*	Yellow birch
Platanus occidentalis	Eastern sycamore		Reduced understory
Kalmia anguistifolia	Sheep laurel	*Picea mariana*	Black spruce
Crop plants			
Lupinus albus	White lupine	*Chenopodium album*	Lambs-quarters
		Amaranthus retroflexus	Redroot
Cereal grains		*Brassica Kaper*	Charlock
Cucumis sativus	Cucumber (some cvs.)	*Brassica hirta*	White mustard
		Panicum miliaceum	Broomcorn
Spinacia oleracea	Spinach cv. F_1 Selma	*Spinacia oleracea*	Spinach cv. Early Hybrid
Glycine max	Soybean	*Sorghum*	Semidwarf cvs.
Helianthus annuus	Sunflower hulls		Lawn grasses, ornamental flowers

There are also a number of tree species, including important ornamentals, that produce allelopathic compounds inhibitory to herbaceous and woody plants growing under the trees. Examples are several of the oaks including white oak (*Quercus alba*), sugar maple (*Acer saccharum*), and black walnut (*Juglans nigra*). Poor growth of garden flowers or lawn grasses under these tree species is not necessarily due to too much shade or competition for nutrients and water, but may be a result of the leaching of allelopathic compounds.

Allelopathy must be considered in the conversion of weedy, overgrown areas to fields and gardens. Successful seed germination and seedling growth may well be hindered because of allelopathic compounds in the soil coming from dead roots and leaf litter of various weeds.

DISEASES

Origins of Disease and Natural Resistance to Disease

The economic losses, worldwide, due to crop devastation by viral, bacterial, and fungal pathogens are enormous and seem a never-ending upward spiral. It is curious that descriptions of fungi have been published since the late seventeenth century, but these microorganisms were not associated with a specific plant disease until the early nineteenth century when smut of wheat was convincingly shown to be caused by a fungus. The first bacterial disease of plants to be described was fireblight of pear. This disease was reported in the late nineteenth century, just two years after the first description of a bacterial disease of a higher animal, anthrax, was published. The first viral disease of plants to be reported was tobacco mosaic in 1885, but it was initially thought to be a bacterial disease. It would be another 20 years before the biological nature of the virus particle would begin to be understood.

The disease-producing agents must first gain entry into the plant. Stomata and wounds allow bacteria and fungi to enter subepidermal tissues. These organisms may also produce enzymes that soften plant cell walls, facilitating their entry into the plant's interior. Plants provide some barriers to entrance. The shape of a stoma or the thickness of a cuticle may slow down or prevent the entrance of the pathogen into leafy tissue. Wounds heal naturally by developing a corky layer which walls off or prevents the entrance of the potential pathogen.

Once inside the host plant, a disease may be established by the pathogen in a number of ways. Some pathogenic bacteria and fungi may produce a specific toxic compound, a phytotoxin, that kills plant tissue. The pathogen may enter water-conducting cells, clogging them and preventing their normal function.

The host plant may show a resistance and prevent the establishment of the pathogen. There is increasing evidence that plants can resist invading microorganisms by producing antibacterial and antifungal compounds. A commonly cited example is the resistance of onion bulbs with colored outer scales to the fungus causing the onion smudge disease. Chemicals in the dead, outer scale leaves prevent the growth of the pathogen. Production by the plant of specific inhibitory compounds may play a role in the resistance of pear cultivars to the bacterial fireblight disease and of apple cultivars to the fungal disease called scab.

Phytoalexins, which are compounds produced by some plants only in tissues where pathogens are present, appear to "ward off" invading microorganisms. Numerous natural compounds, such as tannins, compounds that are responsible for the brown color of tea, seem to provide a degree of protection against pathogens. Phytolectins, which are complex organic compounds isolated from seeds of legumes, may play a role in disease resistance of these plants by inhibiting soil bacteria and protecting legume seeds and young seedlings against fungal attack. Allelopathic compounds produced by plant roots may also aid the plant in resisting invasion.

Taking advantage of these genetically programmed mechanisms may be a way to enhance the natural disease resistance of important crop and garden plants. The plant geneticist has played a vital part, and will continue to do so, in breeding new horticultural varieties that are less susceptible to many common diseases. Tomato is an excellent example. Many new tomato cultivars are resistant to several fungal pathogens and to tobacco mosaic virus and some cultivars may be resistant to as many as five microbial diseases and to nematodes. Seed catalogues give specific information on the disease resistance of garden flowers and vegetables.

Viral Diseases

Viruses are all obligate, intracellular parasites; they are able to reproduce or multiply only when inside a living host cell. Infected plants show a wide range of symptoms and diseased plants are more often dwarfed or stunted than killed. There may be malformation of tissue leading to curvature of leaves as in leaf roll diseases. Patterns of flower color may be changed as in "broken" flowers, where the normal color is interrupted by colorless areas giving a streak effect. This is sometimes considered a desirable effect in ornamentals and is seen in sweet pea, petunia, stock, and tulip. Broken tulip flowers date from the sixteenth century and modern ones are often prized specimens. Nonbroken tulips should not be planted in areas where broken tulips have been grown because the virus persists in the soil for several years, even though it cannot reproduce there, and may infect susceptible cultivars.

The most common symptom of virus disease is the modification in leaves of the green pigment chlorophyll. In mosaic diseases chlorotic or yellow regions are interspersed with normal green areas. In yellows diseases the leaf chlorosis is usually nearly uniform. The effects of some mineral deficiency diseases (Chapter 7) are similar to these viral diseases, and the correct diagnosis is obviously important in determining the appropriate treatment.

Viral diseases are spread from plant to plant in a number of ways. Viruses may persist in the soil. Viruses also remain viable in vegetative parts of perennial plants such as bulbs, tubers, and roots, and these organs become a reservoir for transmission of virus to susceptible plants. Virus-infected nursery stock is also a common source. Some viral diseases are transmitted by some microorganisms, including fungi, mites, nematodes, and the parasitic angiosperm dodder. Viruses in the soil may enter living cells through wounds as when seed potatoes are cut or iris divided with dirty tools. Most pathogenic viruses are carried from plant to plant by sucking insects (vectors) in the taxonomic order Homoptera. Mosaic diseases are most often transmitted by aphids and yellows diseases by leafhoppers. Tobacco mosaic virus (TMV) is more usually spread by humans via contaminated hands or tools or cigarette smoke. A few diseases can be spread by other insects including whiteflies, spittle insects, mealybugs, and leafhoppers.

Virus-caused diseases are controlled through sanitation practices and destruction of insect vectors. The removal of virus-infected plants should be routine and is an obvious part of sanitation. Virus-infected plants should not be composted, but should be burned or bagged for disposal. Maintaining clean garden tools is perhaps less obvious. Where viral disease is suspected, tools used on these plants should be thoroughly washed with hot soapy water, dried, and then wiped with 70 percent alcohol or dilute sodium hypochlorite. Another line of attack is to eliminate insect and other vectors. Growing resistant cultivars and planting virus-free seeds or stock, where possible, is highly advisable.

Bacterial Diseases

The bacteria that cause plant diseases are not obligate parasites, as are the viruses and many fungi, but rather they are facultative parasites, which means they can live either in the soil using dead plant and animal remains as a source of food or in living plant hosts. These organisms belong to the large group of bacteria that are rod-shaped and do not form endospores (Table 10-3). Included with the pathogenic bacteria are the mycoplasma-like organisms, an unusual group of exceedingly small bacteria that do not form cell walls. These organisms are now known to cause as many as 40 yellows diseases formerly thought to be viral, including potato witches' broom and aster yellows. They also infect other flower and garden vegetables (gladiolus, phlox, carrots, lettuce, tomatoes, and others). Mycoplasma-like organisms that are pathogenic for plants are, like viruses, transmitted by leafhoppers and aphids.

Table 10-3   SOME PLANT PATHOGENIC BACTERIA

Genus	Diseases
Agrobacterium	Crown gall in more than 40 families, galls on black and purple cane raspberries, hairy root
Corynebacterium	Fasciation disease, gumming disease of various grasses, vascular wilts
Erwinia	Necrotic disease (fireblight), vascular wilts, blackleg of potato, crown rot
Pseudomonas	Wilts of many plants
Xanthomonas	Vascular diseases, leaf spot, leaf scald, gummosis, canker
Streptomyces	Scab of potato

Table 10-4   SOME PATHOGENIC FUNGI (DIVISION EUMYCOTA)

Taxonomic category	Genus	Diseases
Subdivision Mastigomycotina		
Class Plasmodiophoromycetes		
Order Plasmodiophorales	*Plasmodiophora*	Club root of crucifers
	Spongospora	Powdery scab of potatoes
Class Chytridiomycetes		
Order Chytridiales	*Synchytrium*	Black wart of potato
	Physoderma	Brown spot of maize
Class Oomycetes		
Order Saprolegniales	*Aphanomyces*	Root rot of pea
Order Peronosporales	*Peronospora*	Downy mildews
	Plasmopara	Downy mildews
	Pythium	Root rots, damping-off
	Phytophthora	Damping-off, late blights
	Albugo	White rust of crucifers
Subdivision Zygomycotina		
Class Zygomycetes		
Order Mucorales	*Rhizopus*	Soft rot of sweet potato, leak of strawberries, raspberries, peaches
Subdivision Ascomycotina		
Class Hemiascomycetes		
Order Taphrinales	*Taphrina*	Peach leaf curl, witches' broom of plum, pocket plums
Class Plectomycetes		
Order Erysiphales	*Erysiphe*	Powdery mildews of cereals, cucurbits, peas
Class Pyrenomycetes		
Order Spheriales	*Ceratocystis*	Dutch elm disease
	Venturia	Apple scab
	Glomerella	Bitter rot of apple
	Endothia	Chestnut blight
Order Hypocreales	*Gibberella*	Scab and seedling blights of cereals
	Claviceps	Ergot of cereals and grasses
Class Discomycetes		
Order Helotiales	*Monilinia*	Brown rot of stone fruits
	Sclerotinia	Water soft rot of vegetables
Subdivision Basidiomycotina		
Class Teliomycetes		
Order Uredinales	*Puccinia graminis*	Black stem rust of cereals
	P. malvacearum	Hollyhock rust
	Gymnosporangium	Apple and red cedar rust
	Cronartium	White pine blister rust
Order Ustilaginales	*Ustilago*	Smuts of cereals
	Tilletia	Wheat bunt
	Urocystis	Onion smut
Class Hymenomycetes		
Order Auriculariales	*Helicobasidium*	*Rhizoctonia* diseases, damping-off, stem canker, root rot, storage organ disease, foliage blight
Order Aphyllophorales	*Fomes*	White heart rot of hardwood trees
Order Agaricales	*Armillariella*	Root rot of orchard and other trees

(Continued

Table 10-4   SOME PATHOGENIC FUNGI (DIVISION EUMYCOTA) *(Continued)*

Taxonomic category	Genus	Diseases
Subdivision Deuteromycotina		
Class Hyphomycetes		
Order Moniliales	*Alternaria*	Early blight of potato, tomato
	Botrytis	Neck rot of onion
	Fusarium	Cabbage yellows, wilt of tomato, aster
	Rhizoctonia	White rot of onion
Class Coelomycetes		
Order Melanconiales	*Colletotrichum*	Onion smudge, bean anthracnose
Order Sphaeropsidales	*Phoma*	Black leg of crucifers
	Septoria	Late blight of celery, leaf spot of chrysanthemum

A common result of bacterial infection is rotting, where the bacteria secrete enzymes that dissolve cell walls. In potato tuber rot the bacteria destroy the tuber, and then, as the tuber disintegrates, the bacteria are released into the soil to become a source of further infection. Pathogenic bacteria may release toxins and the infected tissue first becomes chlorotic and then necrotic (dead). The lesions, slow-growing and limited in size, are dry and discolored. In vascular wilt diseases the bacteria produce large amounts of polysaccharide compounds that physically clog xylem vessels. The symptoms of some bacterial diseases reflect their production of growth-regulating substances or the increased synthesis of these compounds by the host plant in response to the bacterial infection. Leaf gall diseases, for example, show excessive development of shoots at the root-shoot junction (carnation, dahlia). Crown gall diseases of roses and fruit trees are characterized by large outgrowths at graft unions or pruning wounds.

Bacteria may be carried from plant to plant by rain or by insects, including the honeybee. The bacteria enter into tissues through natural openings, such as stomata and lenticels, or through wounds.

The control of bacterial diseases involves several lines of attack. Rigorous sanitation must be practiced, and the use of disease-free seed and disease-resistant cultivars, where possible, is essential. Crop rotation is advisable to prevent a buildup in the soil of pathogenic bacteria. The use of antibiotics has been successful for fireblight disease (streptomycin) and for mycoplasma diseases (tetracyclines). In some diseases, including bacterial wilt of cucumber, the insect vector (cucumber beetle) can be controlled by appropriate insecticides. As with herbicides, when using any insecticide, even one of low human toxicity like rotenone, it is highly important to follow directions for application and the recommended time after application before harvesting.

Fungal Diseases

Fungi are the cause of most plant diseases (Table 10-4). They may be either obligate or facultative parasites. A few of the more advanced fungi require two host plants in order to complete their life cycle from asexual to sexual stages of development.

The symptoms of disease associated with the obligate parasitic fungi include stunting and deformation of plant organs, while common symptoms associated with the facultative parasites include softening and rotting of tissues due to the breakdown of cell walls and the pectic compounds that glue plant cells together. Symptoms of rot develop rapidly and the affected tissues are soft and watery. Seedlings that damp-off show these characteristics.

Some pathogenic fungi produce toxins. The resulting blight diseases are distinguished by brown, necrotic lesions. In the toxin-induced vascular wilt diseases, symptoms include necrotic spots on leaves and desiccation of tissues. These are quite common in a number of garden vegetables (tomato, pea, cabbage, and many others). Other vascular wilt diseases are due to the growth of the fungus itself in the water-conducting cells of the xylem (Dutch elm disease). Some fungi release growth-regulating compounds that greatly modify the growth and appearance of the host plant. These responses include distorted leaf growth (cherry), premature loss of leaves (black currant), leaf galls (azalea), and club root (cauliflower and cabbage) where diseased roots are many times larger than healthy ones, but contain few normal vascular cells.

Fungi make enormous numbers of reproductive cells, called spores, which are sufficiently light to be carried by the wind from plant to plant. Water and insects also disseminate the spores. Fungal filaments, or hyphae, grow in the soil or on leaves and can penetrate directly into plant tissues as well as into stomata and wounded surfaces.

It is fortunate that fungal diseases are in general more easily controlled than viral or bacterial diseases. As for these other diseases, control begins with sanitation methods to eliminate or destroy the pathogen. Small amounts of soil may be pasteurized or watered with solutions of fungicides. Infected plant parts must be burned or bagged for disposal. Disease-free seed or fungicide-treated seed should be used where available. Using disease-resistant cultivars is important in being able to grow many vegetables to maturity in soil where the pathogenic fungus is normally present. Proper spacing between plants to permit good air movement is an important aid in controlling disease.

One unusual aspect of fungal disease control is related to the requirement by certain fungi of two host plants to complete their life cycle. The elimination of one host plant protects the other from disease. For example, wheat rust disease has been kept in check by eradicating barberry in wheat-growing areas, and white pine blister rust is not a problem if wild and cultivated currants and gooseberries are removed from white pine areas. In states where the disease is a problem, it is illegal to import these edible fruits, and there are restrictions on how near pines one can plant currant or gooseberries.

Rainy and cool weather patterns enhance the growth of most fungi and may make the use of fungicides an essential part of control. (Problems associated with the use of any pesticide are considered later in this chapter.) Some commonly used fungicides are given in Table 10-5; it is impossible to give an up-to-date, complete list because those in use today may be discontinued and new products are constantly being introduced.

Table 10-5   SOME COMMONLY USED FUNGICIDES

Type of Plant	Fungal disease	Fungicide
Lawns	Fusarium blights Dollar spot	Chlorothalonil, Dyrene Tersan
Fruits	Various	Captan plus ferbam plus an insecticide
Ornamental trees (horse chestnut, maple, London plane)	Leaf spots Twig blights	Maneb, zineb
Flowers	Rusts, mildews, wilts	Benomyl, captan, zineb
	Black spot (rose)	Benomyl, folpet, triforine
Vegetable crops seed diseases	Rot, damping-off	Thiram, captan
Various	Various	Benomyl, captan, maneb, zineb

INSECTS AND OTHER PESTS

Insects

There are at least 3 million species of arthropods, the taxonomic phylum that contains spiders, crustaceans, millipedes, and centipedes in addition to the insects. Over 80 percent of all animals are in this taxon. The class Insecta contains about a million species and, if the still-unclassified members are estimated, there may be 2 million (Table 10-6). Of these, about 15,000 are of direct importance to Man. Close to 3000 are pests of animals and about 2000 directly affect our food supply. Many insects are useful. The most obvious are honeybees and other pollinators of flowers and the silkworm, but the insects involved in the breakdown of litter and other debris and those that serve as food for other animals (not excluding people) also affect our lives. This fact is of great importance in our efforts to control undesirable species, since the loss of useful species and even the loss of species we label undesirable can seriously disrupt the Web of Life.

Insects are highly successful organisms in the evolutionary sense. They tend to have high reproductive rates and high reproductive potentials and many are adaptable to a wide range of environmental conditions. Reproduction is usually sexual, and some insects can also reproduce by parthenogenesis (the development of unfertilized eggs into adults, usually females) to permit a rapid increase in numbers when food supplies are adequate. The population explosions in aphids are due to parthenogenesis.

There are a number of variants in the life cycles in different taxa of insects which bear directly on the methods used in control. The dissemination of insects is rapid; not only can they crawl and fly, but they are also lightweight and so can be carried long distances by the wind, and on other animals. Many food and

Table 10-6   CLASSIFICATION OF THE PHYLUM ARTHROPODA

Taxon	Common Name	Number of Species
Class Xiphosure	Horseshoe crabs	4
Class Arachnida	Spiders, ticks, mites	55,000
Class Crustacea	Lobsters, crabs	25,000
Class Chilopoda	Centipedes	3,000
Class Diplopoda	Millipedes	8,000
Class Insecta	Insects	1,000,000+
Order Collembola	Springtails	2,000
Order Thysanura	Bristletails	700
Order Orthoptera	Grasshoppers, roaches, crickets	23,000
Order Isoptera	Termites	1,800
Order Dermaptera	Earwigs	1,100
Order Anoplura	Sucking lice	200
Order Hemiptera	True bugs	40,000
Order Homoptera	Aphids, scale insects, leafhoppers	20,000
Order Ephemeroptera	Mayflies	1,500
Order Odonata	Dragonflies	5,000
Order Neuroptera	Lacewings, ant-lions	4,600
Order Lepidoptera	Butterflies, moths, skippers	110,000
Order Coleoptera	Beetles	280,000
Order Trichoptera	Caddis flies	4,500
Order Diptera	True flies, mosquitoes, gnats	85,000
Order Siphonaptera	Fleas	1,100
Order Hymenoptera	Wasps, bees, ants	100,000
Order Thysanoptera	Thrips	6,000

flower plants have accidentally been bred or selected to provide excellent habitats and nutritional supplies for specific insects, adding to the problems of their control. In gardens and agricultural plantings, large stands of similar or identical plants may facilitate the rapid increase of insects that feed on these plants so that dramatic losses can be seen in a short time. Some insects infest and can destroy stored grains and fruit. In addition to the direct damage they inflict, insects can transmit and spread plant diseases. Virus-caused yellows and mosaics are carried by leafhoppers and other sucking insects, bacterial wilts and fireblight bacteria are spread by beetles, and serious fungal diseases like the Dutch Elm disease are also transmitted by beetles.

Insect control strategies are divided into several major categories: legal, cultural, physical, biological, and chemical.

Legal Control   Legal controls include quarantine laws designed to restrict the movement of pests, certification of plant freedom from pests, licensing of control methods, and surveillance and predictive determinations of the movement and environmental potential for insect depredations. Quarantine and certifications are generally the first line of defense and most governments have well-conceived regulations regarding importation and spread of infested materials. As our world has become more interdependent, the dangers of importing and dispersing pests have become greater and more difficult to regulate.

Cultural Control   The second strategy is called cultural control. The rotation over a period of years of planted species can reduce the number of species of insect pests and decrease the number of individuals. Even shifting the sequence of rows of vegetables or flowers can be useful. By removing the primary food source, an insect's life cycle can be disrupted, sometimes permanently.

In a few instances the timing of planting can reduce the possibility of insect infestation where the two life cycles are not synchronized. Some insects emerge, go through their heavy feeding stage, and lay eggs at the same time each year. Crops can sometimes be planted to mature in between insect generations, before or after heavy feeding times, and before or after egg laying. For example, the maggots of carrot rust fly may die of starvation if carrots are not planted until late in the season.

Another important aspect of cultural control is sanitation. The removal and destruction of infested plants, adequate cleaning up of residues left after harvest, and proper storage of seeds, bulbs, and corms is the cheapest and most effective method known for insect control. Infested residues should not be composted since resistant eggs may not be killed by composting temperatures.

Physical Control   Many injurious insects can be trapped. White flies, a serious pest in greenhouses and homes, are attracted to bright yellow surfaces; a thin film of grease on boards painted yellow can trap the insects and quickly reduce the population to manageable levels. The destructive Japanese beetle can be trapped in commercially available units placed in the garden. Since many insects see well in the deep blue and ultraviolet regions of the spectrum, the purple BLB fluorescent lamps attract flying insects into traps but are of limited value for commercial plantings.

It has recently been discovered that many insects produce chemicals that induce particular behaviors or developmental responses in other individuals of the same species. These substances, given the general name of pheromones, include sex attractants and substances that modify maturation or alter fecundity. Some of these have been synthesized and are now being used to attract males or even whole populations to where they can be captured and destroyed. Since the pheromones are active in low concentrations and are insect-specific, the potential for control is great.

Biological Control   A third strategy is biological control. Potential pests have natural enemies—other insects, birds, amphibians, and diseases caused by viruses, bacteria, and fungi. Deliberate use of these natural biological controls was probably invented by the Chinese who introduced predatory ants into citrus orchards to control boring beetles. The disruption of natural biological control by alteration of ecosystems has been an important factor in the present problems of pest control. While some environmental alteration has been necessary—the widespread planting of crops and the need for monocultures of important food plants—some modifications have been unnecessary and deleterious. There are several advantages in biological control. In many cases the introduced insect predator is persistent, control is relatively inexpensive, resistance of the pest to

Table 10-7 BIOLOGICAL CONTROL OF INSECTS: PREDATORS AND PARASITES

Organism or disease	Prey or parasitic host
Bacteria	
Serratia marcescens	Many moths and butterflies
Bacillus cereus	Many moths and butterflies
Bacillus popilliae	Milky spore disease of Japanese beetle grubs
Bacillus lentimorbus	Milky spore disease of grubs
Bacillus thuringiensis	Cabbage looper, larvae of other insects
Rickettsiella spp.	Japanese beetle
Fungi	
Beauveria spp.	Pine sawfly
Metarrizium spp.	Wireworm
Entomophthoraceous fungi	Many insect hosts
Viruses	
Nuclear polyhedrosis	Corn earworm, army worm, loopers
Granulosis	Loopers, various worms
Insects	
Vedalia beetle	Cotton scale
Lady beetle	Aphids, mealybug
Praying mantis	Tomato worm, borer
Apanteles	Tomato hornworm
Ooencyrtus	Elm spanworm
Encarsia	Whitefly
Aphytis	Red scale
Macrocentrus	Corn borer
Green lacewing	Aphids, thrips, mites
Flywasp	Eggs of many insects
Ground beetle	Gypsy moth
Exenterus	Pine sawfly
Chelonus	Corn borer
Itoplectis	Caterpillars
Tiphis	Japanese beetle
Trioxys	Walnut aphid
Nematodes	
Neoaplectana	Japanese beetle
Vertebrates	
Many birds	Many insects
Toads	Many insects

the predator is minimal, human health hazards are minimal, and usually any alteration of natural ecosystems has limited consequences. However, control is rarely quick, and for a particular crop in a particular season a severe insect infestation may require immediate action.

Biological controls for insects take a variety of forms. In several highly successful instances, sterilizing males by chemicals or irradiation and then releasing them to breed with wild females has reduced the insect population to manageable levels. This type of control is still under investigation for plant-infesting insects.

Some success has been achieved, mostly with agronomic crops, in breeding plants for insect resistance or tolerance. Such breeding programs involve shifting the time relations of the plant's life cycle, programming the plant to synthesize a distasteful compound, or altering plant structure so that the pest cannot get at the desired plant part. Inbred resistance to nematodes (which are not insects) has been highly successful for many vegetable crops including tomato. Other genetic research looks highly promising.

Insects, like all other forms of life, are subject to a variety of diseases and pests and a growing aspect of biological control utilizes the knowledge that entomologists have obtained on this topic. Viruses, bacteria, fungi, protozoans all attack insects, and insects also eat other insects (Table 10-7). At least some of these insect pathogens and predators have been developed commercially for use on horticultural and garden crops. These biological control agents are usually safe. If the research involved in evaluating their effects on the undesirable insect and on all other aspects of the ecosystem is carefully done, the future of such controls is bright.

Although long known to perceptive gardeners, the concept of companion planting has only recently been considered a useful tool in biological insect control. Plants that repel insects can be interplanted with vegetable or flower crops to keep them free of pests. Since many of the suggested repellent plants have not been rigorously tested for activity, a good deal of the information is hearsay and possibly unreliable. A partial list of companion plants and the insects said to be repelled is included in Table 10-8.

Chemical Control Most insect control strategies involve the use of chemicals. This, too, is not a modern development; the ancient Greeks used sulfur and the Chinese used arsenic compounds over 3000 years ago.

Decisions on if, when, and how to use insecticides must include consideration of a number of factors. The insect can be examined from several different, but equally important points of view. Some insects have high reproductive rates and rates of population increase, good dispersal mechanisms, and high adaptability with broad plant-feeding ranges. These are called *r*-strategists. They are rarely controlled by means other than insecticides. Leafhoppers are a typical *r*-species insect. *K*-strategists have lower fecundities, long generation times, poor dispersal mechanisms, and highly specialized food preferences. Many of the scale insects are *K*-species. They are usually difficult to eradicate or even control. Insecticides may not be very effective, and cultural practices may be the best

Table 10-8   BIOLOGICAL CONTROL OF INSECTS: COMPANION PLANTING

Plant	Pest repelled
Onion, garlic	Aphids
Horseradish	Potato bug
Larkspur	Aphids
Marigold	Nematodes
Crotalaria	Nematodes
Mint	Cabbage butterfly
Nasturtium	Cucumber beetle
Rosemary	Cabbage maggot
Sage	Carrot fly
Radish	Spider mite

means of control. Most of the common insect pests tend to be intermediate between r and K types.

Attention should also be paid to the habits and life cycles of the insects. Those insects that feed by sucking juices from plants are usually resistant to contact poisons and must be controlled with substances that are already within the plant such as the systemic insecticides. The chewing insects, on the other hand, are susceptible to insecticides on the leaf surfaces. Other insects are susceptible, because of their structure, to dusts or sprays that coat their bodies so that the compound enters through the respiratory system. The specific routes of penetration and the modes of action of various insecticides are complex topics beyond the scope of this book.

Until about 1940, most insecticides were inorganic compounds —arsenicals, fluorides, sulfur, or borax. These are primarily stomach poisons suppressing one or another part of the metabolic machinery of the insect. They have to be ingested and hence are ineffective against sucking insects. Some are still used against specific insects, but many are so poisonous to other animals that their use is restricted or banned. Some of the plant-derived insecticides were developed in the nineteenth century and are still effective. They are primarily contact poisons with good penetration into the insect. The nicotine alkaloids derived primarily from tobacco, rotenoids from the roots of jewel vine (*Derris* spp.), and the pyrethroids from flowers of pyrethrum (*Chrysanthemum cinerariifolium*) are, in some cases, the insecticides of choice because of low toxicity to mammals. They are, however, destroyed by heat and light and require frequent applications. Recently developed synthetic pyrethrums are more stable.

Beginning in 1939 with the discovery of the insecticidal properties of DDT, several thousand insecticides have been synthesized and exhaustively tested. They are grouped into four major chemical families: the chlorinated hydrocarbons (DDT, Chlordane), the organophosphates (Diazinon, malathion), the carbamates (Sevin, Furadon), and the pyrethroids (Allethrin, Resmethrin). Each family contains chemicals that are systemic or contact poisons. Depending on formulation, they are applied as dusts, granular soil additives, or sprays. Some insecticides have broad-spectrum effects, killing many insects including desirable species, while others are specific, affecting only one or a few related insects. Since many insect exoskeletons are composed of impenetrable cutins, (the exoskeleton of the lobster is a cutin), many insecticides are formulated with stickers, spreaders, and other compounds to facilitate entrance and distribution of the insecticide within the insect. It must be remembered that the biochemistry of insects is similar to that of other animals, including humans, domesticated animals, and birds. All insecticides should be considered potentially toxic and handled with extreme caution as noted on the label.

In any large population of organisms a few individuals fortuitously acquire, over evolutionary time, a mechanism that may prove to be effective in resisting the effects of a pesticide, such as a detoxification pathway or a barrier to penetration. When the population is stressed by a lethal factor, those that possess the genetic capacity for resistance will, because the lethal factor reduces their competition, increase and come to dominate the population. They will be resistant to the pesticide in concentrations normally used and it becomes necessary either to increase the concentration (which is usually effective for only a short time) or to switch to another pesticide. Many available formulations attempt to circumvent this problem by including several insecticides on the assumption that if one doesn't kill the insect, another will. To some extent, this concept has been successful, but its utility over the long term is doubtful. It is very likely that the chemical and biological war will continue.

Many insecticides are persistent, resisting degradation for several years. As an insect-control strategy this has much to recommend it, but it does present dangers for humans and other animals. Based on the testing and certification process, recommendations have been developed for the safe use of pesticides. Failure to follow such recommendations is frequently punishable under law. The container label is required to note how soon after application plants may be used for food. Strict and even overcautious adherence to these recommendations is wise. Pesticides must be recognized as dangerous materials and must be properly labeled and securely stored away from children and pets. Most municipalities and all health centers have or are in direct telephone communication with one of the poison-control centers in North America where precise information for treatment of pesticide poisonings can be obtained and relayed to the physician.

A major, still unsolved problem for homes, gardens, and agriculture is the safe disposal of pesticide containers, residues, and wash water. Materials deposited in sanitary landfills or poured into sewers can and do move into bodies of water where they disrupt plant and animal ecosystems and present potential dangers in drinking water. Few municipal agencies have considered this problem and the only recommendation has been to bury the material and containers—a wholly impractical solution in many cases.

Control of insect pests on house plants presents special problems. Dusts and sprays developed for gardens can rarely be used inside where food can be contaminated, where children and pets can be exposed, and where some formulations may damage fabrics and furniture. Breakdown of persistent pesticides is usually slow in the restricted conditions of pots whose soil usually lacks the spectrum of microorganisms that detoxify pesticides. Various formulations are available in pressurized spray cans that are effective against many of the common insect pests of house plants and are relatively nonhazardous to other animals. Not infrequently the carrier or propellant can damage plants and the nozzles should be kept at least 30 cm (1 ft) from the plant. Less persistent and less hazardous pesticides such as malathion can be used as sprays or as soil drenches. In general, the concentrations recommended for agricultural or horticultural use tend to be too high for the more delicate house plants and a reduction in concentration by a third is advisable.

Quarantine and sanitation are the first line of defense. Introduction of a recently purchased plant among clean plants may be an invitation to disaster and the new arrival should be kept away from the rest of the collection for several weeks. Removal of dead plant parts and attention to the accumulation of fallen leaves or flowers should be routine. The use of sterilized soil is also advisable. Red spider, spider mite, and white fly are among the more insidious pests of house plants and, not incidentally, among the more difficult to control. Frequent washing of the plants will help control many of these organisms and spraying with dilute soap solutions is valuable; 4 tablespoons of a mild dishwashing detergent in 1 gallon of water is effective. Mealy bugs can be controlled with a spray of 1 tablespoon of dishwashing detergent in 1 gallon of water. Insecticidal soaps are now commercially available. A good, all-purpose, inexpensive, and safe spray consists of $\frac{1}{4}$ teaspoon of olive oil, 2 tablespoons of baking soda, and 1 teaspoon of dishwashing detergent in 2 gallons of water. Alcohol on a cotton swab will kill individual aphids, mealy bugs, and some other pests of indoor plants without damage to the plant. Since eggs of many of these insects are inconspicuous and are resistant to pesticides, repeated treatments at three- to five-day intervals may be necessary to achieve control or eradication.

Nematodes

The invertebrate phylum Nematoda has 30,000 species of organisms known variously as eelworms, hookworms, or pinworms and includes a wide variety of animal pathogens. Reproduction is primarily sexual. Nematodes may be free-living, feeding on bacteria and fungi in soils and in water. Most of them are small, from 1 to 10 mm ($\frac{3}{8}$ in.) long, and they tend to be inconspicuous. Species in at least 12 genera are plant pests. These are divided into two groups, ectoparasites and endoparasites. The ectoparasites inhabit soils and feed by pushing a sharp stylet into root epidermal cells where they suck out protoplasm. Although the punctured root cell may die, the host plant is not killed, but growth and fruiting are severely reduced. The endoparasites invade plant cells and, as part of their parasitism, induce the formation of giant cells, root knots, and overgrowths of the roots that disrupt vascular connections between root and stem. Death of the host plant frequently occurs.

    The physiology and pathology of nematode infestations and infections of plants is of considerable research interest because of the crop losses caused by nematodes. Both the endo- and ectoparasites are attracted to plants by carbon dioxide released during respiration of root cells and by electrical charges on the roots. Immature (larval) stages as well as adults can infect root systems. Both can serve as carriers (vectors) for viral, bacterial, and fungal disease, and the disrupted roots can be secondarily invaded by disease organisms.

    Control strategies involve fumigation of seed beds and vegetable and flower beds with one of several volatile compounds. These require expert attention since the compounds are toxic to mammals and many plants, and the treated soils must be aerated for a week or more before planting. For small areas a pint of 35 percent formalin (formaldehyde) in 6.5 gallons of water is an inexpensive and fairly safe soil drench; aeration for several weeks before planting is necessary. Several organic, broad-spectrum insecticides have also been used for large areas, but only registered applicators are authorized to conduct such treatments. Planting stock, including woody perennials, can be treated with soil drenches. Hot water dips, 46° C (115° F) for 8 min, will kill nematodes found in bulbs and corms. It is always advisable to obtain planting materials certified to be free of nematodes.

Biological controls for nematodes are not generally available. Cucurbits seem to serve as nematode traps and the dwarf French marigold (*Tagetes* sp.) has been reported to repel them. Although nematodes are known hosts for bacteria, fungi, and protozoans, no effective interaction among these organisms has developed as a control. It is possible to breed some vegetable plants for nematode resistance, particularly tomatoes and cucumbers. Such information is supplied on seed packets. Some plants produce specific compounds called phytoalexins that are capable of killing a variety of invading parasites. Many legumes (lima beans, soybeans) produce phytolectins that are effective against nematodes, and there are indications that other vegetable and flower plants may also produce similar substances.

Other Pests and Predators

Garden plantings are subject to the depredations of domesticated and semidomesticated animals. Rabbits, groundhogs, mice and rats, squirrels, raccoons, and deer can devastate gardens and orchards. Adequate fencing, inserted at least 10 cm (4 in.) into the soil and sufficiently high to at least discourage the animals, is in many instances the best that can be done. Hardware-cloth cylinders around ornamental and fruit trees provide a barrier, but must be firmly embedded in the soil to prevent burrowing. Several repellents for rabbits, squirrels, deer, and dogs are available. A mixture in equal volumes of dried blood and napthalene flakes is the least expensive repellent; 1 teaspoon of Lysol plus 3 oz of Epsom salts in 1 gallon of water is used as an anti-squirrel spray. Several rodenticides are commercially available.

Birds, a serious pest of cereal grains, injure ornamental plantings, and are attracted to ripening fruits. Scarecrows, clanging tin pans, and even periodic cannon blasts have only limited value. In view of their importance in insect control and as indicators of environmental stability, killing birds is inadvisable and protection with nets is probably the gardener's only defense.

POLLUTION

The industrial regions of the world produce massive amounts of an almost unlimited number of substances capable of injuring plants. To some extent governments attempt to limit those pollutants that directly affect human health and occasionally those that may affect agronomic crop plants, but relatively little attention has been paid to those that injure home and garden plants. Industry may be responsible for the production of the bulk of the pollutants, but individuals contribute considerable quantities via the automobile, home heating units, and the use of a variety of common household products. While it is virtually impossible to prevent some pollution, the individual as citizen, horticulturist, agronomist, and gardener should be aware of the problem and attempt to have limits imposed on the amount and variety of pollutants.

Major pollutants of concern to the plant grower occur in air, water, and soil. Industrial and automobile sources contribute sulfur and nitrogen oxides convertible to acids that fall as acid rain. Even where acid formation does not occur, gaseous sulfur and nitrogen oxides can directly affect plant growth. In general, acidic precipitation does not present a serious threat to cultivated lands where adequate nutrients are provided and where soil pH and base saturation are controlled. Of more immediate concern are the increased concentrations of heavy metals (cadmium, copper, lead, and zinc) accompanying acid rain. These and the aluminum naturally present in soils are solubilized by acidic precipitation and can decrease plant growth. In regions where automobile exhausts persist, the brown and yellow smogs composed of unburned gasoline, ozone, and organic materials are damaging to plants, and present technology has been inadequately applied to prevent the pollutions. Breeding or selection of resistant cultivars is currently an active research area. In regions where smelting activities exist, waste products such as fluorine compounds are serious pollutants.

Water-borne pollutants include more compounds than are found in air. Metals, including aluminum and the heavy metals, leach from soil to accumulate in water used in homes and in gardens. Industrial wastes are deliberately or inadvertently discharged into rivers and lakes, eventually to flow from your water tap. Since few adequate regulations on these substances exist, the grower cannot know what in the water may be causing damage or whether the substances are accumulating in crops. Residues of pesticides leached from landfills or from sewage treatment plants and the effluent from home products poured down the sink or thrown away as garbage can all return in the water used in homes, gardens, and for irrigation.

Soils are the recipients of air and water pollutants as well as salts used in winter road maintenance and the previous burial of all sorts of strange things that suddenly appear when soil is tilled. It is fortunate that the capacity of soils to absorb and neutralize many potential pollutants is as great as it is. We are now beginning to realize that the capacity of soils to neutralize pollutants is not infinite and that, once the holding ability is exceeded, the degradation of soils is not easily reversible.

SUPPLEMENTARY READINGS

Bohmont, B. L. 1986. *The New Pesticide User's Guide.* Reston, West Nyack, N.Y.
Cox, G. W., and M. D. Atkins. 1979. *Agricultural Ecology.* Freeman, San Francisco.
Crafts, A. S. 1975. *Modern Weed Control.* University of California Press, Berkeley.
DeBach, P. 1974. *Biological Control by Natural Enemies.* Cambridge University Press, New York.
Dickinson, C. H., and J. A. Lucas. 1977. *Plant Pathology and Plant Pathogens.* Wiley, New York.
Dropkin, V. A. 1980. *Introduction to Plant Nematology.* Wiley, New York.
Duke, S. O. (ed.). 1985. *Weed Physiology.* Vol. 1. *Reproduction and Ecophysiology.* Vol. 2. *Herbicide Physiology.* CRC Press, Boca Raton, Fla.
Fedtke, C. 1982. *Biochemistry and Physiology of Herbicide Action.* Springer-Verlag, Berlin.
Flint, M. L., and R. van den Bosch. 1981. *Integrated Pest Management.* Plenum, New York.
Fry, W. E. 1982. *Principles of Plant Disease Management.* Academic Press, New York.

Gillott, C. 1980. *Entomology.* Plenum, New York.

Hance, R. 1981. *Interactions Between Herbicides and the Soil.* Academic Press, New York.

Hill, T. A. 1977. *The Biology of Weeds.* Studies in Biology No. 79. University Park Press, Baltimore, Md.

Holm, L. 1971. The role of weeds in human affairs. *Weed Sci.* 19:485–490.

Horsfall, J. G., and E. B. Cowling (eds.). 1977–1983. *Plant Disease: An Advanced Treatise.* Academic Press, New York.

Hoy, M., and D. Herzog. 1985. *Biological Control in Agricultural IPM Systems.* Academic Press, New York.

Klingman, G. C., F. M. Ashton, and L. J. Noordhoff. 1982. *Weed Science: An Advanced Treatise.* Academic Press, New York.

Kydonieus, A. F., and M. Berger. 1982. *Insect Suppression with Controlled Release Pheromone Systems.* CRC Press, Boca Raton, Fla.

Loehr, R. C. 1984. *Pollution Control for Agriculture.* Academic Press, Orlando, Fla.

Lowrance, R., B. R. Stinner, and G. L. House (eds.). 1984. *Agricultural Ecosystems: Unifying Concepts.* Wiley, New York.

Lucas, G. B., C. L. Campbell, and L. T. Lucas. 1985. *Introduction to Plant Diseases: Identification and Management.* Avi Books, Westport, Conn.

Mandava, B. 1985. *CRC Handbook of Natural Pesticides: Methods.* Vol. 1. *Theory, Practice and Detection.* Vol. 2. *Isolation and Identification.* CRC Press, Boca Raton, Fla.

Marshall, J. K. (ed.). 1977. *The Below Ground Ecosystem.* Colorado State University Press, Fort Collins.

Matthews, G. A. 1979. *Pesticide Application Methods.* Longman, London.

Metcalf, R. L., and W. H. Luckman. 1982. *Introduction to Insect Pest Management.* 2nd ed. Wiley, New York.

Nelson, R. R. 1973. *Breeding Plants for Disease Resistance: Concepts and Applications.* Pennsylvania State University Press, University Park.

Nickell, L. G. (ed.). 1983. *Plant Growth Regulating Chemicals.* 2 vols. CRC Press, Boca Raton, Fla.

Ormrod, D. P. 1978. *Pollution in Horticulture.* Elsevier, New York.

Page, B. G., and W. T. Thomson. 1986. *The 1986 Newly Revised Insecticide, Herbicide, Fungicide Quick Guide.* Thomson, Fresno, Calif.

Palti, J. 1981. *Cultural Practices and Infectious Crop Diseases.* Springer-Verlag, New York.

Pimentel, D. (ed.). 1981. *CRC Handbook of Pest Management in Agriculture.* 3 vols. CRC Press, Boca Raton, Fla.

Pirone, P. P. 1978. *Diseases and Pests of Ornamental Plants.* 5th ed. Wiley, New York.

Putnam, A. R., and W. B. Duke. 1978. Allelopathy in agro-systems. *Annu. Rev. Phytopath.* 16:431–451.

Pyenson, L. L. 1981. *Plant Health Handbook.* Avi Books, Westport, Conn.

Radosevich, S. R., and J. S. Holt. 1984. *Weed Ecology: Implications for Vegetation Management.* Wiley Interscience, New York.

Roberts, D. A. 1978. *Fundamentals of Plant-Pest Control.* Freeman, San Francisco.

Russell, G. E. 1978. *Plant Breeding for Pest and Disease Resistance.* Butterworth, London.

Sharvelle, E. G. 1979. *Plant Disease Control.* Avi Books, Westport, Conn.

Shepard, J. F. 1981. Protoplasts as source of disease resistance in plants. *Annu. Rev. Phytopath.* 19:145–166.

Sill, W. H., Jr. 1982. *Plant Protection: An Integrated Interdisciplinary Approach.* Iowa State University Press, Ames.

Thomson, W. T. 1984. *Tree, Turf and Ornamental Pesticide Guide.* Thomson, Fresno, Calif.

U.S. Department of Agriculture. 1980. *Suggested Guidelines for Weed Control.* U.S. Government Printing Office, Washington, D.C.

Vanderplank, J. E. 1984. *Host-Pathogen Interactions in Plant Disease.* 2nd ed. Academic Press, New York.

Ware, G. W. 1982. *Pesticides: Theory and Practice.* Freeman, San Francisco.

Weed Science Society of America. 1979. *Herbicide Handbook.* Champaign, Ill.

Wheeler, B. E. J. 1976. *Diseases in Crops.* Studies in Biology No. 64. University Park Press, Baltimore, Md.

Yepson, R. B., Jr. 1976. *Organic Plant Protection.* Rodale Press, Emmaus, Penn.

Note: The American Phytopathological Society has published compendiums of plant disease, a series of books dealing with diseases of specific crop and horticultural plants.

PART THREE

ENERGY

C H A P T E R   1 1

PHOTOSYNTHESIS

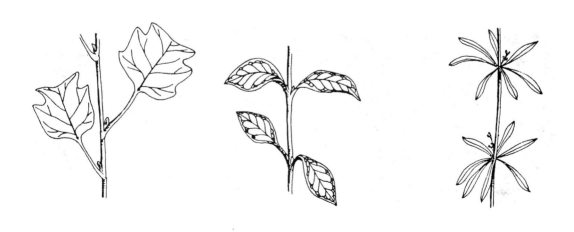

STRUCTURE OF THE PLANT PHOTOSYSTEM

It has been said that photosynthesis is the most important chemical process on earth. The evidence is overwhelming that the presence of oxygen in the atmosphere of the primitive earth was due to the oxygen-yielding photosynthesis of archaic blue-green algae that developed in the Precambrian era, about 2.5 billion years ago. The maintenance of a stable amount of oxygen in the present atmosphere is also due to the photosynthetic process, with a large proportion of the oxygen generated by algae living in the oceans. Without oxygen, life as we know it could not exist; the respiratory processes of most organisms are tied to oxygen and even a short period of deprivation can lead to death.

With the exception of blue-green algae and red algae, the structure of the photosynthetic apparatus of all plants is essentially the same, with identical pigments, unit structure, and photosynthetic pathways. The fact that there is essential unity in the photoapparatus of plants is an indication that it evolved early in the development of plants with nuclei (eukaryotes) and, being efficient, has been carried along during evolution in essentially the same form.

Chloroplasts

The photosynthetic unit consists of a flattened membrane or disc, the thylakoid, on and in which are embedded the pigments and other compounds required for the conversion of light energy into the chemical forms used in the fixation of carbon dioxide into sugar. A number of thylakoid discs are arranged on top of one another to form a stack called a granum (*pl.* grana), much like a stack of coins. Grana are connected by a membranous matrix called the intergranal lamellae (Figure 11-1). These interconnected membranes are enclosed in a double-membraned sac, the chloroplast membrane. The entire unit is called the chloroplast—a green plastid. Depending upon the plant and on the cells in which chloroplasts are found, there may be one or up to a hundred chloroplasts in a cell. The characteristic green color of leaves is due to the presence of large numbers of chloroplasts.

Chloroplasts are self-replicating entities, reproducing within cells by division. They originate as small, colorless bodies lacking mature structure and their development is controlled by light. Chloroplasts float in the cytoplasm of the cell and, if the cytoplasm moves, the chloroplasts also circulate in the cell. This movement of the cytoplasm, called cyclosis, is an energy-requiring process and is controlled by the cell in response to environmental factors. Although studied primarily in algae, it is believed that chloroplasts in higher plants can orient themselves to light so that they can capture the maximum amount of radiation

Table 11-1   CHARACTERISTICS OF PHOTOSYNTHESIS

1. It occurs in cells containing chlorophyll.
2. It proceeds only in the light.
3. Carbon dioxide and water are raw materials.
4. Sugars, oxygen, and water are end products.
5. Energy is stored.

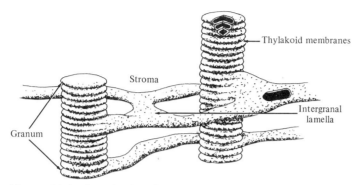

Figure 11-1 Organization of thylakoid membranes into grana.

for the photosynthetic process. The volume of the chloroplast not occupied by photosynthetic membranes consists of the stroma. The stroma is a gel-like mixture of enzymes involved in the carbon-fixation portion of the photosynthetic process. In some plants starch grains remain in the chloroplast for a period of time before being reconverted into sugar and moved out of the plastid. A pigment is a chemical compound capable of absorbing radiation, whether visible light, ultraviolet, or infrared. It is a law of photophysics that for radiation to cause some change, it has to be absorbed by a pigment. Since an important part of photosynthesis is the conversion of the energy of light into chemical energy used in the fixation of carbon dioxide, the pigments of the chloroplast are light absorbers. The color of these pigments is due to those wavelengths of visible light that are not absorbed by the pigment and are either reflected back to the eye or transmitted through the pigment.

Pigments

The most abundant pigments in the chloroplasts are the chlorophylls, which are responsible for the green color. There are two chemical types of chlorophyll differing only slightly in chemical composition, but with very different roles in the photosynthetic process. Chlorophyll *a* (Figure 11-2) is usually present in higher concentrations than chlorophyll *b*. In many plants the ratio between the two is close to 3:1; the ratio varies with the plant as well as with environmental conditions. Chlorophyll *a* seems to be more prone to chemical degradation than chlorophyll *b*, so that as green leafy vegetables age after harvest, the a:b ratio shifts closer to 1:1. This fact can sometimes be used to assess the time that has elapsed since harvest and can be important in grading of produce.

Although it is convenient to speak of chlorophylls *a* and *b*, they are not single compounds. Chlorophylls *a* are divided into two groups, those which capture light (antenna chlorophylls *a*), and those directly involved in the conversion of light to chemical energy (photoactive chlorophylls *a*). All of the chlorophylls *b* are antennae pigments; none participate directly in the light conversion process.

A second major group of pigments found in and on the thylakoid mem-

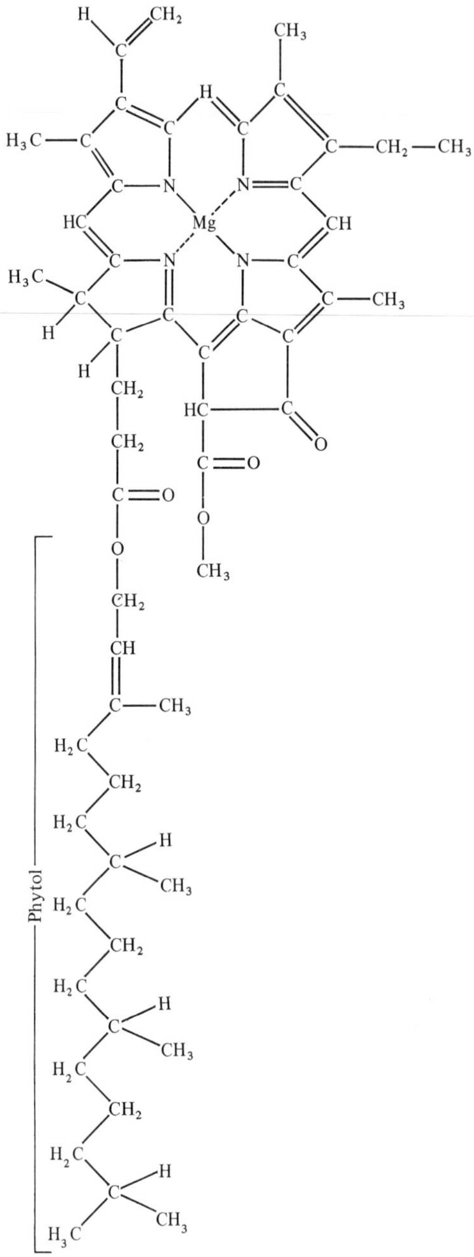

Figure 11-2 Structure of chlorophyll a.

branes are the carotenes. The name is descriptive; they are bright orange in color and were first isolated from carrot roots. In high concentrations they appear reddish. In the higher plants one carotene, beta carotene, dominates, but smaller concentrations of others are found in some plants. There are more carotenes in algae than in flowering plants. The carotenes serve as antennae pigments and also play an important role in preventing the destruction of chlorophylls by high intensities of visible and near-visible light.

Compounds chemically related to the carotenes, the carotenoids (carotene-like), are also found in the thylakoid membranes. They are usually yellow to the human eye. The most prominent carotenoids are the xanthophylls (yellow leaf pigments). They, like the carotenes, are antennae pigments.

Several other types of compounds are found in the membranes, but usually in too small a concentration to be visible to the eye. Several red compounds, cytochromes, are important components in the energy-transformation process.

Every year people in some regions of North America are treated to the spectacle of autumnal coloration. Because of the distribution of certain species, notably the maples (*Acer*), ashes (*Fraxinus*), and sumacs (*Rhus*), the color change is spectacular in New England and adjacent Canada and in the upper Midwest. Signaled by the decreasing photoperiods of September and concomitant reduction in day and night temperatures, leaves begin to reduce both their photosynthetic and respiratory activities. The chlorophylls, because of their high concentrations in the chloroplasts, begin to break down faster than they can be resynthesized, and the carotenes and carotenoids, normally masked by the chlorophylls, begin to be visible. These changes in relative pigment concentration are responsible for the gradual appearance of the orange (carotene) and yellow (carotenoid) colors. The brown colors are produced by the breakdown products of the chlorophylls and the accumulation of tannins (substances that give the brown color to tea) in the leaf cells. The red colors are primarily anthocyanins, which are synthesized when the temperatures are reduced and when sugars, formed in photosynthesis, do not move out of the leaves as rapidly as they did in midsummer. The spectrum of greens, oranges, yellows, browns, and reds brings hillsides into flame (and, not incidentally, is a significant factor in the economies of the states and provinces in which these trees are found). Although not as dramatic, the juxtaposition of the bright yellows of the western aspens (*Populus*) with the dark green of the conifers in the Rockies is also appreciated. In years when frosts come sooner than normal or when the plants have been stressed by drought or pollution, the change from green to the dull brown of dead leaves is quicker and frequently autumnal colors do not appear.

THE ROLE OF LIGHT

Chlorophyll Synthesis and Plastid Formation

Independent of its role in the photosynthetic process itself, light is required for the formation of the photosynthetic apparatus and its maintenance. Chloroplasts are not initiated *de novo* in a plant, but are derived from chloroplasts of the female parent transmitted to the embryo in the seed through maternal inheritance. In embryos the chloroplast is not found in its mature, functional form, but is present as a proplastid whose structure is not immediately recognized as being that of a chloroplast. Certain photosynthetic enzymes, but not all of them, are present in the proplastid and, with a few exceptions among the gymnosperms and in members of the citrus family (Rutaceae), light is required for the initiation of the chlorophylls as well as the plastid. This can be seen in the embryo of a bean seed; the hypocotyl and cotyledons are white or pale yellow rather than green.

Light has two major roles in the synthesis of chloroplasts and of chlorophylls. One of the early steps in the biosynthesis of chlorophyll a involves the formation of a key intermediary designated ALA (α levulinic acid). Its biosynthesis is light-regulated and evidence now available suggests that the photoreceptor for the enzyme activation is phytochrome, with red light activating biosynthesis and far red light turning the synthesis off. ALA is enzymatically transformed into another compound which in darkness may accumulate without being converted into chlorophyll. Red light also activates the final conversion of this precursor into chlorophyll a. The compound itself is its own light receptor and phytochrome is not involved. The end product of these light-activated steps is the complete chlorophyll a molecule. Chlorophyll b is formed by several reactions from chlorophyll a.

The formation of chlorophylls occurs rapidly; measurable chlorophyll a is found within a few hours following irradiation of nonchlorophyllous cells that contain proplastids. Detailed studies, using electron microscopic and biochemical techniques, show that in addition to the synthesis of chlorophyll, irradiation activates the synthesis of enzymes required for the fixation of carbon dioxide into sugar. The light-activation of chlorophyll and enzyme synthesis is a continuous process, with new molecules being formed throughout the active photosynthetic life of the cell.

Although there is at present no explanation for the phenomenon, it is known that the synthesis of the grana and other parts of the chloroplast cannot occur until chlorophyll has been synthesized. The maximum amount of chlorophyll need not have been formed; in many instances chloroplast development will occur when less than 10 percent of the maximum amount of chlorophyll has been produced.

Etiolation

The failure to produce either chlorophyll or the chloroplast is most commonly seen in seedlings grown in darkness or in light lacking the red end of the visible spectrum. The result is etiolation. Etiolated plants have pale yellow leaves due to the presence of small amounts of carotenoids. Structural alterations are also observed. Leaves and stems remain underdeveloped, elongate, and become succulent. Poor development of primary and secondary xylem occurs. The cell walls of the cortical collenchyma frequently do not thicken, leading to the succulence and tenderness of the tissues. Commercially, these traits may be valuable. Hearts of celery, leeks, endive, and a few other crops are etiolated by piling soil up around them during their development.

Red light, acting primarily through the phytochrome system, is required for the prevention of etiolation. Although it appears that the structural alterations are due to failure of the phytochrome system to function, there has not been enough research on the topic to warrant further speculation. Certainly, the topic is of both scientific and applied importance.

Etiolation is not an all-or-none phenomenon. Plants receiving low levels of light may show partial etiolation (chloronemia) with elongated stems and small light-green leaves that are not structurally mature. The internal modifications in cell development and tissue organization may be part way between fully etiolated and fully developed. Although the formation of chlorophyll and the photosynthetic apparatus can be brought to full development by supplying appropriate light, the internal structures will tend to remain in the etiolated form. This is important when starting seeds; inadequate radiation during the early stages of seedling development, even if corrected later, will produce plants that are not well formed and "thrifty." Photosynthetic rates of seedlings receiving inadequate light will be lower.

Light Acclimation and Bleaching

Plants that have been growing under one particular light regime and are then transferred to another usually require time for their metabolism to adjust to the new regime. Such adjustments are necessary if the plant is transferred from a high to a low light situation or the reverse. The reasons for the need for acclimation have received little research attention. Certainly, there are modifications in chlorophyll content and in chloroplast numbers with attendant alterations in the rates of photosynthesis. Some research on the effects of transfer from low to high light conditions has shown that plants that had been growing under low light conditions have lower concentrations of carotenoids than those under high light conditions. As noted above, the carotenoids have the ability to screen the chlorophylls from destruction by light—the phenomenon called photochemical oxidation.

The need for acclimation should be considered in several common situations. Plants growing under shaded conditions or those growing under artificial lighting should not be transferred directly into full sunlight. They should, instead, be exposed to full light for only an hour or two on the first day with the time gradually increased over a period of a week until the adjustment period has been completed. To move plants from full light to shaded conditions the time in the lower light is gradually increased. Too rapid a change may result in a decrease in the rate of growth, loss of leaves or, in extreme situations, death of the plant. Nurseries carefully regulate light exposure; if seed germination and seedling development occur in shade, the radiation intensity is increased slowly. The same procedure is practiced when seedlings are to be transplanted into the field. Greenhouse-grown plants, especially those grown with high humidities and luxury amounts of nitrogen fertilizer, are particularly prone to damage when transferred to homes where the light intensities, relative humidities, and temperatures are likely to be different.

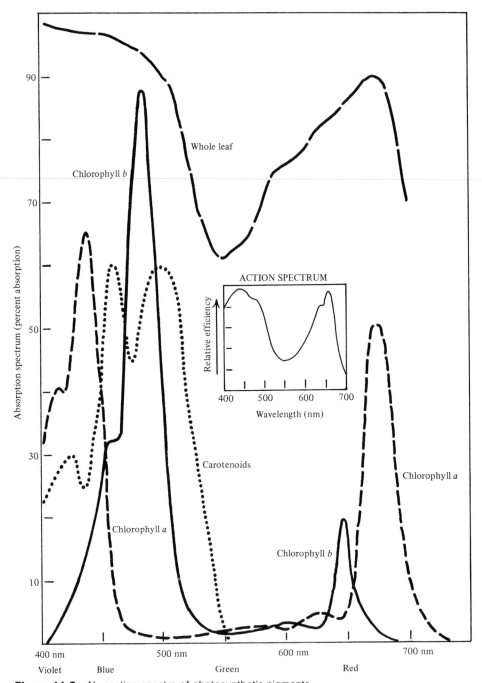

Figure 11-3 Absorption spectra of photosynthetic pigments.

TRANSFORMATION OF LIGHT ENERGY INTO CHEMICAL ENERGY

The Light Reactions

The photosynthetic processes collectively called the light reactions result in the formation of three compounds. ATP (adenosine triphosphate), reduced NADP, or $NADP_{red}$ (nicotinamide adenine dinucleotide phosphate), and O_2 (molecular oxygen). ATP and $NADP_{red}$ are needed for the fixation of carbon dioxide (CO_2) into sugar. The carbon-fixation reactions (described later in this chapter) do not require light. The light-capturing reactions are photochemical, that is, they involve the excitation of molecules, are not enzymatic, and are unaffected by temperature. They occur as efficiently at or below freezing as they do at midsummer temperatures. This means that the overall photosynthetic process is limited by the formation of ATP, reduced NADP in the light reactions, and the carbon-fixing dark reactions which, being enzymatic, are temperature sensitive. Even in midwinter, if the leaves or needles of evergreens absorb enough solar heat to raise their temperature above freezing, overall photosynthesis can occur. Trees with bark cells that contain chloroplasts can photosynthesize in winter.

The photosynthetic light reactions start with the absorption of radiant energy by the chloroplast pigments. Light is absorbed efficiently by the carotene, carotenoids, chlorophyll *b* and most of chlorophyll *a* pigments. Each different molecule absorbs light only within certain wavelength bands of visible and near-visible light. Such absorptions can be measured and are appropriately called absorption spectra (Figure 11-3). The absorption spectra of antennae pigments show that blue and red wavelengths are efficiently absorbed, with relatively little absorption of green wavelengths. The complex of antennae pigments absorbs the bulk of the light in the visible electromagnetic spectrum.

Antennae pigment molecules, once they have absorbed light, are "excited," that is, one or more electrons (e^-) are shifted from their normal or ground state into a higher state. Unless the energy absorbed is moved to another molecule, it is lost and the molecule is again in the ground state, having had no effect on the photosynthetic process. When, however, the energy is transferred to the photoactive chlorophyll *a* molecules in the reaction center, photosynthetic light reactions occur (Figure 11-4). The transfer of excitation energy from antennae to

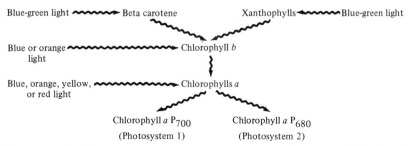

Figure 11-4 Interrelations among antennae pigments and photosynthetically active chlorophylls *a*.

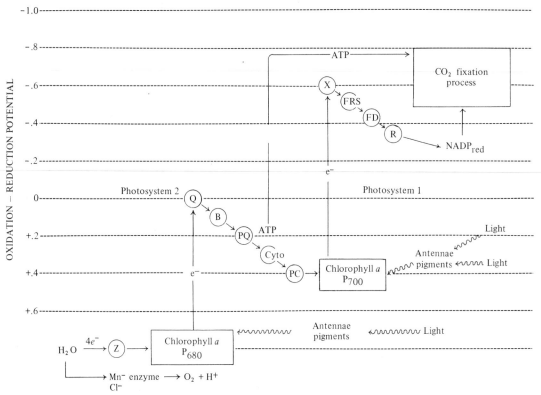

Figure 11-5 The Z-plan of photosynthetic light reactions.

photoactive chlorophyll molecules is extremely rapid and almost 100 percent efficient.

Among the three major types of chlorophyll *a*, two are of special importance because they are the photoactive molecules. They are named on the basis of the absorption maximum at the red end of the visible spectrum. Chlorophyll *a* P_{700} acts in the first part of the light reactions (photosystem 1), and chlorophyll *a* P_{680} acts in the other part of the light reactions (photosystem 2). They differ from the chlorophyll *a* antennae molecules by being attached to special thylakoid proteins. Although each of these special chlorophyll *a* types absorbs light at its peak absorption wavelength, sunlight does not contain enough of these wavelengths for active photosynthesis. The radiation absorbed by all of the antennae pigments is, by yet unknown means, shifted to the energy absorption maxima of the photoactive chlorophylls *a*. By this photophysical method, solar energy is used efficiently.

The sequence of the light reactions of photosynthesis is called the Z-plan (Figure 11-5). The light reactions are divided into two parts. In photosystem 1 light is absorbed directly by chlorophyll *a* P_{700}, and light is absorbed by antennae pigments and transferred to P_{700}. The light excites the chlorophyll molecules, and electrons are shifted to a higher energy state (indicated by the arrow pointed up).

The activation energy, unless quickly moved to a receptor molecule, will "decay," the energy will be dissipated as fluorescence, and the activated electron will return to its ground state in the molecule. In photosystem 1, however, the activated electron is captured by another compound in the thylakoid, designated as X because its exact composition is unknown. The electron is then transferred to FRS, then to FD (an iron-containing compound called ferredoxin), then to R (a poorly characterized substance), and finally to the oxidized form of NADP, which by the receipt of the electron is converted to the reduced state. This $NADP_{red}$ is one of the two compounds required in the carbon-fixation reactions.

Some means has to exist to provide an electron to chlorophyll a P_{700} to replace the one lost to $NADP_{red}$. As in photosystem 1, photosystem 2 is activated by light absorbed directly by chlorophyll a P_{680} or received by P_{680} from the antennae pigments. As in photosystem 1, the light energy absorbed activates an electron which is moved to a higher energy state and captured by a receptor named Q (its composition is unknown). This electron is moved through an electron transport chain to chlorophyll a P_{700} so that it is again capable of undergoing photoactivation to provide more $NADP_{red}$ for the carbon-fixing reactions. Very important for the fixation reactions is the formation of the high-energy chemical ATP. The ATP is formed as the electron moves down an energy cascade, in much the same way that water can provide electrical or mechanical power as it cascades down a spillway. The cascade is the series of

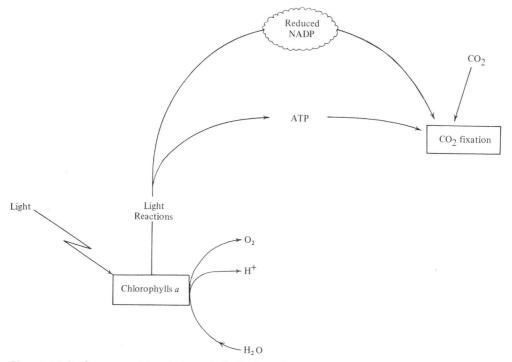

Figure 11-6 Summary of the photosynthetic light reactions.

compounds that constitute the transport chain arranged on the thylakoid membrane in a precise order so that the electron provides energy for the synthesis of the required ATP. When the electron reaches a particular energy state, it can be captured by chlorophyll a P_{700}, reactivating it for another photoreaction.

We have, as you see, accounted for two of the end products of the photosynthetic light reactions, but two more reactions are still required. One is the restoration of an electron to chlorophyll a P_{680} so that it can again participate in the light reactions. The other is the formation of molecular oxygen. Both of these processes involve photosystem 2 and both involve the participation of water. When chlorophyll a P_{680} absorbs the light energy, it not only moves an electron to the higher energy state, but it also causes water to be split. The splitting of water into its component hydrogen ($2H^+$) and oxygen (O^-) releases an electron which is captured by chlorophyll a P_{680}. Oxygen atoms combine to form molecular oxygen (O_2), which is released into the atmosphere. The entire series of light reactions is summarized in Figure 11-6. They can be written simply as:

$$\text{chlorophylls } a + \text{light energy} + \text{oxidized NADP} + H_2O \rightarrow$$
$$\text{chlorophylls } a + \text{ATP energy} + \text{reduced NADP} + O_2$$

Practical Implications

There are many implications of the light reactions. Some of them are obvious. An effective way to kill plants is to supply a substance that interferes or blocks one of the steps in the light reaction series. Several herbicides, Monuron and Diuron, block the splitting of water in photosystem 2. Other herbicides such as Diquat, interfere with other parts of the reaction scheme.

We can also see where some of the inorganic plant nutrients fit into photosynthesis. The chlorophylls are magnesium-containing compounds and their biosynthesis involves a step in which iron plays a role. The formation of oxygen requires the participation of manganese and chlorine ions, and sulfur is needed as part of the proteins of the thylakoid membranes.

Obviously, the intensity, duration, and quality of the radiation available to the chloroplasts determine the speed and the efficiency of the light reactions. Many plants, particularly those adapted to high-light conditions, will respond poorly to reductions in light intensity. Conversely, low-light or shade plants cannot handle high intensities. The total amount of photosynthate formed also depends on the number of hours per day during which photosynthesis can occur; the shorter days of spring and fall result in lower amounts of sugars synthesized.

Considerable attention has been paid to the quality of the light reaching plants. This is particularly important for plants receiving artificial light in which the balance among the various wavelengths differs markedly from that of sunlight. No inexpensive light source has the balance or intensity of sunlight, and it is common practice to increase the duration of irradiation to compensate. Shading, too, is related to the light reactions (Figure 11-7). Garden and field plots are usually laid out with row orientation and spacing that minimizes the shading

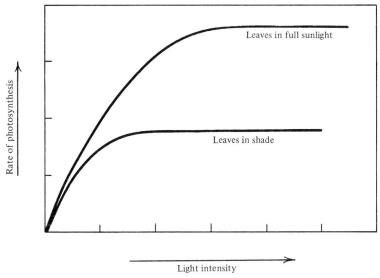

Figure 11-7 Photosynthetic rates in leaves in full sunlight and in shade.

problem. Shading also occurs within individual plants. The upper leaves change the intensity and quality of light to which the lower and interior leaves are exposed. They efficiently absorb the blue and red wavelengths leaving much lower intensities of these wavelengths available to leaves below. The lower leaves, which start out as full-sun leaves, to some extent become shade leaves as the season advances and they compensate for the changed intensity and quality. Breeding and pruning of some plants are directed toward opening the canopy to allow adequate penetration of light. Computer-assisted programs have been developed to determine the optimum tradeoff between making rows wider (with resulting fewer plants per unit area) and facilitating the penetration of light into the planting.

CARBON FIXATION

Calvin-Benson Cycle

The total amount of carbon fixed into all plant material is truly enormous. The U.S. corn crop alone amounts to 14 metric tons per hectare per year and sugar cane yields 45 metric tons of dry matter per hectare. All this material, collectively called biomass, results from photosynthesis and conversion of simple sugars into cellulose, starch, and other carbohydrates, and many plant components.

The mechanism or reaction pathways of photosynthesis leading to the synthesis of sugar through fixation of carbon dioxide (CO_2) from the atmosphere requires two of the end products of the light reactions, ATP and $NADP_{red}$. The

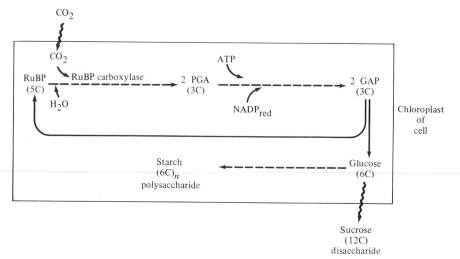

Figure 11-8 C_3 pathway of carbon dioxide fixation (Calvin-Benson cycle).

availability of these compounds can control the rate of sugar synthesis and determine how much dry weight or biomass will be formed.

The principal pathway for the fixation of carbon dioxide is known as the Calvin-Benson cycle, the reductive pentose cycle, or, more commonly, the C_3 cycle. The name Calvin-Benson cycle honors the scientists who contributed to our knowledge of this process. Fixation is the process by which carbon dioxide, an inorganic molecule, present in the atmosphere and entering the leaves through the stomata, is incorporated into an existing organic five-carbon sugar molecule. All green plants, flowering and nonflowering, possess the C_3 cycle of carbon fixation.

All reactions of the C_3 cycle occur within the chloroplasts (Figure 11-8). The specific reactions of fixation occur within the stroma of the chloroplast. Any tissue containing photosynthetic pigments and enzymes will carry on photosynthesis. A five-carbon sugar, ribulose bisphosphate (RuBP), reacts with carbon dioxide to form two molecules of a three-carbon compound, phosphoglyceric acid (PGA). The enzyme ribulose bisphosphate carboxylase (RuBP carboxylase) is a catalyst for this reaction. The PGA is converted into two molecules of a three-carbon sugar, glyceraldehyde phosphate (GAP), in reactions that require ATP and $NADP_{red}$. The reactions operate in a cycle like an endless belt. It is referred to as C_3 because the three-carbon organic compound PGA is the first identifiable, stable product, and the three-carbon sugar GAP is the end product. Every revolution of the cycle regenerates the starting compound RuBP, and six turns of the cycle yield one molecule of the six-carbon sugar glucose. Each of the carbons in this sugar has been fixed from carbon dioxide from the atmosphere.

A large number of glucose molecules are bonded together to make the polysaccharide starch, which can be stored in the chloroplast. The disaccharide sucrose can also be synthesized, but it is largely translocated to other parts of the plant via the sieve elements of the phloem tissue.

Several enzymes that regulate the process of photosynthesis require light for their activation; ribulose bisphosphate carboxylase, the carbon-fixing enzyme of the C_3 cycle, is one of these.

The photochemical and enzymatic reactions of photosynthesis are influenced and modified by several physical factors of the environment, each of which can change independently of the others. The relative rate and the maximum rate can increase or decrease depending upon the concentration of carbon dioxide, light intensity, and temperature. Each of these environmental factors has its own effect, but also interacts with and is changed by the others.

The concentration of carbon dioxide in the earth's atmosphere is 0.035 percent or 350 parts per million (ppm). Concentrations of 400 ppm are commonly found in swampy areas where microorganisms, actively decomposing dead plant remains, release large amounts of carbon dioxide through their respiratory processes. In greenhouses tightly closed to conserve heat, carbon dioxide concentrations may drop below 350 ppm, creating a deficiency that will depress photosynthesis.

In greenhouse experiments, where conditions of light, temperature, and fertilization are optimum, increasing the carbon dioxide level to 1000 to 1500 ppm (concentrations not harmful to people) has been found to have positive effects on plant productivity (Figure 11-9). The positive effects include increased stem length and weight, faster flowering, larger number of flowers, and better rooting of cuttings. This technique, called carbon dioxide enrichment, has been successful with such greenhouse crops as roses, chrysanthemums, carnations,

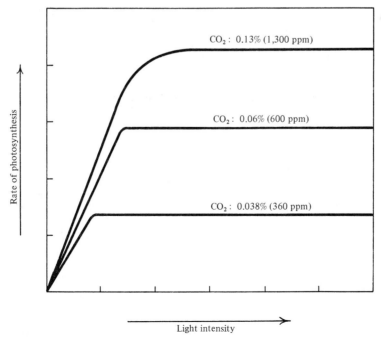

Figure 11-9 Effect of increased carbon dioxide concentration on rate of photosynthesis.

snapdragons, Dutch iris, orchids, poinsettias, geranium cuttings, and vegetable crops of lettuce, cucumbers and tomatoes. Carbon dioxide enrichment in greenhouses has been particularly beneficial in colder regions where greenhouse-grown vegetables and flowers have an important market and is now used widely in northern Europe and the Soviet Union.

Hatch-Slack Cycle

Until the mid 1960s the C_3 pathway for the synthesis of sugar was thought to be the only route for carbon fixation in green plants. Kortshak and Hatch and Slack found that another enzyme capable of fixing carbon dioxide, phospho-enolpyruvate carboxylase (PEP carboxylase), is the initial and major carbon-fixing enzyme in certain groups of flowering plants. It is present in grasses that grow in tropical or in warm arid environments. These include corn (*Zea Mays*), sorghum (*Sorghum bicolor*), sugar cane (*Saccharum officinarum*), carpet grass (*Axonopus*), crabgrass (*Digitaria*), finger grass (*Chloris*), and love grass (*Eragrostis*). PEP carboxylase is also found in some tropical dicots from cool oceanic and cool desert areas including *Portulaca oleracea* and some species of *Atriplex, Amaranthus,* and *Euphorbia* (see Table 11–2).

It was recognized that these plants also show a unique leaf structure (Figure 11-10). This Kranz anatomy, or halo appearance, was first observed in the nineteenth century. The leaf veins are surrounded by two rings of mesophyll cells. Those immediately surrounding the vein, the bundle sheath cells, are large and contain many chloroplasts, giving this ring a green appearance in living tissue. Surrounding the bundle sheath ring is another ring of more typical mesophyll cells containing fewer chloroplasts.

The alternate pathway of photosynthesis was named the Hatch-Slack cycle after its discoverers. In this pathway, also called the C_4 pathway, most of the

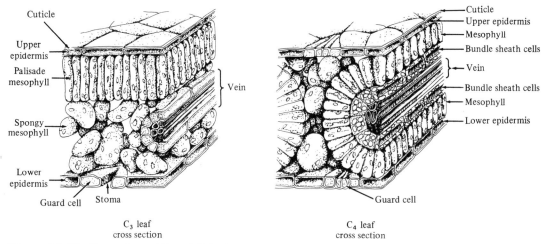

Figure 11-10 Comparison of C_3 and C_4 leaf anatomy.

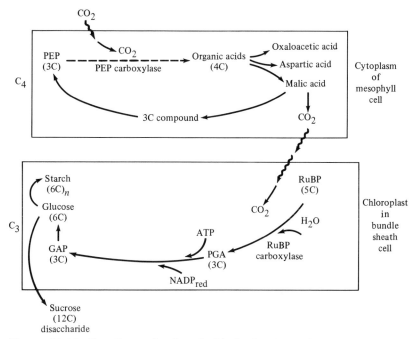

Figure 11-11 C_4 pathway of carbon dioxide fixation (Hatch-Slack cycle).

carbon from carbon dioxide entering the leaf reacts with phosphoenolpyruvic acid (PEP) to form the four-carbon organic compounds oxaloacetic acid, aspartic acid, and malic acid (Figure 11-11). The reactions leading to the synthesis of these compounds take place in the cytoplasm of the mesophyll ring of cells, because the enzyme PEP carboxylase is a cytoplasmic enzyme. These compounds are the source of carbon dioxide for the C_3 cycle occurring in chloroplasts in the inner ring of bundle sheath cells. Thus, in C_4 plants two carbon-fixing enzymes are functioning: RuBP carboxylase in the C_3 cycle and PEP carboxylase in the C_4 cycle. PEP carboxylase is a very efficient enzyme able to fix both much higher and much lower concentrations of carbon dioxide than can RuBP carboxylase. Many of the plants possessing this pathway are able to photosynthesize at close to double the rate of C_3 plants. Clearly, this has important positive consequences for the growth and development of plants possessing the C_4 pathway.

   C_4 plants show little or no photorespiration (discussed below). Consequently, they retain most or all of the carbon dioxide fixed by the carboxylase enzymes. C_4 plants are resistant to photosaturation (Figure 11-12). C_4 plants are able to maintain high rates of photosynthesis even when water is in short supply, a clear advantage over C_3 plants in which photosynthesis is depressed during water stress. In addition, C_4 plants tolerate higher temperatures than do C_3 plants.

   The C_4 advantage can be seen by comparing two forage grasses, western wheatgrass (*Agropyron smithii*), a C_3 grass, and blue grama grass (*Bouteloua gracilis*), a C_4 grass. *A. smithii* shows its most active growth during the cool

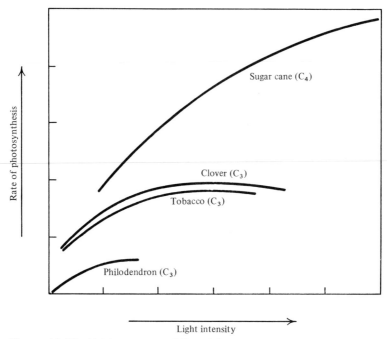

Figure 11-12 Light responses of C_3 and C_4 plants.

portion of the growing season; as the summer temperature increases, net photosynthesis decreases. *B. gracilis,* on the other hand, grows most actively during the hot summer months and shows an increased net photosynthesis as the temperature increases. Lawngrowers are familiar with the all-too-successful growth of the C_4 hairy crabgrass (*Digitaria sanguinalis*) in eastern and southern United States where, during hot, dry summers, it can overgrow the finer, more attractive C_3 lawn grasses such as Kentucky bluegrass (*Poa pratensis*).

Photorespiration, or the C_2 cycle, is defined as the sequence of reactions through which plants release carbon dioxide during the day, although the carbon dioxide so released does not arise from any of the usual cell respiration pathways (Chapter 12). The source of this gas is glycolic acid, a two-carbon compound synthesized in chloroplasts during the C_3 cycle. When this compound is metabolized, carbon dioxide is formed and eventually released into the atmosphere. In contrast to cell respiration no ATP is synthesized during photorespiration. In fact, the metabolism of glycolic acid requires ATP and is wasteful in terms of energy conservation.

A large number of plants have been tested for the presence of photorespiration. All C_3 plants readily release carbon dioxide into the air during the day by metabolizing glycolic acid and thus all show photorespiration. C_3 plants may lose as much as 50 percent of the carbon dioxide initially fixed. As discussed below, C_4 and CAM plants release little or no carbon dioxide from photorespiration. The most reasonable explanation is that although this gas is formed and diffuses into the leaf mesophyll, the extremely efficient PEP carboxylase captures and fixes it before it can escape through the stomata. The C_4 and CAM plants are more efficient in retaining the carbon dioxide released when glycolic acid is metabolized. Another consequence for C_4 plants is the increased gain in biomass because of their ability to retain and utilize the photorespiratory carbon dioxide for synthesis of sugar.

In view of the marked advantages of plants possessing the C_4 cycle of sugar synthesis, attempts are underway to explore the possibility of converting agriculturally and horticulturally important C_3 plants into C_4 plants, using genetic engineering and classical genetic techniques.

CAM Cycle

Plants that make sugar via the CAM (crassulacean acid metabolism) cycle were first described morphologically around 1884. They are succulent plants, usually perennials, whose leaves, stems, or both, are thick, fleshy, and juicy. Examples include jade tree, (*Crassula argentea*), prickly pear (*Opuntia vulgaris*), and starfish plant (*Stapelia variegata*). The CAM cycle occurs in 18 different flowering plant families (Table 11-2). In two of these, the cactus (Cactaceae) and orpine or stonecrop (Crassulaceae) families, all species have the CAM capability. Other families are variable, with not all members of a genus showing the CAM cycle.

CAM plants are anomalous because their stomata close during the day and

Table 11-2   PLANT FAMILIES THAT HAVE SPECIES SHOWING THE C₄ OR CAM CYCLES OF CARBON FIXATION

C_4 cycle	CAM cycle
Monocotyledonae	Monocotyledonae
Cyperaceae	Agavaceae
Gramineae	Bromeliaceae
Dicotyledonae	Liliaceae
Aizoaceae	Orchidaceae
Amaranthaceae	Dicotyledonae
Asteraceae	Aizoaceae
Chenopodiaceae	Asclepiadaceae
Euphorbiaceae	Asteraceae
Nyctaginaceae	Cactaceae
Portulacaceae	Crassulaceae
Zygophyllaceae	Curcurbitaceae
	Euphorbiaceae
	Geraniaceae
	Labiatae
	Oxalidaceae
	Piperaceae
	Portulacaceae
	Vitaceae

open at night, just the reverse of the usual pattern. The unusual behavior is an adaptation to very hot and dry habitats where water conservation is essential for survival. Closing the stomata during the day reduces transpirational water loss markedly; carbon dioxide can enter the leaf at night for participation in photosynthesis. The mesophyll of the leaves of these plants is primarily spongy parenchyma in contrast to the bilayer appearance of C_3 plants and the halo appearance of C_4 plants.

CAM species are, in general, slow-growing due to their limited ability to make sugar, but they utilize water more efficiently and tolerate periods of drought. They rarely become the ecologically dominant plant, except in habitats such as the American Sonoran or African deserts, and they are few in number where competition is high. But they are survivors.

The CAM pathway of sugar synthesis is similar in several ways to the C_4 cycle. The enzyme PEP carboxylase, present in mesophyll cell cytoplasm, fixes carbon dioxide into PEP during the night when stomata are open to permit the gas to enter the leaf. The end product, malic acid, is stored in the mesophyll cell vacuole. During the day, when the stomata are closed, the malic acid becomes the internal source of carbon dioxide which diffuses into the chloroplast reacting with RuBP of the C_3 cycle.

The CAM cycle appears to be modifiable. When *Agave americana* is well watered, it shows daytime C_3 sugar synthesis as well as the nighttime carbon dioxide fixation characteristic of the CAM cycle. In *A. deserti* watering causes the CAM cycle to stop altogether, with the plant exhibiting only the daytime C_3 process. *Portulacaria afra,* a fodder plant grown in South Africa, uses the CAM cycle when there is a water deficiency and the C_3 cycle when the plant is well watered.

STORAGE OF PHOTOSYNTHATE

Sugars and Starches

The primary product of photosynthesis is the six-carbon sugar glucose. Other compounds, such as malic and glycolic acids, are also produced. All these

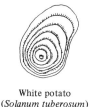

| White potato (*Solanum tuberosum*) | Bean (*Phaseolus vulgaris*) | Sweet potato (*Ipomoea Batatas*) | Banana (*Musa acuminata*) | Rice (*Oryza sativa*) |

Figure 11-13 Leucoplasts in which starch is stored.

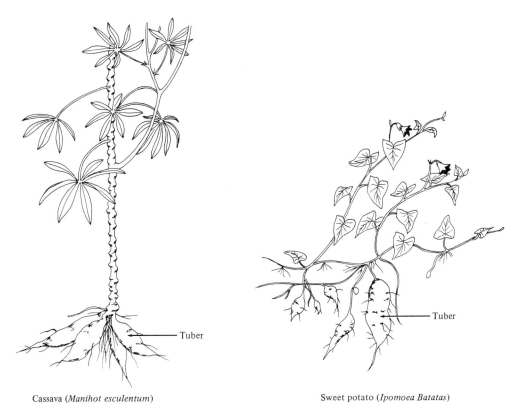

Cassava (*Manihot esculentum*)

Sweet potato (*Ipomoea Batatas*)

Figure 11-14 Two root tubers that store starch.

substances are collectively called photosynthate. The total organic matter of a plant is referred to as biomass. Glucose may be converted to the polysaccharide starch and stored within the chloroplast; it may also be transformed into the disaccharide sucrose, the major sugar translocated from the leaf to stem, root, or fruit via sieve tube cells of the phloem tissue. Sucrose can be reconverted to glucose which, in turn, is polymerized to starch. Starch, thus formed, will be stored in leucoplasts (Figure 11-13) present in a variety of storage cells. A few important crop plants, including sugar cane, sorghum, and sugar beet, do not store starch, but rather sucrose.

Most of our food plants contain starch as their major storage substance. These include the fruits (grains) of cereals (barley, corn, millet, oat, rice, rye, sorghum, wheat); tuberous root crops such as sweet potato (*Ipomoea Batatas*) and cassava or tapioca (*Manihot esculenta*) (Figure 11-14); and stem tubers such as white potato (*Solanum tuberosum*). Various legume seeds (soybeans, beans, peas, peanuts) and other edible seeds (buckwheat) store starch as well as protein and lipid.

In plants starch occurs in two structural forms (Figure 11-15). Amylose consists of a large number of glucose molecules bonded together like beads on a

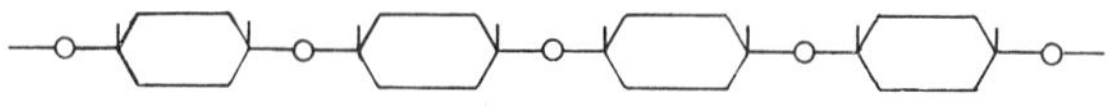

Figure 11-15 Structural forms of starch: amylose, a straight chain, and amylopectin, a branched chain.

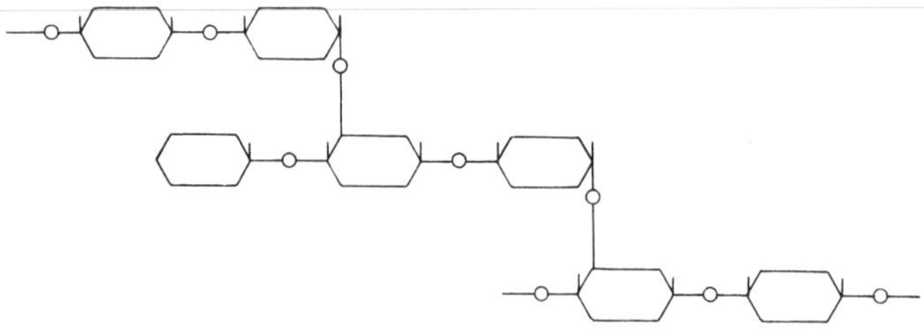

string to form a long, straight chain. Amylopectin is a more complex molecule, composed of straight chains connected by short chains branching from the straight chains. The type of starch can markedly affect the texture of food. In corn grains of the type called waxy maize, the endosperm cells contain primarily the amylopectin starch which, when cooked, becomes glutinous or sticky. Certain glutinous or soft cultivars of rice also have mostly amylopectin in the endosperm, while the hard rices contain three-fourths amylopectin and one-fourth amylose and do not become sticky when cooked. The soft types of corn and rice are popular in Asia where glutinous cereals are preferred, but hard rices are more important in world trade.

The starch extracted from corn is a highly valuable commercial product in its familiar powdered form. It may be chemically converted to a liquid form containing dextrins, fructose, and glucose. As a liquid sweetener, used in soft drinks and the baking industry, it is an economically important competitor of cane and beet sugars.

A few plants store sucrose. The most important economically are sugar cane (*Saccharum officinarum*), in which the thick stems, or canes, accumulate high concentrations of sucrose, and the beet root (*Beta vulgaris*) (Figure 11-16). Although the major use of sorghum (*Sorghum bicolor*) in the United States is as a grain for livestock feed, sorghum syrup is also derived from the sugar stored in the juicy stems of some sorghum cultivars. Some cultivars of corn—the sugar maizes—also accumulate sucrose in their stems (Figure 11-17).

The polysaccharide inulin, a polymer of fructose, is a rare storage form. It is

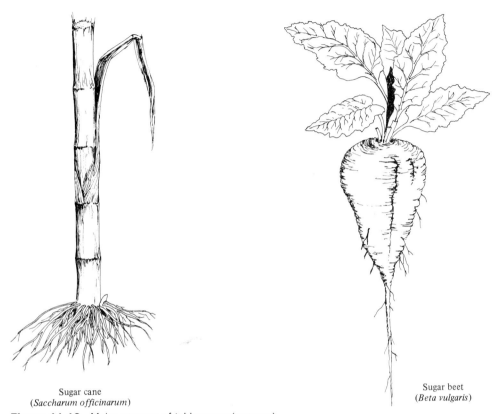

Sugar cane
(*Saccharum officinarum*)

Sugar beet
(*Beta vulgaris*)

Figure 11-16 Major sources of table sugar (sucrose).

stored in the potato-like tuber of Jerusalem artichoke (*Helianthus tuberosus*) and in the root tubers of dahlia (*Dahlia pinnata*). Inulin has been used as a carbohydrate food for diabetics.

Storage of carbohydrate in underground organs—corms, bulbs, tubers, and roots—is common and highly important for successful overwintering of perennial plants. For example, in carrot (a biennial that is harvested as an annual as a food crop) photosynthate stored in the large tap root during its first year's growth is used as a source of energy for the resumption of growth and the formation of flowers during the second year.

Temperature is an important environmental control and may modify the form of the carbohydrate stored. The flow of sugary sap in sugar maple in late winter is due to the fact that carbohydrate stored in ray cells of the stem (trunk) is converted to sucrose as the temperature increases. Young corn kernels of sweet corn are sweet because of the high concentration of sucrose. If the freshly harvested ears of sweet corn are kept at a low temperature, but above freezing, sucrose conversion to starch will be inhibited and the kernels remain sweet for some time. White potatoes are stored at 4° C (39° F). At higher temperatures

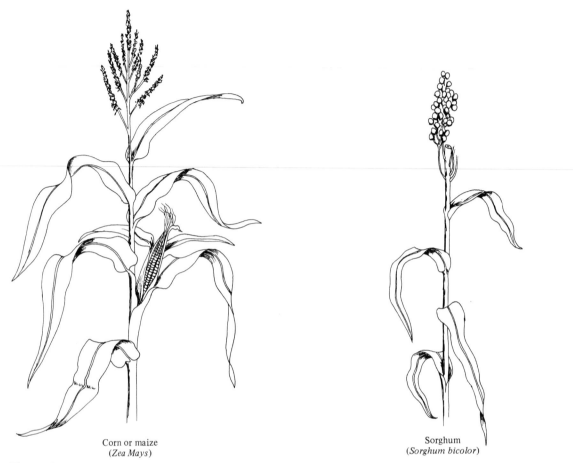

Corn or maize
(*Zea Mays*)

Sorghum
(*Sorghum bicolor*)

Figure 11-17 Two agricultural grasses that store sucrose in their stems.

sprouting occurs, and the potatoes become soft as starch is converted to sugars and water is lost by transpiration from young shoots. At temperatures below 4° C starch is also converted to sugar.

SUPPLEMENTARY READINGS

Benzing, D. G. 1980. *The Biology of the Bromeliads.* Mad River Press, Eureka, Calif.

Burris, R. H., and C. C. Black. 1976. *CO₂ Metabolism and Plant Productivity.* University Park Press, Baltimore, Md.

Carlson, P. (ed.). 1980. *The Biology of Crop Productivity.* Academic Press, New York.

Cobley, L. S., and W. M. Steele. 1977. *An Introduction to the Botany of Tropical Crops.* 2nd ed. Longman, London.

Davies, D. D. (ed.). 1980. *The Biochemistry of Plants.* Academic Press, New York.

Enoch, H. Z., and B. A. Kimball. (eds.). 1986. *Carbon Dioxide Enrichment of Greenhouse Crops.* 2 vols. CRC Press, Boca Raton, Fla.

Hall, D. O., and K. K. Rao. 1977. *Photosynthesis.* 2nd ed. Studies in Biology No. 37. University Park Press, Baltimore, Md.

Halliwell, B. 1981. *Chloroplast Metabolism: The Structure and Function of Chloroplasts in Green Leaf Cells.* Oxford University Press, Oxford.

Hesketh, J. D., and J. W. Jones. 1980. *Predicting Photosynthesis for Ecosystem Models.* CRC Press, Boca Raton, Fla.

Jones, C. A. 1985. *C_4 Grasses and Cereals: Growth, Development and Stress Response.* Wiley-Interscience, New York.

Nelson, P. V. 1981. *Greenhouse Operation and Management.* 2nd ed. Reston, Reston, Va.

Pearson, C. (ed.). 1984. *Control of Crop Productivity.* Academic Press, New York.

Ting, I. P., and M. Gibbs. (eds.). 1982. *Crassulacean Acid Metabolism.* American Society of Plant Physiologists, Rockville, Md.

Woolhouse, H. W. 1978. Light gathering and carbon assimilation processes in photosynthesis: Their adaptive modifications and significance in agriculture. *Endeavour* 2(1):35–46.

C H A P T E R   1 2

RESPIRATION

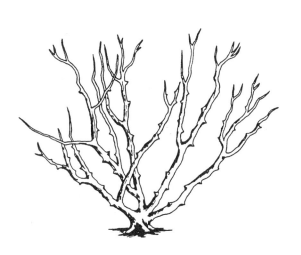

SUGAR INTO ENERGY

We have seen how, in photosynthesis, radiant energy of sunlight or artificial light is captured, converted to chemical energy, and stored primarily as starch and sucrose. The plant must change that stored energy into utilizable energy in the form of ATP (adenosine triphosphate) in order to synthesize protein, fats, vitamins, alkaloids, lignin, cellulose, and all the other compounds required to maintain the life of the plant and permit its growth and development. This energy is also needed to maintain the integrity and viability of cells. The mechanism by which this occurs is the process of cellular aerobic respiration. The mechanism is also called dark respiration to distinguish it from photorespiration discussed in Chapter 11.

Aerobic respiration goes on continually, day and night, in all living cells. It is an enzyme-controlled process that releases the energy stored in glucose at a steady, slow rate so that the energy can be utilized efficiently (Table 12-1). Heat is

Table 12-1   CHARACTERISTICS OF AEROBIC CELLULAR RESPIRATION

1. It occurs in all living plant cells.
2. It proceeds continually in light and dark.
3. Sugar and oxygen are raw materials.
4. Carbon dioxide and water are end products.
5. Energy is released.

also generated and if respiration were to occur rapidly, as in the combustion of wood or coal, there would be a rise in temperature above that which cells and the organism could tolerate. There are a few notable exceptions to this general rule, one of these being the skunk cabbage or polecat weed (*Symplocarpus foetidus*) in which the internal temperature of the flower may rise as much as 20° C (36° F) above that of the ambient air.

The complex process of cell respiration requires a large number of enzymes as well as a specific organelle, the mitochondrion. The process is divided into three parts: glycolysis, occurring in the cell cytoplasm; the Krebs or citric acid

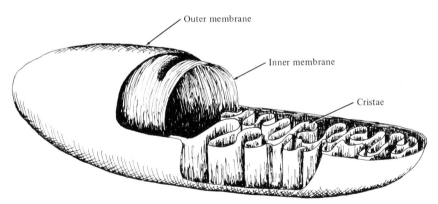

Figure 12-1   The mitochondrion, the organelle that is the site of the Krebs cycle and the electron transport system.

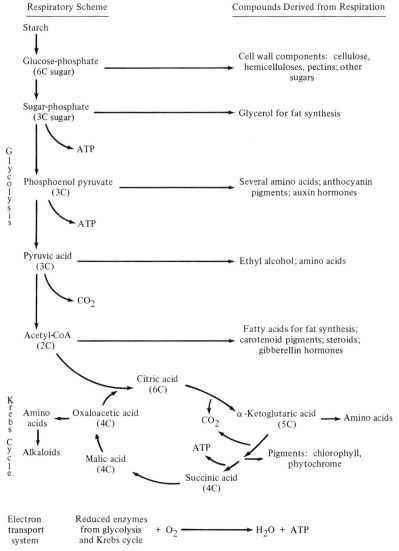

Figure 12-2 Aerobic cellular respiration and the compounds derived from glycolysis and the Krebs cycle.

cycle; and the electron transport system, the latter two parts taking place in the mitochondrion (Figure 12-1).

Sugar, in the form of starch or glucose, is the starting point for the series of reactions of glycolysis (Figure 12-2). Starch is broken down (hydrolyzed) to glucose, an enzymatic step requiring inorganic phosphate. Phosphorylated glucose is converted, through a series of enzymatic steps, to pyruvic acid during the course of which a small amount of the energy of glucose is released and used to synthesize ATP. These glycolytic reactions do not require the participation of molecular oxygen; we shall return to this point in the discussion of fermentation.

**Table 12-2   RESPIRATORY QUOTIENT (RQ) OF SEVERAL SEEDS DURING
GERMINATION**

Plant	Common name	Type of storage compound	RQ
Zea Mays	Corn	Starch	1.0
Fagopyrum esculentum	Buckwheat	Protein	0.50
Linum usitatissimum	Flax	Oil	0.64
Pisum sativum	Pea	Organic acids	1.5–2.4

Acetyl-CoA enters the mitochondrion where it is further broken down via the Krebs cycle with ATP and carbon dioxide being generated as end products. The electron transport system is a sequence of oxidation reactions where reduced enzymes generated in glycolysis and in the Krebs cycle are oxidized, releasing a large amount of energy used for the synthesis of ATP. About 40 percent of the energy of glucose is converted to ATP energy; the remaining 60 percent is lost as heat. The final step of this sequence, leading to the synthesis of water, requires the presence of oxygen. Where oxygen is deficient, as in waterlogged or heavy clay soils or in overwatered potted plants, the health of root systems is seriously jeopardized. Spring floods, common in low lying areas adjacent to rivers, can create a temporary but devastating situation. As the respiration rate decreases, cells do not make enough ATP to maintain themselves. Dead and injured cells are particularly prone to infection. Certain plants, however, grow in waterlogged soils. Rice plants have continuous air spaces extending vertically through the stem and into the root system. Oxygen, entering the aerial shoot, diffuses through these air spaces into the root system permitting normal aerobic respiration to continue.

The reactions may be summarized as:

$$C_6H_{12}O_6 \quad + \quad 6O_2 \quad \rightarrow \quad 6CO_2 \quad + \quad 6H_2O + \text{energy}$$

glucose $\qquad$ oxygen $\qquad$ carbon dioxide $\qquad$ water

The summary shows that each of the six carbon atoms of glucose is oxidized to carbon dioxide and that an equal number of molecules of oxygen are taken up to complete these oxidations. Thus, when glucose (or starch or sucrose) is respired, the ratio of carbon dioxide released to oxygen taken up is 1.0. This ratio is called the respiratory quotient (RQ). When respiratory gas exchange is measured, an RQ of 1.0 means that sugar is being respired (Table 12-2). Plants can also use proteins or lipids for respiration. These types of molecules require less oxygen for this conversion to carbon dioxide and ATP energy and the RQ for their respiration is less than 1.0. Fats, in particular, are very concentrated sources of energy and many seeds, including legumes, tomato, and the embryos or "germs" of cereal grains, utilize their lipid reserves early in germination with RQ values below 1.0.

USE OF SUGAR FOR BIOSYNTHESIS OF PLANT COMPONENTS

Green plants synthesize directly all of the various molecules they require to sustain life, in contrast to animals which must ingest a variety of foodstuffs. A

Table 12-3 AMINO ACIDS AND VITAMINS FROM PLANTS THAT ARE ESSENTIAL FOR HUMAN NUTRITION

Amino acids	Vitamins
Isoleucine	Ascorbic acid (vitamin C)
Leucine	Folic acid
Lysine	Niacin (vitamin B_3)
Methionine	Pyridoxine (vitamin B_6)
Phenylalanine	Riboflavin (vitamin B_2)
Threonine	Thiamine (vitamin B_1)
Tryptophan	Cobalamin (vitamin B_{12})
Valine	Vitamins A, D

large number of important compounds are derived from various molecules formed in glycolysis and the Krebs cycle.

The basic constituents of the primary cell wall—cellulose, hemicellulose, and pectins—are all compounds whose synthesis begins with glucose. Calcium pectate is found in the middle lamella and is the sticky glue holding plant cells together. Pectins, available commercially, are used to gel fruit syrups into jellies and jams. Cellulose is a long chain of glucose molecules linked together by chemical bonds different from those linking glucose into starch. This difference results in cellulose molecules being able to form fibrils, which is not true for starch.

Several compounds formed in glycolysis and in the Krebs cycle are the starting point for the biosynthesis of important structural and metabolic substances. Amino acids, the building blocks of protein, are derived from pyruvic acid and other organic acids of the Krebs cycle by enzymatic processes involving the addition of ammonium ion. There are 20 or 21 different amino acids found in proteins in various ratios. Plants can make all of the amino acids, but humans must obtain certain amino acids, termed essential amino acids, from their foods (Table 12-3). In general, plant proteins tend to be low in several human essential amino acids.

Proteins play many roles in plants. All enzymes are protein; some proteins are not enzymes, but are important structural constituents of cell membranes and cell walls. Proteins are storage or reserve products in seeds, roots, and tubers.

Cereal grains contain about 8 to 15 percent protein (Table 12-4) with adequate levels for human nutrition of the important sulfur-containing amino acid cysteine and the essential amino acid methionine. Corn (*Zea Mays*) kernels store a large amount of a protein zein, which is low in the amino acids lysine and tryptophan, both essential for human nutrition. Several new cultivars of corn have been developed that contain higher levels of these two amino acids. These new cultivars, with increased nutritional value, are potentially important in human and animal nutrition. Rice kernels, on the other hand, contain high concentrations of protein adequate in both lysine and tryptophan for human nutrition. The successful intergeneric cross of rye and wheat yielded a new genus, *Triticale,* with higher lysine than either parent. This new grain may become important for feeding the hungry people of the world. Cottonseed (*Gossypium*) and sunflower seed (*Helianthus*) contain up to 25 percent protein, and those of

Table 12-4   PROTEIN CONTENT OF VARIOUS FOOD CROPS

Plant	Common form of food	Percent protein
Cereal grains		
Oryza sativa	Whole rice	7.5–9.0
	Polished rice	5.2–7.6
Triticum aestivum	Wheat flour	9.8–13.5
Zea Mays	Corn meal	7.0–9.4
Legume seeds		
Cicer arietinum	Chick-pea	22–28
Glycine max	Soybean	33–45
	Soybean meal, defatted	49
	Soyprotein, concentrate	70–72
Arachis hypogaea	Peanut	25–30
Tubers		
Solanum tuberosum	Potato	10–13
Manihot esculenta	Cassava	1.3
Others		
Medicago sativa	Alfalfa meal	17
Various yeasts	Single cell protein	52–54

legumes, such as soybean (*Glycine max*) contain up to 45 percent good quality protein (Figure 12-3). Soybean protein is generally underutilized for human nutrition in the United States compared to its importance as a basic food in Asia. It has, in general, low concentrations of the sulfur-containing amino acids, but contains adequate levels of lysine.

The synthesis of lipids—fats and oils—is initiated by enzymatic bonding of two-carbon acetate units derived from pyruvic acid to form fatty acids with specific, even numbers of carbon atoms. Abundant in plants are 12-carbon lauric acid, 14-carbon myristic acid, 16-carbon palmitic acid, and 18-carbon stearic acid. These are straight-chain, saturated fatty acids where adjacent carbon atoms are joined by a single bond; unsaturated chains are those where one or more adjacent pairs of carbon atoms are joined by double bonds. The most common unsaturated fatty acid in plants, oleic acid, has 18 carbon atoms and 1 double bond. Linoleic acid, an essential fatty acid, has 18 carbon atoms and 2 double bonds. Oleic acid is found in high concentration in olive oil and peanut oil; linoleic acid is the dominant one in cotton and sunflower seed oils. Fatty acids, when bonded to glycerin, produce fats (solid at room temperature) and oils (liquid at room temperature). These lipid compounds are constituents of plant

Table 12-5   OIL CONTENT OF VARIOUS SEEDS

Plant	Common name	Percent oil
Cocos nucifera	Coconut	65
Helianthus annuus	Sunflower	up to 50
Zea Mays (germ or embryo)	Corn or maize	50
Arachis hypogaea	Peanut	36–45
Gossypium spp.	Cottonseed	35
Glycine max	Soybean	13–25
Carthamus tinctorius	Safflower	up to 40
Juglans spp.	Walnut	15

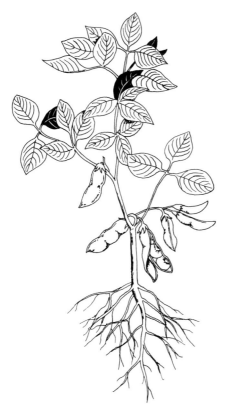

Soybean (*Glycine max*)   **Figure 12-3** The soybean plant (*Glycine max*).

membranes and are important storage products in certain seeds (Table 12-5) and in endosperm cells of coconut (*Cocos nucifera*) (Figure 12-4).

Organic acids are formed via Krebs cycle reactions and via both C_4 and CAM types of carbon dioxide fixation reactions. Krebs cycle compounds may accumulate to high levels: citric acid in citrus (*Citrus*), malic acid in apples (*Malus*), succinic acid in periwinkle (*Vinca*) and alfalfa (*Medicago sativa*), and fumaric acid in marigold (*Tagetes*) and sunflower (*Helianthus*). Leaves of rhubarb (*Rheum Rhabarbarum*) are poisonous due to the high concentration of calcium oxalate, although the red petioles are quite edible when cooked. Oxalic acid accumulates in *Oxalis, Begonia,* and spinach (*Spinacia oleracea*), while tartaric acid levels are high in grapes (*Vitis*) and geraniums (*Pelargonium*). They play roles as reservoirs of substances for the Krebs cycle and may control the acid-alkaline balance of plant cells.

Higher plants also synthesize vitamins, a heterogeneous group of complex molecules having a variety of routes of synthesis. These compounds function as cofactors of a number of enzymes, that is, they are nonprotein compounds essential for the functioning of those enzymes. Several of these cofactor-containing enzymes participate in cellular respiration. Although intact higher plants do not require vitamins, tissue culture medium for growing roots and

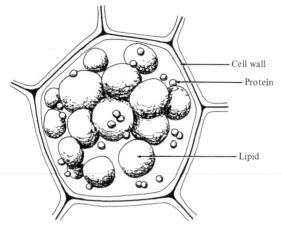

Figure 12-4   Endosperm cell of coconut (*Cocos nucifera*) storing both oil in large globules
and protein in smaller ones.

young embryos must contain several of the B vitamin group because not all plant
cells are capable of making vitamins. Vitamin B_{12} is not made by higher plants
and is the only one that plants cannot supply for human nutrition.

FERMENTATION

Fermentation is a term with a long and interesting history. Louis Pasteur's
significant experiments on fermentation saved the wine industry of France, when
he showed how to prevent wine from becoming vinegar by excluding air during
the fermentation process. Glucose present in wine grapes is converted to ethyl
alcohol and carbon dioxide by yeasts naturally present on the grapes.

   Fermentation, or anaerobic respiration, is a term used to describe the
glycolytic breakdown of glucose, in the absence of molecular oxygen, to pyruvic
acid and then to ethyl alcohol and carbon dioxide (Figure 12-5). Glucose may be
fermented to lactic acid, but this end product is much less frequently formed in
higher plant cells than is ethyl alcohol. Where molecular oxygen is absent, the

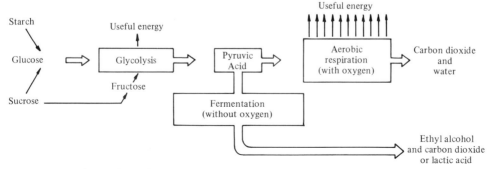

Figure 12-5   Comparison of aerobic respiration with fermentation.

electron transport system cannot function and, more importantly, the amount of ATP energy generated in fermentation is limited to that coming from glycolysis.

The process of fermentation occurs in cells of higher plants when oxygen is deficient, such as bulky storage organs when stored at too high a temperature. Low levels of oxygen in the central tissues leads to fermentation, rather than aerobic respiration, and to the accumulation of ethyl alcohol and carbon dioxide, both of which may become toxic. In the initial stages of germination of some seeds, impermeable seed coats may slow down the penetration of oxygen resulting in a period of fermentation rather than aerobic respiration. If oxygen did not become available, the embryo would soon die due to the accumulation of ethyl alcohol and to a deficiency of ATP energy.

An interesting question comes up here: How do living cells in the internal areas of trees with thick trunks obtain sufficient oxygen to carry on aerobic respiration? At least part of the answer is the presence of lenticels, openings in the bark surrounded by cork cells. The underlying tissue also has a high proportion of intercellular space. Lenticels seem to function by permitting gaseous diffusion into the tree trunk. Cherry and birch trees have prominent, evenly arranged lenticels on their bark; the small dots on the skins of apple and pear are lenticels.

The fermentation process is used by the baking and brewing industries. Leavened bread develops when an elastic protein, gluten, found in both wheat and rye flours, is "stretched" by the carbon dioxide released as baker's yeast ferments sugar in the flour-water mixture. In the brewing of beer, malted barley (sprouted, dried, and powdered barley grains) is the source of the enzyme amylase, which converts starch to glucose, which, in turn, is fermented by brewer's yeast to ethyl alcohol and carbon dioxide.

EFFECTS OF ENVIRONMENT ON RESPIRATORY PROCESSES

Cellular respiration in plants responds to changes in air (ambient) or soil temperature because all of its reactions are enzymatic and temperature sensitive. The term Q_{10} refers to the effect of temperature on enzyme reactions. For every 10° C rise in temperature between 5° C (41° F) and 25° C (77° F), the rate of an enzyme reaction will at least double as measured by either oxygen consumed or carbon dioxide released. This means that cell respiration at 10° C (50° F) goes on at a slower rate than at 20° C (68° F). Above 35° C (95° F) cell respiration begins to decrease as the activity of individual enzymes is depressed or enzymes are inactivated or destroyed. Respiration can be modified by oxygen concentration (Figure 12-6); the rate decreases slowly as concentration decreases from 21 percent (that of air) to about 10 percent at which point the rate begins to decrease more rapidly.

Such information has led to improvement in procedures for the long-term storage of several crops. Apples, in particular, benefit by being stored in controlled atmosphere storage (CAS). The temperature is kept at 0° C (32° F) and ambient oxygen is decreased to 1 to 3 percent, slowing down cell respiration and

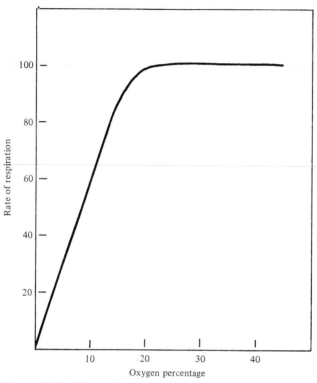

Figure 12-6 Effect of oxygen concentration in air on rate of respiration.

decreasing the amount of stored photosynthate metabolized. (This is discussed in more detail in Chapter 15.)

Other environmental factors also modify respiration rates. Cells infected by fungi may have rates that are higher than normal; roots in waterlogged soils show depressed respiration; herbicides may interfere with cellular respiration. It is pertinent here to mention thermoperiod. One consequence of a high nighttime temperature is high nighttime cellular respiration. If daytime photosynthesis does not exceed overall respiration, stored photosynthate will gradually be depleted leading to a depression of the general growth of the plant.

Changes in respiration rate may be related to the age of cells or tissues as well as to the stage of growth. Young expanding cells have a higher rate than maturing cells. During the germination of some seeds, carbon dioxide production increases during the first week of growth and then levels off.

SUPPLEMENTARY READINGS

Arms, K., and P. S. Camp. 1982. *Biology.* 2nd ed. Saunders, Philadelphia.
Beard, B. H. 1981. The sunflower crop. *Sci. Amer.* 244(5):150–161.
Davies, D. D. (ed.). 1980. *The Biochemistry of Plants.* Vol. 2. *Metabolism and Respiration.* Academic Press, New York.

Goodwin, T. W., and E. I. Mercer (eds.). 1983. *Introduction to Plant Biochemistry.* 2nd ed. Pergamon Press, London.

Klein, R. M. 1987. *The Green World.* 2nd ed. Harper & Row, New York.

Krogman, D. 1973. *The Biochemistry of Green Plants.* Prentice-Hall, Englewood Cliffs, N.J.

Milthorpe, F. L., and J. Moorby. 1979. *An Introduction to Crop Physiology.* 2nd ed. Cambridge University Press, Cambridge.

Opik, H. 1982. *The Respiration of Higher Plants.* Studies in Biology No. 120. University Park Press, Baltimore, Md.

Palmer, J. M. 1984. *Physiology and Biochemistry of Plant Respiration.* Cambridge University Press, Cambridge.

Salisbury, F. B., and C. W. Ross. 1985. *Plant Physiology.* 3rd ed. Wadsworth, Belmont, Calif.

Ting, I. P. 1982. *Plant Physiology.* Addison-Wesley, Reading, Mass.

Vickery, M. L., and B. Vickery. 1981. *Secondary Plant Metabolism.* University Park Press, Baltimore, Md.

PART FOUR

PLANT GROWTH AND DEVELOPMENT

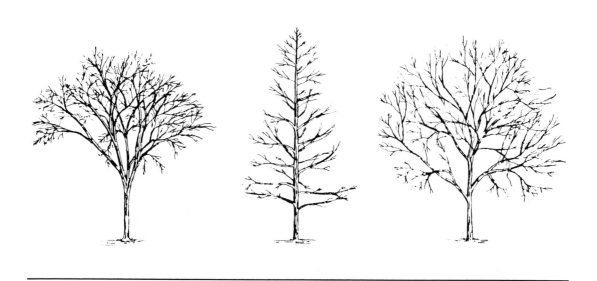

C H A P T E R 1 3

INTRODUCTION TO PLANT GROWTH

CONCEPTS AND COMPONENTS OF GROWTH

Division, Enlargement, and Differentiation

Plant growth is a complex process that can be examined in many different ways depending on what aspect is to be considered. It is convenient to examine growth in terms of three cellular processes. Plant cells divide, they enlarge, and they differentiate. The first two of these growth processes are easily visualized; cell division involves growth in number and enlargement involves growth in size. Differentiation is more complex. A cell can become different by changes in structure, as when chloroplasts develop or a secondary cell wall is formed. Differentiation may also involve a change in function; a cell that develops chloroplasts can photosynthesize and is both structurally and functionally changed. A cell may mature and die. Cells of the xylem are functional in moving water only after they have formed secondary walls and have died. The sequence of division, enlargement, and differentiation starts with a meristematic cell. It undergoes division to form two cells, one or both may divide again, and one or

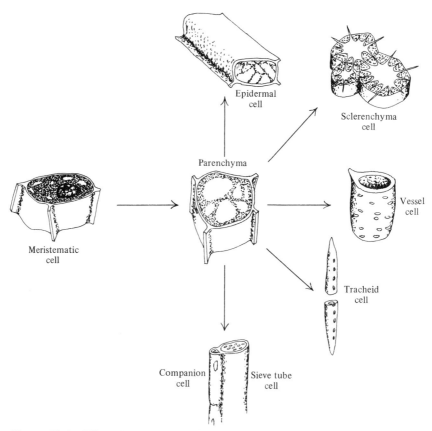

Figure 13-1   Differentiated cell types.

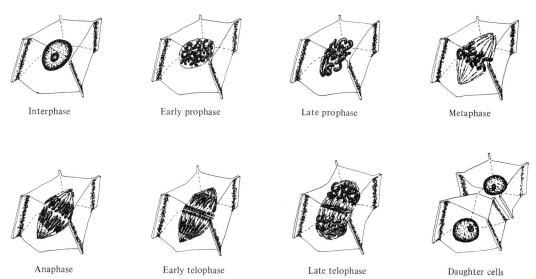

| Interphase | Early prophase | Late prophase | Metaphase |

| Anaphase | Early telophase | Late telophase | Daughter cells |

Figure 13-2   Stages in cell division (mitosis) of plant cells.

both may begin to enlarge and then mature and differentiate into the various cell types that make up the plant body (Figure 13-1). These cellular activities are the foundation for the growth of the entire plant.

Vegetative cell division, called mitosis, is the most fundamental process in plant growth. In mitosis a cell divides by a regular sequence of events that ensures that each of the two resulting cells contains enough cytoplasm to maintain metabolic processes and also contains the full genetic complement possessed by the original or parent cell (Figure 13-2). In many instances the two resulting cells are the same size, but occasionally cell division may be unequal, with one cell being larger than the other. A critical feature in cell division is the plane in which the new cell wall that separates the two cells forms. If, in a series of divisions, all the planes of division are oriented parallel to each other, a file or column of cells is formed. This occurs in both roots and shoots. If the planes of division alternate at right angles, a sheet of cells results. If the planes of division are unoriented, a mass of cells results. This is seen in meristems and in several disease conditions. Other patterns also occur. Continued cell division can also result in increases in the mass or volume of the organ or tissue.

Cell enlargement involves the accumulation of water into cell vacuoles. The resulting wall pressure, combined with a loosening of the cell wall, causes cell enlargement (Figure 13-3). If the enlarged cell forms new cell wall material, the enlargement is permanent. Depending on the location of the cell in the plant body, its genetic programming, and other factors, cells may enlarge in all dimensions to become essentially spherical or the enlargement may result in an increase in length (elongation) or in girth. Much of the increase in the length of young roots and shoots is due to cell elongation. The formation of columns of cells by a series of divisions with parallel wall formation and the subsequent

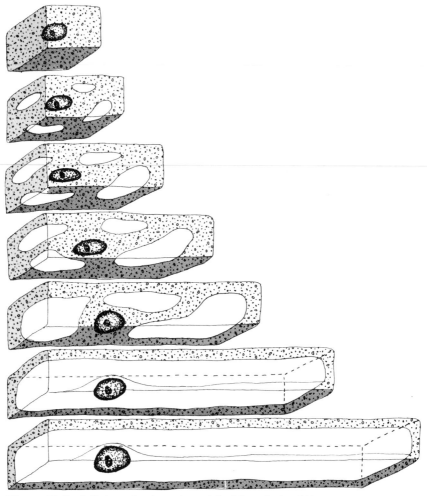

Figure 13-3 Cell elongation by water uptake into cell vacuoles.

elongation of these cells results in cell columns that will, by differentiation, form the vascular systems of shoots and roots.

Chemical Control of Growth

The processes of division, enlargement, and differentiation must, for the acquisition of the typical form and function of the plant, be precisely regulated and controlled. The physical and chemical factors involved in cell development are varied and complex and many of the details are poorly understood. All of the metabolic activities are involved. Photosynthesis and respiration supply the energy and many of the compounds needed for growth. Water and nutrients, proper temperature, genetic regulation, and other factors are part of the controlling complex.

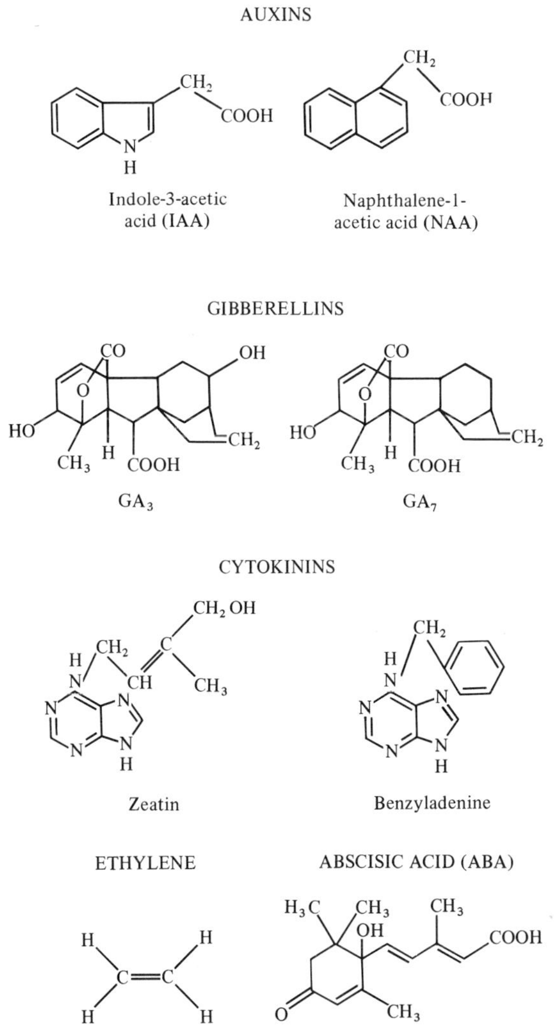

Figure 13-4 Structural formulas for plant growth-regulating compounds.

Sparked by experiments of Charles Darwin in the nineteenth century, there has been continued research on the roles of the specific chemicals that are the major components of growth regulation. Plant growth regulators are best defined as organic (carbon-containing) compounds other than nutrients that are utilized in small amounts to affect growth processes. Plant hormones are growth-regulating compounds that are made by the plant and usually move within the plant from the site of synthesis to the site of action—a cell, tissue, or organ. Here the term plant hormone is restricted to naturally occurring compounds, while the term plant growth regulator includes both natural hormones and synthetic compounds. There are five major groups of growth regulators (Figure 13-4) and several minor groups. There are both natural (endogenous) and synthetic members of each group.

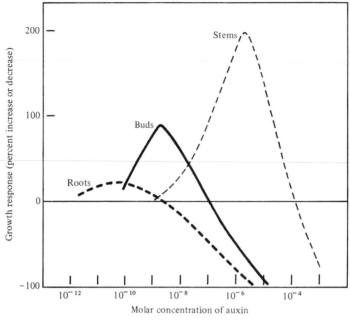

Figure 13-5 Differential sensitivity of roots, buds, and stems to auxin.

The first group of these growth-regulating substances is the auxins (Greek *auxein,* "to increase"). The major auxin is indoleacetic acid (IAA), although other related natural compounds are found and many valuable synthetic compounds have been made. It was first believed that auxins were active only in cell elongation, but they are now known to be required for division, differentiation, and a number of metabolic reactions. Natural auxins are synthesized in most young cells and tissues with meristems, young leaves or flowers, with developing fruits and seeds being the most active. They diffuse polarly, almost always down (basipetally) from the region of synthesis so that there is a gradient in concentration in plant tissues and organs. Although the modes of action of auxin are still speculative, it is known that growth responses depend largely on the concentration of the substance and the "readiness" of the cells to respond. Cells in different organs are responsive to different concentrations of auxin with growth effects on root cells and tissues requiring less than buds or stems (Figure 13-5). Higher concentrations tend to be inhibitory, which is itself a control process in plant growth.

Auxins play many specific roles in plant growth and development. Natural and particularly the synthetic auxins are important aids in regulating plant production. Many are herbicides in low concentrations, selectively killing undesirable plants. Since monocots, particularly grasses, are less sensitive to being killed by auxins than are most dicots, auxins are used to rid lawns of weeds and to control weeds in grain fields (Figure 13-6). They are used to root cuttings, regulate plant height, induce flower formation, control fruit set and fruit drop, and in many other processes.

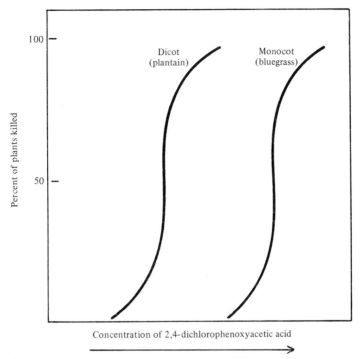

Figure 13-6 Differential sensitivity of a monocot, such as a lawn grass, and a dicot, such as plantain, to an auxinic herbicide.

The gibberellins, of which gibberellic acid (GA_3) is the best known, were discovered as the causal factor of a disease of rice. There are many gibberellins, each given a number. Some plants may contain 6 to 10 chemically distinguishable GAs. They are found in low concentrations and move in all directions from the zone of synthesis. Cell and tissue response depends not only on readiness to react and gibberellin concentration, but also on the presence of other growth-regulating substances including auxins. They affect a number of growth processes including cell division, elongation, and differentiation and are known to activate enzymes and to overcome dormancy. Auxins also are involved in these processes, but appear to affect different parts of the process than do the gibberellins.

GAs are widely used in horticulture. Sprays of 5 to 10 ppm increase grape size and cluster number by up to 100 percent. They maintain freshness in leafy vegetable crops, prevent rind discoloration in citrus fruits, and cause size increases in stems and leaves of ornamental plants. Soaking some seeds (peas, beans, citrus, grape, apple, and stone fruits) in a 5000 ppm solution of GA for 24 hours greatly speeds up germination. GAs can cause induction of parthenocarpy (formation of seedless fruits) in blueberry, cranberry, pome, citrus, and grape fruits. Tuber initiation and uniformity of sprouting of potato pieces can be synchronized by GAs to permit more economical harvesting. Using GA to break dormancy in flowering bulbs and corms is being studied and has already had some commercial success. GA_3 has also become important in the brewing industry by activating germination of barley used for malt. There is great potential for GA in increasing the yields of many crops and ornamentals and new applications are being made at a rapid rate.

The third major group of plant growth-regulating substances is the cytokinins. The first to be reported, kinetin, is not found in plants, but was isolated from fish sperm. There are a large number of natural cytokinins in plant cells. Tissues undergoing rapid cell division synthesize these compounds which can move from cell to cell. They, like auxins and gibberellins, are active in low concentrations, are effective in various tissues in different concentrations, and interact strongly with other growth regulators. Their structural similarity to components of nucleic acids suggests that their mode of action is related to the activity of nucleic acids.

Working in conjunction with auxins and GAs, the range of growth processes affected by the cytokinins is large: germination stimulation, differentiation and regulation of buds, breaking of dormancy, modification of fruit set, modification of fruit and seed development, and a role in the senescence and death of leaves. In spite of this spectrum of activity, they have only a few practical roles. Their main application at present is in the asexual reproduction of plants by tissue and cell culture methods of cloning plants (Chapter 15). However, as we learn more about them, their use will increase.

Although it was known for many years that some substance in air could cause malformations in plants, break dormancy in buds of potato tubers, and accelerate the ripening of fruit, the chemical nature of the gas was not established until the 1930s. The gas is ethylene, a simple organic compound found in artifical illuminating gas and produced by soil microorganisms and plants. Like other growth-regulating substances, ethylene production and activity is bound up with other substances, notably auxins, and both its synthesis and activity are modified by light, temperature, and the stage of development of cells, tissues, and organs. It is active in extremely low concentrations and is measured by gas chromatography.

The first horticultural use of ethylene was in the ripening of fruit, initially citrus fruits, but now many commercially available fruits and some vegetables. Green but mature fruits are placed in gas-tight rooms containing ethylene gas where they ripen in a short time. As knowledge of ethylene advanced, a search was made for a synthetic substance that could release controlled amounts of the gas. The ethylene-releasing compound Ethephon has been used since 1965, and it has assumed a greater role in horticultural crop production as its effects have become better known. For ripening, harvested fruits are dipped in a 5000 ppm Ethephon solution. Its use allows commercial producers to harvest an entire crop at one time rather than having to pick several times. In addition to its use in ripening Ethephon sprays at 2500 ppm are used to induce flower formation in apples and bromeliads and to cause uniform flowering of bananas. Female cucumber plants are treated with Ethephon to cause a few flowers to change into males, while maintaining a preponderance of female flowers for fruit development. Spraying nut trees with ethylene-releasing compounds speeds up development of the abscission layer and the fruits are more easily shaken from the trees. Similar treatments can loosen grapes and cherries and speed up their maturation.

Since injured or diseased plants produce ethylene, storage problems exist; a single diseased apple can speed up the ripening of an entire lot.

We have considered only those plant growth substances that promote developmental processes, but there are also natural inhibitors involved in growth regulation. The best known of these is abscisic acid (ABA). Initially found in 1953, details of its structure, synthesis, and roles were worked out only in the last decade. ABA is a general growth inhibitor, affecting seed and bud dormancy, leaf, flower, and fruit drop, and stomatal action. At the cellular level it represses the elongation of cells regulated by auxins or gibberellins and may affect maturation processes in several tissue systems. Its synthesis is regulated by environmental conditions, especially photoperiod operating through the phytochrome system. ABA is therefore an important compound in dormancy induction and release in perennial species. Like other regulators, it is effective in low concentration and interacts with other regulators in producing the observed responses. Practical uses for ABA have not yet been extensively developed.

These five groups of growth-regulating substances do not complete the spectrum of natural compounds that affect plant growth and development. Whether classified as growth regulators or not, many compounds play significant roles by themselves or through interactions with growth regulators. Each regulator group may contain several to many compounds and different members of each group are individually and selectively effective in a wide range of concentrations. The stage of development and the cell or tissue type determine the direction and extent of response, and the ratios among one, two, or more regulators elicit different responses. It is obvious that plant growth and development is under exquisite control. As knowledge of these interactions increases, it is expected that translation of research into applications will continue to be an important facet of plant science.

With increased knowledge of the types and roles of natural growth-regulating compounds, development of synthetics soon followed. Some resemble natural compounds and are used to control plant growth through interaction or interference with natural substances. These include the phenoxy acids, of which 2,4-dichlorophenoxyacetic acid (2,4-D) is the best known weed killer, and naphthaleneacetic acid (NAA) and indolebutyric acid (IBA), which are used to root cuttings, enhance fruit set, and for other purposes.

For both lawns and some crop plants, the lowered sensitivity of monocots such as the grasses and the cereal crops to auxinic herbicides compared with the higher sensitivities of many broad-leaved dicots is the basis for the selective killing of weedy species in the plantings (Figure 13-6).

Other growth-regulating chemicals bear little structural or metabolic relationship to natural compounds, but are tailored for specific horticultural and agronomic roles (Figure 13-7). Synthetic growth-retarding compounds have considerable importance in manipulating the growth of horticultural plants. Maleic hydrazide and other compounds have been used to prevent the growth of lawn, turf, and roadside grasses. The development of growth retardants and dwarfing compounds has been an economic boon to the floriculture industry, allowing the production of plants with short internodes and, in some cases,

NATURAL PHENOLIC INHIBITORS

Benzoic acid 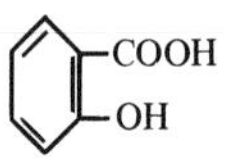   Salicylic acid 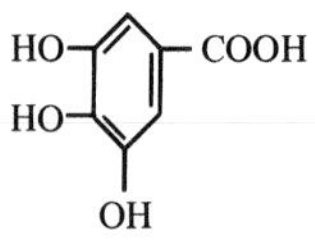   Gallic acid

SYNTHETIC DWARFING COMPOUNDS

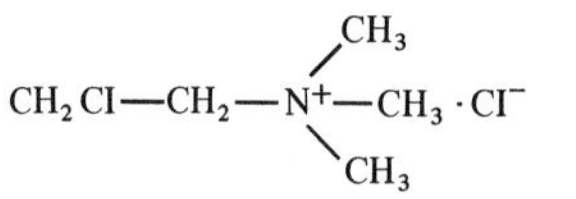

CCC, or Cycocel (2-Chloroethyl trimethylammonium
chloride)

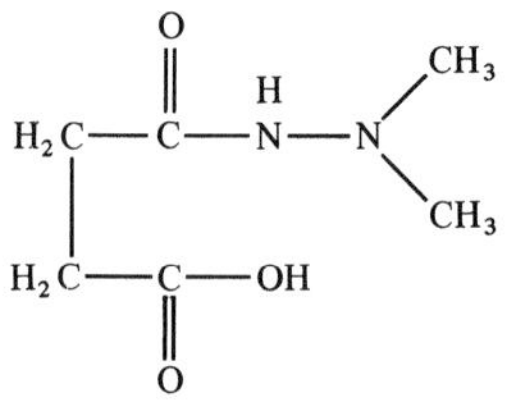

B Nine, or B-995
(Succinic acid 2,2-dimethylhydrazide)

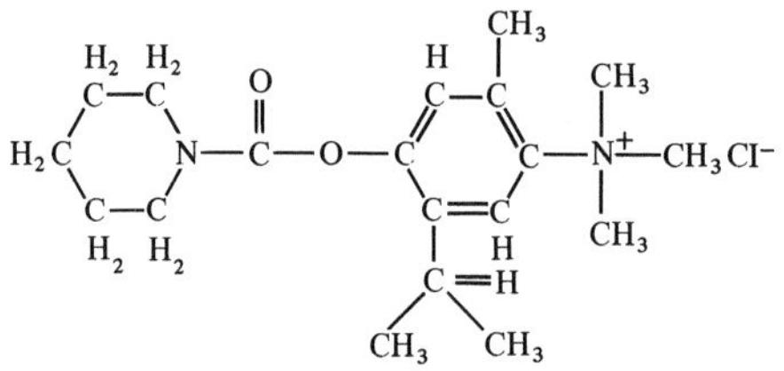

AMO 1618 (2-isopropyl-4-dimethylamino-5
-methylphenyl-1-piperidine-carboxylate methyl chloride)

SYNTHETIC AUXINLIKE INHIBITORS

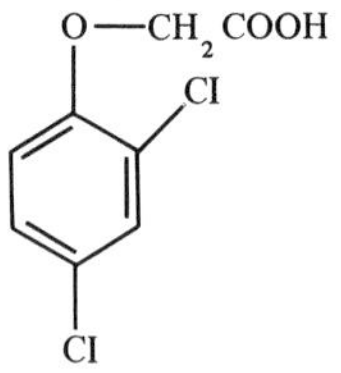

2,4-D (2,4-dichlorophenoxyacetic acid)

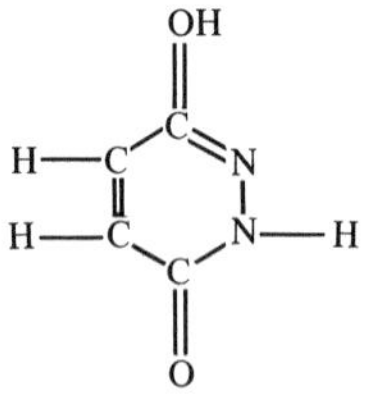

Maleic hydrazide

Figure 13-7 Structural formulas of plant growth-retarding compounds.

shorter stems produced by decreased cell elongation. A number of these with
different chemical formulae are now available. Where bushy plants are desired,
as in market chrysanthemum, begonia, azalea, and fuchsia, removal of the
terminal stem bud had been done by hand pinching (Chapter 14), but chemical

"pinchers" that selectively kill the cells of the apical meristem are routinely used for some plants. In nursery stock production treatment with chemical pruners results in desirably branched trees and shrubs and the application of these chemicals has been extended to orchard trees. Controlled abscission is a prelude to mechanical harvesting of crops like cotton where leaves interfere with the collection, the harvesting of oranges, sweet cherries, and other crops, and the defoliation of nursery stock for fall pruning and planting.

Natural and synthetic growth-regulating substances are still being isolated and compounded. Among the newest are morphactins, organic fluorine compounds. They are effective growth suppressants in very low concentrations, prevent normal auxin transport, and seem to interfere with normal gibberellin regulation. Because of their low toxicity, they probably will be useful.

Environmental Control of Growth

It is obvious that any environmental factor can affect plant growth. Because of the economic importance of many plants, considerable theoretical and applied research has been devoted to determining the direction and extent of growth modification caused by light, water, temperature, and nutrients. With few exceptions the impact of any environmental factor is determined by the interplay of that factor with the genetic makeup of the plant. The genetic constitution determines the limits of possible plant response; environment determines the degree of response. The genetic spectrum is called the genotypic potential and the plant resulting from the interaction of heredity and environment is the phenotypic expression, that is, what the plant actually looks like.

$$\left. \begin{array}{l} \text{Genotype} \\ \text{Environment} \end{array} \right\} \rightarrow \text{Internal metabolic processes} \rightarrow \text{Phenotype}$$

Shade-requiring annuals like sea lavender *(Statice latifolia)* may show a much different phenotype when grown in full sun than when grown in shade; the common house plant split-leaf philodendron *(Monstera deliciosa)* will have small, entire leaves in low light, but large, deeply lobed leaves in adequate light. Plants under long-term water stress or receiving inadequate nutrition will frequently be less vigorous and may bear leaves, flowers, or fruit that are different in shape or size. If an environmental stress occurs for even a short time at a critical stage in development, the plant may never express its full genetic potential.

Genotype-phenotype interactions bear strongly on selecting plants for particular locations. Plants grown outside the range optimum for their development require special attention and even then may not exhibit their full developmental potential. In the continual search for new economically important plants, the provenance (the place of origin) of the individual plant is an important consideration. Within a wild species there are usually individuals or populations that have been genetically adapted to particular environmental conditions.

These ecotypes (ecological types) represent a pool of genetic potential (germ plasm) useful for selection and breeding of cultivars.

MEASURING AND MODELING PLANT GROWTH

Many aspects of plant growth can be analyzed quantitatively. No single measurement provides a complete picture of growth, but each type of measurement has value. With the development of sophisticated statistical methods and computers, growth measurements for research and crop evaluation observe fairly rigid standards, and any study should be preceded by full consideration of statistics. This is particularly necessary for field studies since genetic uniformity is difficult to achieve and even slight alterations in environmental conditions can cause large changes in plant growth.

Growth measurements may be destructive, with plants harvested for weight determinations or chemical analyses. They may also be nondestructive, leaving plants uninjured and unaltered. Nondestructive methods allow measurements to be made over a period of time to provide a kinetic record of growth. Kinetic analyses can be made with destructive sampling by using a large enough number of plants to allow periodic sampling. Since any imposed variable or condition of an experiment can be expressed through several types of response, the controls or checks used as the base for evaluation of the effects of the variable must be extensive and chosen with care. This is easier in laboratory or greenhouse studies than in field trials where many environmental factors cannot be adequately regulated.

Measurements can be grouped into several major categories: number, size, weight, and physical and chemical analysis, the last including the wide range of metabolic activities of plants. Both destructive and nondestructive methods are used and the techniques available are many and varied.

The most fundamental kinetic measurement is the growth rate, usually presented as a time-related process (Figure 13-8). Virtually the same sigmoid (S-shaped) curve is obtained with such diverse growth phenomena as increase in number of a bacterial population, size of tomato fruits, weight of cucumbers, and height of pea plants. A period of little or no observable growth, called the lag phase, is followed by a period of rapid growth, the grand or log phase, followed by a period of no observable growth, called the stationary phase. When time is plotted against the logarithm of the growth measurement, the resulting graph is a straight line whose slope is the rate of growth. Such slopes are used to compare growth rates of two or more populations, variables, or cultivars. Growth rate curves can be transformed (first derivative) to show the daily or weekly growth rate providing a visual measure of when growth is most or least rapid. Such analyses are valuable to determine when a crop requires water or fertilizer to ensure maximum development.

Under field conditions, where water, temperature, light, or nutrients may vary during the growing season, growth rate curves are complex, with several sequences of lag-log-stationary phases. These have considerable value in plant

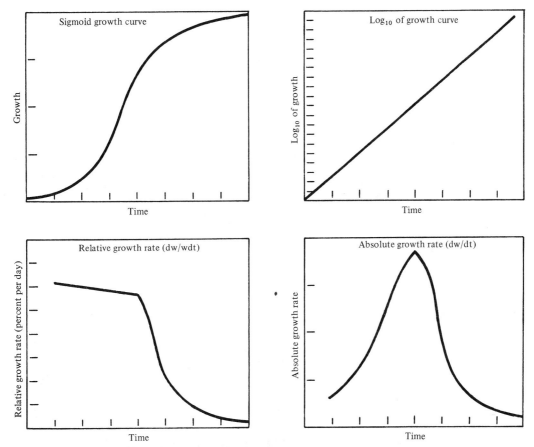

Figure 13-8 Types of growth rate curves.

growth analysis. The repeating patterns in growth of perennials are used to predict health and vigor over several years.

Some growth phenomena occur on an annual cycle and are not easily handled by standard growth analyses. One of the more important of these is the influence of climate on growth processes like leaf abscission, winter bud formation, bud break in the spring, flowering, and fruiting. This study is called phenology and is of great importance. In order to evaluate the potential use of an ornamental perennial over a wide geographical range, genetically identical plants are grown throughout the range and the dates of selected events are determined. Analysis of these dates can establish the effective range of a cultivar or species. Such studies require many years to complete, but are invaluable for horticulturists and landscape designers. They also provide useful information on the influence of climate on plant growth and development that could not otherwise be obtained. Phenological analysis is not restricted to changes that are visually apparent, but also includes the timing and sequence of changes that occur at cell

and tissue levels. The effect of meteorological factors on the initiation and
development of secondary vascular formation, dormancy, or stages in fruit
ripening can be measured on phenological scales.

In horticulture and agriculture predicting the success of a planting or crop
has great economic importance. Hardiness zone selection, determination of soil,
nutritional and water needs, site selection, and other factors are well understood.
Many environmental factors are beyond our control, such as diseases and pests
and poor growing seasons. To evaluate the potential impact of these variable
factors, modeling schemes have been developed that attempt to calculate the
possible effect on yield of all the internal and external factors that affect the
growth of a plant or a crop. A model, to have predictive value, must include and
evaluate as many of the factors affecting plant growth as possible, realizing that
this is an impossible task. It is made even more difficult because the impact of an
environmental condition on growth and development changes at different stages
in the plant's life cycle, and there are great variations in the responsiveness of
cultivars.

In spite of these obvious difficulties, models for major agricultural crops
have been developed. Growth models fall into two categories. The empirical
model transforms field data into formulas that describe the data in mathematical
terms without generating any information that was not contained in the field
data. Another, more useful approach, is the development of a mechanistic
model. It attempts to bring together all of the environmental and biological
factors that might affect plant growth, to determine the relative importance of
each factor, and by computer transformations to predict how an alteration in any
one factor will affect growth and yield. Calculated predictions can be tested
against an empirical model to determine the adequacy of the mechanistic model
and, if the "fit" is good, the mechanistic model can have predictive value in
future years. In general, such models have proved to be valuable with predictive
efficiencies above 75 percent. It appears that the single most important component of crop-yield models is the total amount of photosynthetically active
radiation received during the growing season. Temperature is the second most
important factor. Together, these two factors account for 85 to 90 percent of the
variability from year to year. This assumes that water, nutrient supply, competition, and injury by biotic and nonbiotic factors can be completely controlled.
With improved understanding of the complex internal and external regulation of
growth, both genetic and environmental, computer modeling of plant growth will
become even more useful to the producer and the consumer.

GROWTH MOVEMENTS

Plants orient themselves in space. These orientations are accomplished by
growth movements. Growth movements are classified into two groups, those that
involve reversible alterations in turgor pressure and those that involve irreversible changes in cell length. The forcible dispersal of geranium seeds by coiling
and uncoiling of fruit structures and the sudden splitting of legume pods are due
to tensions developed and released by changes in hydration of cells. Impatiens,

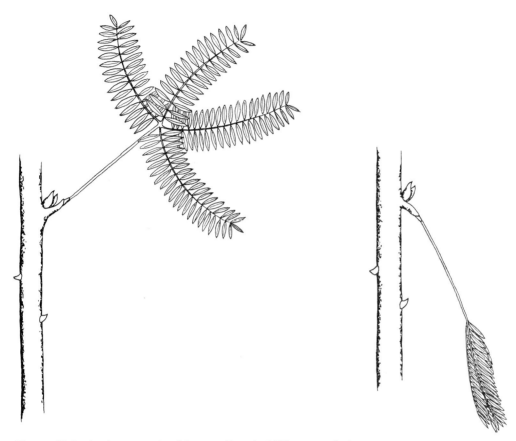

Figure 13-9   Leaf movements of the sensitive plant (*Mimosa pudica*).

squirting cucumber (*Ecballium elaterium*), and other seeds may be ejected much like a cork from a champagne bottle. Leaf rolling in grains and grasses, the drooping of rhododendron leaves in cold weather, and changes in leaflet position in the sensitive plant (*Mimosa pudica*) involve alterations in turgor pressure in special structures (Figure 13-9).

   Growth movements are responses to external stimuli including gravity, light, water, chemicals, and touch. Stems are usually negatively geotropic, tending to grow upward, and roots are positively geotropic, growing downward. Branches may grow laterally at right angles (diageotropism) or at some other fixed angle to the vertical axis (plagiogeotropism), and roots may grow out from the tap root at specific angles. Some plant organs are ageotropic. The angle of lateral growth is genetically determined, with a number of important ornamental tree cultivars exhibiting the desirable "weeping" habit that can be maintained by vegetative propagation. Geotropic response can change with time. Flower buds of oriental poppy (*Papaver orientale*) are recurved and become negatively geotropic when mature, while many lilies (*Lilium* spp.) show the reverse response with positive geotropic curvatures developing after fertilization. Daffodil flower

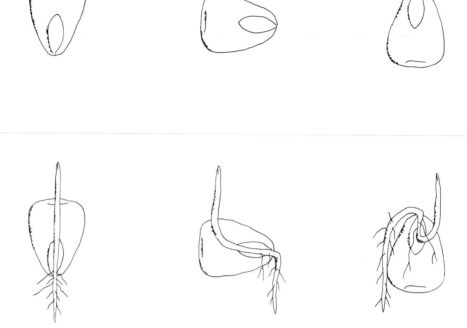

Figure 13-10   Geotropic growth of stem and root of a corn seedling.

buds become horizontal just before bud opening. The peanut (*Arachis hypogaea*) flower stalk is negatively geotropic and, after fertilization, becomes positively geotropic and buries the fruit in the ground.

There are several theories on gravity sensing. Auxins are involved since the movement requires differential cell elongation which is known to be mediated by auxins. If a normally vertical stem is placed in the horizontal position, it will bend upward because cells on the lower portion of the organ elongate more than those on the upper portion (Figure 13-10). Bending reactions are restricted to young, elongating areas or zones of the organ. In most plants planting seeds upside down or sideways is accommodated by geotropic movements, allowing mechanical sowing or little attention to seed placement, but in some species, accommodation does not occur readily and the seedling will become twisted and may not survive. In some ornamental woody perennials including many conifers, the geotropic angle of growth persists, and rooted shoot cuttings will not grow upright, but will maintain the predetermined angle.

As a horizontal branch of a tree becomes heavier, it would be expected to bend of its own weight. Except for weeping forms of trees, this rarely occurs. Bending stimulates formation of what is called reaction wood. In hardwood species (angiosperms) more cambial activity occurs on the upper side of the branch with the formation of tension wood having fewer and smaller vessels, more cellulose, and less lignin than normal wood. In softwoods (gymnosperms) the excess cambial activity occurs on the lower side of the branch resulting in compression wood in which the xylem tracheids have more lignin and less cellulose than normal. The formation of reaction wood is exploited by forcing a branch into the desired position and holding it for a period of time sufficient to allow development of reaction wood. This is accomplished in bonsai by wiring a branch into the desired position. In orchard trees scaffolding branches are positioned by inserting a stiff brace between the main stem and the branch to force the branch into the semihorizontal position. Once in the desired position and with reaction wood formed, the branch can withstand the weight of a heavy fruit crop.

Phototropism has been discussed in the chapter on light. The bending toward (positive phototropism) or away (negative phototropism) from blue-violet wavelengths is caused by an unequal distribution of auxin on the sides facing and away from the source of unilateral illumination, with more auxin accumulating on the shaded side. The cells receiving more auxin elongate more than those receiving less with consequent bending of the organ. In positive phototropism the reorientation of the plant places it in a position to receive more light for photosynthesis (Figure 13-11). Negative phototropism occurs in many vines where the roots are brought into closer contact with walls or tree trunks. In

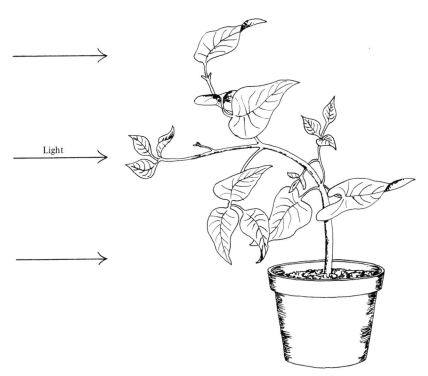

Light

Figure 13-11 Phototropic growth of stem and leaves.

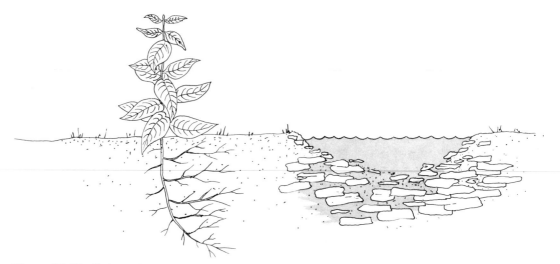

Figure 13-12 Hydrotropic growth of roots.

homes, where the primary source of light is frequently unilateral, it is necessary to turn the pots a quarter turn every day or two to prevent the plant from becoming directionally oriented.

Hydrotropism is seen in legumes and curcubits, but is not as common as other tropisms. Since geotropism is a more dominant growth reaction, hydrotropism is overwhelmed in most plants. The "seeking" of water by growth of roots is

Figure 13-13 Thigmotropic growth of stem.

more properly considered to be the growth of the root along a concentration gradient of water without tropic, differential cell elongation (Figure 13-12).

Little is known of the reactability of plants to chemicals, electric fields, and temperature, although chemo- and thermo-tropisms have been observed for over a century. Roots appear to exhibit avoidance reactions, with tropic growth responses away from certain chemicals, unfavorable temperatures, or electric fields, followed by the more usual response to gravity.

Many plants exhibit thigmotropic growth movement, the stimulus arising from a touch of the plant organ to some solid structure such as a pole, or another plant stem (Figure 13-13). As with other tropisms, it involves a differential growth response resulting in the coiling of the tendril or stem about the support. Many peas, beans, and other legumes show this tropism, and it is exploited in the design of supports for these plants.

SUPPLEMENTARY READINGS

Baker, N. R. 1985. *Control of Leaf Growth.* Cambridge University Press, Cambridge.

Burgess, J. 1985. *Introduction to Plant Cell Development.* Cambridge University Press, Cambridge.

Carlson, P. S. (ed.). 1980. *The Biology of Crop Productivity.* Academic Press, New York.

Causton, D., and J. Venis. 1981. *The Biometry of Plant Growth.* Edward Arnold, London.

Charles-Edwards, D. A. 1982. *Physiological Determinants of Crop Growth.* Academic Press, New York.

Crosier, A. (ed.). 1983. *The Biochemistry and Physiology of Gibberellins.* 2 vols. Praeger, New York.

Dale, J. E. *The Growth of Leaves.* Studies in Biology No. 137. University Park Press, Baltimore, Md.

Erickson, R. O., and W. K. Silk. 1980. The kinematics of plant growth. *Sci. Amer.* 242(5):134–151.

Evans, G. C. 1972. *The Quantitative Analysis of Plant Growth.* Blackwell, Oxford.

Firn, R. D., and J. Digby. 1980. The establishment of tropic curvatures in plants. *Annu. Rev. Plant Physiol.* 31:131–148.

Hill, T. A. 1980. *Endogenous Plant Growth Substances.* 2nd ed. Edward Arnold, London.

Hunt, R. 1978. *Plant Growth Analysis.* Studies in Biology No. 96. University Park Press, Baltimore, Md.

Leopold, A. C., and P. E. Kriedemann. 1975. *Plant Growth and Development.* 2nd ed. McGraw-Hall, New York.

Letham, D. S., P. B. Goodwin, and T. J. V. Higgans. 1978. *Phytohormones and Related Compounds: A Comprehensive Treatise.* 2 vols. Elsevier-North Holland, Amsterdam.

Loomis, R. S., R. Rabbinge, and E. Ng. 1979. Explanatory models in crop physiology. *Annu. Rev. Plant Physiol.* 30:339–367.

Luckwill, L. C. 1981. *Growth Regulators and Crop Production.* Studies in Biology No. 129. University Park Press, Baltimore, Md.

Milthorpe, F. L., and J. Moorby. 1979. *An Introduction to Crop Physiology.* 2nd ed. Oxford University Press, Oxford.

Moreland, D. E. 1980. Mechanisms of action of herbicides. *Annu. Rev. Plant Physiol.* 31:597–630.

Nickell, L. G. 1982. *Plant Growth Regulators: Agricultural Uses.* Springer-Verlag, New York.

Nickell, L. G. (ed.). 1983. *Plant Growth Regulating Chemicals.* 2 vols. CRC Press, Boca Raton, Fla.

Pearson, C. J. (ed.). 1984. *Control of Crop Productivity.* Academic Press, Orlando, Fla.

Wareing, P. F., and I. D. G. Phillips. 1981. *Growth and Differentiation in Plants.* 3rd ed. Pergamon Press, Elmsford, N.Y.

Weaver, R. J. 1972. *Plant Growth Substances in Agriculture.* Freeman, San Francisco.

Wilkins, M. B. (ed.). 1984. *Advanced Plant Physiology.* Pittman, London.

C H A P T E R   1 4

VEGETATIVE GROWTH

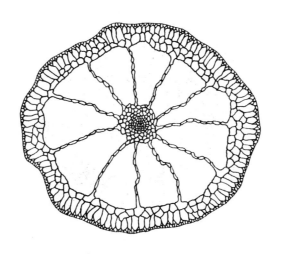

SEED GERMINATION

Storage and Longevity

Seeds may be successfully stored for long periods of time, but particular environmental conditions are a prerequisite to maintain the viability and developmental ability of the embryo. Temperature, moisture, and oxygen concentration must be controlled. The conditions that are conducive to seed viability in storage are essentially opposite those that promote germination. Optimum temperature for storage is quite low, around 0° C (32° F), although seeds can be held at somewhat higher temperatures if the relative humidity is below 10 percent. Keeping seeds cool and dry is the basic requirement.

The moisture levels of freshly harvested seed may range up to 20 percent. Drying to less than 12 percent for cereal grains and legume seeds and to 4 to 7 percent for most others is necessary if seed is to be maintained for long periods of time. However, embryos of a few seeds die when dried to this low moisture level. Some trees, such as sugar maple, oak, hickory, and walnut and citrus species, are in this category.

The other environmental condition conducive to successful storage is low atmospheric oxygen with increased carbon dioxide. As the level of carbon dioxide increases, respiration decreases, which slows down utilization of food reserves and extends the viability of the seed. Storage of seeds in sealed containers, such as the aluminum foil packets now used by many suppliers, controls the ambient atmosphere of the seed. As the seeds slowly respire, oxygen decreases and carbon dioxide increases.

Longevity of seeds has a curious fascination for people since many seeds remain viable for decades and even centuries. Seeds of arctic lupine (*Lupinus arcticus*), discovered in dry, frozen soil in an animal burrow and reputed to be 10,000 years old, germinated and produced normal plants. Lotus seed discovered in an Asian lake bed and proved to be at least 400 years old by radiocarbon dating germinated and formed apparently normal plants.

One of the first studies on seed longevity was started in 1879 by Professor W. J. Beal at Michigan State University. Seeds of 23 wild plants were harvested, mixed with sandy soil, placed in unsealed containers, and buried in the ground. Samples were tested at intervals during the next 100 years and seeds of a few species germinated after 100 years and produced normal plants. These were common round-leaved mallow (*Malva rotundifolia*), common mullein or flannel plant (*Verbascum thapsus*), and moth mullein (*V. blattaria*).

One problem in determining whether seed from wild plants will germinate is that seeds may be dormant when tested but capable of germination if tested at a time of the year when they would normally germinate. There is accumulating evidence that seeds go in and out of dormancy. If germination does not occur because environmental conditions are not favorable, the seeds become dormant again and will not germinate although still viable. This situation seems not to be the case for seeds of ornamental and agricultural crops which germinate at any time of the year when conditions are favorable.

Table 14-1 AVERAGE NUMBER OF YEARS SEEDS OF SOME FLOWERS REMAIN VIABLE WHEN STORED UNDER APPROPRIATE CONDITIONS

Latin name	Common name	Latin name	Common name
One to two years		**Four years**	
Aster	Aster	*Lobularia*	Sweet alyssum
Delphinium	Larkspur	**Five years**	
Phlox	Phlox	*Alcea*	Hollyhock
Lathyrus	Sweet pea	*Calendula*	Field marigold
Three years		*Centaurea*	Dusty miller
Antirrhinum	Snapdragon	*Chrysanthemum*	Chrysanthemum
Arctotis	African daisy	*Dianthus*	Carnation
Artemisia	Dusty miller	*Matthiola*	Stock
Chrysanthemum	Shasta daisy	*Salpiglossis*	Painted tongue
Cosmos	Cosmos	*Tropaeolum*	Nasturtium
Petunia	Petunia	*Zinnia*	Zinnia
Scabiosa	Scabiosa		
Tagetes	Marigold		
Verbena	Verbena		
Viola	Pansy		

The length of time flower and vegetable seeds remain alive depends upon both storage conditions and innate genetic constitution (Tables 14-1 and 14-2). Onion seed remains viable for one to two years, while tomato seed may be viable for at least five years. Tobacco and chrysanthemum seed have been shown to retain their ability to germinate for 30 years. Percentage germination, however, decreases with time.

Table 14-2 AVERAGE NUMBER OF YEARS SEEDS OF SOME VEGETABLES REMAIN VIABLE WHEN STORED UNDER APPROPRIATE CONDITIONS

Latin name	Common name	Latin name	Common name
One to two years		**Five years**	
Abelmoschus esculentus	Okra	*Apium graveolens*	Celery
Allium ampeloprasum	Leek	*Brassica oleracea*	Kohlrabi
A. cepa	Onion	*B. rapa*	Turnip
Pastinaca sativa	Parsnip	*Citrullus lanatus*	Watermelon
Zea Mays	Sweet corn	*Cucumis melo*	Muskmelon
Three years		*C. sativus*	Cucumber
Asparagus officinalis	Asparagus	*Cucurbita pepo*	Squash
Daucus carota	Carrot	*Lactuca sativa*	Lettuce
Phaseolus spp.	Bean	*Raphanus sativus*	Radish
Pisum sativum	Pea	*Solanum melongena*	Eggplant
Four years		*Spinacia oleracea*	Spinach
Beta vulgaris	Beet		
Brassica oleracea	Broccoli		
B. oleracea	Brussels sprouts		
B. oleracea	Cabbage		
B. oleracea	Cauliflower		
B. nigra	Mustard		
Capsicum annuum	Bell pepper		
Cucurbita pepo	Pumpkin		
Lycopersicon esculentum	Tomato		

Imbibition

Germination of dry seed depends upon the presence of a number of factors. They must, of course, be viable and in a nondormant state. Water in sufficient quantity must be available to hydrate the enzymes and other molecules within the seed. Various proteins and carbohydrates, stored in the tissues of the seed, are hydrophilic (water-loving) and are important in the absorption of water. The uptake of water by dry seed is referred to as imbibition. This is the initial event in the process of germination.

Seeds enlarge and become softer as the hydrophilic compounds imbibe water. The rate of germination of large seeds—peas, corn, nasturtium, and others—can be enhanced by soaking them in water for a few hours or overnight before planting. The seeds are placed in a shallow container and cool water is added to just cover the seed. They should not be covered with large volumes of water since oxygen must penetrate to the embryo to allow normal aerobic respiration and other reactions to go on. Water in the bottom of a deep pail may well become anaerobic.

Seed coats of some seeds (many legumes, morning glory, and others) are sufficiently impervious so as to prevent imbibition of water and diffusion of oxygen into the interior of the structure. The term scarification applies to any method that makes hard seed coats more permeable. In nature this occurs when microbial activity or passage through the digestive tracts of animals softens the coat. Temperature changes also modify hard coat. Fire that is not so intense as to kill the embryo will scarify the coats. Abrasion by rocks or soil can score or break them.

Numerous artificial methods are used to scarify seed coats. Mechanical techniques, such as shaking with sharp sand or rubbing between sheets of sandpaper, are useful where large numbers of seed are to be processed. Nicking hard seed coats with a knife or file can be used when only a few seeds need to be treated. Care must be exercised, however, to avoid damage to the embryo.

Chemical methods are also useful for treating large numbers of seed. Organic solvents, acetone or alcohol, will dissolve waxy outer layers. The seeds are soaked for a few minutes, the solvent is poured off, and the seeds are washed thoroughly with running, cool tap water before planting. Concentrated sulfuric acid can be employed the same way, but such a caustic compound is hazardous to work with. Another technique is to place the seeds in water that has just come to a boil; the water is allowed to cool and the seed is planted after 24 hours.

Temperature

The optimum temperature for germination is species-dependent, and seed will not germinate below the minimum temperature required by the species. Flower and garden vegetable seeds can be categorized on the basis of soil temperature essential for maximum germination. Cool-season plant seeds may be planted outdoors when the soil can be easily worked and its temperature has reached at least 2° C (34° F). Moderate-season plants require a soil temperature of at least 4°

C (39° F) and warm-season plants a minimum of 15° C (59° F). Temperatures above 30° C (86° F) during germination are frequently damaging.

Information on the length of the growing season needed by the plant is essential since many seeds can be started indoors 6 to 10 weeks before being planted outdoors to provide the required germination temperature before it is reached in the soil and in effect artificially lengthen the growing time of the plant. Seed catalogues provide days to harvest information based on the time of planting out of young plants or time from seed germination when seed are planted directly outdoors.

Seeds of many plant species will not germinate unless exposed to cold temperatures for a period of time. Under natural conditions the temperature of a normal winter in temperate North America ensures adequate exposure. The horticulturist must provide conditions that mimic this environment in order to promote the germination of a number of desirable woody and herbaceous ornamental plants. Chill requirements and stratification as a technique to meet these requirements were discussed in Chapter 8. In stratification seeds are placed in alternate layers with a moist, clean substrate, such as sand, peat, or vermiculite. The containers are then held at a temperature below 7° C (45° F); the temperature need not go below freezing. The containers, covered with plastic to prevent evaporation and still permit adequate aeration, may be stored in a refrigerator or outdoors.

Seeds of stone fruits (peach, plum, cherry), other members of the Rosaceae family (apple, pear), certain deciduous and coniferous trees, and many garden flowers require stratification for successful germination (Table 14-3). As we have seen, the time required varies with the species. Pitch pine (*Pinus rigida*) requires one month at 5° C (41° F). When exposed to temperatures adequate for germination 90 percent of the stratified seed germinates in 10 days compared to 30 percent germination after 50 days for nonstratified seed. Three months is the usual time required by rosaceous species to assure maximum germination, although 30 days are sufficient for apricot seeds (*Prunus armeniaca*).

There is no adequate explanation for this cold requirement, although several hypotheses have been suggested. It seems most likely that inhibitors of

Table 14-3 **SOME GARDEN FLOWERS WHOSE SEEDS REQUIRE STRATIFICATION TO PROMOTE GERMINATION**

Latin name	Common name	Latin name	Common name
Aconitum spp.	Monkshood	*Gentiana septemfida*	Crested gentian
Adonis vernalis	Pheasant's eye	*Globularia cordifolia*	Blue globe daisy
Alstroemeria spp.	Lily of the Incas	*Helleborus niger*	Christmas rose
Arnica montana	Arnica	*Lewisia rediviva*	Bitter root
Clematis spp.	Virgin's bower	*Paeonia lactiflora*	Common garden peony
Daphne cneorum	Garland flower	*Phlox paniculata*	Perennial phlox
Dicentra spectabilis	Bleeding heart	*Thalictrum aquilegifolium*	Meadow rue
Dryas octopetala	Mountain avens	*Trillium* spp.	Wake robin
Eranthis hyemalis	Winter aconite	*Trollius europaeus*	Globe flower
Eremurus spp.	Desert candle	*Viola odorata*	Sweet or English violet
Eryngium alpinum	Sea holly		

seed germination, such as the hormone abscisic acid, that are present in the seed coats or other tissues disappear under cold conditions. Certain growth-promoting hormones, cytokinins and gibberellins, simultaneously increase in concentration or begin to be synthesized.

The process of vernalization, in which imbibed seeds and very young seedlings are exposed to cold temperatures, speeds up flowering of the plants during the following growing season (Chapter 8). A few plants respond to vernalization at the seed stage including beet, kohlrabi, cereal grains, and mouse-ear cress (*Arabidopsis thaliana*).

Light

Early work on seed germination showed that exposure to light during germination enhances the response. Of the almost 1000 species tested, 70 percent responded with improved germination in the light. Light is not required, in general, by horticulturally important plants, although seeds of some flowers (Table 14-4) and a few vegetables (lettuce, celery, Belgian endive, garden cress and mustard) require light for maximum germination. Lettuce, (*Lactuca sativa*), particularly the cultivar, Grand Rapids, has an absolute requirement for light and the percentage of germination in the dark may be as low as 10 percent. Light activation of germination of this and other test species has been shown to involve the pigment phytochrome. Seeds of a few plant species are inhibited by light and therefore require darkness during the germination process (Table 14-4).

These requirements for light or darkness apply to freshly harvested seed. As seeds age under proper storage conditions, light or dark requirements tend to disappear and the seed germinates under appropriate environmental conditions. Descriptions in seed catalogues indicate the required conditions for maximum

Table 14-4 LIGHT AND DARK REQUIREMENT FOR GERMINATION OF SEEDS OF SOME ORNAMENTALS

Light		Dark	
Latin name	**Common name**	**Latin name**	**Common name**
Antirrhinum	Snapdragon	*Achillea*	Yarrow
Aquilegia	Columbine	*Amaranthus*	Love-lies-bleeding
Begonia	Begonia	*Echeveria*	Hen and chickens
Browallia	Bush violet	*Echinacea*	Purple coneflower
Calceolaria	Slipperwort	*Echium*	Viper's bugloss
Coleus	Coleus	*Nemophila*	Baby blue eyes
Digitalis	Foxglove	*Saintpaulia*	African violet
Ficus	Fig	*Tithonia*	Mexican sunflower
Fuchsia	Lady's eardrops	*Tropaeolum*	Nasturtium
Heuchera	Alumroot		
Impatiens	Jewelweed		
Lobelia	Cardinal flower		
Matthiola	Stock		
Petunia	Petunia		
Primula	Primrose		
Sinningia	Gloxinia		

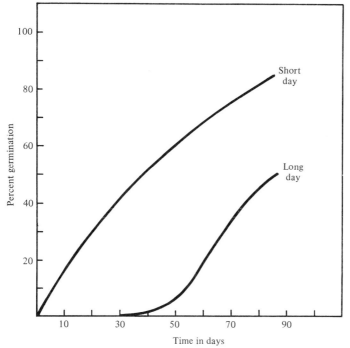

Figure 14-1   Effect of photoperiod on seed germination of rest-harrow (*Ononis sicula*).

germination. In general, 12 to 14 hours of light each day is about optimum for most species.

The germination of a few seeds is enhanced when the length of the photoperiod is controlled. Hardy begonia (*Begonia grandis*) and umbrella sedge (*Cyperus inflexus*) have long-day seeds that require a 15- to 20-hour period of light each day. The seeds of one of the speedwells (*Veronica persica*), rest-harrow (*Ononis sicula*), and baby blue-eyes (*Nemophila menziesii*) respond best to the short-day conditions of an 8- to 10-hour period of light each day (Figure 14-1).

Activation of Metabolism and Growth

Once the seed has imbibed water, the cells of the embryo begin to enlarge, which causes the seed to increase in size. This early enlargement growth of the embryo is usually sufficient to cause the rupture of the seed coats and also to permit the embryonic root, the radicle, to push out of the seed. A seed is said to have germinated when the radicle is visible.

But even before the radicle emerges, numerous enzymatic reactions occur, including those of aerobic respiration. The imbibition of water activates a number of enzymes that cause the breakdown (the hydrolysis) of the food molecules stored in the seed.

The best studied system is that of the barley grain (*Hordeum vulgare*). As

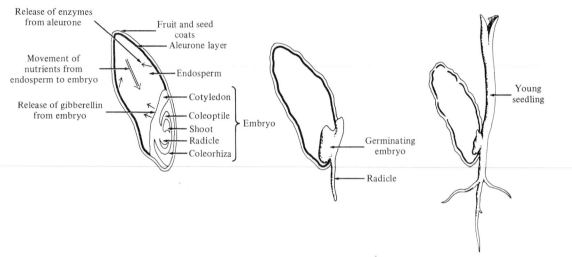

Figure 14-2 Germination of barley (*Hordeum vulgare*).

cells of the embryo become hydrated, they begin to synthesize the growth-promoting hormone gibberellin, which moves into the aleurone layer surrounding the endosperm tissue (Figure 14-2). Gibberellin is the signal from the embryo that activates enzymes in the aleurone cells. These enzymes move into the endosperm tissue and digest the various food molecules. Starch is hydrolyzed to the simple sugar glucose and protein to amino acids. Cell walls are also broken down. The grain shrinks in size as digestion of the endosperm continues. Sugars and amino acids move to the embryo, providing it with nutrients and energy for

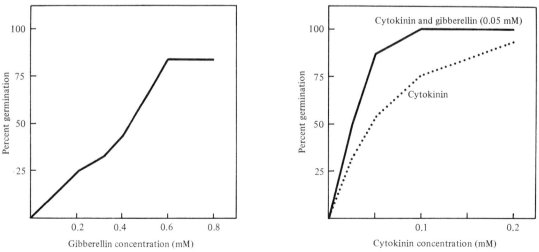

Figure 14-3 Effect of plant hormones on seed germination of milkweed (*Asclepias*).

its growth processes. The embryo is completely dependent upon this stored food until the first true leaves emerge and begin active photosynthesis. Laboratory studies have shown that germination may be greatly enhanced when seeds of certain plants imbibe in low concentrations of gibberellin or cytokinins (Figure 14-3).

Starting Seeds

A variety of substrates for starting seeds can be made or purchased. It may be less expensive, where large volumes are required, to prepare the medium. It is, however, absolutely vital that the ingredients are not contaminated by disease-producing microorganisms or weed seeds. The use of soil dug from the garden is unwise unless it is sterilized (Chapter 5) because of the presence of potential pathogens. Milled sphagnum peat used alone is satisfactory for some seeds. Commercially available mixes combine sphagnum moss with vermiculite or perlite and nutrients and are disease and weed free (see Chapter 5 for a description of available mixes). An excellent substrate for starting seeds is Cornell mix which combines equal volumes of shredded sphagnum peat and vermiculite plus small amounts of ground lime, superphosphate, and chelated iron. When plants are to remain in substrates that do not contain mineral soil for longer than three or four weeks, they should be supplied with a dilute soluble fertilizer until planted out.

The seed-starting medium should be dampened before it is placed in containers. Convenient volumes can be put into plastic bags and room-temperature water added to just moisten the ingredients.

Containers must have drainage holes or be sufficiently porous to allow water to drain through. Flats and square or round pots made of compressed peat are generally satisfactory. Peat pots holding individual plants can be planted directly into the garden. This minimizes transplantation shock, particularly important for cucurbits (cucumber, squash, melons). Peat flats hold a large number of seeds, but the seedlings must usually be transplanted to individual pots to give the plants room to grow and become established before transplanting to the garden. Another type of peat pot is a ball or disc of compressed starter mix, some types covered with nylon mesh. When submerged in water, it swells to about 5 cm (2 in.). The nylon mesh should be removed before planting out.

Larger seeds are covered by the moist substrate and pressed firmly down. A general rule-of-thumb is to cover seeds with twice their thickness of substrate. Small or very small seeds (petunia) or those that require light for germination are just pressed into the moist medium and are not covered.

After seeding, the pots or flats should be put into a tray of water so the substance can absorb moisture from the bottom. Sprinkling water on the surface is likely to disturb the seeds. Sufficient water to keep the substrate just moist is essential. Too much moisture promotes the growth of pathogens and also impedes aeration of the substrate, hindering seed germination since this process is oxygen requiring. The trays should be covered with clear plastic to minimize evaporation and maintain an even moisture level. Many seeds are quite sensitive to drying out, particularly when the radicle is emerging.

Temperature control is essential to promote rapid germination. Flats or pots containing seeds that require warm temperatures for maximum germination may be placed on heating cables or heating trays with a built-in thermostat set for 21° C (70° F). Seeds requiring cool germination temperatures would not be put on these heating units. The flats are then placed under artificial lights or in a window receiving bright light. They should not be put into direct sunlight to avoid overheating.

Some seeds, during germination, respond positively to higher levels of nutrients and these may be incorporated into a coating which surrounds the individual seed. These are called pelleted seed. Popular garden vegetable seed may be attached to a soluble tape that makes handling the seed and achieving proper spacing very simple.

Some seeds are particularly susceptible to attack by fungal pathogens and many of these seeds are treated with antifungal agents. This information appears on the seed packet. The major disease problem during germination is damping-off. The characteristic symptom is the young seedling falling over and the stem at the soil line appearing water-soaked and discolored. This disease can be prevented in a number of ways. Seed coated or dusted with fungicide can be used. Seed can be immersed before planting in a 0.5 percent solution of sodium hypochlorite for 10 minutes (1 part household bleach plus 9 parts water). Only sterile soil should be used in any soil-containing mix. Sphagnum moss incorporated into the seed starting medium will tend to prevent fungal growth as it contains natural inhibitors of these organisms. Proper levels of moisture and temperature and adequate air circulation also ensure vigorous seedling growth.

When seeds are to be planted directly out of doors, essentially the same techniques are used as detailed for starting seeds indoors. The major limiting factor is soil temperature; there is a great tendency to plant before the soil is sufficiently warm. Garden vegetables and flower bed soils should be properly tilled, amended with fertilizers and organic substances, and pH adjusted. To prevent damping off or rotting of seedlings, fungicide-treated seed can be used or fungicide may be incorporated directly into the planting area. The soil moisture must be maintained at close to field capacity. Field-grown agronomic crops are usually seeded mechanically, although many vegetable and flower crops are started indoors in pots or flats.

VEGETATIVE DEVELOPMENT

Utilization of Seed Reserves

Although plant physiologists define germination as the protrusion of the radicle through the seed coat, practical germination occurs when both the primary root and primary shoot are visible. Seedlings are assumed to have become established

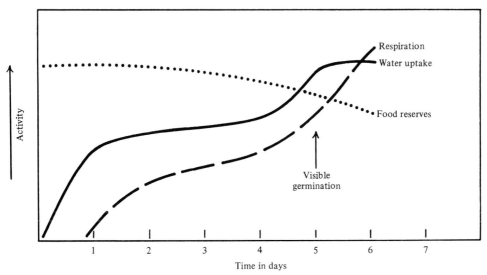

Figure 14-4 Metabolic changes accompanying seed germination.

when the endosperm expands or when the cotyledons expand and turn green, the first leaves have unfolded, the primary root has elongated, and lateral roots have formed. Although the shoot may be photosynthetically active, the amounts of sugar formed are insufficient for seedling needs and the required amounts are provided primarily by food reserves in endosperm or cotyledons. The larger the seed, the more food reserves available and the longer the time the plant can develop without total dependence on photosynthesis. Light, particularly red wavelengths needed for the activation of phytochrome, is required since the seedling will become etiolated in its absence.

Mobilization of reserves is enzymatic, with starch, protein, and lipid converted into soluble compounds that are translocated from their source in the cotyledons to the sinks of growing regions of the seedling. Inorganic ions stored in cotyledons of dicot plants are also mobilized and translocated. Loss of a cotyledon will reduce the growth of a seedling, suggesting that ions and major nutrients are not the only materials supplied from cotyledonary reserves. Some of the enzymes needed for conversion of reserves into soluble products are present in the seed, but many are synthesized during the germination process. Water uptake and respiration tend to parallel each other and food reserves slowly are depleted (Figure 14-4). Since enzyme synthesis, activation, and activity are temperature-dependent, large deviations from optimum temperatures for development of the species may prevent thrifty seedling development.

As food reserves are used for growth and energy processes, cotyledons shrivel and eventually abscise (Figure 14-5). At this time, the seedling is fully autotrophic, that is, entirely dependent on water and minerals taken up through the root system and on the photosynthesis of stem and leaves. Leaves become net exporters of photosynthate to growing points.

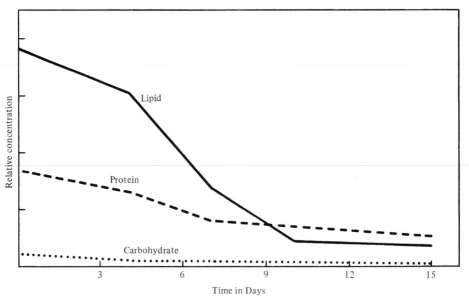

Figure 14-5   Decrease in concentration of food reserves during seed germination.

Figure 14-6   Seedling development in corn (*Zea Mays*).

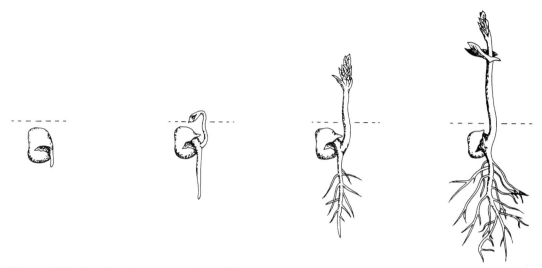

Figure 14-7 Seedling development in pea (*Pisum sativum*).

Early Seedling Development

Seedling development occurs by one of two modes: hypogeous or epigeous. In monocots stored food in the endosperm is mobilized and translocated via the single cotyledon to the coleoptile and epicotyl (see Figure 14-2). Germination in monocots and some dicots, such as pea, is hypogeous with the seed reserves remaining below ground and only the epicotyl emerging (Figures 14-6 and 14-7). In bean and most dicots germination is epigeous with a hypocotyl bringing up both cotyledons and the epicotyl (Figure 14-8).

Growth of seedling organs is not uniform. The primary root shows most elongation toward its tip, while the shoot elongates from the upper portion of the epicotyl (Figure 14-9). This elongation pattern, due to both cell division and cell elongation, continues throughout the life of the plant with each internode and root repeating the pattern. In leaves, too, various areas enlarge more than do others, so that the leaf develops the form characteristic of the species.

Young seedlings are notoriously tender and are retarded or even killed by conditions in their environment that might not affect more mature plants. Stems and roots have not developed bark and their epidermal layer is an inadequate barrier to harsh conditions. More care must be taken to ensure that seedlings receive adequate nutrition, water, and light and are protected against diseases and insects.

Hardening and Transplantation

Although many species are started from seed where the plants are to develop, it is frequently necessary or convenient to start seedlings under controlled conditions for later transplantation to their permanent site. For very small seeds such as petunia, ageratum, and some culinary herbs, transplantation is virtually a necessity. In colder climates it is possible to start plants indoors for transplanta-

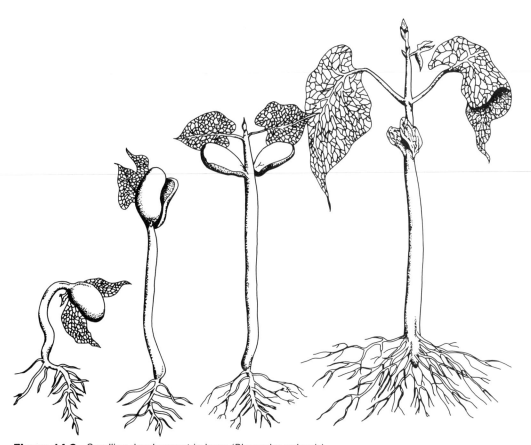

Figure 14-8 Seedling development in bean (*Phaseolus vulgaris*).

tion to the garden when seedlings are well developed and weather conditions are more favorable.

Seedlings can be transferred either into the garden or into small pots when one or two true leaves have reached full size. Plants that have not yet developed many lateral or branch roots are easier to transplant and are less injured than are older seedlings. If the seedlings develop so rapidly that roots of adjacent plants become tangled, attempts to separate them result in excessive root damage. Plants started in soilless mixes should also be transplanted relatively quickly or supplied with dilute soluble fertilizer to maintain their growth and development. Rooted cuttings, too, require transplantation as soon as the new roots are well formed.

Seedlings started in peat pots can be transplanted as a unit into the desired garden location, inserting the pot so that the soil level in the pot is the same as the garden soil level. If seedlings are to be removed from their original containers, the substrate should be moderately, but not fully dry and should be loosened with a pointed stick or dibble to permit the seedling to be removed with minimal injury. A hole is punched into the new soil, the seedling is transferred to the same

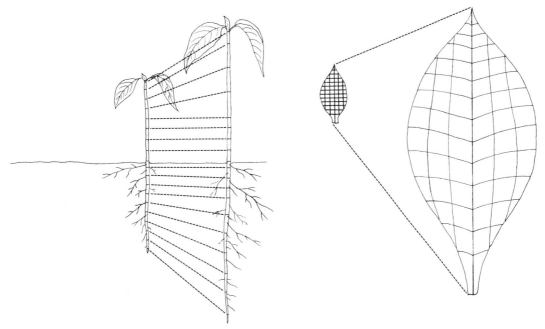

Figure 14-9 Differential growth of seedling root, stem, and leaf.

or slightly greater depth as in the germination medium, and the soil is gently firmed around the seedling and immediately watered. Watering with soluble fertilizer as a starter solution at one-half to one-third recommended full strength is advisable to provide the plant with a readily absorbable source of nutrients.

Transplantation shock is reduced by supplying a starter solution of diluted, soluble fertilizer, by reduction in transpirational water loss (covering with clear plastic), and by exposure to moderate light with little or no direct sunlight. Commercial installations may place transplanted seedlings or rooted cuttings under misting conditions for a few days until the root system has recovered and can again meet the water needs of the plant.

Greenhouses usually have high relative humidities and temperatures above those which the plant will experience out-of-doors. When artificial lights are used, the intensities are much lower than those found naturally. As a consequence, seedlings will be tender and succulent and may succumb when exposed to the harsher natural conditions. To lessen the severity of the adjustment, transplants are usually hardened off, that is, made less succulent by gradual exposure to natural conditions. In greenhouses this is accomplished by placing the plants at night temperatures a few degrees lower than that used for germination and early seedling development. The horticulturist can harden seedlings by placing them outside for a few hours each day in a cool shaded place and gradually increasing the exposure time for a week until the plants have acclimated to ambient conditions. Rooted cuttings to be grown in the garden and plants in peat pots or similar containers are hardened in the same way. It is

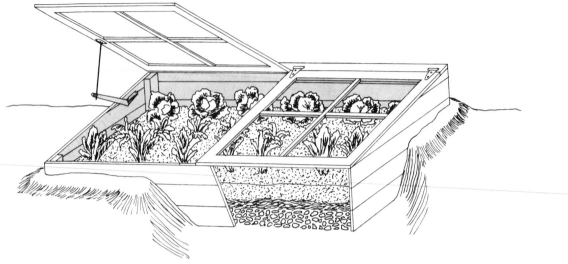

Figure 14-10   Cold frame.

possible to overharden plants by temperatures that are too low and, when moved to their permanent location, their growth will be depressed.

Cold frames are effective for hardening off plants prior to outplanting. These solar-powered and energy-efficient units serve as a transition between propagating conditions and the harsher external environment. Basically, the cold frame is a bottomless box with a transparent lid that collects heat during the day and radiates it back through the unit at night (Figure 14-10). In harsh climates it can be warmed with heating cables. The cold frame is installed in south-facing areas to maximize solar absorption. On sunny days the lid is raised to keep the temperature from becoming too high and to provide good air circulation. The lid can be raised by hand or by thermostatic devices without electrical connections. Small, thermostatically regulated exhaust fans can provide additional temperature and ventilation control. Cool-season crops can be started from seed in a cold frame and warm-season crops can be held in it until conditions allow outplanting. Plants that have borderline winter hardiness can be overwintered in a frame.

Plants that wilt or die after transplantation usually have been injured by water stress, heat stress, or disease. Plants that have been exposed to inadequate illumination or to excessive light by being placed too suddenly in direct sunlight frequently do poorly following transplantation. Those that have been overfertilized or underfertilized may die soon after transplantation. None of these stresses need develop if adequate attention is given them.

Temperature

There is considerable variation in the ability of different species or even cultivars to develop optimally under different temperature regimes. Although excessively high temperatures may, in a number of cool-season crops, cause bolting or stop development, the more critical problem is outplanting as early as possible to obtain full season growth. This is particularly acute in more northern regions where the frost-free growing season may be scarcely adequate. Starting plants indoors for transplantation into the garden is valuable, but when the danger of late spring frosts is great, plants must be given some protection after being set out.

Soil temperatures can be increased by covering the planting beds with black plastic which absorbs heat and transmits it to the upper layer of the soil. In normally warm areas (Hardiness Zones 7 to 10), the black plastic is removed after danger of frost damage is past as soil temperatures may become high enough to retard or kill roots. In cooler regions (Hardiness Zones 3 to 5) keeping black plastic in place is useful for warm-season crops such as the cucurbits. Hot caps (cloches), consisting of conical translucent paper covers, can be placed over each plant when frost is expected (Figure 14-11). Hot caps can be improvised from newspaper, plastic jugs, or other readily available materials. Horticultural supply companies sell wire cones on which shading strips can be pasted, but these are too expensive for large plantings. They should be removed as soon as possible.

For rows of plants several innovative techniques have proved to be valuable. Tunnels can be constructed of 3 mil clear plastic draped over wire hoops and secured by stones, wood, or soil along the length of the tunnel. The plastic is lifted along the sides on warm days to prevent overheating. Slitted row covers consist of sheets of clear plastic film, usually 1.5 mil thick, with slits 5 inches long and 3/4 inch apart along the length of the sheet. The sheets are supported by wire hoops (Figure 14-11). The slits allow aeration and permit

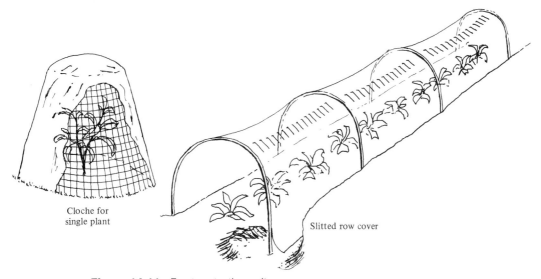

Cloche for
single plant

Slitted row cover

Figure 14-11 Frost protection units.

warm air to dissipate so that the plants are not overheated. When used with black plastic soil coverings to retain soil moisture and provide weed control, survival and early yields of warm-season plants are greatly enhanced. A somewhat similar row covering material is composed of woven polyester film that does not require wire supports since the sheets are light enough to lay directly on the tops of the plants. It is sometimes possible to start plants from seed directly under the polyester sheets. They must be lifted during hot sunny periods to prevent excess heat buildup in the row. Row covers are usually removed when the air temperature warms up, usually within 2 to 3 weeks.

Light and Photoperiod

In warm regions, where high temperatures are experienced early in the growing season, young plants may require protection from high light intensities and correspondingly high temperatures. Temporary lath houses placed over garden beds are inexpensive and effective. A lath house is a wooden frame to which are attached thin strips of wood separated by spaces equal to the width of the strips. Such a construction results in approximately a 50 percent reduction in light intensity and a 30 percent reduction in heat load during the warmest part of the day, and transpiration is also reduced. The same or somewhat greater reductions in light and temperature can be achieved by draping a dark plastic shading cloth on uprights over a bed. Both allow easy access to the planting for watering, weeding, and fertilization. If allowed to remain in place after the plants are well established, plants may become etiolated, tender, and susceptible to wilting or disease.

Light intensity during the rest of the growing season is usually not controllable and the location of plants in the garden or field should be selected with attention to the light requirements of the planting.

Table 14-5 INFLUENCE OF PHOTOPERIOD ON FORMATION OF STORAGE ORGANS

Latin name	Common name	Organ affected
Favored by short days		
Apios tuberosa	Groundnut	Root tuber
Begonia grandis	Hardy begonia	Aerial stem tuber
B. socotrana	Semituberous begonia	Aerial stem tuber
B. tuberhybrida	Tuberous begonia	
cv. Camelliaflora		Underground stem tuber
cv. Multiflora		Stem tuber
Dahlia hybrida	Dahlia	Root tuber
Phaseolus coccineus	Scarlet runner bean	Underground stem tuber
Solanum tuberosum	White potato	Underground stem tuber
Favored by long days		
Allium cepa	Shallot	Bulb
A. cepa	Onion	Bulb
A. sativum	Garlic	Bulb
Triteleia laxa	Triplet lily	Corm

In addition to the requirement for light in photosynthesis, light is also involved in a number of photoperiodic responses including flower induction and regulation of some vegetative growth responses. For example, the formation of storage organs is under photoperiodic control (Table 14-5). Most young seedlings should not be outplanted in midsummer where photoperiods exceed 20 hours (latitudes above 60° north) since seedlings generally do poorly in long photoperiods.

Water

Watering of most flower and vegetable plantings is best done in the early morning since foliage watered in the evening may remain wet overnight and will be more prone to disease. Plants in soil with high organic matter or covered by natural or artificial mulchings usually require less frequent watering. Container-grown plants in commercial production are watered as needed to prevent desiccation. Trickle irrigation (discussed in Chapter 6) has proved to be economical and effective under both greenhouse and field conditions. As plants increase in size, transpiration increases and watering may be required at more frequent intervals. Plantings will generally lose, by combined evaporation and transpiration, about 2 to 3 cm (1 in.) of water a week or about 450 liters/100 m² (125 gal/1000 ft²). When rainfall is inadequate, additional water should be provided through permanent irrigation systems or by hose watering in smaller plots. Soil type and species requirements must be considered when watering to ensure adequate penetration. Two cm of water will penetrate to a depth of 15 cm (6 in.) in sandy soil, but only to 8 to 10 cm (4 in.) in heavier loams. Deeper rooted plants will require proportionally more water; tomatoes should have water down to 35 cm (32 in.) and weekly water supplies should be 4 to 5 cm (2 in.).

When sprinklers or hoses are used, the water should be provided slowly to prevent puddling of the soil and to allow time for penetration. In flower beds thorough watering can be accomplished with soaker hoses that allow water to ooze out slowly through the fabric of the closed-end hose. Woody perennials, particularly young plantings, may require as much water as flower or vegetable plants; the water can be poured into a dished soil area surrounding the individual plant. Bath or dish water may, if necessary, be used for woody perennials, but must not be used for vegetable or flower beds.

Nutrition

With few exceptions, supplies of nutrients promote healthy, vigorous, vegetative growth. Again with a few exceptions, better vegetative growth can be obtained by supplementing the natural soil with additional fertilizer. The nutrients required by plants were surveyed in Chapter 7. The first step in determining fertilizer needs is a soil test to determine the level of nutrients already available to the plants.

The nutritional requirements of plants vary greatly. Some, such as corn, potatoes, and tomatoes, are heavy feeders, needing up to 225 kg/ha (200 lb/acre) of nitrogen and 22 kg/ha (20 lb/acre) of phosphorus for maximum development and yield. Light feeders, such as lettuce, members of the cabbage family, and carrots, require about half these amounts. Woody perennials require about one-tenth of these amounts and most flowers require about one-fifth of the amounts needed for vegetables. Care must be exercised to avoid oversupplying, for example, plants taking up too much nitrogen become excessively succulent and tender and more susceptible to wilting and to disease.

Some methods of supplying nutrients were also surveyed in Chapter 7. Soluble fertilizer can be applied at the time of watering; granular fertilizer can be applied as a side dressing, a band of granules around each plant or along rows. For valuable plantings compressed nutritive spikes or granules that release nutrients slowly over a long period of time are efficient, but for most annuals they are too expensive. A 5-10-5 granular formulation at the rate of 1 kg/10 m^2 (2.5 lb/100 ft^2) incorporated into the soil when it is turned over prior to planting can meet the needs of many plants for the season. Legumes, which can fix nitrogen, should not receive nitrogen fertilization since it represses nodulation and fixation processes. The incorporation into the soil of organic compost and mulches provides some nutrients, improves soil textures and enhances moisture-holding ability. Liming and acidifying are also done during soil preparation before planting to adjust soil pH to required levels as determined by soil analysis.

Chemical Regulation

Most research on chemical regulation of plant growth is still in the experimental stage and few substances have been cleared for control of vegetative development in field or garden plots. Some show considerable promise for controlling branch number and size, modifying leaf number and size, and regulating the initiation and development of storage organs. Gibberellic acid sprays have been used to increase stem length, but most plants do not require such treatment. Dwarfing compounds and chemicals are used commercially, but rarely have a place in home gardens. As discussed later, there are a number of compounds that are used in the control of reproductive development and senescence.

CONTROL OF PLANT FORM

Apical Dominance

The growth of one part of the plant is regulated by another, usually by the movement of growth-regulating substances formed in one organ and transported to another. The phenomenon called apical dominance is the most striking of these growth correlations and is of fundamental importance in the control of plant form. Apical dominance is the process by which the stem apical meristem

Removal of apical bud   Release of axillary buds   Replacement of apical bud with auxin in lanolin

Figure 14-12 Apical dominance in chrysanthemum.

suppresses the development of shoots from axillary buds. The physiological basis for apical dominance is not completely understood. It is known that indoleacetic acid (auxin) formed in the metabolically active terminal bud and in young leaves moves down the stem and can repress the development or breaking of axillary and lateral buds (Figure 14-12). The tip of the plant can be replaced by auxin. Cytokinins have been shown experimentally to oppose this inhibitory action of auxin. The nutritional, light, and water status of a plant may affect dominance with vigorous shoots showing less repression than those with less active growth.

Plant species differ in their degree of apical dominance. For some, like the sunflower (*Helianthus annuus*), apical dominance is virtually complete; only when the apical meristem is injured will a sunflower develop lateral branches. In other plants, such as coleus, apical dominance is not complete; axillary buds at a distance from the apex of the stem will develop into shoots even if the apex is intact, and the farther from the apex, the more active is shoot development. In potato tubers dormancy of the buds is complete in midwinter and usually only one of the stem buds (eyes) will form a shoot. This shoot becomes dominant, and subsequent shoots are weak. When the tuber is cut into "seed pieces" each can form a dominant shoot (Figure 14-13). Tomato (*Lycopersicon esculentum*) shows weak apical dominance and side shoots may have to be removed several times during a growing season.

Dominance may become less complete as plants age. Many ornamental trees have a single stem when young and then begin branching by shoot development as they mature. Among ornamental trees, decurrent species such as oak (*Quercus*) and maple (*Acer*) exhibit strong apical dominance during a

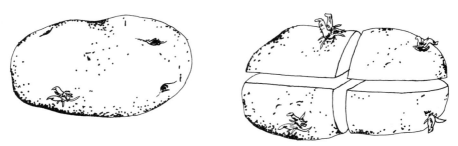

Figure 14-13 Apical dominance in potato tubers.

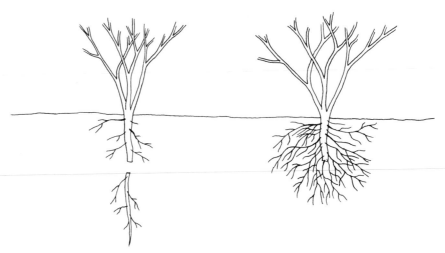

Figure 14-14 Root development following pruning of tap root.

growing season when the leader is actively growing and producing auxin. No apical control is exerted in the early spring. The lateral buds develop quickly in the spring and themselves become dominant shoots that may outgrow the original leader. This results in the umbrella shaped plants seen when these species grow in the open. Conifers and other excurrent tree species that normally retain a single, dominant stem usually have moderate apical dominance and the form of the tree is conical.

Where bushy plants are desired, apical dominance can be overcome by the horticultural technique of pinching back. The apical meristem and the first sets of young leaves—the primary sources of auxin—are removed, allowing axillary buds to develop into shoots. This process can be repeated several times, resulting in a plant with many shoots and a bushy appearance. This is effective with bedding plants, such as cushion chrysanthemums where a mass of flowers is desired, with many bushes and shrubs, and with bonsai. Release of apical dominance by chemicals is now used for large-scale plant production.

When a primary root or the tip of a strong lateral root is removed, the response may be the initiation and development of additional lateral roots (Figure 14-14). Root apical dominance may not have the same control mechanisms as stem apical dominance. Nevertheless, removal of the tap root or trenching around a plant to cut lateral roots (Figure 14-15) is practiced extensively to increase the number of feeder roots, to train the root system into a compact ball prior to lifting and transplanting, or to produce the shallow root system needed in bonsai.

Pruning

Pruning, the removal of plant parts, occurs naturally and is also a major horticultural activity. Pruning serves several functions. Plants may, by selective

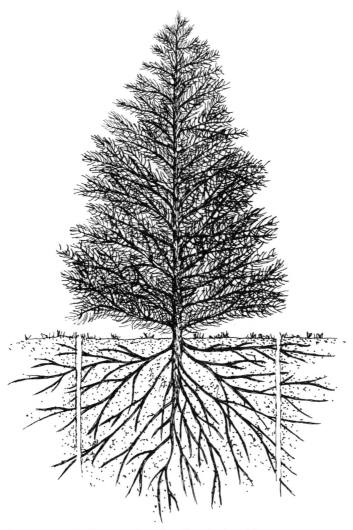

Figure 14-15 Root pruning of conifers by trenching.

pruning, be trained into a desired shape or size, an important consideration in the maintenance of ornamental woody perennials, fruit and nut trees, and speciality crops like Christmas trees. Overcrowded branches may block the penetration of light and air and can injure each other; thinning out allows better growth. The removal of dead or diseased branches promotes healthy, vigorous growth and invigorates those left on the plant. Pruning may, depending on the timing and the nature of the treatment, either repress or promote reproductive activity. Altering the relative balance between shoot and root systems by pruning is almost essential when transplanting where injured roots cannot supply adequate amounts of water and nutrients to the above-ground portion of the plant.

Pruning practice relates directly to the phenomenon of apical dominance.

When a dominant apical meristem is pruned off, one or more axillary buds are capable of developing into shoots. This heading back can change the direction of the branch or leader, exercising a selective control over the form of the plant.

Although some plants require special pruning techniques, there are general rules applicable to most species. It is usually poor practice to prune in the middle of the growing season since photosynthesis and the accumulation of food reserves will be decreased and there is also a tendency for repressed buds to break into soft shoots susceptible to winter or drought injury. Except for the immediate removal of injured shoots or those found to be diseased, plants in poor condition should not be pruned until their overall health has been improved. Top pruning of plants with small root systems will alter the shoot-to-root ratio in favor of the root system to permit the uptake of adequate amounts of water and nutrients for the smaller top. Pruning or pinching back at the time of transplantation of annuals or perennials is useful for this reason. In many plants severe pruning will delay flower and fruit development and enhance vegetative growth, but in fruit trees that are low in nitrogen, pruning out vegetative growth may result in better flowering.

The time of pruning is critical for many plants. Many flowering shrubs and trees initiate their flowers the previous year and spring pruning will remove flower buds. This is usually the case in spring-flowering plants. Those that flower later in the growing season usually (but not invariably) form flower buds in the early part of that growing season and should be pruned after the flowers have

Table 14-6   TIME OF PRUNING OF FLOWERING PERENNIALS

Latin name	Common name	Latin name	Common name
Spring-flowering plants pruned in early summer			
Amelanchier	Serviceberry	*Lonicera*	Honeysuckle
Azalea	Azalea	*Magnolia*	Magnolia
Berberis	Barberry	*Malus*	Crabapple
Celastrus	Bittersweet	*Philadelphus*	Mock-orange
Cercis	Redbud	*Pieris*	Andromeda
Chaenomeles	Quince	*Pyracantha*	Firethorn
Cotinus	Smoketree	*Prunus*	Flowering cherry
Cornus	Dogwood	*Prunus*	Flowering plum
Crataegus	Hawthorn	*Rosa*	Shrub rose
Deutzia	Deutzia	*Sorbus*	Mountain ash
Forsythia	Forsythia	*Spiraea*	Bridal wreath
Jasminum	Jasmine	*Styrax*	Snowbell
Kalmia	Laurel	*Syringa*	Lilac
Kerria	Japanese rose	*Weigela*	Weigela
Kolkwitzia	Beautybush	*Viburnum*	Arrowwood
Ligustrum	Privet		
Summer-flowering plants pruned in fall, winter, or early spring			
Acanthopanax	Aralia	*Hydrangea*	Hydrangea
Abelia	Abelia	*Koelreuteria*	Golden-rain
Albizia	Silk tree	*Lagerstroemia*	Crape myrtle
Buddleia	Butterfly bush	*Mahonia*	Oregon holly
Clematis	Vasevine	*Nerium*	Oleander
Clethra	White alder	*Rosa*	Hybrid teas
Cotoneaster	Cotoneaster	*Symphoricarpos*	Snowberry
Hibiscus	Mallow	*Vitex*	Indian spice

Figure 14-16 Heading back woody shoots.

faded. Spring-flowering plants should be pruned immediately after flowering since new flower primordia are laid down later in the season (Table 14-6). Although there is some debate on this point, it is usual practice to remove dead flowers or unwanted fruit from plants as soon as possible. Fruit and seeds are active sinks for the accumulation of nutrients and can deprive the rest of the plant of these needed substances.

Ornamental and Fruit Trees Pruning ornamental trees and many fruit trees can be mild or drastic. Heading back is mild pruning. The terminal growing point of a shoot or branch is removed, allowing lateral buds to develop and limiting the extension of the pruned branch (Figure 14-16). The shoot is headed back just above a large, healthy bud that is facing the direction in which it is desired the branch should grow. Only under special circumstances should this bud be facing inward; a good rule is always cut to the outside. The pruning cut should be made about 0.5 cm above the retained bud at an angle of 30° (Figure 14-17).

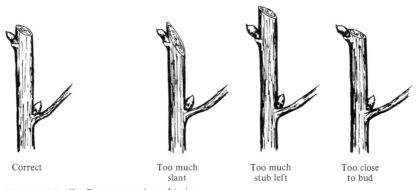

Correct   Too much   Too much   Too close
                           slant   stub left   to bud

Figure 14-17 Proper pruning of twigs.

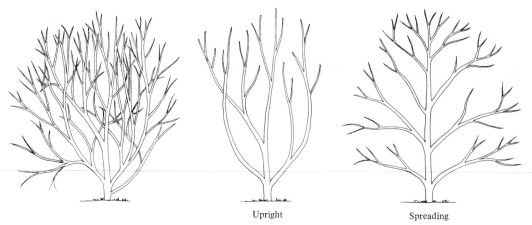

Upright   Spreading

Figure 14-18   Removal of excess branches.

Moderately drastic pruning involves selective removal of entire branches (Figure 14-18). One of a set of terminal branches can be removed to permit the unimpeded development of a single leader. Root suckers should be removed to prevent diversion of water and nutrients, and slow-growing, drooping branches (hangers) should be cut out. Water sprouts, vigorous, vertical shoots arising from latent buds or from tissues surrounding a healing cut, are usually removed since they interfere with the proper development of major branches and are unsightly. The removal of a large branch requires several cuts—a cut from below about a foot from the main trunk, a cut from above farther out on the branch to sever the

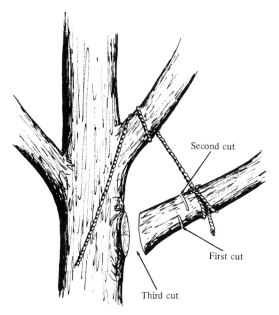

Second cut

First cut

Third cut

Figure 14-19   Removal of a large tree limb by over-
and undercutting the branch (jump
method).

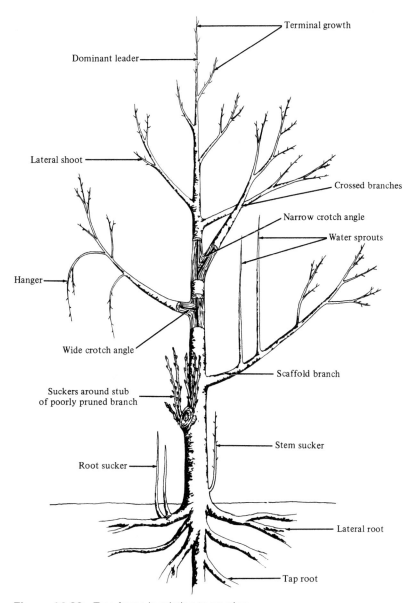

Figure 14-20 Tree frame in relation to pruning.

limb, and a cut to remove the stub as close to the tree as possible; the branch is sometimes supported by a rope to prevent tearing damage. (Figure 14-19).

In trees with large side branches that will become heavy, be weighted down with snow, or bear heavy fruit crops, the angle at which the limb joins the trunk is important. Wide angles make the side or scaffolding branch stronger because of the formation of reaction wood, while narrow angled branches are inherently weak and tend to break away from the main trunk when under load (Figure

Figure 14-21 Pruning for central leader arrangement of branches.

14-20). Where possible, branches with narrow crotches should be removed. Prevention is a better option; when the tree is young, the crotch angle can be improved by spreaders, wooden strips, or metal rods which are inserted between the trunk and the branch to force them apart.

Small to moderately sized ornamental and fruit trees can be trained by selective pruning. Most nursery trees should be severely pruned, keeping few branches, when planted. In subsequent years pruning becomes more selective, leaving those branches that will become the main scaffolds. Pome fruits (apple and pear) and several stone fruits (cherry and plum) normally have a spiral organization of scaffolding branches and develop best in the central leader arrangement (Figure 14-21) or in the modified leader arrangement (Figure 14-22). Other stone fruits (peach, nectarine, and apricot) have a spreading branch pattern with limbs radiating out like spokes of a wheel. These are best trained in the open center arrangement (Figure 14-23). The open center pattern is effective for many of the flowering trees such as dogwood (*Cornus*), redbud (*Cercis*), crabapple (*Malus*), and hawthorn (*Crataegus*) when these are used as

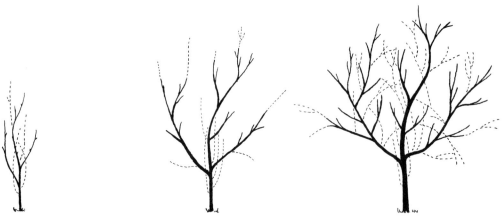

Figure 14-22 Pruning for modified leader arrangement of branches.

Figure 14-23 Pruning for open arrangement of branches.

free-standing ornamentals. When used as street plantings, the central leader system is preferred.

Conifers Most conifers grow in flushes, with the major flush at the end of the dormant period. Pruning is most effective soon after growth is initiated or, in the case of junipers (*Juniperus*) and yews (*Taxus*) during the dormant period. Most conifers have few dormant or latent buds in branches that are capable of forming shoots. Junipers, yews, and arborvitae have some latent buds in the foliage area. Pinching back by removal of the terminal or shearing of lateral shoots should be done in spring or early summer when new growth will increase the density of the foliage.

Young growth of spruce (*Picea*), fir (*Abies*), and Douglas fir (*Pseudotsuga*) as well as junipers and yews can be sheared as the shoots expand (Figure 14-24).

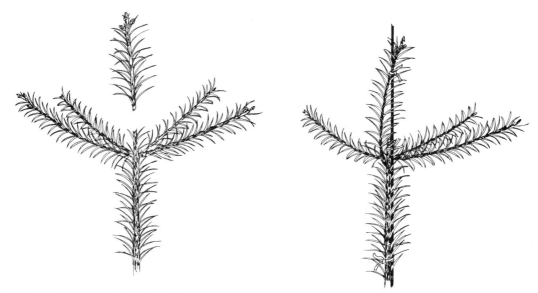

Figure 14-24 Shearing of conifers.

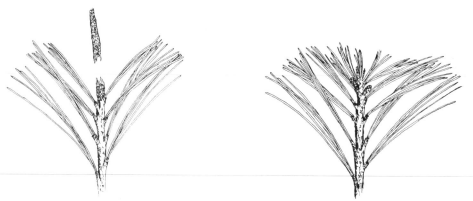

Figure 14-25 Heading back pine by removal of new growth (candle).

When shearing, it is advisable to cut back just above any latent buds or to tufts of visible foliage, but not below the point where foliage is present. Pines (*Pinus*) can be sheared or can have the "candles" cut or preferably broken in half when they are almost fully expanded (Figure 14-25) which forces the development of latent buds at the base of the new growth.

Thinning, by removal of entire branches, is best done during the dormant period to reduce the leaking of resins that discolor the stems. Few conifers withstand severe pruning; shaping or reducing the height of the plant should be done over several growing seasons. However, dead or diseased branches should be removed as soon as possible.

Hedges Hedges, rows of closely spaced shrubs or trees, are important in landscape design. They outline and separate different areas and can be visual and noise screens. Many species are used, depending on location and desired effect, but it is wise to use a single species or cultivar in a hedge. Both conifers and broad-leaved species are planted as hedges. Desirable species have small leaves with dense branching patterns (low apical dominance), the ability to resist shearing damage, and the ability to form new shoots. Either single or multiple stemmed plants can be used.

Pruning practice differs little from that used on other woody perennials, although it is difficult to prune individual stems. Shearing is usually the method of choice with attention paid to flowering time (see Table 14-6). Shearing is best done either in early spring when the plants are showing their first growth flush or late in the growing season when plants have started to enter dormancy.

Hedges can be pruned to several shapes and heights, but it is important to keep the hedge somewhat narrower at the top to allow light penetration to branches near the ground (Figure 14-26). For rapidly growing hedges, shearing may be required several times during a growing season. Generally, two to three young leaves are left below the pruning cuts. Such pruned plants develop dominant apical meristems that prevent rapid side growth and can reduce the number of shearings needed. Conifer hedges of yew, juniper, Canada hemlock, and some cypresses should be sheared only into young foliage.

Figure 14-26 Examples of good hedge shapes.

Shrubs, Roses, and Berries Shrubs and bushes are woody perennials with several stems developed at or below ground level. Most have large numbers of latent buds at the base of each stem and along branches and show weak apical dominance so that they tend to be quite dense. Pruning is needed to maintain form, to allow the free flow of air, and to permit light penetration. Although slowly growing shrubs require little pruning, those that grow rapidly should be pruned each year. Dead, diseased, or weak branches and those rubbing against other branches should be removed at any time, but flowering shrubs should be pruned in relation to flowering time. Badly overgrown but vigorous shrubs can be severely pruned to allow the latent buds to develop into new shoots or the plant may be thinned by selective shoot removal to shape it into a spreading or an upright form (Figure 14-27). Fertilization after pruning will supply needed nutrients and adequate watering is essential.

For pruning, roses are divided into two groups. The first group consists of roses that bloom on the canes of the current year. The group includes the bedding

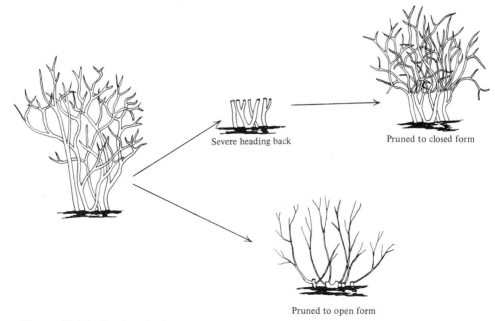

Severe heading back

Pruned to closed form

Pruned to open form

Figure 14-27 Pruning shrubs.

roses (hybrid teas, floribundas, and grandifloras) and bush and shrub roses. Hybrid tea roses are vigorously growing shrubs that normally form one dominant flower at the end of each cane with smaller blooms lower on the stems. Floribundas produce a panicle of flowers at the ends of each cane and tend to be more bushy than hybrid teas. Grandiflora roses are hybrids between teas and floribundas that combine the bloom and growth qualities of teas with the flower abundance of floribundas. The second group includes climbing roses, ramblers, low-climbing pillar roses, and polyanthus cultivars. These initiate flower buds in late summer on wood that is at least a year old and flowers develop in the spring or early summer of the following year. Many roses in this second group will produce blooms on the same stems for several years.

For both groups, primary pruning operations concentrate on removal of all dead, injured, or diseased canes. Since roses are highly susceptible to both bacterial and fungal infections, pruning tools must be disinfected with denatured alcohol after every pruning cut. Insect-damaged canes are cut back below the point of infestation without sacrificing the whole cane. Dead canes are dark brown to black and should be removed well below the killed region. Weak, thin, and crossing canes are removed next and excessively long canes are headed back. For best shoot development, all roses should be pruned just above a bud (eye) facing to the outside; these form sturdy canes capable of initiating flowers. In grafted roses sucker shoots initiated from the rootstock must be removed because they are genetically different from, and usually inferior to, the scions.

Roses are usually pruned more severely than other shrubs to maintain a balance between vegetative and reproductive growth and to keep the plants neat and thrifty. Except for the climbers, most are pruned to less than 0.5 m (20 in.) although in Hardiness Zones 7 to 10 they may be left somewhat taller. Annual pruning of teas, floribundas, and grandifloras is done in early spring before bud break (Figure 14-28). Climbing and rambler roses are trained on trellises to six or eight vigorous canes after blooming and should be headed back before the spring growth flush (Figure 14-29). These may not need pruning every year in contrast to the tea rose group.

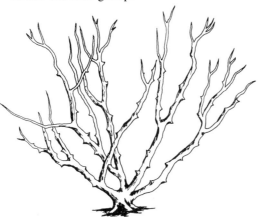

Figure 14-28 Pruning hybrid tea rose bushes.

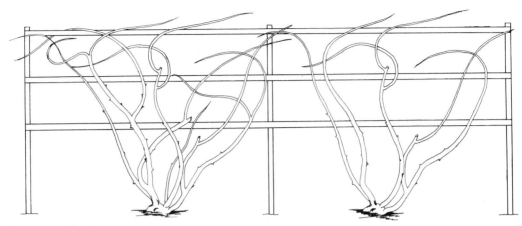

Figure 14-29 Pruning climbing roses.

Berry canes should be pruned in late fall or early spring before bud break (Figure 14-30). Red raspberry is pruned to leave five to seven sturdy canes that formed the previous summer. All canes that bore fruit should be removed; they tend to have thick bases and brown, cracked bark. Canes may be headed back to 1.5 m (5 ft) at the time they are thinned. Black raspberry canes, which form a much more tangled growth, should be pruned to leave three to four canes per plant. Side branches should be headed back severely. Unless pruned each year, berry rows soon become unmanageable.

Training for Special Effects Grape vines, some fruit trees, and a few ornamentals can be shaped by pruning into espaliers, that is, plants trained to grow with branches held flat against a support, such as a wire frame, or wall. The branches may be arranged in free forms, cordons, fans, or any of several geometric patterns (Figures 14-31 and 14-32). The espalier form can be a decorative element in a landscape design, and it also can facilitate the gathering of a crop and allow trees to be grown in a small space. It is sometimes possible to maintain bearing fruit trees against south-facing walls in a hardiness zone one number colder than that recommended for the species.

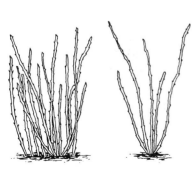

Red raspberry

Black raspberry

Figure 14-30 Pruning berry canes in early spring.

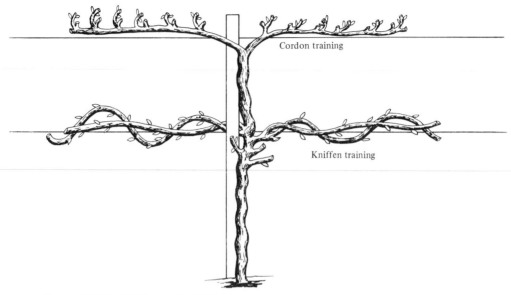

Figure 14-31   Training grape vines.

Development of arbors requires frequent heading back of shoots. Shearing of plants into geometric forms or shapes resembling animals, called topiary, can be done with many small-leaved, rapidly growing shrubs or small trees.

Bonsai   Fundamentally, bonsai merely means "plant-in-a-pot," but this horti-cultural art is based on the concept of miniaturizing woody perennials so that the construction assumes the appearance of an ancient tree. The form originated in China at least a thousand years ago and entered Japan by the tenth century as a garden art form and as a part of Zen Buddhism. Bonsai is a rewarding hobby and

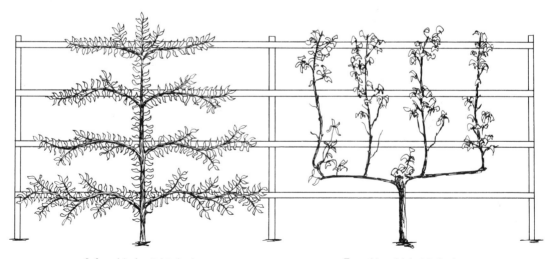

Informal (palmette) trained   Formal (candelabra) trained

Figure 14-32   Espalier forms.

a thriving horticultural business both in the Far East and, most recently, in the West. Over the centuries major styles of Bonsai have been codified (Figure 14-33), each representing plant forms that are seen in nature. Many species can be used to construct bonsai. Some plants are selected because they have small leaves or needles or have foliage that can be prevented from reaching its full growth potential. With some exceptions, bonsai are not house plants, but are grown outside where the interaction of environmental factors with the plant can enhance the rugged, venerable look associated with age. The true age of a bonsai is unimportant; a masterpiece may be only a few years old or it may be several centuries old as is the case for some of the famous Japanese plants.

Bonsai are started from seed or cuttings or are gathered from exposed, harsh environments. Nursery stock is an excellent source for many specimens. Bonsai techniques differ little from standard horticultural practices. It is important to use light soils or soil mixes with adequate provisions for drainage. Nutrition is controlled by judicious fertilization, using relatively low nitrogen levels to avoid soft, rapid growth and higher phosphorus levels to promote woodiness. Root pruning reduces water and mineral uptake, with the frequency of root pruning dependent upon the growth rates of the specimen. Top pruning also depends on growth rate and is required to maintain or develop the desired style and size. Pinching out growing points on twigs reduces apical dominance and heading back is widely used to control the direction and bushiness of a branch. A major consideration in bonsai construction is bringing individual branches into proper alignment as part of the composition. This is accomplished by tying, wiring, and bracing branches, techniques used for other woody perennials, but rarely at the small scale required for bonsai.

Dwarfs and Other Genetic Forms

The rate of growth of a plant is determined by the interaction of heredity (genotype) and the plant's total environment. Many plants can be kept small and growing slowly by control of nutrition, water supply, and soil composition. Such plants are not true dwarfs, since they will express their genetic potential under optimum growth conditions. Dwarfing can be induced by regulation of natural and applied growth-regulating substances, although the plant may eventually resume full growth. Grafting of plants to special rootstocks or the use of interstocks (Chapter 15) will cause some plants to grow as semidwarfs; this is extensively done with fruit trees. Most apple trees are now propagated on size-controlling rootstocks. Selection of rootstock and scion combinations in nursery trees is a valuable tool in predetermining the mature size of the trees which are then classified as dwarf, semidwarf, semistandard, and standard.

There are, however, plants that for a variety of genetic reasons will grow slowly under optimum conditions. These are the true dwarfs. The words *nana* or *pygmeae* in a plant name identify the growth habits, for example, *Juniperus procumbens cv.* nana (dwarf trailing juniper) and *Chamaecyparis obtusa cv.* pygmeae (highly dwarfed Hinoki cypress). The genetic and physiological basis for the dwarf habit is usually not known. It may be reduced cell division or reduced enlargement, which results in plants with fewer and smaller cells, or cells

Black pine formal upright (*Chōkkan*)

Juniper informal upright (*Moyugi*)

White pine slanting (*Shakan*)

Mugo pine cascade (*Kengai*)

Figure 14-33   Major styles of Bonsai. (Illustration courtesy of Dr. Patrick Daily)

Table 14-7   GENETIC FORMS OF WOODY PERENNIALS

Compacta	Branches close together, usually slow growing
Contorta	Branches twisted
Fastigiata	Small stem-branch angle, branches erect
Pendulata	Branches drooping or hanging down (weeping)
Procumbens	Trailing branches, very low growing
Prostrata	Branches lying almost flat on the ground
Torulosa	Branches irregularly swollen or gnarled

may be of normal size, but exhibit reduced rates of division or an earlier cessation of cellular and tissue development. In some instances root systems are poorly developed so that smaller quantities of water and nutrients are absorbed. Some dwarfs have been obtained from abnormal growths found on otherwise normal plants, suggesting that they are the result of a mutation in apical cells of shoots. These are called bud sports.

Dwarfs are horticulturally valuable, with many propagated by grafting or from cuttings to provide the landscaper with useful and unusual specimens. They are also used in bonsai and in miniature gardens. Some appear to be less adaptable than their full-sized equivalents, although there is no overall rule for the hardiness of dwarf plants.

In addition to genetic dwarfing, there are many cultivars that exhibit aspects of form that differ from the standard specimen of the species. These, like dwarfs, are important in landscape design. All originated as bud sport mutations in standard plants and are propagated vegetatively. Table 14-7 lists some of the more common genetic forms used horticulturally.

SUPPLEMENTARY READINGS

Bewley, J. D., and M. Black. 1978–1982. *Physiology and Biochemistry of Seeds.* 2 vols. Springer-Verlag, New York.

Bleasdale, J. K. A. 1985. *Plant Physiology in Relation to Horticulture.* 2nd ed. Avi, Westport, Conn.

Brown, G. E. 1977. *The Pruning of Trees, Shrubs and Conifers.* Faber & Faber, Salem, N.H.

Devlin, R. M., and F. H. Witham. 1983. *Plant Physiology.* 2nd ed. Willard Grant Press, Boston.

Duffers, C. M., and J. C. Slaughter. 1980. *Seeds and Their Uses.* Wiley, New York.

Gardner, F. P., R. B. Pearce, and R. L. Mitchell. 1985. *Physiology of Crop Plants.* 2nd ed. Iowa State University Press, Ames.

Grounds, R. 1973. *The Complete Handbook of Pruning.* Macmillan, New York.

Kozlowski, T. T. (ed.). 1972. *Seed Biology.* 3 vols. Academic Press, New York.

Leopold, A. C., and P. E. Kriedemann. 1975. *Plant Growth and Development.* 2nd ed. McGraw-Hill, New York.

Mayer, A. M., and A. Poljakoff-Mayber. 1982. *Germination of Seeds.* Pergamon Press, Elmsford, N.Y.

Murray, D. (ed.). 1984. *Seed Physiology.* 2 vols. Academic Press, N.Y.

Naka, J. Y. 1984. *Bonsai Techniques Vols. I and II.* Bonsai Institute of California, Los Angeles.

C H A P T E R   1 5

REPRODUCTIVE GROWTH

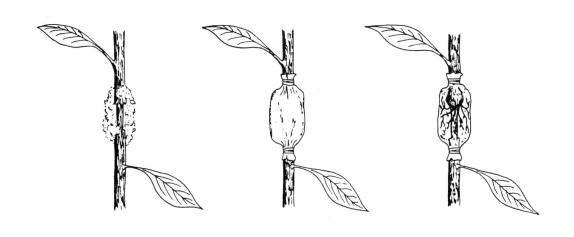

ASEXUAL REPRODUCTION

Genetic Uniformity

Plant cells, in contrast to animal cells, have the capacity to reproduce the entire multicellular organism. This ability, called totipotency, requires that the original cell not only can reproduce itself by mitosis, but also can undergo the selective enlargements and differentiations that result in integrated tissue and organ systems. Essentially, the vegetative plant cell retains full competence for differentiation and development in much the same way as the fertilized egg cell (the zygote). All the cells of the plant that develop from the embryo have the same heredity—the same genotype—and when new plants are obtained from preexisting plants, they will possess the same heredity as the original plant. Populations of plants derived from a single plant are called clones. Although all members of a clone have the same heredity, the development of individual members may be modified by environmental conditions, that is, the genotype is uniform, but the expressed development—the phenotype—may be different.

Production of a clone is called asexual reproduction since the sexual process is not involved. Genetic uniformity is rarely found in plants reproduced sexually because during the sexual process each parent supplies different genetic information and there may be recombinations of genetic information. There are cultivars, called lines, that do maintain almost all of their characteristics through sexual reproduction; they are usually self-fertile plants that have mechanisms that prevent cross-fertilization or that can be so controlled that cross-fertilization is prevented. But in most cases sexual reproduction produces diversity. Asexual reproduction has many advantages in horticulture and agriculture. For many cultivated plants, populations of genetically uniform plants may be highly desirable. Many economically important plants, the banana, for example, rarely produce seeds. Other important crop plants may exhibit male sterility (corn, sugar beet, sorghum) and may be polyploid so that the desirable characteristics can be transmitted only by asexual processes. The chance development of a mutation (sport) with superior properties can be saved through perpetuation by asexual means, but it would be lost during sexual reproduction. Most of our fruit and nut cultivars are asexually maintained. Ornamentals rarely breed true to type and color variation; differences in growth and reproductive rates and other dissimilarities cannot be controlled in the sexual process. Coleus leaves, for example, have a number of genetically determined color patterns maintained only by asexual reproduction, and various clones of woody perennials that normally crossbreed are maintained by asexual processes.

Genetic uniformity has some drawbacks. In populations that have exactly the same genetic capacity, deviations from optimum environmental conditions may cause severe damage to the entire population or crop. A disease that in a heterogeneous population may cause the death of only a few plants will result in the loss of an entire planting of a clone or line. Since many diseases are not transmitted through seeds, asexually reproduced plants may accumulate viruses, mycoplasmas, and other organisms and "run down." This occurs in potato and other plants. Elimination of virus infections can be accomplished by certain asexual reproduction techniques. When a cultivar has been maintained only by asexual reproduction, potentially valuable genetic information may be lost and will not be available for future breeding purposes.

Rooting of Cuttings

Asexual reproduction of plants utilizes a large number of techniques and processes. The most common is the rooting of cuttings. A cutting is an isolated part of an organ (leaf, stem, or root) which, when placed under suitable conditions, will allow some totipotent cells to develop into the missing organs. Techniques used for propagation by cuttings vary with the vegetative organ used.

Stem cuttings are classified as hardwood, semihardwood, softwood, and herbaceous. Hardwood cuttings are segments of mature stems collected at the end of a growing season after leaves have fallen and winter buds are present (Figure 15-1). They are usually stored in a cool, humid environment until their dormancy requirements are fulfilled (see Chapter 8). Semihardwood cuttings consist of partly matured stems of broad-leaved evergreens or deciduous plants collected after a flush of growth of new leaves. They can be rooted immediately. Softwood cuttings are collected in spring from coniferous or deciduous twigs bearing leaves. They usually root more quickly than more mature material. Herbaceous cuttings are succulent slips or stems. A juvenile characteristic in English ivy and other plants is that cuttings from juvenile plants root rapidly while cuttings from mature ones infrequently form roots. Large numbers of house plants and many herbaceous perennials are rooted from these cuttings.

Some house plants are propagated from leaf cuttings consisting of a leaf blade with or without the petiole attached (Figure 15-2). In some species leaf

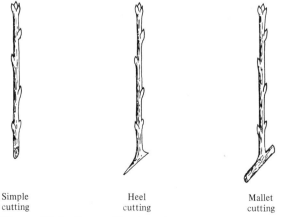

Simple
cutting

Heel
cutting

Mallet
cutting

Figure 15-1 Types of hardwood cuttings.

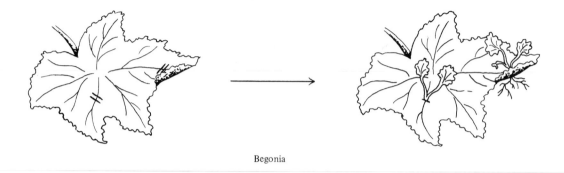

Begonia

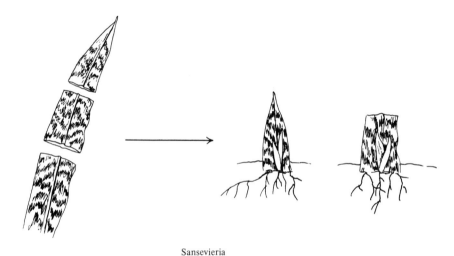

Sansevieria

Figure 15-2   Leaf cuttings from begonia and sansevieria.

cuttings will form roots, but do not develop stems. Leaf-bud cuttings, consisting of a small piece of stem with an attached leaf are used. African violets (*Saintpaulia*) are frequently propagated by leaf cuttings. Plants like maternity plant (*Kalanchoe*) form propagules in notches of the leaf that, when removed, will root and form new plants.

Although fewer species are involved, some plants can be reproduced from root segments (Figure 15-3). Smaller roots, taken from young plants in late winter or early spring when the roots contain stored food reserves, are most frequently used.

Successful propagation from cuttings depends upon the formation of totipotent cells out of which the organized root and shoot systems differentiate. In stem cuttings this group of cells is called a callus, an irregular mass of thin-walled, actively dividing parenchyma cells formed at the basal end. Callus is derived from cells of the vascular cambium and immature xylem or phloem.

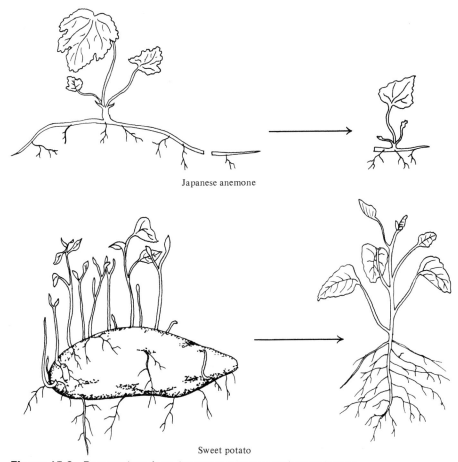

Japanese anemone

Sweet potato

Figure 15-3 Root cuttings from Japanese anemone and sweet potato.

Associated with the callus and sometimes arising from callus cells, initials of new roots develop and grow out as normal roots. (An initial is the first recognizable cell that will develop into an organ or part.) When this has occurred, the cutting is said to have struck roots and can be transplanted. In some cuttings adventitious root primordia are already present. These latent or preformed roots are normally suppressed, but will develop into roots when the cutting is separated from the influences of the whole plant.

For callus and root initials to form, there must be activation of cell division and organization of new cells into the initials. In addition to the maintenance of adequate temperature, light, and moisture, chemical control is necessary. A number of known and some unknown chemical growth regulators are involved. Auxin (indoleactic acid, IAA) activates the cell division that leads to callusing and promotes the differentiation of root initials. In rooting procedures synthetic

Table 15-1 EFFECTIVE CONCENTRATIONS OF AUXIN IN ROOTING POWDERS

Latin name	Common name	Latin name	Common name	Latin name	Common name
		0.1 percent indolebutyric acid			
Abelia	Bush arbutus	Euphorbia	Poinsettia	Philodendron	Philodendron
Ageratum	Ageratum	Forsythia	Forsythia	Populus	Poplar
Andromeda	Andromeda	Gardenia	Gardenia	Ribes	Currant
Azalea	Azalea	Geranium	Geranium	Rosa	Rose
Begonia	Begonia	Hydrangea	Hydrangea	Rubus	Raspberry
Berberis	Barberry	Iberis	Candytuft	Saintpaulia	African violet
Buddleia	Butterfly bush	Jasminum	Jasmine	Salix	Willow
Callicarpa	Beautyberry	Kerria	Kerria	Salvia	Sage
Chrysanthemum	Chrysanthemum	Lantana	Lantana	Sansevieria	Snake plant
Clerodendron	Clerodendron	Lavandula	Lavender	Spirea	Spirea
Codiaeum	Croton	Maclura	Osage orange	Symphoricarpos	Snowberry
Coleus	Coleus	Morus	Mulberry	Thunbergia	Clockvine
Crassula	Crassula	Myrica	Bayberry	Tilia	Linden
Deutzia	Deutzia	Parthenocissus	Parthenocissus	Veronica	Speedwell
Dianthus	Carnation	Penstemon	Penstemon	Viburnum	Viburnum
Dracena	Dracena	Philadelphus	Mock orange	Weigela	Weigela
		0.3 percent indolebutyric acid			
Ardisia	Ardisia	Hedera	Ivy	Picea	Spruce
Chionanthus	Fringe tree	Laburnum	Golden-chain tree	Teucrium	Germander
Clematis	Clematis	Lonicera	Honeysuckle	Thuja	Arborvitae
Corylus	Hazelnut	Juniperus	Juniper	Sambucus	Elder
Cystisus	Broom	Nerium	Oleander	Vaccinium	Blueberry
Daphne	Daphne	Potentilla	Cinquefoil	Vinca	Periwinkle
Fagus	Beech	Pyracantha	Firethorn	Wisteria	Wisteria
Hamamelis	Witch hazel			Zelkova	Zelkova
		0.8 percent indolebutyric acid			
Abies	Fir	Cotoneaster	Cotoneaster	Olea	Olive
Acer	Maple	Crataegus	Hawthorn	Oxydendron	Sourwood
Acanthopanax	Acanthopanax	Cryptomeria	Cryptomeria	Pecan	Pecan
Betula	Birch	Elaeagnus	Russian olive	Pinus	Pine
Buxus	Boxwood	Epigaea	Arbutus	Quercus	Oak
Calluna	Heather	Erica	Heath	Rhododendron	Rhododendron
Camellia	Camellia	Ilex	Holly	Robinia	Locust
Catalpa	Catalpa	Kalmia	Laurel	Sciadopitys	Umbrella pine
Celastrus	Bittersweet	Kolkwitzia	Beautybush	Syringa	Lilac
Chaenomeles	Quince	Ligustrum	Privet	Taxus	Yew
Citrus	Orange	Liriodendron	Tulip tree	Vitis	Grape
Cornus	Dogwood	Magnolia	Magnolia	Zenobia	Zenobia

auxin analogues, naphthaleneacetic acid (NAA) and indolebutyric acid (IBA), are used in preference to the natural auxin because they are not as affected by enzymes that destroy IAA. Rooting powders, consisting of an auxin dispersed in an inert material like talc and sometimes containing fungicides, are convenient to use. Concentrations of the active ingredient range from 0.1 percent for easy to root herbaceous material to 4.0 percent for very difficult to root cuttings such as conifers and many deciduous hardwood cuttings (Table 15-1). Selection of a concentration should be done carefully; too low a concentration will be ineffective and too high a concentration can suppress root development. Manufacturers of rooting powders provide information on the appropriate powder to use for different species.

Many other substances and special treatments can promote rooting of cuttings, and for some species these may be necessary. Information on plants requiring special handling can be found in appropriate reference works.

For many species the presence of leaves promotes rooting, but since leaves transpire and the rootless cutting does not take up water efficiently, water stress is always a consideration in rooting, particularly in cuttings that take a long time to form new roots. Maintaining high relative humidities around the cuttings reduces transpirational water loss. This may be accomplished with elaborate misting chambers. Misting also coats leaves with a film of water that through evaporation keeps leaves cooler and further reduces transpiration. Misting for long periods of time may, however, leach both organic and inorganic substances from leaves, but the inorganic nutrients can be replaced by incorporating water-soluble nutrients into the mist for foliar uptake. For small numbers of cuttings, covering the rooting container with a clear plastic bag is effective. Water loss is reduced and light can reach the leaves. Temperature control is particularly important with the bag techniques since overheating can occur if cuttings receive direct sunlight.

Cuttings bearing leaves can conduct photosynthesis and synthesize substances that promote the rooting process. Direct sunlight is usually disadvantageous because the resulting heat load increases transpiration and creates water stress. Rooting of many woody plants is speeded up due to increased photosynthesis and activation of the phytochrome system when the daylength is extended to 14 to 16 hours with incandescent light. Photoperiod is important for some species and in some plants the photoperiodic regime of the parent plant at the time cuttings are taken becomes a factor in rooting ability (Table 15-2). Vernalization of the parent plant may also promote the rooting of cuttings taken from the plant. Cuttings should be taken only from vegetative plants. For yet unknown reasons, the presence of flowers depresses rooting capacity.

The composition and temperature of the rooting medium are factors in determining the success of rooting. The medium serves to maintain the cutting in a desired position (usually upright) and is the reservoir for the water and air necessary for proper callus and root initial metabolism. Ideally, the medium should be porous, have high water-holding capacity, and drain freely. It should be sterile and should not support the development of microorganisms. Many

Table 15-2   EFFECT OF PHOTOPERIODIC CONDITIONS ON THE ROOTING CAPACITY OF CUTTINGS

Latin name	Common name
Root initiation increased when parent plant is in LD	
Begonia X*cheimantha* (leaf cuttings)	Christmas flowering begonia
Bryophyllum tubiflorum	Chandelier plant
Cornus florida cv. alba	Flowering dogwood
Populus X*canadensis*	Carolina poplar
Populus X*robusta*	Poplar
Root initiation increased when parent plant is in SD	
Abelia X*grandiflora* cv. Prostrata	Prostrate glossy abelia
Dianthus caryophyllus	Carnation
Ilex crenata	Japanese holly
Salix babylonica	Weeping willow
Root initiation increased when cutting is in LD	
Abelia X*grandiflora*	Glossy abelia
Cornus florida	Flowering dogwood
Ilex Aquifolium	English holly
Ilex opaca	American holly
Juniperus horizontalis	Creeping juniper
Magnolia X*soulangiana*	Chinese magnolia
Populus X*robusta*	Poplar
Rhododendron mucronulatum	Asian azalea
Salix X*blanda*	Wisconsin weeping willow
Weigela florida	Weigela
Root initiation increased when cutting is in SD	
Bryophyllum tubiflorum	Chandelier plant
Ilex crenata	Japanese holly
Juniperus chinensis	Juniper
Taxus cuspidata cv. Nana	Dwarf Japanese yew
No effect of daylength on rooting	
Abelia X*grandiflora* cv. Prostrata	Prostrate glossy abelia
Buxus sempervirens	Boxwood
Juniperus horizontalis cv. Plumosa	Creeping juniper
Taxus cuspidata	Japanese yew

different media have been developed, but an all-purpose medium consists of equal volumes of milled sphagnum and either vermiculite or perlite. Well-washed sand is widely used, although the roots formed may be highly branched and brittle. Some herbaceous cuttings can be propagated in water, but since light suppresses root development, the container must be covered to exclude light; the water should be changed periodically to eliminate microorganisms.

Striking of roots is, for many species, promoted by temperatures in the rooting medium slightly above the ambient temperature (21° to 27° C, or 70° to 80° F). Some plants form roots more rapidly with lower night temperatures. Heating cable units such as are used for starting seeds are excellent for the home gardener and larger, more versatile hotbed units are available commercially.

Figure 15-4 Asexual propagation of cactus by articulation.

Reproduction from Specialized Stems

As noted in Chapter 3, there are a number of specialized stems and many of these can be used to propagate the entire plant. In cacti, including most species of *Opuntia*, a segment of stem will root if broken from the plant (Figure 15-4). This is called articulation. Runners of strawberry (*Fragaria* sp.), flowering stems of spider plant (*Chlorophytum comosum*), and stolons of spearmint (*Mentha spicata*) root easily (Figure 15-5). Segments of rhizomes of iris and tubers of potato, each containing a node with a bud, will sprout when planted (Figure 15-6). Bulbs of hyacinth can be scored or sectioned, the cut surface allowed to heal and then planted (Figure 15-7). Dahlia tubers develop from roots in the

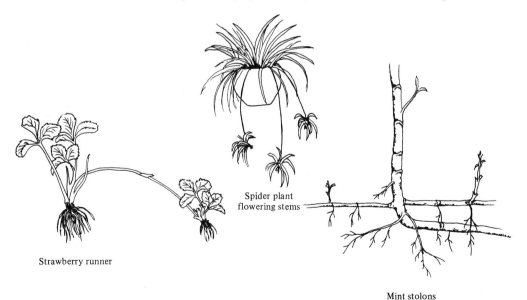

Spider plant flowering stems

Strawberry runner

Mint stolons

Figure 15-5 Asexual propagation from modified stems.

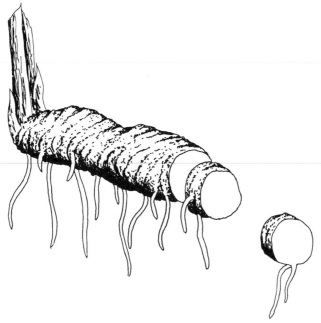

Figure 15-6 Asexual propagation of iris rhizome.

shorter days of late summer and form a clump connected to the central stem. When the plant is lifted after the first frost, the clump is stored over winter at temperatures slightly above freezing and is divided in the spring to obtain separate tubers for planting (Figure 15-8). Several members of the lily family and some other monocots form bulbils, small vegetative stem buds that can be removed and planted (Figure 15-9). Gladiolus forms both daughter corms and cormlets (Figure 15-10).

Scoring

Sectioning

Figure 15-7 Asexual propagation of hyacinth bulbs.

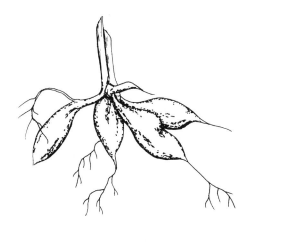

Figure 15-8 Dividing dahlia root tubers.

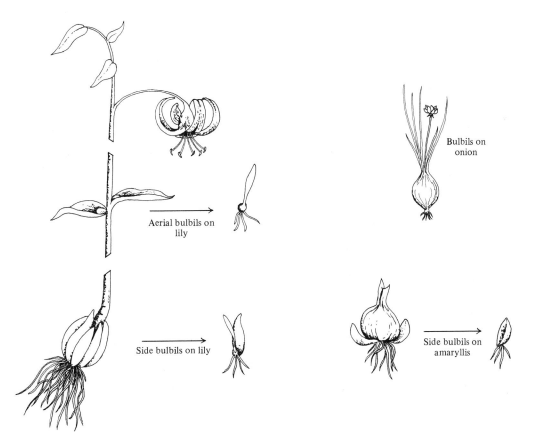

Bulbils on onion

Aerial bulbils on lily

Side bulbils on lily

Side bulbils on amaryllis

Figure 15-9 Asexual propagation from bulbils.

Figure 15-10 Asexual propagation of gladiolus cormels.

Layering

Layering differs from other methods of stem propagation in that the new plant is induced to produce adventitious roots before it is separated from the original plant. It is particularly useful for hard-to-root species since the plant to be propagated receives its water and nutrients from the parent plant no matter how long it takes to strike roots. As is true for other methods of rooting, an adequate supply of moisture, good aeration, and satisfactory temperatures are all required. Layering is time consuming, labor intensive, and has not been mechanized. The simplest technique is tip layering where the upper portion of a stem is bent into the ground and held in place with a wire or wooden hook (Figure 15-11). In a modification of this technique the subterminal portion of the cane is buried, with the tip of the shoot left exposed. Berry canes, grapes, and blueberries are commonly propagated by either of these methods. Shrubs with dormant buds at

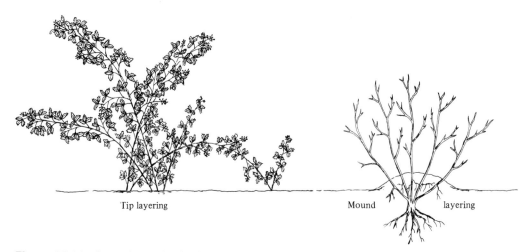

Tip layering   Mound   layering

Figure 15-11 Asexual reproduction by layering.

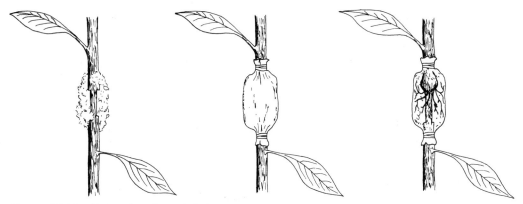

Figure 15-12   Air layering of woody twig.

the crown can be propagated by stool or mound layering. After severe pruning, soil is heaped about the plant to facilitate the formation of adventitious roots at the base of each stem (Figure 15-11). After rooting, new plants are cut from the parent plant.

In air layering the stem portion to be rooted is girdled (the cambium is removed) and kept open so that photosynthate and growth substances accumulate above the wound to provide a source of nutrients for the formation of new roots. The cut or girdle is dusted with a rooting powder to increase callus formation, the area is wrapped with damp sphagnum, and the sphagnum is covered with plastic to keep the sphagnum in place maintaining darkness and high humidity (Figure 15-12). Callus forms at the upper end of the girdled region and root formation can be observed through the plastic.

Apomixis

Apomixis is the development of seeds without a complete sexual process and can be considered a specialized type of asexual reproduction. The embryo develops from an egg cell or associated cells having the same chromosome number as the vegetative plant and has only the hereditary capacity of the female parent. Although a fairly common phenomenon, it is not utilized extensively in plant propagation. Apomixis is discussed in Chapter 3.

Micropropagation

The newest techniques of asexual propagation involve tissue and cell cultures. Not only can large numbers of genetically uniform plants be developed quickly, but the resulting plants are usually pathogen free. By suitable procedures, unique cell lines or even genetic crosses can be propagated.

Conceptually, micropropagation is based on the hypothesis, announced early in the century by G. Haberlandt, that living plant cells from vegetative tissues and organs possess, like the fertilized egg, all the potential needed to form an entire plant. The earlier development of mineral salt nutrient solutions (see Chapter 7) provided the basis for media in which tissues and organs could be grown hydroponically.

The technique of micropropagation is based on research started in the 1920s when it was discovered how to culture plant organs, primarily root tips, under sterile conditions in complex mineral salt-sugar solutions. By the 1930s excised bits of tissue from most vegetative organs could be grown as unorganized callus masses, initiating the era of plant tissue culture. Although far from a micropropagation method, tissue cultures allowed investigators to refine their growth media by substituting known amounts of pure chemicals for the complex natural additives—yeast extract, coconut water, protein hydrolysates—that had been necessary to allow growth to occur in culture. Such additives are necessary because tissue fragments, unlike the intact plant, cannot synthesize all of the organic substances required for the growth and development of plant cells. The obligatory role of the then newly discovered plant growth-regulating substances was determined during this same time period. Only rarely, and usually spontaneously, did callus cultures show any differentiation into roots and shoots and the potential for plant propagation was still speculative.

By 1950 renewed interest in the sterile cultivation of apical meristems resulted from the finding that many viruses multiply more slowly than the cells of the meristem and that it was possible to free stem tips of viruses and then root them to develop intact plants. The potato industry depended upon such virus-free seed potato stock. When growth-regulating chemicals were added to the medium in which meristems were growing, it was found that many new buds or meristems developed about the base of the original meristem. These could be excised, grown individually in sterile culture, and eventually used as rooting stock, so that from a single meristem culture it became possible to obtain hundreds of genetically identical plants from one desirable plant. Meristem micropropagation is now an important horticultural and agricultural industry, providing growers with millions of clonal plants each year. Since only months, rather than years, are required for commercial production, such plants have become important in floriculture, vegetable and small fruit crops industries, and in the production of coniferous forest tree species. Only a few agricultural crops are grown from clonal meristem cultures, although the techniques are being used to develop clonal material for research and crop breeding work.

Since many hundreds of individual callus tissue cultures can easily be started from a single plant, interest in using these cultures for clonal micropropagation has continued. As information accumulated on the various roles of plant growth substances, these were supplied singly and in combinations to tissue cultures. By 1956 it was found that appropriate mixtures of auxins and cytokinins would cause tissue cultures to differentiate roots and shoots. These could be excised and used to produce intact plants (Figure 15-13).

At about the same time it was discovered that the tiny seeds of many orchids could be germinated and grown into plantlets under sterile conditions. This revolutionized the orchid industry, long plagued by erratic seed germination and low growth rates of commercially desirable species and cultivars. The

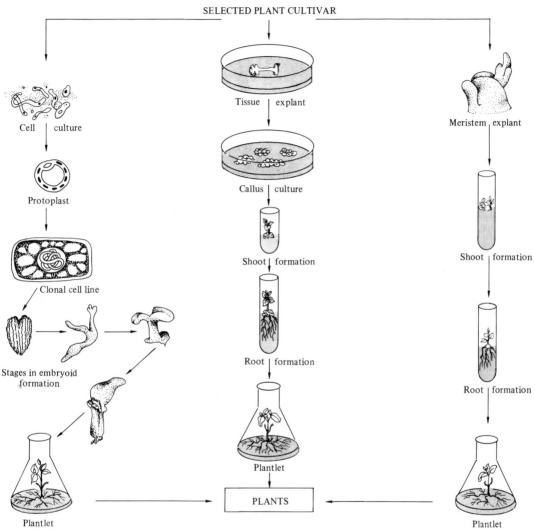

Figure 15-13 Outline of procedures used in the micropropagation of vegetative plants. Sketches not to scale.

concepts and techniques were then used for the development of intact plants from embryos isolated directly from seeds of species that normally had low germination capacities, required months or years for seed germination, or were the products of intraspecific crosses that germinated poorly because of defective endosperm seed reserves.

As part of research programs evaluating tissue culture development, investigators transferred solid callus cultures from agar into liquid media. In many species, notably tobacco and carrot, the cells separated and continued to divide, forming cell cultures that could be manipulated by bacteriological techniques. Excellent growth was soon obtained by supplementing the known media with other organic additives needed to meet the more complex nutritional requirements of single cells as compared with tissues. By 1960 it became possible to start cell cultures from plant organs in one step by incubating a root or a leaf in enzymes that dissolved cell walls. Such cells, obtained from either tissue cultures or from intact organs, were manipulated so that they would proliferate and would eventually differentiate into cell masses that had the potential to form entire plants. In addition to vegetative organs, floral parts were also tested and, when anthers or stamen tips or pollen grains were used, some of the resulting cells and plantlets were haploid and could be used for breeding purposes.

Using cell cultures, many investigators attempted to control the rates and directions of differentiation by additions of growth substances in varying qualitative and quantitative ratios. As such cell cultures developed, some of the multiplying cells remained attached to each other and, instead of forming irregular callus masses, they began to organize into forms that are almost identical to those seen in normal embryos within a fertilized embryo sac. This asexual embryogenesis can result in hundreds of embryoids being formed in a single culture flask. Using the techniques developed for the growth of orchid embryos, they can be isolated, grown in culture until they are large plantlets, and then potted up. Most recently, embryoids have been encapsulated in resins and sown like seeds (see Figure 15-13).

A recently developed variant of the explant procedure is the protoplast technique (see Figure 15-13). Bits of tissue are treated with enzymes that dissolve the cell wall leaving the naked protoplast surrounded by its cell membrane. The protoplasts can be grown in suitable liquid medium where they undergo the same series of morphological changes as do the explant cells. The protoplast technique has, however, an important advantage in that protoplasts can be individually selected for development into plants.

Grafting

Grafting is the establishment of a permanent union between stems or roots with the development of vascular connections and continued growth as one plant. The upper portion is termed the scion and the lower portion is the stock. When the scion is only a bud, the process is called budding. Where graft incompatibility may exist, a third plant, an interstock, can be introduced between stock and scion. This technique is called double-working.

Grafting and budding are done for many reasons. Fruit, nut, and many ornamental woody perennials are difficult to propagate from cuttings, cannot easily be multiplied in large numbers, and, when propagated sexually, rarely come true to type. Grafting is necessary to perpetuate sterile cultivars (navel oranges), to obtain large populations of desirable clones (most fruit and nut trees), and to grow plants whose roots or tops are better adapted to cultural conditions (disease resistance, winter hardiness). Almost all wine grapes (*Vitis vinifera*) are grown on rootstocks of American species that are resistant to phylloxera insects. Some greenhouse cucumbers and tomatoes are grafted to disease-resistant roots. Rootstocks may confer upon the scion other desirable characteristics including early fruiting, dwarfism, or rapid vegetative development.

Topworking is the grafting of desirable cultivars to already established trees. Unproductive, wild, or disease-prone trees can be replaced in a few years with the lower stem and root system remaining as a foundation. Where species are unisexual, one or more staminate (male) branches for pollination of large numbers of female flowers can be introduced by topworking a few trees. For example, pistillate (female) holly (*Ilex*) can be made fruitful by insertion of a single staminate branch. The production of apple, pear, stone fruit, and citrus trees with scaffold branches of different cultivars allows the grower to harvest a number of fruit types from a single plant.

Over the years specific rootstocks have been developed to regulate the size, growth habit, and reproductive vigor of scions. Size-controlling rootstocks are now available for most fruit and nut species and for many ornamentals. For apple and other pome and fruit trees, the famous East Malling (EM) and Malling-Merton (MM) series of stocks, developed at British research stations, are used throughout the world (Figure 15-14). These rootstocks are now propagated through layering to maintain genetic uniformity. The trees produced range from dwarf to very vigorous standard size.

Other rootstocks can alter the growth habit of the scion to produce

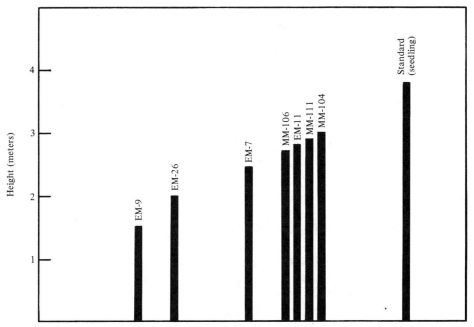

Figure 15-14 Sizes of apple trees produced when grafted to various East Malling (EM) and Malling-Merton (MM) rootstocks.

spreading, contorted, or other desired habits. The level of reproductive vigor, size and quality of fruit, winter hardiness, and disease resistance can be enhanced by appropriate stocks. There are some scions that can modify the development of rootstocks, but these are not as well developed.

Successful grafting and budding depends upon the ability of both meristematic (actively dividing) and mature cells to initiate rapid cell division to form layers of undifferentiated parenchyma cells. These callus cells from both stock and scion interlock and intermingle. Within the resulting callus, some of the parenchyma cells that are in line with the cambia of stock and scion differentiate into primary vascular xylem and phloem, while others differentiate into a new vascular cambium that can form secondary xylem and phloem. These establish bridging vascular connections between vascular strands of the stock and scion, permitting the movement of materials between them. Failure to form vascular connections results in an unsuccessful graft. The development of buds on the scion leads to establishment of a new shoot.

Considerable research has been directed toward understanding the structural and physiological basis for grafting and budding. The initiation of cell division and the proliferation of cells to form the callus and the differentiation of cells into vascular elements and cambia involve the participation of growth-regulating substances (auxins, gibberellins, cytokinins) derived from both stock and scion. Temperature, moisture, light, the past history of stock and scion, diseases, and many other factors are involved.

A major problem in grafting is that of graft incompatibility. It is generally accepted that graft success is highest between related cultivars, usually high within a species, less high between closely related species, low between genera, and almost absent across family lines. Graft incompatibilities exist even among related cultivars. The failure of grafts to become established can be related to many factors, such as the movement of toxic substances across the graft union, differential growth of scion and stock, viruses, and imbalances in growth-regulating compounds, but in many instances the reasons are not known. There is some evidence that cellular recognition factors are involved, but at the present time much of our knowledge is speculative.

Successful grafting depends not only on environmental and compatibility factors, but also on the physiological status of the scion and stock. In general, higher rates of success are achieved when the cambium is active in the spring; this is usually referred to as the time the bark is "slipping." Buds are usually beginning to swell, although shoot formation has not occurred. Deciduous species are grafted in late winter or early spring using the previous year's growth for scions, although older twigs can be used if they bear strong, vigorous buds. In some cases, twigs to be used as scions are collected in late fall and allowed to complete dormancy under controlled conditions.

There are several fundamental considerations in successful grafting. Stock and scion must be compatible. The surfaces to be joined must be placed in intimate contact with the cambial regions of both partners in juxtaposition. The surfaces must be held together firmly during the period of callus formation and graft union establishment and must be protected from desiccation by wrapping

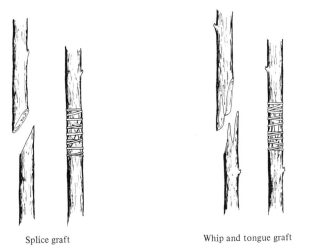

Splice graft   Whip and tongue graft   Side graft

Figure 15-15   Common twig grafts.

or the use of a grafting wax or both. Prevention of infection through the use of clean equipment is necessary.

There are many different grafting techniques, each developed for specific purposes. Whip and tongue grafts, splice grafts, and side grafts (Figure 15-15) are used primarily with relatively small shoots and, when done properly, establish quickly and form a strong union. The scion should possess at least two or three buds. Cleft grafts involve a stock of greater diameter than the scion and are used to introduce new shoots on established shoots (Figure 15-16). Cleft, wedge, and saddle grafts are extensively used for topworking of trees with the main trunk or scaffolding branches forming the stock.

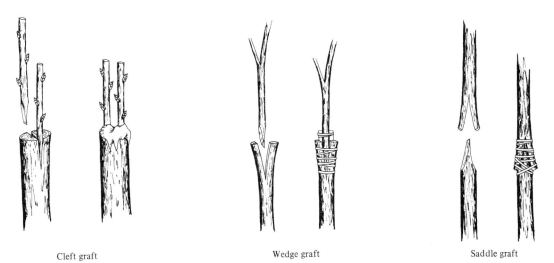

Cleft graft   Wedge graft   Saddle graft

Figure 15-16   Cleft, wedge, and saddle grafts.

Bridge graft

Approach graft

Figure 15-17 Bridge and approach grafts.

Bridge grafts are used to repair the severe injury to trunk or stem that results from girdling by animals or disease (Figure 15-17). Approach grafts involve the joining of two independent plants (Figure 15-17). When the graft union is established, the top of one plant and the bottom of the other are removed, usually in stages, so that a single stem remains. Approach grafting is a difficult procedure, but is sometimes necessary when more conventional grafting techniques cannot be used.

Budding, in contrast to stock-scion grafting, involves the insertion of a single bud with or without bark or wood into a stem that serves as the stock (Figure 15-18). Bud grafting is usually done only with young plants and is frequently used to topwork nursery stock of fruit and nut trees and some ornamental species. The stock may be a rooted cutting, a young seedling, or a small branch on an established tree. Bud grafts form strong unions and are used to produce large numbers of genetically identical plants for commercial orchards and plantations.

Figure 15-18 T-bud graft.

SEXUAL REPRODUCTION

Flower Induction

The formation of the flower is the culmination of the angiosperm life cycle. The flower is the organ where sexual reproduction occurs (see Chapter 3). As we saw in Chapter 9, the mechanism whereby vegetative (asexual) meristems are converted to floral meristems in light-sensitive plants begins with the perception by the leaves of the number of hours of light received each day (photoperiod). The ability to respond to this environmental control is inherited and many plants have specific photoperiod requirements. Short-day plants (SDP) flower when the photoperiod is less than some specific number of hours per day, long-day plants (LDP) when the photoperiod is longer than some specific number of hours per day, and day-neutral plant (DNP) under any photoperiod. The specific number of hours is different for each species and even different cultivars in the same species may have different daylength requirements (Figure 15-19).

Interaction between photoperiod, light intensity, and growth temperature may modify the flowering response in some plants. African violet (*Saintpaulia*) is a day-neutral plant, but its flowering is delayed or minimal when the nighttime temperature falls below 20° C (68° F) and when light intensities are low. Commercially important flowering plants like chrysanthemum and poinsettia also show photoperiod-temperature interactions. Some plants (the June-bearing garden strawberry, orange, Japanese morning glory) are strictly short-day plants when the nighttime temperatures are 20° C or above, but become day-neutral

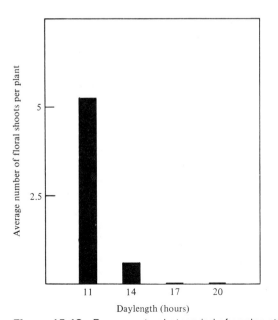
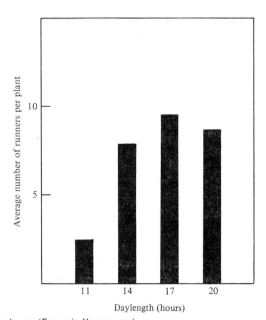

Figure 15-19 Response to photoperiod of garden strawberry (*Fragaria Xananassa*).

**Table 15-3 PHOTOPERIOD REQUIREMENT FOR FLOWERING FOR SOME
COMMON CROP PLANTS**

Latin name	Common name	Latin name	Common name
Short-day plants (SDP)		**Day-neutral plants (DNP)**	
Allium cepa	Onion	*Apium graveolens*	Celery
Capsicum frutescens	Tabasco pepper	*Cucumis sativus*	Cucumber
Fragaria Xananassa	Garden strawberry	*Daucus carota*	Carrot
Glycine max	Soybean	*Fragaria vesca*	Woodland strawberry
Ocimum basilicum	Basil	*F. Xananassa*	Everbearing garden strawberry
Phaseolus vulgaris	Kidney bean	*Lycopersicon esculentum*	Tomato
Solanum tuberosum	Potato	*Pisum sativum*	Pea
Long-day plants (LDP)		*Poa annua*	Bluegrass
Anethum graveolens	Dill	*Vicia faba*	Broadbean
Beta vulgaris	Sugar beet	*Zea Mays*	Corn
B. vulgaris	Swiss chard		
Brassica oleracea	Cabbage		
B. rapa	Chinese cabbage		
B. rapa	Turnip		
Cichorium endiva	Endive		
Lactuca sativa	Lettuce		
Lolium spp.	Ryegrass		
Mentha Xpiperita	Peppermint		
Raphanus sativus	Radish		
Solanum tuberosum	Potato		
Spinacia oleracea	Spinach		

plants when exposed to lower nighttime temperatures during photoperiodic
induction.

The photoperiodic response of a large number of flowering plants has been
determined and only a representative sample can be given here. Table 15-3 lists
the photoperiod requirements of some common crop plants and Table 15-4 lists
the requirements for some important ornamental plants.

The pigment phytochrome, occurring in leaves, perceives daylength. The
interconversion of the two forms of phytochrome (P_r and P_{fr}) acts as a trigger for
the formation of the floral-inducing hormone, which moves to the vegetative
meristems. Florigen, the hypothetical flowering hormone, has never been isolated and is probably more than one substance. The floral stimulus modifies the
vegetative meristems so that these cells and tissues now form flowers.

Responsiveness to photoperiod by the plant is a function of ripeness-to-
flower. A certain amount of vegetative growth must take place, as measured by
the number of leaves or nodes formed, before the plant becomes photoperiodically sensitive. A very few plants can be photoperiodically induced at the
cotyledonary stage (Japanese morning glory). Some plants become day neutral
when fully mature. During the juvenile growth phase, flower induction either
does not occur or proceeds only minimally. Brussels sprouts plants are in a
juvenile stage and will not flower until they are about 11 weeks old. English ivy
(*Hedera helix*) has a distinctive juvenile form which is a creeping vine with lobed,

Figure 15-20 Juvenile and mature forms of English ivy (*Hedera helix*).

palmate leaves. This form persists an indefinite period of time and the growth habit rarely changes to the mature, flowering form of an upright bush with entire leaves (Figure 15-20).

The effect of nutrition on flowering is quite variable. There is no direct effect on photoperiodic induction, but the nutritional status may have a bearing on the number and rate of development of the flowers formed. Flowering in short-day plants can be hastened or delayed by reducing nitrogen nutrition, while flowering in long-day plants is often speeded up by low nitrogen levels (Chapter 7).

Pollination and Fertilization

Although the existence of male and female in animal sexual reproduction was understood in the sixth century in China and by the fourteenth century in Europe, plants were believed to be pure and sexless until the end of the eighteenth century when Christian Sprengel demonstrated that flowers had sexual parts and possessed features that attracted insects. By the middle of the nineteenth century, studies by Charles Darwin and others led to the conclusion that sexual processes analogous to those of animals were characteristic of plants.

As described in Chapter 3, pollen grains contain two nuclei, one of which serves to fertilize (combine with) an egg cell nucleus in the embryo sac to initiate the first cell of the next generation. This zygote, and the plant developed from it, has a genetic constitution determined by the hereditary units (genes) borne by both male and female sexual nuclei. Pollination is the process by which pollen is transferred from its site of formation in the anther to the receptive surface of the stigma of the female entity, the carpel. The fusion of male and female nuclei is

Table 15-4 PHOTOPERIOD REQUIREMENT FOR FLOWERING FOR SOME COMMON ORNAMENTALS

Latin name	Common name	Latin name	Common name
Short-day plants (SDP)		**Day-neutral plants (DNP)**	
Amaranthus caudatus	Love-lies-bleeding	*Alyssum* spp.	Madwort
Ananas comosus	Pineapple	*Browallia speciosa*	Bush violet
Billbergia nutans	Friendship plant	*Calendula officinalis*	Pot marigold
Cattleya trianaei	Christmas orchid	*Coleus Xhybridus*	Painted nettle, coleus
Celosia spp.	Woolflower	*Cyclamen persicum*	Florist's cyclamen
Chrysanthemum indicum	Chrysanthemum	*Draba* spp.	Draba
Chrysanthemum Xmorifolium	Chrysanthemum	*Fuchsia* spp.	Lady's eardrops
Cleome spp.	Spider plant	*Gardenia jasminoides*	Cape jasmine
Coffea arabica	Coffee	*Gerbera jamesonii*	Transvaal daisy
Coleus Xhybridus	Painted nettle, coleus	*Geum* spp.	Avens
Cosmos bipinnatus	Cosmos	*Gladiolus* spp.	Gladiolus
C. sulfureus	Yellow cosmos	*Helianthus annuus*	Sunflower
Euphorbia pulcherrima	Poinsettia	*Impatiens* spp.	Balsam
Hydrangea macrophylla	French hydrangea	*Ilex aquifolium*	English holly
Ipomoea purpurea	Common morning glory	*Lobelia* spp.	Lobelia
Kalanchoe blossfeldiana	Kalanchoe	*Lunaria annua*	Honesty
K. pinnata	Airplant	*Rhododendron* spp.	Rhododendron
Perilla frutescens	Perilla	*Rosa* spp.	Rose
Pharbitis nil	Japanese morning glory	*Saintpaulia* spp.	African violet
Primula spp.	Primrose	*Saxifraga* spp.	Saxifrage
Rhododendron spp.	Azalea	*Tagetes* spp.	Marigold
Salvia splendens	Scarlet sage	*Vinca* spp.	Periwinkle
Schlumbergera bridgesii	Christmas cactus	*Viola XWittrockiana*	Pansy
S. truncata	Crab cactus		
Senecio cruentus	Cineraria	**Short-day followed by long-day plants (SDLD)**	
Tagetes erecta	African marigold	*Campanula medium*	Canterbury bells
Viola spp.	Violet	*Iberis* spp.	Candytuft
Zinnia spp.	Zinnia	*Poa pratensis*	Kentucky bluegrass

Long-day plants (LDP)

Ageratum spp.	Flossflower
Alcea spp.	Hollyhock
Anagallis arvensis	Common pimpernel
Antirrhinum majus	Snapdragon
Begonia semperflorens-cultorum	Hybrid bedding begonia
B. socotrana	Begonia
B. tuberhybrida	Hybrid tuberous begonia
Calceolaria crenatiflora	Pocketbook flower
Callistephus chinensis	China aster
Camellia japonica	Common camellia
Campanula isophylla	Falling stars
C. persicifolia	Willow bellflower
Centaurea cyanus	Cornflower
Chrysanthemum parthenium	Feverfew
C. maximum	Max chrysanthemum
Cichorium intybus	Common chicory
Coreopsis spp.	Tickseed
Dahlia spp.	Dahlia
Delphinium Xcultorum	Hybrid delphinium
Dianthus barbatus	Sweet william
D. caryophyllus	Carnation
D. gratianopolitanus	Cheddar pink
D. superbus	Pink
Digitalis purpurea	Common foxglove
Fuchsia spp.	Lady's eardrops

Long-day plants (LDP)

Gaillardia spp.	Blanket flower
Gypsophila spp.	Gypsophila
Hibiscus syriacus	Rose-of-Sharon
Matthiola incana	Stock
Nicotiana alata	Flowering tobacco
N. sylvestris	Flowering tobacco
Nigella damascena	Love-in-a-mist
Oenothera spp.	Evening primrose
Petunia Xhybrida	Common petunia
Phlox paniculata	Perennial phlox
Rosa spp.	Rose
Rudbeckia hirta	Black-eyed Susan
Salpiglossis spp.	Painted tongue
Scabiosa ucranica	Pincushion flower
Sedum spectabile	Showy stonecrop
S. telephium	Orpine
Sempervivum spp.	Liveforever
Senecio Xhybridus	Cineraria
Tropaeolum majus	Garden nasturtium
Verbena spp.	Verbena

Long-day followed by short-day plants (LDSD)

Aloe albiflora	Aloe
Kalanchoe laxiflora	Kalanchoe

Table 15-5   POLLINATION REQUIREMENTS FOR COMMON FRUIT AND NUT TREES AND SHRUBS

Latin name	Common name	Pollination	Exceptions
Carica Papaya	Pawpaw	S	
Carya Illinoensis	Pecan	S	
C. ovata	Hickory	S	
Castenea sativa	Chestnut	X	
Corylus spp.	Filbert	X	
Cydonia oblongata	Quince	S	
Diospyros spp.	Persimmon	X	
Fragaria spp.	Strawberry	S	
Juglans nigra	Black walnut	X	
J. Regia	English walnut	X	
Malus spp.	Apple	X	
Prunus armeniaca	Apricot	X	Except 'Moorpark'
P. avium	Sweet cherry	X	
P. cerasus	Sour cherry	S	
P. domestica	European plum	S	Except 'Greengage,' 'Big Blue,' 'Italian' prune, 'Stanley,' 'Fellemberg,' 'Yellow Egg'
P. maritima	Beach plum	X	
P. Persica	Peach	X	Except 'J. H. Hale'; other cultivars with Hale in the name usually self-fertile
P. P. Nucipersica	Nectarine	S	Can be pollinated by peach
P. salicina	Japanese plum	X	Except 'Santa Rosa,' 'Superior,' 'Abundance'; Shiro has infertile pollen
P. tomentosa	Bush cherry	S	
Pyrus communis	Pear	X	Except 'Seckel,' which is incompatible with 'Bartlett'
Ribes sativum	Currant	S	
R. uva-crospa	Gooseberry	S	
Rubus spp.	Raspberry	S	
Sambucus spp.	Elderberry	X	
Vaccinium spp.	Blueberry	X	
Vitis spp.	Grape	S	

S = self-pollinating; X = requires cross-pollination. Even when the plant is self-fruitful, better fruit development occurs when the plant is cross-pollinated. In most instances different cultivars are satisfactory for cross-pollination.

preceded by the development of a pollen tube which grows down to the ovule containing the egg nucleus. The two male nuclei are in the pollen tube.

Many economically and horticulturally important plants are self-fertile, that is, the male nuclei in pollen grains of the same plant or even of the same perfect flower are capable of fertilizing the egg nuclei (Table 15-5). Many legumes (peas, beans), tomato, and other plants are usually self-fertile. The resulting embryo and, eventually, the plant derived from that seed, will possess the same genetic information as the parent plant with, possibly, some modification in genetic constitution due to mutation or reassortment of chromosomal material.

When the parent is a hybrid, the seeds do not come true to type and should not be used the following year.

Genetic uniformity in nature is not necessarily desirable since variations in genetic constitution allow a population of plants to adapt to a variety of environmental stresses. Over evolutionary time many structural and physiological mechanisms evolved to prevent self-pollination and self-fertilization and to increase the chance of a plant's being fertilized by another plant of the same species. In addition to maintaining a diverse gene pool, cross-pollination may also result in heterosis, the display of great vegetative or reproductive vigor in the offspring (the F_1 generation). Available hybrids of many agronomic crops such as corn and wheat and horticultural vegetables and flowers are deliberately cross-bred to enhance hybrid vigor.

Even in perfect flowers, self-pollination may be prevented by having the stamens or receptive carpelate surface (the stigma) mature at different times or by having male or female so placed that selfing does not readily occur. Stigmas and styles may protrude beyond the stamens as in fuchsia or the reverse as in clerodendron. There are chemical incompatibilities in many plants with perfect flowers. Pollen of the same genetic constitution may land on the stigma, but will not form a pollen tube or will abort its male nuclei.

Many structural modifications have evolved to ensure cross-pollination. Most obvious is the dioecious state in which male and female flowers are borne on separate plants. Common examples include holly (*Ilex*), spinach (*Spinacia oleracea*), willow (*Salix*), and other deciduous trees. Corn (*Zea Mays*) and many ornamental and nut trees bear imperfect flowers on the same plant. Members of the squash family are effectively dioecious and both male and female plants must coexist. In cucumber (*Cucumis sativus*) and squashes (*Cucurbita* spp.), the first-formed flowers are male, followed by a flush of both male and female flowers and, eventually, all female flowers. Auxin sprays accelerate femaleness, while gibberellins promote maleness. In cucumber, maleness is favored by short days and femaleness by long days. Both photoperiodic and chemical control of sex expression are used commercially.

In many important plants, whether monoecious or dioecious, cross-pollination is required for fertilization. Wind is an important vector of pollination in conifers and many broad-leaved species, and water carries the pollen of many plants to the receptive surfaces of other plants. The collaboration of plants and pollinating animals is one of the most astounding and fascinating aspects of evolutionary theory. Insects (bees, flies, wasps, butterflies), birds (hummingbirds), and rodents (bats, mice, rats) carry pollen from one plant to another. In many instances the association of vector and plant is very precise, with structural and functional adapations of the animal and the plants to ensure the transfer of pollen. Humans act as vectors of pollination through genetic crossbreeding work and in greenhouse conditions where natural pollinators are not present. Greenhouse tomatoes, peppers, squashes, and other plants require pollination by human intervention.

Once appropriate pollen has reached the stigmatal surface of the carpel, it may germinate and send a pollen tube down the style to the ovule (see Chapter

3). Some pollen tubes take more than a year on their journey, while other species complete the route in a few hours. The speed is genetically as well as environmentally controlled. Temperature, moisture, nutritive and regulatory relationships, and other factors are involved. The sperm nuclei of a single pollen tube can fertilize only one egg and polar nuclei set. Where there are multiple ovules, a number of pollen tubes must simultaneously traverse the style to effect the multiple fertilizations that are required for full development of the fruit.

Fruit Development and Maturation

Following successful pollination and fertilization, the ovary begins to enlarge and the petals abscise. The initiation of development of the young fruit is called fruit set.

The increasing size of the ovary results from both cell division and cell enlargement, activities that require an adequate supply of nutrients. Mobilization of food materials for transport into the developing fruit occurs in nearby leaves. The nutrient reserves of the plant are finite, and average fruit size generally decreases as the total number of fruits on a plant increases.

At the end of their growth phase fruits have reached their maximum size and have accumulated a large variety of storage compounds such as carbohydrates, proteins, lipids, and acids. Other compounds (phenolics), which give a bitter or sharp tastes to unripe fruit, are in high concentration and volatile compounds, which give flavor and aroma to ripe fruit, begin to accumulate. At the end of the maturation phase some fruits have high levels of starch (apple) or organic acids (citrus, berries).

Several growth-regulating substances (auxins, gibberellins, cytokinins) are involved during fruit development and maturation in order for the fruit to reach its full size potential. The source of these hormones is primarily the developing seed although other fruit tissues may also play a role. Parthenocarpic fruits (those in which seed formation did not take place or where the seed aborted) can continue to grow normally. Application of one or more hormones to certain developing fruit to alter fruit size, to change fruit shape, to delay fruit drop, to increase fruit color, or to promote or delay maturity has become common pomological practice. In the case of tomato use of auxin spray results in fruit with fewer seeds.

Genetic Engineering

Micropropagation techniques result in the production of plants that are genetically identical. Thus, micropropagation is a technique for the asexual production of plants. It is also desirable to be able quickly and uniformly to reproduce plants sexually. A more diversified genetic potential is present when the parent plants possess different genetic attributes. Important barriers to desirable sexual recombinations exist, however. These include the general failure of distantly related plants to be crossed, barriers to pollen tube germination and growth in

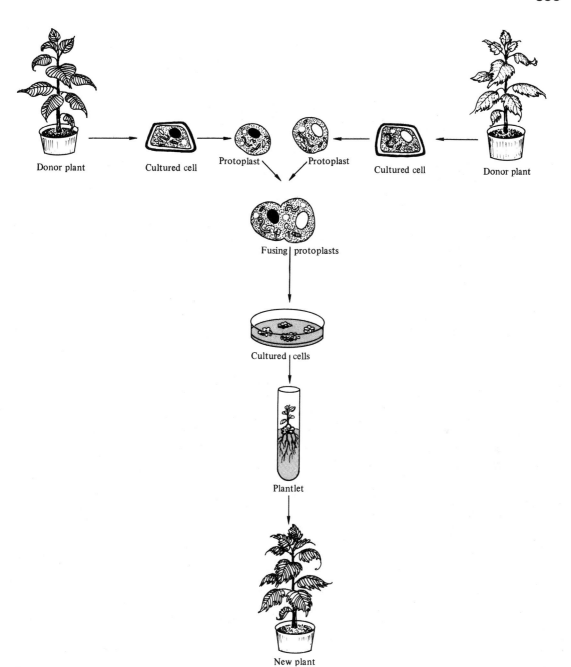

Figure 15-21 Outline of the procedure for genetic engineering of plants using the protoplast fusion method. Sketches not to scale.

incompatible strains or races of particular species, the long time needed for completion of many plant life cycles, and the inability to insert precisely those genetic characters that are desired or to eliminate undesirable characters. It is for these and other reasons that genetic engineering concepts and techniques have become so important in plant breeding.

Two major methods are used for genetic modification of plants under micropropagation conditions (Figure 15-21). The first is the protoplast fusion method. Cells in culture or even from an intact plant whose genetic potential is known can be freed of their cell walls by appropriate treatment with enzymes. These protoplasts can be made to fuse with other protoplasts obtained from genetically different plants that may be distantly related or even unrelated. The two nuclei fuse to form a single nucleus that contains the genetic information from both cells. Depending on the nuclear condition of the original protoplasts, the new cell may be the normal diploid, triploid, or even polyploid. In protoplast fusion experiments with cells that are closely related, the cell will form a new wall, survive, and grow into a cell culture. A few of these cultures have, via micropropagation techniques, developed into plantlets. Although still at the laboratory level, it is now at least theoretically possible to develop plants possessing desirable characteristics of both parents and to do this in a short period of time. Standard protoplast fusion is, in general, a modification of classical breeding methods because the entire genome of both parent plants is included in the new plant.

An exciting development in genetic engineering has the potential to allow specific genetic information to be inserted into plant cells. For many years it has been known that when plants are inoculated with the bacterium (*Agrobacterium tumefaciens*) that causes crown gall or with the related bacterium (*A. rhizogenes*) that causes hairy root, tumor development or unusual root systems are initiated by an organized plasmid, a subcellular particle that contains a special DNA (the tumor-inducing plasmid). The tumor-inducing plasmid fuses with the normal DNA of the host cell, conferring on the infected cells the capacity for unlimited growth. This transformation has been used as the basis for genetic engineering. It is possible to insert, in the bacterium, higher plant DNA fragments bearing genes controlling specific characteristics of value. If the plants are then inoculated with the altered bacterium, the tumor-inducing plasmid bearing useful genetic information fuses with the normal plant DNA. Methods are being developed for the isolation from plants of segments of the DNA that code for desirable characteristics. These can be multiplied in a suitable bacterium (frequently the colon bacterium *Escherichia coli*) and then introduced into the plasmids of the crown gall bacterium. These bacteria, in turn, are inoculated into plants where they will induce tumor formation. The tumors are isolated, grown as cell cultures, and new, genetically altered plants obtained by micropropagation techniques (Figure 15-22). Thus, it is now at least theoretically possible to transfer specific genetic information from one plant to another resulting in new plants whose capacities and attributes are tailored to specific needs. It is hoped that genetically engineered plants may be available within the next few years. Alteration of cereal crops, food legumes, and other major food crops have high priority. Attention is

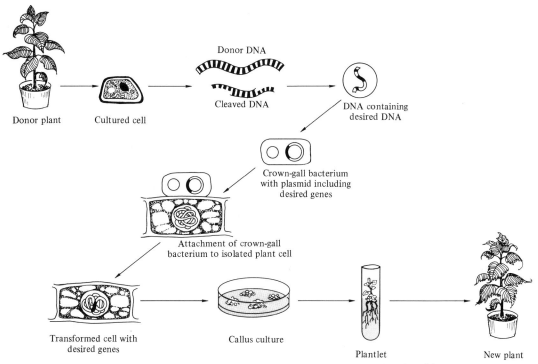

Figure 15-22 Outline of the procedure for genetic engineering of plants using the plasmid vector method. Sketches not to scale.

also being paid to the possibility of conferring disease resistance, ability to grow in arid and saline environments, more efficient use of fertilizers, and other agricultural needs.

SENESCENCE

Differentiated cells have finite lives that range from weeks to years depending on their location and function. The gradual or abrupt deterioration of cell function is termed senescence and leads to cell, tissue, and organ death. Although most plants, because they contain both primary and secondary meristems, are theoretically immortal, they have species-specific life spans. We recognize this in our assessment of short-lived and long-lived species, and landscape or garden plants are chosen accordingly. The senescence of plant organs, too, is species specific. Needles of evergreen plants may be functional for one growth season (larch) or for many years (some pines); reproductive organs may persist on plants for several years (pine cones) or, like many flowers, may mature, senesce, and be displaced in a few days.

As evidenced by the name, annual or biennial plants (monocarpic) usually die after flowering and fruiting even when the plants are maintained in optimum growing conditions. Polycarpic plants are perennials that, when mature, will flower and fruit for a number of years. There is growing evidence that whole plant senescence involves the production by developing fruits and/or seeds of several substances that move from fruit into the rest of the plant. Removal of faded flowers and developing fruit will prevent or delay normal senescence of monocarpic, but not polycarpic plants. Removal of flower buds and unfertilized flowers is also effective. The nature of these senescence or "death" factors is not known, but knowledge of their chemical constitution and concentrations may have considerable economic and significance.

Fruit Ripening

Fruit ripening is an example of senescence. A mature, but unripe fruit progresses to a soft, usually nongreen, sweet-tasting ripe fruit; an overripened fruit is one in which cells are dead or dying.

The events leading to fruit ripening have been studied intensively and the knowledge utilized at the practical level. For example, controlling the gaseous atmosphere during storage (controlled atmosphere storage) has meant that apples and other fruits are available throughout the year rather than for a few months following harvest.

The ripening process involves a number of striking changes in the appearance, texture, and taste of the fruit. The internal region of the fruit begins to soften due to the enzymatic breakdown of the pectins of the middle lamella between cells as well as the cellulose in cell walls. Storage compounds are also degraded. The ripening fruit becomes sweet as simple sugars are formed by hydrolysis of complex carbohydrate. Grapes and cherries accumulate the simple sugars fructose and glucose and for some cultivars of grapes their concentrations may reach very high levels. A decrease in sharp or bitter flavors is due to the breakdown of various phenolics and organic acids. (The acids in lemon continue to accumulate, making the fruit sour rather than sweet, and the same is true to a lesser extent for orange and grapefruit.)

Chlorophyll, the green pigment of unripe fruit, decreases and unmasks the yellow xanthophyll pigments; or pigments are newly synthesized such as the red anthocyanin (apple) or orange-red lycopenes (tomato). The color change from green to yellow in banana (*Musa*) occurs as the fruit ripens, while the change in orange (*Citrus*) goes on only during the early stages of ripening. It is unusual for a color change to occur after the fruit is ripe (pear), and some fruits are green when ripe (some cultivars of apple).

The synthesis of the various storage compounds as well as other activities of cells requires energy and cells of maturing fruit are metabolically quite active. During the early stages of fruit ripening, respiration, as measured by carbon dioxide released, is occurring at a relatively high level, but this activity slows down. The gradual decrease in respiration may, for some fruits, show a sudden, sharp reversal as carbon dioxide output becomes quite pronounced and then tapers off again (Figure 15-23). The rapid increase in respiration is called the climacteric rise. The time frame of this rise corresponds to the time during which ripening occurs and when storage compounds are being broken down.

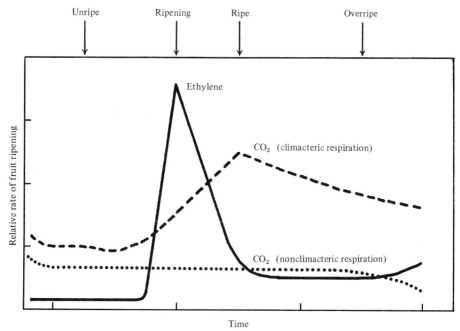

Figure 15-23 Sequence of events in fruit ripening.

The climacteric peak may occur at the peak of ripeness and flavor (pear) or just before full ripeness is reached (apple, banana). The climacteric peak may occur much before the fruit is at the peak of ripeness (tomato). Some stone fruits also show the climacteric (peach, apricot, plum). Avocado (*Persea americana*) exhibits a marked climacteric rise only after the fruit is picked; it does not ripen until after removal from the plant. A number of fruits do not show the climacteric rise in respiration (citrus, fig, pepper, peanut, strawberry, pineapple, grape), but rather exhibit a gradual respiratory decrease during the period when the fruit is undergoing changes associated with the ripening process.

The climacteric is initiated by ethylene, a gaseous compound produced by cells in the maturing fruit. Ethylene accumulates in the intercellular air spaces and, for most fruits, reaches its maximum concentration at or just before the beginning of the climacteric respiratory rise. It acts as the chemical trigger that sets off the chain of events that start the ripening process. It has been called the fruit-ripening hormone.

It is common knowledge that a ripe apple or banana will hasten the ripening of unripe fruit when these are together in a closed container. The biochemical explanation is that ethylene released from the ripe fruit stimulates the ripening process of the other fruit by accelerating ethylene production. In fact, exogenous ethylene can induce a climacteric rise in fruits that normally do not show this characteristic. Use of ethylene in commercial fruit and vegetable ripening is discussed in Chapter 13.

Fruit Storage

The accumulated information concerning ethylene, respiration, and their inter-actions in promoting fruit ripening has been instrumental in the development of storage facilities where fruit can be maintained under conditions that prevent further ripening and the deterioration characteristic of overripe fruit. If respira-tion is inhibited, fruit ripening will be suppressed. Low temperature will, of course, decrease the rate of respiratory activity. Elevated levels of carbon dioxide inhibit respiration as well as the synthesis of ethylene. Lowered levels of oxygen will delay the onset of the climacteric since respiratory processes require oxygen, although too low levels lead to excess breakdown of sugar and poor fruit quality.

These facts define the environmental conditions necessary for optimum storage (controlled atmosphere storage). Air-tight containers have a gaseous atmosphere of 5 to 10 percent carbon dioxide and 1 to 3 percent oxygen, the specific level determined by the fruit being stored. The temperature of storage is also critical. Some fruits (banana, tomato, lemon, grapefruit, pineapple) are damaged when stored below 10° C (50° F). The minimum storage temperature for others (papaya, olive, avocado) is 7° C (45° F). Some fruits (apple, pear, grape) store well at 0° C (32° F).

Root cellars have long been used as convenient areas for storage of fruit and root crops. They are sufficiently cool and, depending upon the plant material being stored, sufficiently humid to prevent excess loss of water. The use of plastic bags for storing fruit provides an atmosphere within the bag necessary to retard overripening. As the cells of the fruit respire, oxygen is used up and carbon dioxide is released.

Abscission

Fruit drop and the autumnal falling of leaves is termed abscission. Since the fruit stalk (the peduncle) is developmentally and structurally a leaf stalk (a petiole), the processes leading to abscission are essentially identical in both structures, although much more information is available on leaf abscission than on fruit drop. Developing and maturing fruits are notable nutrient sinks, causing the mobilization and translocation of nutrients from leaves that function as sources.

Abscission is the final stage in senescence. The sequence of loss of cell function leading to abscission has been studied in a number of fruits. There is a gradual reduction in chlorophyll and associated reductions in respiration, nucleic acid, and biosynthetic metabolism. Protein disappears as it is broken down to its constituent amino acids. Soluble inorganic ions are transported from the fruit or the leaf to storage areas or to younger growth. As physiological activity decreases, the production of auxins, cytokinins, and gibberellins de-creases while ethylene and abscisic acid synthesis increases. These growth substances, now present in very different ratios than in metabolically active fruits or leaves, affect a band of cells in the peduncle or petiole called the abscission layer (Figure 15-24). Abscission layer cells maintain an active meta-bolic state only when auxins, gibberellins, and cytokinins are being synthesized

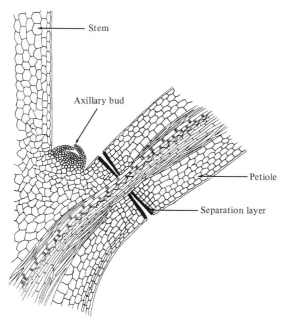

Figure 15-24 Formation of leaf abscission layer.

in fruit or leaf blade cells and when ethylene and abscisic acid are absent. As the chemical balance at abscission zone cells is altered, they begin to develop corky cell walls and die. When most are dead, they separate easily from one another and the weight of the now senescent fruit or leaf and the action of wind or rain will allow the fruit or leaf to abscise and fall from the plant. The layers of corky abscission cells close to the twig form the impervious, protective outer layers of the leaf or fruit scar.

The decrease in the activity of fruit or leaf blade cells can be triggered by a variety of factors. Under normal conditions senescence of a plant is controlled by the decreasing photoperiods of late summer and the alterations in the day and night temperatures. Drought, injury, disease, and insect infestations can initiate premature senescence and the development of the abscission layer. Applications of auxins, gibberellins, or cytokinins can reverse or retard senescence. These substances are now used commercially to lengthen the time that fruits remain in their mature stage prior to harvest and they have also been used as postharvest treatments of green leafy vegetables to retain freshness during storage and shipping.

Abscission of fruits before maturity is termed drop. It is an important horticultural problem. Fruit drop may occur at any time, but is most commonly seen after fruit set or during the early growth phase of the embryo and fruit. In apple (*Malus*) there are two periods of fruit drop. Early drop occurs when the ovary begins to enlarge and June drop occurs when the embryo is developing rapidly. The basis for senescence of immature fruits leading to drop is not well understood. It is suggested that trees bearing large numbers of fruits cannot provide adequate water and mineral supplies for all fruits, each of which is an active sink. In some fruits growth substances are produced in developing seeds and inadequate seed set may be a factor in fruit drop. By spraying trees with appropriate growth-regulating compounds, fruit drop can be minimized. Conversely, treatment with growth substances that metabolically oppose the action of endogenous growth substances or with ethylene-forming substances can increase fruit drop. Both enhancing and decreasing premature fruit drop are used commercially. Where agronomic crops such as cotton fruits are machine harvested, pretreatment with substances that activate leaf abscission facilitate harvesting. Fruit and nut trees are sprayed with ethylene-forming substances to loosen the fruit and facilitate mechanical harvesting. For tomato and related plants, compounds are used to retain young fruits on the plant. These are called setting substances and function to prevent the formation of the abscission layer.

Senescence and abscission of flowers, fruits, and leaves of house and garden plants have the same physiological and structural basis as in trees. In house plants senescence may be progressive and sequential. As plants develop, older leaves and the first-formed flowers or fruit may yellow and abscise progressively from older to younger nodes. Water, nitrogen and other mobile nutrients, or radiation may be limiting and the younger portions of the plant are favored. This is particularly noticable in house plants that are root-bound and inadequately fertilized or illuminated. In many instances the only solution is to root the apical, leaf-bearing portion of the plants, although sometimes repotting and fertilization allow dormant axillary buds to break.

SUPPLEMENTARY READINGS

Addicott, F. T. (ed.). 1982. *Abscission.* University of California Press, Berkeley.

Allen, O. 1978. *Pruning and Grafting.* Time-Life Encyclopedia of Gardening. Time-Life Corp., Alexandria, Va.

Ammirato, P. V. (ed.) 1984. *Handbook of Plant Cell Culture.* Vol. 3. *Crop Species.* Macmillan, New York.

Baird, L. A. M., and B. D. Webster. 1975. Anatomy and histochemistry of fruit abscission. *Hort. Rev.* 1.

Bajaj, Y. P. S. (ed.). 1986. *Biotechnology in Agriculture and Forestry.* Springer, New York.

Baker, R. J. 1986. *Selection Indices in Plant Breeding.* CRC Press, Boca Raton, Fla.

Bernier, G., J.-M. Kinet, and R. M. Sachs. 1981. *The Physiology of Flowering.* 2 vols. CRC Press, Boca Raton, Fla.

Brouse, P. M. 1979. *Plant Propagation.* Simon & Schuster, New York.

Burton, W. G. 1982. *Post-harvest Physiology of Food Crops.* Longman, London.

Collins, G. B., and J. F. Petolino. 1984. *Applications of Genetic Engineering to Crop Improvement.* Kluwer, Hingham, Mass.

Conger, B. V. (ed.). *Cloning Agricultural Plants via In Vitro Techniques.* CRC Press, Boca Raton, Fla.

Evans, D. A., and W. R. Sharp (eds.). 1984. *Handbook of Plant Cell Culture.* Vol. 1. *Techniques for Propagation and Breeding.* Vol. 2. *Crop Species.* Macmillan, New York.

Fehr, W. R. (ed.). 1987. *Plant Breeding.* 2 vols. MacMillan, New York.

Fowke, L. C., and F. Constabel (eds.). 1985. *Plant Protoplasts.* CRC Press Boca Raton, Fla.

Guse, W. E., and F. E. Larson. 1975. *Herbaceous Plants from Cuttings.* Pacific Northwest Cooperative Extension Publ. 151, Pullman, Wash.

Gustafson, J. P. 1984. *Gene Manipulation in Plant Improvement.* Plenum Press, New York.

Hammett, K. R. W. 1973. *Plant Propagation.* Drake, New York.

Hartmann, H. T., and D. E. Kester. 1983. *Plant Propagation.* 4th ed. Prentice-Hall, Englewood Cliffs, N.J.

Helmer, M. J. 1980. *House Plant Propagation for Modern Living.* Merchants, Kalamazoo, Mich.

Hutchinson, W. A. 1980. *Plant Propagation and Cultivation.* Avi, Westport, Conn.

Kosuge, T., and C. P. Meredith (eds.). 1983. *Genetic Engineering of Plants: An Agricultural Perspective.* Plenum Press, New York.

Kyte, L. 1986. *Plants from Test Tubes.* ISBS/Timber Press, Beaverton, Ore.

Larson, F. E. 1977. *Layering to Renew or Multiply Plants.* Pacific Northwest Cooperative Extension Publ. 165, Pullman, Wash.

Larson, F. E. 1977. *Propagating Plants from Seed.* Pacific Northwest Cooperative Extension Publ. 170, Pullman, Wash.

Larson, F. E., and W. E. Guse. 1975. *Propagating Deciduous and Evergreen Shrubs, Trees and Vines with Stem Cuttings.* Pacific Northwest Cooperative Extension Publ. 152, Pullman, Wash.

Lewis, D. 1979. *Sexual Incompatability.* Studies in Biology No. 10. University Park Press, Baltimore, Md.

MacDonald, A. B. 1987. *Practical Woody Plant Propagation for Nursery Growers.* ISBS/Timber Press, Beaverton, Ore.

Magnien, E., and D. de Nettercourt (eds.). 1985. *Genetic Engineering of Plants and Microorganisms Important for Agriculture.* Kluwer, Hingham, Mass.

Monselese, S. P. (ed.). 1986. *CRC Handbook of Fruit Set and Development.* CRC Press, Boca Raton, Fla.

Murashiga, T. 1974. Plant propagation through tissue cultures. *Annu. Rev. Plant Physiol.* 25:135–166.

Neyra, C. A. (ed.). *Biochemical Basis of Plant Breeding.* 2 vols. CRC Press, Boca Raton, Fla.

Panopulos, N. J. 1982. *Genetic Engineering in the Plant Sciences.* Praeger, New York.

Proctor, M., and P. Yeo. 1973. *The Pollination of Flowers.* Taplinger, New York.

Salisbury, F. B. 1982. Photoperiodism. *Hort. Rev.* 4:66–105.

Sen, S. K., and K. L. Giles (eds.). 1983. *Plant Cell Culture in Crop Improvement.* Plenum Press, New York.

Smock, R. M. 1979. Controlled atmosphere storage of fruits. *Hort. Rev.* 1.

Styer, D. J., and C. K. Chin. 1983. Meristem and shoot tip culture. *Hort. Rev.* 5.

Thorpe, W. 1981. *Plant Tissue Culture: Methods and Applications in Agriculture.* Academic Press, New York.

Torres, K. C. 1986. *Tissue Culture Techniques for Horticultural Crops.* Avi, Westport, Conn.

Wetherall, D. 1981. *Introduction to In Vitro Propagation.* Avery, Wayne, N.J.

Vose, P. B., and S. G. Blixt (eds.). *Crop Breeding: A Contemporary Basis.* Pergamon Press, Elmsford, N.Y.

Zimmerman, R. H. 1972. Juvenility and flowering in woody plants. *Hort. Sci.* 7:417–445.

PART FIVE

APPLIED PLANT SCIENCE

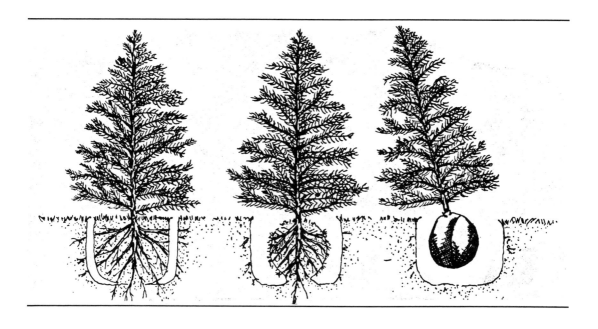

C H A P T E R   1 6

VEGETABLES

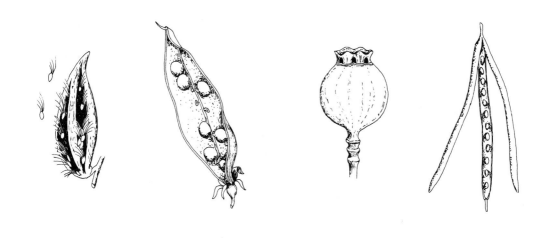

Vegetables are usually distinguished from fruits in the marketplace even though some of the most popular vegetables are true fruits (tomato, cucumber, bell pepper). Plant parts consumed as food in the raw or cooked state and termed vegetables include flowers (broccoli, cauliflower, globe artichoke), leaves (lettuce, cabbage, collards), stems (asparagus, kohlrabi, bamboo shoots), petioles (rhubarb, fennel, celery), bulbs (onion, garlic), tubers (white potato), roots (sweet potato, carrot), and fruits (string beans).

Olericulture is the horticultural term for the growing of vegetables for the home or commercial market. Production of vegetables in the United States for the fresh vegetable market or for processing and canning is small compared to the production of cereal grains, but is still a significant aspect of North American agriculture. White (Irish) potatoes account for about 35 percent of total vegetable production, and five other vegetables (tomatoes, sweet corn, lettuce, onions, cabbage) form 40 percent of total vegetable production. These same vegetables are also among the most popular in the home garden.

SELECTION OF CULTIVARS

Information on growing vegetable crops geared to a particular climatic region may be obtained from the appropriate Cooperative Extension Service (see appendix). Lists of available publications on growing specific crops and on general aspects of gardening may be obtained from the Superintendent of Documents, Government Printing Office, Washington, D.C. 20402. The selection of cultivars may be aided by looking for those designated All America Selection (AAS). Extensive field trials are made of newly developed cultivars and those designated AAS are superior in one or another characteristic compared to similar cultivars.

Cultivars appropriate for a particular region are selected partly on the basis of information on days to harvest and length of the growing season. Days to harvest indicates the average number of days for the maturation of the crop from the time seeds are planted in the garden or from the time transplants are set out (Table 16-1). Seed catalogues supply this information. The actual number of days before a crop can begin to be harvested will depend upon soil type, amount of rainfall or extra water supplied, temperature, fertilization, and specific location within a climatic zone.

Days to harvest information will determine the advisability of planting a specific crop or cultivar. Tomatoes, for example, are classified as early, midseason, or late. A tomato cultivar requiring 75 or more days to form ripe fruit cannot usually be grown to full harvest in cool areas of northern United States and southern Canada that have short growing seasons.

Growth zones are a measure of the average number of days in an area that are frost-free, that is, where the temperature will not fall below freezing. The time frame so encompassed is the growing season; it commences at the time of the last frost in the spring and ends with the first frost of the fall. The average number of days that are frost-free varies from about 100 in southern Canada and the most northern United States to about 300 in regions bordering the Gulf of

Mexico. This number is the major limiting factor in the decision as to which crops can reliably be grown to maturity. In southern United States, the long growing season permits planting and harvesting a second crop of fast-growing vegetables such as beans, beets, carrots, lettuce, radishes, and spinach.

The time of the average last frost of spring determines the time for planting out and for starting seeds that will be set in the garden as vigorous, young plants (Table 16-2). To determine the indoor planting date note the age in weeks of transplants, determine the average date of the last frost in spring and add one week, and count back to determine the date for starting seeds. The time to plant out seeds or transplants depends not only on the average last frost of spring but also on the tolerance to cold temperature of the plant material (see Chapter 8). Cool-season vegetable crops are those that grow optimally around 15 to 18° C (59 to 64° F). Some of these will tolerate a limited exposure to freezing temperatures (Brussels sprouts, turnips, rutabaga, spinach, beets), while others do not (cauliflower, carrots, lettuce, onions, potatoes, peas). Vegetables classified as warm-season crops do best at temperatures around 18 to 27° C (64 to 80° F). These plants do not tolerate freezing temperatures or long exposure to near-freezing temperatures. This category includes cucumber, eggplant, melons, okra, peppers, pumpkins, squash, tomato, sweet corn, and sweet potato. Some are quite sensitive to cool temperatures; for example, a temperature below 13° C (55° F) causes blossom drop in tomato. Bean seeds, planted in cold and wet soils, will most likely rot before germinating.

Using specific information on frost-free time, days to harvest, last and first frosts, and temperature requirements for the growth of seeds or transplants, appropriate cultivars can be selected and planted out with the full expectation of an abundant harvest.

There are a few general rules to follow when disease resistance and disease treatment are considered. Many resistant cultivars of vegetable crops are available and more are developed each year. The exact spectrum of resistance to pathogenic organisms is indicated in seed catalogues. Resistant cultivars should be planted whenever possible. Information about disease prevention and treatment is found in Chapter 10.

Diseased plants must always be removed from the garden and disposed of rather than being added to compost piles or used as mulch. Good sanitation methods are essential to maintain a healthy garden. Crop rotation is beneficial in preventing a buildup of pathogens in the soil. Weeds should be eliminated or kept to a minimum around the vegetable garden as many disease-producing organisms persist in weedy species and survive the winter in these plants.

Pesticides are advisable when the situation demands. Attention must be paid to the time of application before harvest as well as to the toxicity of the material. Identification of the insect, fungus, or nematode pest can be made by Cooperative Extension Services so that the appropriate pesticide can be chosen. Pesticides should be applied only to those crops specified on the label.

Insofar as possible, pesticides of low toxicity for humans and for pollinating bees should be the first choice. Many insecticides have low toxicity for bees including allethrin, pyrethrum, and Rotenone. Many fungicides are minimally

Table 16-1 PLANTING INFORMATION FOR SOME COMMON GARDEN VEGETABLES

Vegetable	Age in weeks of transplants	Seeds/plants per 100 ft row	Final space between plants in row-inches	Space between rows inches	Depth to plant inches	Approximate days to first harvest
Asparagus	1-yr crowns	65–75	12–18	36–60	6–8	2–3 years
Asparagus		4 pkts	12–18	36–60	1	3–4 years
Beans						
Bush-snap	3	½–1 lb	2–4	18–30	1–2	45–60
Pole-snap	3	¼–½	18–36	24–36	1–2	60–75
Lima	3	½–1 lb	6–8	24–36	1–2	70–90
Beets		1 oz	3–4	12	½–1	40–70
Broccoli	5–7	¼ oz	18	36	¼–½	50–80 transplant 80–100 seeds
Brussels sprouts	5–7	¼ oz	18–24	24–36	¼–½	65–75 transplant 100–110 seeds
Cabbage	5–7	½ oz	12–24	20–30	¼–½	60–90 transplant 90–150 seeds
Carrot		½ oz	1–3	10–24	½–1	65–85
Cauliflower	5–7	¼–½ oz	18–24	30–36	½	55–90
Celery	10–12	½ oz	6–8	24–36	¼–½	100–125
Collards	4–6	1 pkt	6–8	24–30	½	75–80
Cucumber	4–6	1 oz	12	60	½–1	50–70
Corn						
Pop		1 pkt	12	30–36	2	80–105
Sweet		1 pkt	12	30–36	2	60–120
Eggplant	7–10	1 pkt	24–30	36	¼–½	72–80
Garlic		1 lb cloves	3–4	12–18	1–2	90–120
Kohlrabi		2 pkts	4–6	12–18	¼–½	50–60
Leeks	8	2 pkts	2–4	12–18	¼–½	100–130
Lettuce						
Head	4–6	1 pkt	8–15	18–24	¼	70–75
Leaf		1 pkt	6–8	12–15	¼	45–75
Melons	3–4	1 oz	36	60	½–1	80–110

Crop		Days to germination / weeks	Amount to plant	Between plants (in.)	Between rows (in.)	Planting depth (in.)	Days to maturity
Onion seeds			1 oz	2–3	12	¼–½	100–200
	Chives						
	Green onions						
	Onions						
	Shallots						
Onion sets			50 bulbs	2–3	12	1–2	60–90
Onion transplants		8		2–3	12	1–2	90–100
Okra			2 oz	18–24	36	½–1	50–55
Parsnip			1 pkt	3–4	18–24	¼–½	100–130
Peas			1 lb	2–3	18–24	1	50–80
	Common						
	Edible podded						
	Southern table						
	Yardlong bean						
Pepper		7–10	2 pkts	18–24	24–30	½	60–80
	Hot						
	Sweet						
Potatoes							
	Sweet		75–100 slips	12–18	36	3–4	150
	White		100 sets	12	30	4	90–120
Pumpkins		3–4	1 oz	48–72	72–96	½–1	90–120
Radish, small			1 pkt	1–2	6–12	½	20–30
Rhubarb			30–50 roots	24–36	36–48	2–3	1–2 years
Rutabaga			1 pkt	6–10	24–36	½	90–100
Spinach			1 oz	3–5	12–18	¼–½	40–70
Squash							
	Summer	3–4	1 oz	24–36	36–48	1	50–60
	Winter	3–4	½ oz	36–48	60–72	1	85–110
Swiss chard			1 pkt	6–8	18–24	½	60
Tomatoes		5–7	½ oz	18–36	36–48	¼–½	50–90
Turnips			2 pkts	4–12	12–18	½–1	40–60

Table 16-2   FROST DATES FOR CONTINENTAL UNITED STATES AND CANADA

State or province	Average date of last killing frost in spring	Average date of first killing frost in fall
Alabama	mid Feb.–mid Mar.	mid Nov.–mid Dec.
Arizona	early Feb.–early Mar.	mid Dec.
Arkansas	mid Mar.	mid Nov.
California	mid Jan.–mid Feb.	late Nov.–mid Dec.
Colorado	late Apr.–early May	mid Oct.–late Oct.
Connecticut	mid Apr.	mid Oct.–late Oct.
Delaware	mid Apr.	late Oct.
Florida	mid Jan.–late Feb.	early Dec.–late Dec.
Georgia	late Feb.–late Mar.	mid Nov.–early Dec.
Idaho	late Apr.–early May	early Oct.–mid Dec.
Illinois	early Apr.–late Apr.	mid Oct.–late Oct.
Indiana	early Apr.–early May	mid Oct.–early Nov.
Iowa	mid Apr.–late Apr.	early Oct.–mid Oct.
Kansas	early Apr.–mid Apr.	late Oct.–early Nov.
Kentucky	early Apr.–mid Apr.	late Oct.–early Nov.
Louisiana	mid Feb.–early Mar.	late Nov.–mid Dec.
Maine	late Apr.–mid May	late Sept.–mid Oct.
Maryland	late Apr.	mid Nov.
Massachusetts	mid Apr.–early May	early Oct.–late Oct.
Michigan	late Apr.–mid May	mid Oct.–late Oct.
Minnesota	late Apr.–late May	late Sept.–mid Oct.
Mississippi	mid Mar.	mid Nov.
Missouri	early Apr.–mid Apr.	late Oct.–early Nov.
Montana	early May–mid May	late Sept.–early Oct.
Nebraska	mid Apr.–late Apr.	mid Oct.–late Oct.
Nevada	mid Mar.–mid May	early Oct.–mid Nov.
New Hampshire	mid May	late Sept.
New Jersey	late Mar.–early Apr.	early Nov.–mid Nov.
New Mexico	early Apr.–early May	early Oct.–late Oct.
New York	early Apr.–early May	early Oct.–mid Nov.
North Carolina	early Mar.–mid Apr.	late Oct.–late Nov.
North Dakota	mid May	late Sept.
Ohio	mid Apr.–late Apr.	late Oct.–early Nov.
Oklahoma	late Mar.	early Nov.
Oregon	early Apr.–mid May	late Sept.–early Dec.
Pennsylvania	late Mar.–late Apr.	mid Oct.–late Oct.
Rhode Island	mid Apr.	late Oct.
South Carolina	mid Feb.–mid Mar.	late Nov.–early Dec.
South Dakota	early May	early Oct.
Tennessee	late Mar.	early Nov.–mid Nov.
Texas	early Feb.–mid Apr.	late Oct.–mid Dec.
Utah	early Apr.–end May	late Sept.–end Oct.
Vermont	mid May	early Oct.
Virginia	mid Mar.–mid Apr.	late Oct.–late Nov.
Washington	late Feb.–late Apr.	mid Oct.–early Dec.
West Virginia	mid Apr.	mid Oct.–late Oct.
Wisconsin	late Apr.–early May	early Oct.–late Oct.
Wyoming	mid May–late May	late Sept.

(Continued)

Table 16-2 *(Continued)*

State or province	Average date of last killing frost in spring	Average date of first killing frost in fall
Alberta	mid May–late May	mid Sept.
British Columbia	late Mar.–mid June	late Aug.–mid Nov.
Manitoba	late May–late June	mid Sept.–late Sept.
New Brunswick	mid May	mid Oct.
Newfoundland	early June	mid Sept.–early Oct.
Northwest Territories	mid June–late June	mid Aug.–late Aug.
Nova Scotia	mid May	late Oct.
Ontario	early May–mid June	early Sept.–mid Oct.
Quebec	early May–late June	late Aug.–mid Oct.
Saskatchewan	late May–early June	early Sept.–mid Sept.
Yukon	early June	early Aug.

Note: Specific frost dates depend on latitude, elevation, and other geographical and climatic factors and may vary from the average by a week or more.

toxic for bees (benomyl, captan, maneb, zineb, folpet, and others). Some herbicides and defoliants can be used when bees are present with minimal effect on these insects. Directions on the labels must always be followed exactly.

STARTING PLANTS

Seed Starting

The germination requirements of vegetable seeds are no different than those of other angiosperms. Specific details are discussed in Chapter 14. The optimum conditions to maximize rapid and uniform germination are warm temperature (21° C, 70° F), even moisture, and adequate aeration. Whether seeds are started indoors or planted directly into the garden, these conditions must be met. Only a few vegetable seeds require light to promote germination (onion, some lettuce cultivars).

Legume seeds (peas, beans, peanuts) should be dusted at the time of planting with commercially available legume inoculants, a dry mixture of nitrogen-fixing bacteria. This will ensure the presence of live bacteria in the soil at germination to effect nodulation, and will reduce the need for nitrogen fertilizer (see Chapter 7).

Planting Out

The usual method for planting vegetable seed or transplants is in narrow, parallel rows with walking space between the rows. The distance apart of individual plants in a row and the space between rows (see Table 16-1) are related to the size of the mature plant.

Wide-row planting, in contrast to the more conventional single-row planting, results in rows of vegetables that are 25 to 30 cm (10 to 12 in.) wide rather

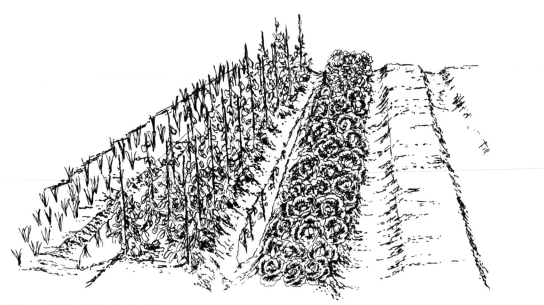

Figure 16-1   Raised beds of vegetables.

than only a few centimeters wide. This method is particularly advantageous for carrots, beets, onions, lettuce, collards, spinach, peas, and beans. Yields are greater per unit area planted since the walking space between rows is decreased. The soil must be properly prepared and the seed is broadcast within the wide row, with small seeds being distributed evenly and larger seed (peas, beans) being planted equidistant across the row.

Raised bed gardening, common in irrigated areas, requires intensive labor to create raised beds for growing crops, but is also practical for the small home garden. The soil beds in which the crops are grown are raised 15 to 25 cm (6 to 10 in.) above the original soil level (Figure 16-1). The narrow walkways between beds can also be used as irrigation channels if warm weather watering is required. The soil in raised beds dries out and warms up more quickly in the spring allowing for earlier planting in colder, northern areas. In warmer areas cool weather crops may be planted earlier and harvested earlier before warm weather creates adverse growing conditions.

The soil bed should be properly prepared before seeds or transplants are set in. This involves adjusting the soil pH to suit the crop (see Chapter 5) and amending the soil to provide adequate levels of nutrients (see Chapters 5 and 7) for the early growth of seedlings or transplants. Transplants also benefit from watering with a dilute solution of soluble fertilizer at the time of setting out.

Transplants must always be hardened off before being planted out (see Chapter 14). A too sudden change from indoor low light and warm temperature to outdoor high light and low temperature will set back, if not kill, tender, young plants. Plants may also need to be given extra protection after planting out (see

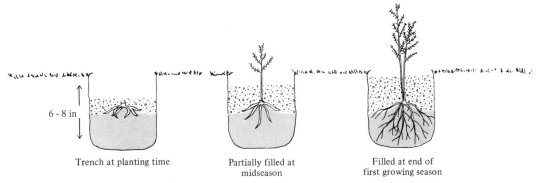

6 - 8 in

Trench at planting time

Partially filled at
midseason

Filled at end of
first growing season

Figure 16-2 Planting crowns of asparagus.

Chapter 14). The use of plastic tunnels or hot caps over seed beds or individual plants has proved to be of value in colder regions as a way of extending the length of the growing season and getting earlier harvests of slow-growing crops.

Asparagus, a perennial, will provide a crop for many years if the planting bed, preferably a sandy loam, has been properly prepared, a high level of fertilization is maintained, and the bed receives full sun. When one-year old crowns are planted, rather than seed, certain special techniques are required which are illustrated in Figure 16-2.

CULTIVATION PRACTICES

The soil between plants should be gently loosened to promote good aeration of the root system, although care must be taken not to cultivate too deeply since this can damage roots growing close to the soil surface.

Thinning, to provide adequate space between plants, is required to decrease competition for water, nutrients, and light. Crowded plants also prevent sufficient air movement, a factor in disease control. Thinning of wide-row plantings is accomplished for lettuce and other small-seed crops by gently dragging a stiff-tooth rake across the wide row when the plants are 1.5 to 2.5 cm (0.5 to 1 in.) high and so removing some of the plants. Large-seed crops (peas, beans) do not need thinning if the initial planting was at an appropriate spacing.

Some vegetable crops require staking to prevent the fruit from coming in contact with the soil. Tomatoes may be staked in a number of ways (Figure 16.3). Peas will grow up a trellis, winding in and out, as their tendrils twine about metal, wood, or string supports. Pole beans require a vertical support, a pole or heavy string, since these plants do not attach themselves to horizontal parts of a trellis, as do peas.

The amounts of nitrogen (N), phosphorus (P), and potassium (K) to be added to soil for optimum growth of a particular vegetable crop should be determined by soil analysis through state cooperative extension services or kits

Central vertical stake

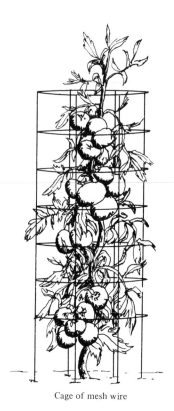

Cage of mesh wire

Figure 16-3 Staking tomatoes.

available for this purpose (see Chapter 7). Many long-season vegetables that are heavy feeders (cabbage, onions) require that fertilizer be incorporated into the soil before planting and applied again as a side-dressing after about 6 to 10 weeks of growth. Carrots, cucurbits, and tomatoes thrive with lower levels of NPK, as do many short-season crops.

Perennial vegetables (asparagus, rhubarb, artichoke) are usually fertilized just before or at the time growth begins. Asparagus responds well to a second fertilization at the end of the six- to eight-week harvest period. Asparagus is a halophyte (salt-loving) and application of agricultural salt to the soil at the end of the harvest period promotes luxurious growth of the plants (the fern stage) during the latter part of the summer.

HERBS

The availability of herbs has increased greatly in the last decade and their cultivation in the home garden has become quite common (Table 16-3). The seeds, with few exceptions, germinate readily and the plants grow rapidly in a friable, limed soil. Most grow well with low levels of fertilizer. Most require full sun or a very sunny location.

Table 16-3 SOME COMMON HERBS, THEIR CULTURE AND USES

Herb	Type	Height (in.)	Space between plants (in.)	Comments	Use
Anise	Annual	18–24	6–8	Low, spreading	Leaves: salads Seeds: candies, breads, pastries
Basil	Annual	20–24	12	Pinch back frequently; pot plant	Tomato, fish, cheese; basis of pesto
Borage	Annual	20–24	12	Seeds slow to germinate, but reseeds easily	Salads
Chives	Perennial	12	8	Pot plant	Salads, soups, eggs, cheese
Caraway	Biennial	12–24	6		Leaves: garnish Seeds: breads, soups
Chervil	Annual	18–24	6	Partial shade	Salads, soups, garnish Leaves: known as cilantro or Chinese parsley; Mexican and Chinese dishes
Coriander	Annual	12–24	7–10	Reseeds itself easily	Seeds: Shellfish, curries, sausage
Dill	Annual	24–36	12	Reseeds itself easily	Leaves: fish, meat, salads Seeds: pickles
Fennel	Perennial	36	12		Leaves: garnish Seeds: soups, breads
Marjoram, sweet	Tender perennial, usually grown as an annual in North America	12	8–10		Lamb, beef, fish, herb tea
Mint	Perennial	18	8–10	Semishade, damp; aggressive spreader by underground runners	Vegetables, jellies, desserts, herb tea
Oregano	Perennial	24	8–10	Pot plant	Tomato, soups, stews
Parsley	Biennial	5–6	6–8	Slow to germinate	Salads, soups, stews, garnish
Rosemary	Perennial	36	24	Grown from cuttings; pot plant; needs protection from temperatures below −4° C (26° F)	Lamb, pork
Sage	Perennial	18	30	Well-drained soil	Stuffing for poultry, sausage, herb tea
Savory, summer	Annual	18	8–12	Grown from cuttings or seed	Bean, pea, poultry
Tarragon	Perennial	24	12	Russian from seed, French from cuttings; Pot plant	Poultry, vinegar
Thyme	Perennial	8–12	10–12	Grown from cuttings or seed	Beef, pork, poultry, soups, vegetables

SUPPLEMENTARY READINGS

Aldrich, S. R., W. O. Scott, and E. R. Leng. *Modern Corn Production.* 2nd ed. A & L, Champaign, Ill.

Bianchini, F., and F. Corbetta. 1976. *The Complete Book of Fruits and Vegetables.* Crown, New York.

Bienz, D. R. 1980. *The How and Why of Home Horticulture.* Freeman, San Francisco.

Boxer, A., and P. Black. 1980. *The Herb Book.* Octopus Books, London.

Calvin, C. L., and D. M. Knudson. 1983. *Modern Home Gardening.* Wiley, New York.

Coon, N. 1974. *The Dictionary of Useful Plants.* Rodale, Emmaus, Penn.

Crockett, J. U. 1972. *Vegetables and Fruits.* Time-Life Books, Alexandria, Va.

Dexon, G. R. 1981. *Vegetable Crop Diseases.* Avi, Westport, Conn.

Doty, W. L. 1973. *All About Vegetables.* Ortho, San Francisco, Calif.

Everett, T. 1981. *The New York Botanical Garden Illustrated Encyclopedia of Horticulture.* Garland, New York.

Faust, J. L. 1975. *The New York Times Book of Vegetables.* Quadrangle/The New York Times, New York.

Ferro, D. N., G. W. Moorman, and R. J. Precheur. 1981. *New England Recommendations for Commercial Vegetable Crops, Insects, Diseases and Weeds.* College of Agriculture, University of Massachusetts, Amherst.

Friend, J., and M. J. C. Rhodes (eds.). 1983. *Advances in the Biochemistry of Fruits and Vegetables.* Academic Press, New York.

Gould, W. A. 1983. *Tomato Production, Processing and Quality Evaluation.* Avi, Westport, Conn.

Haard, N. F., and D. K. Salunkhe. 1975. *Postharvest Biology and Handling of Fruits and Vegetables.* Avi, Westport, Conn.

Hackett, C., and J. Carolane (eds.). 1982. *Edible Horticultural Crops: A Compendium of Information on Fruit, Vegetable, Spice and Nut Species.* Academic Press, New York.

Hagedorn, D. J. 1984. *Compendium of Pea Diseases.* American Phytopathological Society, St. Paul, Minn.

Harris, P. M. 1978. *The Potato Crop.* Wiley, New York.

Hooker, W. J. (ed.). 1983. *Compendium of Potato Diseases.* American Phytopathological Society, St. Paul, Minn.

Hylton, W. 1976. *The Rodale Herb Book.* Rodale, Emmaus, Penn.

Janick, J. 1986. *Horticultural Science.* 3rd ed. Freeman, San Francisco.

Langer, R. H. M., and G. D. Hill. 1982. *Agricultural Plants.* Cambridge University Press, Cambridge.

Lorenz, O. A., and D. M. Maynard. 1980. *Knott's Handbook for Vegetable Growers.* Wiley-Interscience, New York.

McNab, A. A. 1975. *Identifying Disease of Beans, Crucifers, Curcubits, Peas, Sweet Corn and Tomatoes.* Cooperative Extension Service of the Northeast States Publ. NE-31.

Martin, F. W. (ed.). *CRC Handbook of Tropical Food Crops.* CRC Press, Boca Raton, Fla.

North, C. 1979. *Plant Breeding and Genetics in Horticulture.* Wiley, New York.

Nyvall, R. F. 1979. *Field Crops Diseases Handbook.* Avi, Westport, Conn.

Ortho's Complete Guide to Successful Gardening. 1983. Ortho, San Francisco.

Pantastico, E. B. 1975. *Postharvest Physiology, Handling and Utilization of Tropical and Subtropical Fruits and Vegetables.* Avi, Westport, Conn.

Pollack, B. L., and M. Robson (eds.). 1980. *Commercial Vegetable Production Recommendations.* Cooperative Extension Service, Rutgers University, New Brunswick, N.J.

Ryall, A. L., and W. J. Lipton. 1979. *Handling, Transportation and Storage of Fruits and Vegetables.* I. *Vegetables and Melons.* 2nd ed. Avi, Westport, Conn.

Ryder, E. J. 1979. *Leafy Salad Vegetables.* Avi, Westport, Conn.

Salunkhe, D. K., and B. B. Desai. 1984. *Postharvest Biotechnology of Vegetables.* 2 vols. Avi, Westport, Conn.

Simmonds, N. W. 1979. *Principles of Crop Improvement.* Longman, London.

Smith, O. 1977. *Potatoes: Production, Storage, Processing.* 2nd ed. Avi, Westport, Conn.

Soule, J. 1986. *Glossary for Horticultural Crops.* American Society Horticultural Science, Alexandria, Va.

Splittstoesser, W. E. 1984. *Vegetable Growing Handbook.* 2nd ed. Avi, Westport, Conn.

Tindall, N. L. (ed.). *Vegetables in the Tropics.* Avi, Westport, Conn.

U.S. Department of Agriculture. 1978. *Growing Vegetables in the Home Garden.* U.S. Government Printing Office, Washington, D.C.

Ware, W., and G. McCollum. 1985. *Producing Vegetable Crops.* 3rd ed. Thomson, Fresno, Calif.

Wells. R., T. Lee, D. Graham, B. McGlasson, and E. Hall. 1981. *Postharvest: An Introduction to the Physiology and Handling of Fruits and Vegetables.* Avi, Westport, Conn.

Yamiguchi, M. 1983. *World Vegetables: Principles, Production and Nutritive Values.* Avi, Westport, Conn.

C H A P T E R   1 7

FLOWERS

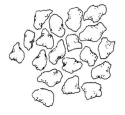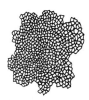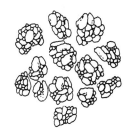

CULTURE OF FLOWERING PLANTS

Growing plants for their flowers and for decorative gardens has a long history in Europe and North America. Some of these gardens became repositories for unusual and exotic plants collected from other areas of the world. The National Arboretum in Washington, D.C., the Royal Botanic Garden (Kew) in London, and the National Arboretum of Canada are three examples. Evergreen and flowering shrubs plantings in home gardens have increased greatly (see Chapters 19 and 20), and flowering herbaceous plants are also of high value in outdoor beds as well as for indoor containers. Whether the home gardener starts these herbaceous plants from seed or buys pregrown stock, their popularity has shown dramatic and consistent increases.

Part of the reason for their increasing popularity is the continued improvement of the plants. An excellent example is the petunia. This plant has been modified genetically by intensive breeding from a single type of upright growing plant that produced small, single and simple petalled, pale-colored flowers to a group of upright and weeping types showing an explosion of colors and bicolors, with double and fringed petals, all of which are long-lasting in the garden. The development of dwarf marigolds, hybrid geraniums, and improved cultivars of begonia, impatiens, and zinnias have also contributed to their enhanced popularity. Other important new cultivars include asters resistant to wilt disease, stocks resistant to mosaic disease, and fuchsias and sweet peas resistant to heat.

Herbaceous flowering plants are propagated by seed, cuttings, or crown divisions (geraniums, chrysanthemums, some perennials). Only the best quality seed which are free of weed seeds, properly harvested, and stored under conditions which maximize longevity should be used (see Chapter 14). The general conditions and materials required for germinating, growing, and transplanting that have been discussed for plants in general (see Chapter 14) apply to flowering plants as well. Seed packets and catalogues of suppliers give specific horticultural information which is generally accurate.

For all garden plants, the soil must be properly prepared and adequate organic materials and fertilizer incorporated into it (see Chapters 6 and 7). Watering on a regular basis when rainfall is inadequate will ensure a long growing season. Faded flowers should be removed to permit renewed blooming since developing seed and fruit are nutrient traps diverting the nutrient supply from the rest of the plant. Dead and diseased plants should be disposed of to prevent disease organisms and insects from overwintering in the soil. Adequate spacing between plants (given in seed catalogues) permits better air circulation and decreases competition for nutrients, water, and light.

The role of photoperiod in planning an outdoor or indoor garden must be considered. Many garden and house plants respond to daylength for flower induction or promotion as well as for vegetative growth. This topic has been discussed in detail in Chapters 9 and 15. The light requirements for house plants has been covered in Chapter 9.

Table 17-1 SOME POPULAR ANNUAL FLOWERING PLANTS   **421**

Latin name	Common name	Bloom time	Sun	Part sun	Shade	Cut	Tall	Border	Rock garden	Pot plant	Winter annual	Tolerates dry soil
Ageratum	Floss flower	S–F	X	X				X		X		
Antirrhinum	Snapdragon	S–F	X	X		X	X	X		X	X	
Arctotis	African daisy	S–F	X			X		X			X	X
Begonia	Bedding begonia	S–F		X	X			X		X		
Brassica	Ornamental kale	S	X					X		X	X	
Browallia	Bush violet	S		X	X			X		X		
Calendula	Pot marigold	S–F	X			X		X		X	X	
Callistephus	China aster	S–F	X	X		X		X		X	X	
Campanula	Canterbury bells	Sp–F	X	X				X	X			
Capsicum	Ornamental pepper	S–F	X					X		X		
Celosia	Cockscomb	S	X			X	X	X				X
Centaurea	Cornflower	S	X	X		X					X	X
Coreopsis	Tickseed	S	X			X		X				X
Chrysanthemum	Chrysanthemum	S–F	X	X		X		X	X		X	
Clarkia	Farewell-to-spring	S	X	X		X				X	X	
Cleome	Spider plant	S–F	X			X	X					X
Coleus	Coleus	S–F	X	X	X			X		X		
Cosmos	Cosmos	S–F	X			X	X					
Delphinium	Larkspur	S		X		X	X				X	
Dianthus	Pink	S	X			X		X	X	X	X	X
Dimorphotheca	Cape marigold	S	X			X		X			X	
Eschscholzia	California poppy	Sp–S	X			X		X	X		X	X
Gaillardia	Blanket flower	S–F	X			X		X			X	X
Gazania	Gazania	S–F	X						X	X		
Helianthus	Sunflower	S–F	X			X	X	X				X
Helichrysum	Everlasting	S–F	X			X	X					
Helipterum	Strawflower	Sp–S	X			X					X	
Iberis	Candytuft	Sp–S	X					X	X		X	
Impatiens	Garden balsam	Sp–F		X	X			X		X		
Ipomoea	Morning glory	S–F	X				X					
Lathyrus	Sweet pea	Sp	X			X	X	X		X	X	
Linaria	Spurred snapdragon	Sp–S		X				X	X			
Lobelia	Edging lobelia	Sp–F		X	X			X	X	X	X	
Matthiola	Stock	Sp–S	X			X		X			X	
Nicotiana	Flowering tobacco	S–F	X	X			X	X				
Nigella	Love-in-a-mist	S	X					X			X	
Papaver	Shirley poppy	Sp–S	X					X			X	
Pelargonium	Geranium	S–F	X					X		X		X
Petunia	Petunia	S–F	X	X				X	X	X		
Phacelia	Scorpion weed	S–F	X					X	X			X
Phlox	Phlox	S–F	X			X		X				X
Portulaca	Moss rose	S–F	X					X	X	X		X
Reseda	Mignonette	S–F	X	X		X		X		X		
Salvia	Sage	S–F	X			X		X		X	X	X
Scabiosa	Pincushion flower	S–F	X			X		X			X	X
Tagetes	Marigold	S–F	X			X	X	X		X		
Tropaeolum	Nasturtium	S	X			X		X	X	X		X
Venidium	Cape daisy	S–F	X					X				
Viola X *Wittrockiana*	Pansy	Sp–S		X	X			X	X	X	X	
Zinnia	Zinnia	S–F	X			X	X	X	X			X

Sp = spring; S = summer; F = fall.

FLOWERING ANNUALS

Flowering plants that complete their life cycle from seed to seed in one growing season are referred to as annuals. They are also called monocarpic. Most annuals can also be grown in containers where outdoor soil or space is inadequate to support their growth. This is especially advantageous for city gardeners. Most annuals require full sun for optimum flowering, but some do well in partial shade (Table 17-1).

Many annuals are warm-temperature plants and planting them out into the outdoor garden too early in the spring may lead to death of the plants or of the flower buds if they are subjected to a late spring frost. Petunias, for example, may be planted out in southern California, southern Texas, or Florida (Zone 10) around March 15, in central Texas around April 1, in northern California between May 1 and May 15. They should not be set out in the central area of the United States and southern Canada (Zones 4 to 6) until between June 1 and June 15. As a general rule, young plants are not planted out until the soil warms to about 16°C (61°F), and this holds true for starting seeds outdoors as well (Figure 17-1). The seeds of a few annuals can be sown in the early spring as soon as the soil can be worked. These include cornflower, cleome, stock, sweet alyssum, and sweet pea.

In areas with warm winters, annuals that tolerate cool weather are called winter annuals—pansies, calendulas, sweet peas—and can be grown during the

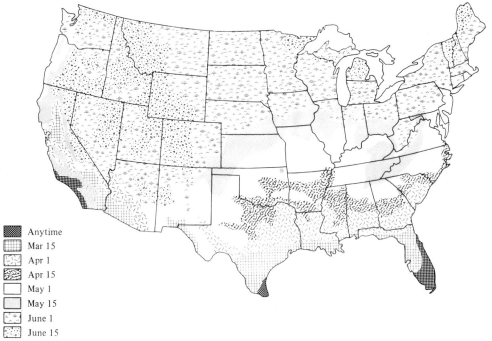

	Anytime
	Mar 15
	Apr 1
	Apr 15
	May 1
	May 15
	June 1
	June 15

Figure 17-1 Approximate time for setting out young plants and planting seeds of tender plants outdoors.

winter, but they will die back as temperatures rise (Table 17-1). At this time heat-tolerant annuals, referred to as summer annuals, are planted out (marigold, zinnia, petunia).

The majority of annuals are grown for their flowers, but a few are utilized for their brilliant colored foliage, such as the many cultivars of amaranthus.

FLOWERING HERBACEOUS PERENNIALS

Herbaceous perennials are plants that live more than two years. The shoots may die back each year, but the crown (the apical meristem) and the roots remain alive and regrow each year as environmental conditions permit. Most herbaceous perennials do not bloom until their second year of growth. Biennials are flowering plants that grow vegetatively during the first year, flower during their second year of growth, and then die.

Some perennials bloom during most of the summer, but most flower for a short time in the spring, summer, or fall (Table 17-2). The varying characteristics of this group permit a stable garden in terms of patterns of color or form throughout the growing season. Low-growing or creeping plants are favored for the rock garden (creeping thyme); tall cultivars are useful as background plantings and for cut flowers (delphinium, phlox, hollyhock). Some perennials thrive in cool summers (violets) and others in shady, moist areas (meconopsis, trollius). Some last for many years if well cared for (peony, bearded iris). A few perennials are grown for their interesting foliage (dusty miller).

Ferns, although not flowering plants, can be a focus of interest in any shady, cool area both in the outdoor garden or in pots for indoor display. Most require an evenly moist, well drained soil, high in peat moss or other fibrous material. Many species, some of which are hardy in colder northern areas, are available from commercial sources. Cacti and succulents form a basis for perennial gardens in hot, dry climates. Palms, bromeliads, and orchids add interest and color in shadier sites in regions where winters are warm.

Many perennials grown in colder areas require some winter protection (see Table 17-2). When the soil has cooled and hardened in the fall, the plantings are covered with a 4- to 6-inch layer of mulch. This covering keeps the soil cold and prevents the alternate freezing and thawing of soil which can severely damage root systems.

Woody perennials, an important feature of outdoor plantings, are discussed in Chapter 20.

BULBS

Growing Flowering Bulbs

Perennial plants that store food in bulbous or fleshy structures are here considered together as bulbs (see Chapter 3). Some, such as tulips, daffodils, lilies, and flowering onion, form true bulbs, while lily-of-the-valley, daylilies, and

Table 17-2   SOME POPULAR PERENNIAL FLOWERING PLANTS

Latin name	Common name	Bloom time	Sun	Part sun	Shade	Cut flower	Tall	Border	Rock garden	Comments
Achillea	Yarrow	Sp–S	X			X		X	X	Tolerates dry soil
Aconitum	Aconite	S–F		X			X	X		
Adonis	Pheasant's eye	Sp–S	X			X		X		Biennial
Alcea	Hollyhock	S–F	X			X	X	X		
Alyssum	Madwort	S–F	X					X	X	
Anchusa	Bugloss	S	X							
Anemone	Pasque flower	S	X	X				X	X	
Antirrhinum	Snapdragon	Sp–S	X			X		X	X	Needs winter protection
Aquilegia	Columbine	Sp–S		X		X		X	X	
Arenaria	Sandwort	S		X				X	X	
Armeria	Thrift	Sp–S	X			X		X	X	
Arnica	Arnica	Sp–S	X			X		X	X	Tolerates dry soil
Asclepias	Butterfly weed	S	X			X		X		
Aster	Michaelmas daisy	S–F	X			X	X	X		Needs moist soil
Astilbe	Spirea	S	X			X		X		
Aubrieta	Aubrieta	Sp		X				X	X	
Belamcanda	Leopard flower	S–F	X	X		X		X		
Bellis	English daisy	Sp		X				X		
Campanula	Bell flower	Sp–S		X				X	X	
Cerastium	Mouse-ear chickweed	Sp	X					X	X	Needs winter protection
Cheiranthus	Wallflower	Sp	X			X		X		Tolerates dry soil
Chrysanthemum	Various	S–F	X			X		X		
Coreopsis	Tickseed	S–F	X			X		X		Needs winter protection
Cytisus	Broom	Sp	X			X		X		
Delphinium	Larkspur	Sp–S	X			X		X		Tolerates dry soil
Dianthus	Carnation	Sp–S	X			X		X		Needs winter protection
Dicentra	Bleeding heart	Sp		X				X		
Echinacea	Purple coneflower	S	X			X		X		Tolerates dry soil
Echinops	Globe thistle	S–F	X			X	X	X		Needs winter protection
Eremurus	Desert candle	Sp	X			X	X	X		
Erythronium	Adder's tongue	Sp		X				X	X	

Genus	Common name	Season							Remarks
Gaillardia	Blanket flower	S–F	X				X	X	Needs winter protection
Gerbera	Gerbera	S–F	X				X	X	
Geum	Avens	Sp–S	X				X		
Globularia	Globularia	Sp–S			X		X	X	
Gypsophila	Gypsophila	Sp–S	X				X	X	
Helenium	Sneezeweed	S–F	X				X	X	Needs winter protection
Helianthemum	Sun rose	S–F	X				X	X	
Heliopsis	Oxeye	S–F	X				X		
Hosta	Plantain lily	S–F			X		X		
Hypericum	St. John's wort	Sp	X				X	X	Tolerates dry soil
Iberis	Candytuft	Sp	X				X		
Iris	Flag	Sp–S		X			X		Needs moist soil
Jasione	Jasione	Sp–S	X				X	X	
Lewisia	Lewisia	Sp–S	X				X	X	Tolerates dry soil
Linum	Flax	Sp–S	X				X	X	
Liriope	Lilyturf	S–F		X	X		X		Needs moist soil
Lobelia	Cardinal flower	S		X	X		X		Needs moist soil
Lunaria	Honesty	S		X			X		Biennial
Lupinus	Lupine	S	X				X		
Lythrum	Loosestrife	S		X			X		Needs moist soil
Meconopsis	Asiatic poppy	S–F		X		X	X		Needs moist soil
Nierembergia	Cupflower	S		X			X	X	Needs winter protection
Paeonia	Peony	S	X	X			X		Needs moist soil
Papaver	Oriental poppy	Sp	X	X			X		
Pennisetum	Flowering grass	S–F	X	X		X	X		
Phlox	Phlox	S	X	X			X		Needs moist soil
Platycodon	Balloon flower	Sp–S		X			X		
Primula	Primrose	Sp–F	X				X		Needs moist soil
Rudbeckia	Coneflower	Sp–F	X	X			X		Tolerates dry soil
Saxifraga	Saxifrage	Sp		X	X		X	X	
Stokesia	Stokes' aster	S	X	X			X		
Thalictrum	Meadow rue	S	X	X		X	X		Needs moist soil
Thymus	Thyme	Sp	X	X			X	X	
Trollius	Globe flower	Sp		X	X		X	X	Needs moist soil
Veronica	Speedwell	S–F	X				X	X	Needs moist soil
Viola X*Wittrockiana*	Pansy	Sp–S		X			X	X	Needs winter protection

Sp = spring; S = summer; F = fall.

Table 17-3   SOME POPULAR SPRING-FLOWERING BULBS

Latin name	Common name	Sun	Part shade	Shade	Hardy	Not hardy	Pot plant	Force for winter bloom
Anemone spp.	Anemone	X	X		X			
Chionodoxa spp.	Glory of the Snow	X	X		X		X	X
Convallaria spp.	Lily-of-the-Valley		X		X		X	X
Crocus vernus	Crocus	X	X		X		X	X
Endymion hispanicus	Spanish bluebell	X	X		X		X	X
Eranthis spp.	Winter Aconite		X		X			
Fritillaria spp.	Fritillary	X	X		X			
Galanthus nivalis	Snowdrops	X	X		X			
Hippeastrum spp.	Amaryllis	X	X			X	X	X
Hyacinthus orientalis	Hyacinths	X	X			X	X	X
Iris spp.	Dutch Iris	X	X			X	X	X
Muscari botryoides	Grape Hyacinth	X	X		X		X	X
Narcissus pseudonarcissus	Trumpet Narcissus	X	X		X		X	X
Narcissus tazetta	Paperwhite Narcissus		X	X		X	X	X
Tulipa spp.	Tulip	X	X		X		X	X

agapanthus form bulblike structures. Gladiolus, colchicum, crocus, and freesia form corms; anemone forms tubers, and begonia and dahlia form tuberous rootstocks. Dutch iris that make a bulbous structure are included in this section, and those that grow from rhizomes are considered with herbaceous perennials.

Spring-flowering bulbs that are hardy are planted in the garden in the early fall to permit them to establish root systems and to fulfill their cool temperature requirements (Table 17-3). The large bulbs in this group include tulips, most daffodils and other narcissi, and hyacinths. The small bulbs include crocus, grape hyacinth, scilla, snowdrops, chionodoxa, and lily-of-the-valley.

Nonhardy bulbs may be planted outdoors in the late spring in colder regions or in fall or very early spring in areas with mild winters. These include tazetta hybrid narcissus and some of the bulbous iris. Very tender bulbs, such as amaryllis (Barbados lily), are usually grown as pot plants for late winter or spring bloom.

Daffodils, other narcissi, and the small bulbs are planted out from September to November (but before the ground becomes hard) in central and northern United States and southern Canada and from October to December in southern or warmer areas of the United States (Figure 17-2). Hyacinth and tulip bulbs are planted out from mid October to mid or late November. Tulips should not be set in the garden until the soil temperature cools to 17° C (62° F), a temperature at

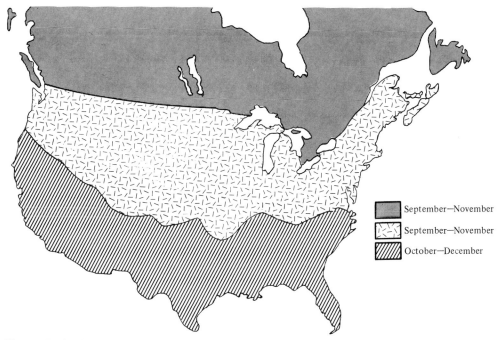

Figure 17-2 Approximate outdoor planting dates for spring-flowering bulbs.

	September—November
	September—November
	October—December

which the growth of the wilt fungus *Fusarium,* a serious disease organism, is minimal. A general rule is to plant bulbs to a depth two to three times their height (Figure 17-3).

Summer-flowering bulbs are not hardy in regions with cold winters, with the exception of daylilies, most true lilies, and a few gladioli (Table 17-4). The nonhardy ones are planted out when the soil temperature warms up in the spring and after all danger of frost is past. They are dug in the fall after the first frost, and stored over winter. Many of these bulbs also do well in pots. Gloxinia is usually grown only as a pot plant. Caladium is a nonhardy bulb grown for its multicolored foliage. It is most useful in shady borders or in pots and grows best at moderate temperatures. Bulbs of these two species are lifted in the fall, dried for a few days, and stored over winter at 16° C (61° F) in damp peat moss.

Tuberous begonias grow best in cool-summer regions or in spring or fall in hot-summer regions. The tubers are started in a fibrous, high moisture-holding medium in flats or small pots and are transplanted to larger containers when they are well rooted, the eyes (buds) have sprouted, and good growth has started. They are not planted out until all danger of frost is past. Flowering is promoted by long days. The tubers, which are killed at soil temperatures below 5° C (41° F), must be dug before soil temperatures drop to this point, dried for several days, and then stored in damp peat moss in a cool area not below 10° C (50° F).

Gladiolus, callas, cannas, and small bulbs are dug after the first frost, dried

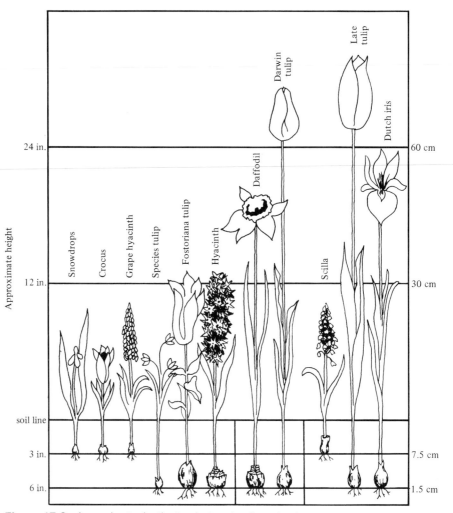

Figure 17-3 Approximate depths to plant spring-flowering bulbs.

off, and stored in cool (4° to 10° C, 5° to 50° F) dry conditions. Dahlia roots are stored at 7° C (45° F) in damp peat moss or vermiculite.

All stored bulbs should be checked occasionally for the presence of insects or mold and treated with an appropriate dust if necessary (Chapter 10).

Forcing Spring-Flowering Bulbs

Many spring-flowering bulbs can be grown in containers so that they will flower indoors in late winter or very early spring before their normal flowering time. There are a few general rules to follow. The medium is usually a soilless mix or a

Table 17-4 SOME POPULAR SUMMER- AND FALL-FLOWERING BULBS

Latin name	Common name	Sun	Part shade	Pot plant	Depth to plant outdoors	
					cm	in.
Hardy, summer-flowering						
Gladiolus Xhortulanus	Gladiolus	X	X		10–15	4–6
Hemerocallis spp.	Daylily	X	X		2.5–5	1–2
Lilium spp.	Lily	X	X		15–20	6–8
Non-hardy, summer-flowering						
Achimenes spp.	Magic flower		X	X	2.5–5	1–2
Agapanthus africanus	Lily-of-the-Nile	X		X	2.5–5	1–2
Begonia Xtuberhybrida	Tuberous begonia		X	X	7.5–10	3–4
Anemone spp.	Anemone	X		X	7.5	3
Bletilla striata	Chinese orchid		X	X	2.5–5	1–2
Canna Xgeneralis	Canna	X			10–12.5	4–5
Dahlia spp.	Dahlia	X	X		10–12.5	4–5
Eucharis grandiflora	Amazon lily	X		X	2.5–5	1–2
Freesia Xhybrida	Freesia	X		X	2.5–5	1–2
Gladiolus Xhortulanus	Gladiolus	X			10–15	4–6
Hedychium coronarium	Butterfly lily	X	X	X	2.5–5	1–2
Hymenocallis narcissiflora	Peruvian daffodil	X	X	X	2.5–5	1–2
Lilium longiflorum	Easter lily	X	X	X	15–20	6–8
Ranunculus asiaticus	Persian buttercup	X	X	X	2.5–5	1–2
Sinningia speciosa	Gloxinia	X	X	X	—	—
Tigridia pavonia	Tiger flower	X	X	X	5–7.5	2–3
Zantedeschia spp.	Calla lily	X		X	2.5–5	1–2
Zephyranthes spp.	Zephyr lily	X	X	X	2.5–5	1–2
Non-hardy, fall-flowering						
Colchicum autumnale	Meadow saffron		X	X	5	2
Lycoris squamigera	Resurrection lily	X	X	X	5–7.5	2–3
Polianthes tuberosa	Tuberose	X		X	7.5–10	3–4

well-drained, light soil mix (see Chapter 5). It must not dry out too rapidly, it must be sterile, and its nutrient level should be low.

The large bulbs (tulip, hyacinth, daffodil) are spaced in containers about 2.5 cm (1 in.) apart. The noses (the elongated upper part of the bulb) should be above the medium. The flat side of the tulip bulb should be against the inside of the pot, as the first leaf emerges from this side. Small bulbs (crocus, scilla, grape hyacinth, and others) are covered by 1 to 2 cm of the planting medium. The medium is saturated with water when the bulbs are potted and then watered as necessary to keep moist.

The containers are kept in the dark at 9° C (48° F) or lower but above 0° C (32° F) to permit rooting to occur and to satisfy the cold-temperature requirement. When the cold requirement time has been completed (Table 17-5) and the leaves are about 5 cm (2 in.) above the nose, the containers can be moved to a lighted area at a higher temperature to permit the more rapid development of the flower. Fungal contamination can be controlled by dusting or watering with a fungicide (Chapter 10).

Polyanthus narcissus (*Narcissus tazetta*), which includes paper-white nar-

Table 17-5   COLD REQUIREMENTS FOR FORCING SPRING-FLOWERING BULBS FOR INDOOR BLOOM

Name	Number of weeks in dark at 9° C (48° F)	Post-cold treatment
Daffodils and other narcissi	15–16	Light + 16–18° C (61–69° F)
Hyacinths	10–12	Light + 20–23° C (68–74° F)
Tulips	15–18	Light + 18° C (64° F)
Small bulbs	15–16	Light + 15–16° C (59–61° F)

cissus and Chinese sacred lily, are easily grown for winter bloom. The bulbs, set in a shallow layer of water and small stones, are placed in the dark at around 16° C (60° F). The water should be replaced frequently. While the bulbs can be placed in the light, rooting is slower and less vigorous. In 2 to 3 weeks, vegetative growth is well advanced and flower heads are several inches tall. At this time, the plants are moved to bright light in a cool area.

FLOWERING HOUSE PLANTS

The general requirements for successfully growing plants indoors have been discussed in previous chapters: various soil mixes appropriate for pot plants (Chapter 5), fertilization (Chapter 7), proper temperature (Chapter 8), and light requirements (Chapter 9). The plants listed in Table 17-6 will usually grow vegetatively and flower well indoors. Some have special requirements to promote flowering. (Bromeliads and orchids are not included in Table 17-6 since species requirements are so variable. Appropriate references are included in the bibliography.) The usual causes of failure to maintain these plants is overwatering during cool, damp weather, inducing root rot, and underwatering in hot, dry home environments, allowing the plant to wilt beyond the recovery stage.

Flowering plants grown indoors may become infested by a number of insects including mealybugs, hardshell scale, spider mites, and whitefly. Cleanliness is the first line of attack. Trays and pots should be washed with soap occasionally and only sterilized soil mix should be used (see Chapters 5 and 10). The foliage can be washed under cool, running water to remove as much of the infestation as possible and then sprayed with insecticidal soap solution following directions on the label for house plants. Other insecticides are available for indoor use, but should be used with caution.

THE COMMERCIAL GREENHOUSE ENVIRONMENT

The greenhouse industry appears to have started in Holland during the seventeenth century to supply lilacs and table grapes for the European market. It quickly expanded to the production of spring flowers and out-of-season vegetables. In North America there were few commercial greenhouses before the nineteenth century, but by the beginning of the twentieth century installations were in operation near the larger cities. Today, greenhouse production of plants has become a large and valuable aspect of horticultural science and technology. The development of relatively inexpensive air freight and refrigerated ground transportation and new packaging technology permitted construction of greenhouses in suitable regions that may be long distances from primary markets. The trend toward the establishment of large greenhouses in southern and southwestern states has been accelerated by rising costs of fuel, although local markets still support flourishing businesses.

The range of species and cultivars grown under glass is limited more by market factors than by technological considerations. Greenhouse crops include fresh flowers cut from plants prior to sale, flowering and foliage plants in containers for indoor and outdoor display, flowering bedding plants, vegetable seedlings, and some high-value vegetables including cucumbers, tomatoes, and bell peppers. In northern Europe, where growing seasons are short, many common vegetables and fruits are grown almost entirely as greenhouse crops.

Greenhouses are loosely defined as buildings in which plants are grown that are covered with some transparent or translucent material to admit natural light. They are usually considered separately from cold frames and hot beds (see Chapter 16), which are not buildings in which a person can work. Designs vary greatly from simple pipe or wood frames to elaborate metal structures. Commercial establishments may consist of a range of attached greenhouses covering several hectares and equipped with mechanized and automated devices for regulation of temperature, radiation, humidity, and carbon dioxide concentration.

Coverings include plastic films, heavier reinforced plastic sheets, and glass (Table 17-7). The principal thin flexible film is polyethylene. Thin polyethylene (4 to 6 mil) has the advantages of initial low cost, light weight, and adaptability to a variety of frame designs. Its disadvantages are a short effective life because of wind damage and photooxidation by solar ultraviolet radiation and excessive heat loss in winter, although double layering with an air space between the layers (air-inflated) provides some insulation. Somewhat thicker films (8 to 12 mil) of Mylar or polyvinyl have longer effective lives, particularly when coated with substances that reduce ultraviolet photooxidation. They can be expected to last for four to six years. Plastic paneling, smooth or corrugated, is available in polyvinyl chloride (PVC) or in fiberglass-reinforced plastics (FRP). These are versatile and are relatively easy to use as greenhouse coverings, although their life is shorter than that of glass even with antiultraviolet coatings. Light penetration is slightly less than that of clear glass, but the diffusion of light by translucent panels is useful. Heat transmission is lower with plastic paneling than with glass, an economic consideration where greenhouse cooling is necessary. Large commercial greenhouse ranges still are covered with glass because of its stability and relatively low replacement costs. For high value crops grown where winters are severe, double glazing may be marginally economical.

Table 17-6 SOME FLOWERING HOUSE PLANTS

Latin name	Common name	Sun	Some sun	Shade	Ever-blooming	Summer	Fall	Winter	Comments
Abutilon	Flowering maple		X			X			Evenly moist soil
Aeschynanthes	Lipstick plant		X		X				Trailing vine
Anthurium	Flamingo flower			X		X			Cool temperature, evenly moist soil, high humidity
Aphelandra	Zebra plant		X			X			Short day required to induce flowering
Aristolochia	Pelican flower		X			X			Vine
Asparagus	Asparagus fern		X			X			Moist soil, drier in winter
Calceolaria	Slipper flower		X			X			13°–16° C night temperature required to induce flowering
Cacti	Numerous	X							Cool winter (10°–13° C), dryish soil
Clivia	Kaffir lily		X					X	Cool winter (10°–13° C), repot infrequently
Columnea	Columnea		X		X				
Crossandra	Firecracker flower		X			X			
Cyclamen	Cyclamen		X			X			13°–16° C night temperature required to induce flowering
Episcia	Flame violet			X		X			Moist soil, high humidity

Genus	Common name						Comments
Exacum	Persian violet		X				13°–18° C required to induce flowering, winter dormant
Fuchsia	Lady's eardrops	X	X				
Gardenia	Common gardenia				X		15°–18° C night temperature, acid soil, evenly moist
Hoya	Wax vine		X				Blooms when pot-bound on two-year-old stems
Lavandula	English lavender		X				Flowers for sachet
Pelargonium	Geranium		X				Long day required to induce flowering
Saintpaulia	African violet		X	X			21° C night temperature required to induce flowering
Senecio Xhybridus	Cineraria		X	X			13°–16° C temperature, moist soil
Schizanthus	Butterfly flower		X				
Schlumbergera	Christmas cactus		X			X	13° C night temperature and short day required to induce flowering
Schlumbergera	Thanksgiving cactus		X		X		13° C night temperature and short day required to induce flowering
Stephanotis	Madagascar jasmine		X				Cool winter, moist soil
Strelitzia	Bird of paradise		X				10° C and dry in winter
Streptocarpus	Cape primrose	X		X			13°–16° C night temperature required to induce flowering
Succulents	Numerous	X					Cool winter, dryish soil

Table 17-7 SOME CHARACTERISTICS OF COVERINGS FOR COMMERCIAL GREENHOUSES

| Material | Thickness | Light transmittance[a] | | Thermal[b] transmittance | Effective durability | Cost/year/ft² ($ US) |
		Single glaze (percent)	Double glaze (percent)			
Polyethylene, clear	4–6 mil	89	81	70	9 months	0.04–0.05
Polyethylene, UV	4–6 mil	88	80	70	15 months	0.04–0.05
Polyvinyl, clear	8–12 mil	91	84	70	48 months	0.05–0.06
Polyvinyl, haze	8–12 mil	89	82	12	48 months	0.05–0.06
Mylar	8–12 mil	90	80	16	72 months	0.05–0.07
Reinforced fiberglass, clear sheet	6 oz[c]	78	64	8	15 years	0.05–0.075
Glass, single weight		90	79	5	30 years	0.04–0.06

[a]Percent of wavelengths between 400 and 700 nm penetrating through covering.
[b]Percent of infrared (heat) wavelengths penetrating through covering.
[c]Sold by weight, not by thickness.

In most of the northern temperate zone winter heating of greenhouses is an important economic consideration. Most of the heat is lost by conduction through the covering material and the framing. Glass conducts heat faster than FRP and thin plastic films lose heat even more rapidly. Infiltration of cold air and some direct loss through panels and around ventilators and doors may cause a complete change of air volume in an hour. Heat is also lost by direct radiation, particularly through thin films.

In northern regions heating costs are a major budget item and almost any modification that conserves heat is cost effective. Conservation measures include adequate insulation of foundations, elimination of leaks between panels, caulking and painting of framings, and similar measures. For north-facing glass or rigid-sheet coverings, translucent plastic bubble insulation can save up to 15 percent in heating costs and reduce the possibility of chill damage to sensitive plants. A sheet of bubble insulation consists of a layer of flat plastic and a layer shaped into a series of air-filled bubbles. The sheets are cut to size and taped to the panes or panels; they can be removed and reused. Because bubble insulation may reduce snow melting and increase the load on the roof, it is installed only on the side walls and gable ends of structures that might not be able to support the additional weight of snow or ice.

Many systems of heat supply have been developed and choices depend on many factors. A major consideration is the discharge of effluent gases that can injure plants. Ethylene and sulfur dioxide are the most dangerous. Solar heating combined with heat storage and exchange equipment is economical in some areas, but is still not practical for northern areas above Hardiness Zone 5. The greenhouse range and its heating system should be designed together to permit rapid and even heat distribution throughout the range and to permit the necessary diurnal rhythm in day and night temperatures (see Chapter 8).

Infrared (heat) rays from the sun penetrate easily through glass and clear plastics and, once inside, are not easily reradiated. This "greenhouse effect" can increase air temperatures within a greenhouse by $10°$ to $15°$ C ($18°$ to $27°$ F) in a few hours with consequent danger to plants. Adequate side and roof ventilation is the first line of control, but it is inadequate in larger installations or in southern regions.

Shading is the second line of control. Glass may be painted on the outside with compounds that reflect infrared radiation with some loss of plant-required wavelengths. These formulations become more transparent when wet to allow more light penetration in gloomy weather and gradually wear away. Shade fabrics can be used to exclude part of the incoming visible and infrared radiation. Polypropylene or Saran fabrics are available to achieve shading of 25 to 75 percent of incoming radiation which, in addition to reducing heat loads, may be necessary for the successful cultivation of shade-requiring plants.

Location and crop may dictate more extensive heat control systems. Blower fans connected to vented plastic tubing bring in outside air and distribute it throughout the greenhouse. These vented tube systems can also be used to distribute heat from wall- or ceiling-mounted heaters. Evaporative cooling units, usually called fan and pad systems, are commonly used in large greenhouses.

They operate on the basis of the absorption of heat during water evaporation. Water is passed over and through a pad of cellulose or similar material and outside air is drawn into the greenhouse by exhaust fans on the opposite wall. The entering air is cooled by water evaporation with a significant (5° to 10° C) reduction in greenhouse air temperatures. The water is discharged into drains or is recycled. If recycling is done, care must be taken to prevent the water from becoming contaminated by bacteria or fungi. The integration of the cooling system with the heating system and the greenhouse design is essential.

Within the greenhouse growing beds may be at ground level or raised. Although ground-level beds are used for tall crops such as carnations and gladiolus, they are hard to maintain and to cultivate. Raised benches may be low or 1 m (3 ft) high, which is a convenient working height. Construction materials vary. Concrete has some water-holding capacity and a long life expectancy, but tends to accumulate algae and other microorganisms. Woods, particularly cypress, redwood, and cedar have some decay resistance which may be enhanced by antirot and algicidic paints such as copper naphthalate, which does not affect plants. Sturdy plastic benches are available and have the advantage of light weight, excellent life expectancy, and ease of cleaning.

Under commercial conditions bench frames are filled with rooting medium or growing soil to depths of up to 30 cm (1 ft). Planting directly in beds or solid frames makes watering the substrate and fertilization easy, but replacement of beds or frames, fumigation between plantings, and temperature and aeration control can be difficult. Plants can also be grown in pots or flats on slatted, lath, or wire benches rather than on the traditional box benches. Not only do these open-topped benches prevent the accumulation of disease-breeding debris, but they facilitate air movement around the plants and permit easier flow of heating or cooling air. Bench width is usually 0.8 to 1.2 m (30 to 40 in.) to allow easy access to the plants. Walkways are rarely narrower than 1 m (3 ft) and must be sufficiently wide to accommodate wheeled carts and spray rigs. Movable bench systems increase the efficiency of space utilization in large greenhouse units and may be used to move plants from one photoperiodic regime to another.

Many of the routine tasks in commercial greenhouses have been made easier by specifically designed machinery. Automated humidity and mist-control units for entire ranges or for individual houses are used for tropical foliage plants. Electric and steam systems sterilize and fumigate soil. Automatic irrigation systems can be combined with programmable proportional water-fertilizer systems. The intended crop and labor costs will determine the level of sophistication of labor-saving equipment needed and it, too, should be part of greenhouse design.

The fundamentals of good horticultural practice (soils, watering, fertilization, etc.) have been covered in appropriate chapters of this book and reference to the supplementary readings in this and related chapters should be consulted for details of technique and operation. Diseases and pests are particularly severe in greenhouses where plants are grown close together and where monocultures of species or cultivars provide excellent conditions for extremely rapid transmis-

Table 17-8 SCHEDULING COMMERCIAL PRODUCTION OF SOME ANNUAL FLOWERING PLANTS

Latin name	Common name	Bloom time in weeks from seed	Comments
Ageratum	Flossflower	12–14	
Antirrhinum majus	Snapdragon	10–12	Cool temperatures, 10–16° C (50–60° F)
Begonia semperflorens	Bedding begonia	16–20	
B. X*tuberhybrida*	Tuberous begonia	16–24	
Browallia	Bush violet	14–16	Cool temperature, 13° C (55° F)
Calceolaria	Slipperwort	28	Night temperature 10° C (50° F)
Calendula officinalis	Pot marigold	16–20	Cool temperature, 7°–10° C (45°–50° F)
Callistephus chinensis	Annual aster	6–8	
Catharanthus roseus	Rose periwinkle	20	Tolerates hot, dry conditions
Celosia cristata	Cockscomb	6	
Coleus	Coleus or painted nettle	6–8	Bright light
Cosmos	Cosmos	8–10	
Dianthus caryophyllus	Carnation	12–14	Sensitive to dwarfing compounds
Dianthus spp.	Dianthus	10–14	
Exacum affine	Persian violet	24	
Fuchsia	Fuchsia	10–12	Night temperature 13° C (55° F)
Gazania	Gazania	12	Full sun for best growth
Impatiens	Impatiens	12	Requires shade
Lobularia maritima	Sweet alyssum	12	
Mimulus	Monkey flower	12	5 hours extra light winter, shade
Nicotiana alata	Flowering tobacco	12	Requires long day for flowering
Pelargonium X*hortorum*	Geranium hybrids	12–16	Night temperature 18° C (65° F)
Petunia X*hybrida*	Petunia	12–16	
Portulaca grandiflora	Rose moss	8	Full sun
Senecio X*hybridus*	Cineraria	20	Cool temperature for flowering, 10° C (50° F)
Sinningia speciosa	Gloxinia	16–20	Night temperature 18° C (65°F)
Streptocarpus	Cape primrose	16	Cool temperature
Tagetes	Dwarf French marigold	8	
Tagetes	Hedge-type marigold	12	
Viola X*Wittrockiana*	Pansy	16–20	
Verbena X*hybrida*	Verbena	24	
Zinnia elegans	Zinnia	6–8	

sion. A program of integrated pest management becomes one of the greenhouse manager's most important tasks.

Growing high-quality annual plants to bloom for spring sale has become a profitable venture. The steps required to produce these plants, such as starting seed, regulating environmental conditions, and controlling pests have been discussed throughout the book. Table 17-8 lists some of the more popular annuals and the time required to bring these plants to their initial flowering condition.

SUPPLEMENTARY READINGS

American Orchid Society. 1975. *American Orchid Society Handbooks.* Botanical Museum of Harvard University, Cambridge, Mass.

Backberg, C. 1977. *Cactus Lexicon.* Blandford, London.

Bromeliads: A Cultural Handbook. 1977. Bromeliad Society, Santa Monica. Calif.

Davenport, E. 1977. *Ferns for Modern Living.* Merchants, Kalamazoo, Mich.

DeHertog, A. A. 1977. *Holland Bulb Forcer's Handbook.* Netherlands Flower-Bulb Institute, New York.

Ecke, P., and O. A. Matkin. 1976. *The Poinsettia Manual.* Paul Ecke, Encinatas, Calif.

Fitch, C. M. 1981. *All About Orchids.* Doubleday, New York.

Foster, C. O. 1975. *Organic Flower Gardening.* Rodale, Emmaus, Penn.

Foster, F. G. 1985. *Ferns to Know and Grow.* Rev. ed. ISBS/Timber Press, Beaverton, Ore.

Galle, F. 1985. *Azaleas.* ISBS/Timber Press, Beaverton, Ore.

Graf, A. B. 1975. *Pictorial Cyclopedia of Exotic Plants.* Roers, East Rutherford, N. J.

Halevy, A. H., and S. Mayak. 1981. Senescence and postharvest physiology of cut flowers. Part 2. *Hort. Rev.* 3:59–143.

Hanan, J. J., W. D. Holley, and K. L. Holdsberry. 1978. *Greenhouse Management.* Springer-Verlag, New York.

Harper, P., and F. McGourty. 1985. *Perennials: How to Select, Grow and Enjoy.* HP Books, New York.

Hay, R., and P. M. Synge. 1982. *The Color Dictionary of Flowers and Plants for Home and Garden.* Crown, New York.

Hieke, I. K. 1976. *Window-box, Balcony and Patio Gardening.* Hamlyn, New York.

Horst, R. K. (ed.). *Compendium of Rose Diseases.* American Phytopathological Society, St. Paul, Minn.

Hoshizaki, B. J. 1975. *Fern Grower's Manual.* Knopf, New York.

Hudak, J. 1986. *Gardening with Perennials.* ISBS/Timber Press, Beaverton, Ore.

Hunt, M. B. 1980. *Basic Organic Gardening.* Rodale, Emmaus, Penn.

Jacobson, H. 1974. *Lexicon of Succulent Plants.* Blandford, London.

Joiner, J. N. (ed.). 1981. *Foliage Plant Production.* Prentice-Hall, Englewood Cliffs, N. J.

Jones, D. 1986. *Encyclopedia of Ferns.* ISBS/Timber Press, Beaverton, Ore.

Kramer, J. 1980. *The Complete Book of Flowering House Plants.* St. Martin's Press, New York.

Kramer, J., and D. Worth. 1977. *Cacti and Other Succulents.* Abrams, New York.

Larson, R. A. (ed.). *Introduction to Floriculture.* Academic Press, New York.

Mastalerz, J. W. 1971. *Geraniums.* Pennsylvania Flower Grower, University Park, Penn.

———. 1976. *Bedding Plants.* Pennsylvania Flower Grower, University Park, Penn.

———. 1977. *The Greenhouse Environment.* Wiley, New York.

Mathias, M. E. (ed.). *Color for the Landscape: Flowering Plants for Sub-tropical Climates.* California Arboretum Foundation, Arcadia, Calif.

Mierhof, A. 1981. *The Dried Flower Book: Growing, Picking, Drying, Arranging.* Elsevier-Dutton, New York.

Nelson, P. V. 1981. *Greenhouse Operation and Management.* 2nd ed. Reston, Reston, Va.

Northen, R. T. 1970. *Home Orchid Growing.* 3rd ed. Van Nostrand Reinhold, New York.

The Ortho Problem Solver. 1984. Ortho, San Francisco.

Peterson, T. 1976. *The New A to Z on Fuchsias.* National Fuchsia Society, San Francisco.

Phelps, H. R. 1985. *Growing and Propagating Wild Flowers.* University of North Carolina Press, Chapel Hill, N.C.

Pirone, P. P. 1978. *Disease and Pests of Ornamental Plants.* 5th ed. Wiley, New York.

Ratij, K., and T. Horeman. 1977. *Aquarium Plants—Their Identification, Cultivation and Ecology.* F. T. H. Publications, Neptune, N.J.

Reilly, A. 1978. *Park's Success with Seeds.* G. W. Park Seed Co., Greenwood, S.C.

Rentoul, J. N. 1980. *Growing Orchids, Cymbidiums and Slippers.* University of Washington Press, Seattle.

Rice, L. W. 1976. *Cacti and Succulents for Modern Living.* Merchants, Kalamazoo, Mich.

Rockwell, F. F., and E. C. Grayson (revised by M. J. Dietz). 1977. *The Complete Book of Bulbs.* Lippincott, New York.

Rowley, G. 1979. *The Illustrated Encyclopedia of Succulents.* Crown, New York.

Seddon, G. 1979. *The Pocket Guide to Indoor Plants.* Simon & Schuster, New York.

Sessler, G. J. 1978. *Orchids and How to Grow Them.* Prentice-Hall, Englewood Cliffs, N.J.

Schuman, D. N. 1980. *Living with Plants: A Gardener's Guide to Practical Botany.* Mad River Press, Eureka, Calif.

Snyder, L. C. 1978. *Gardening in the Upper Midwest.* University of Minnesota Press, Minneapolis.

———. 1983. *Flowers for Northern Gardens.* University of Minnesota Press, Minneapolis.

Strider, D. L. (ed.). 1984. *Diseases of Floral Crops.* 2 vols. Praeger, New York.

Thomas, G. S. 1976. *Perennial Garden Plants.* McKay, New York.

Walls, I. G. 1973. *The Complete Book of Greenhouse Gardening.* Quadrangle/The New York Times, New York.

Watts, L. 1980. *Flower and Vegetable Plant Breeding.* Grower Books, London.

Note: The U.S. Department of Agriculture through the U.S. Government Printing Office, Washington, D.C., and the extension services of state colleges of agriculture (see appendix) have pamphlets and booklets on these topics that are keyed to the various regions of the United States. Similar services are available in Canada.

C H A P T E R   1 8

LAWNS

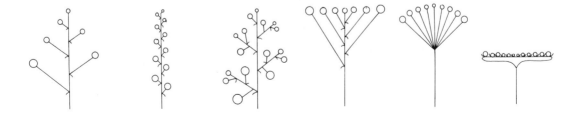

Lawns have been important for centuries, and the lawn and turf business is one of the most active of the horticultural industries. Home lawns, public and private recreational areas, cemeteries, highways, and other lawn installations require maintenance that by itself accounts for several billion dollars each year in North America and Europe. Grass lawns have a minor role in the horticulture of the Far East.

Contrary to expectations, lawn installation and maintenance are among the more expensive and time-consuming horticultural activities. The individual grass plants are not only subject to many pests and diseases, but also are deliberately crowded and in intense competition for space, light, water, and nutrients. Nevertheless, there is great personal desire and community pressure for a beautiful lawn to reduce dust and mud, to soften and enhance the landscape, and to sit and play on.

NEW LAWNS

Site Preparation

Site preparation is undoubtedly the single most critical factor in developing a fine lawn. Preparation is more difficult at new construction sites, since much of the topsoil has been removed, the subsoil has been compacted, and the site almost invariably contains construction debris. All debris must be removed rather than buried since bricks, paint cans, and boards will interfere with lawn development.

Where topsoil has been removed or is less than 7.5 to 10 cm (3 to 4 in.) deep, additional top-grade soil must be added. Before spreading fresh soil, the subsoil is cultivated to a depth of 15 cm (6 in.) by harrowing or rototilling. The soil should not be cultivated if it is water-saturated. Unless the topsoil is excellent, it is usually good practice to treat it as subsoil and incorporate it into the subsoil. Clay or excessively sandy subsoils require the addition of organic matter—peat, manure, or straw—to increase water and air movement and to allow the roots to penetrate easily. Lime is recommended to bring the subsoil to pH 5.8 to 6.8, and if the subsoil is nutrient-deficient (as determined by soil tests), phosphate fertilizer at recommended amounts can be added. When the subsoil is prepared, it is graded to provide a smooth, firm base for the topsoil and to eliminate high or low areas that may affect drainage and be difficult to maintain. Grading is usually done mechanically. A grade or slope away from any building with an 8- to 10-in. drop per 50 linear ft allows adequate drainage.

Topsoil is uniformly distributed over the subsoil by hand raking. Where organic matter in the topsoil is low, appropriate amending with peat, well-rotted manure, or well-decomposed compost is necessary. Well-decomposed sawdust can be used, but it should be at least 8 years old to avoid nitrogen deficiencies in the soil (see Chapter 5). Milled peat is incorporated at a rate of 3 bales/1000 ft^2. Sand to lighten heavy clay soils may be supplied at 200 lb/1000 ft^2. Lime is added as needed, and a light fertilization application (5 lb N/1000 ft^2 of a 10:10:10 formulation) should be made.

The topsoil is graded for uniform depth and raked to remove stones, sticks, and other debris and to break up clods of soil. The surface of the seedbed should be 3 to 5 cm (1 to 2 in.) lower than walks, driveways, and curbs to allow for the additional height of the grass.

The best time to establish a lawn in northern areas is in mid- to late fall, with spring a distant second choice. Where this is not possible, a green manure cover crop of annual ryegrass (*Lolium multiflorum*) or redtop (*Agrostis gigantea*) can be grown to be turned under in August. The cover crop will reduce weed development. In the south (Zones 8 to 10) lawns of warm-season grasses are best started in early summer: fall cover crops of crimson clover (*Trifolium incarnatum*), hairy vetch (*Vicia villosa*), or annual ryegrass are cultivated into the soil prior to planting.

Seeding

Lawn grasses are conveniently divided into cool-season and warm-season species and cultivars. These categories reflect the different growth patterns of the plants, cool-season grasses developing best in the cooler weather of spring and fall and warm-season species exhibiting best growth in the heat of summer. These differences largely determine the choice of grasses for lawns in different lawn climatic areas. Continental United States can be divided into six regions on the basis of conditions for growing lawns (Figure 18-1). There is a transition region

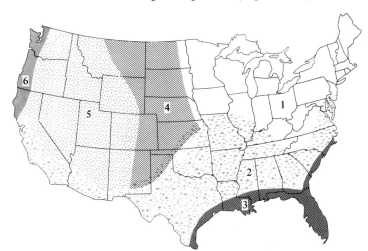

Lawn Area 1: Kentucky blues, red fescues, colonial bent. Bermuda and zoysia in southern portions of Area 1.
Lawn Area 2: Bermuda, zoysia, centipede, carpet, St. Augustine. Kentucky blues and tall fescues in northern portions of Area 2.
Lawn Area 3: St. Augustine, bermuda, zoysia, carpet, bahia.
Lawn Area 4: Crested wheat, buffalo, blue grama in nonirrigated portions. Kentucky blues and red fescues in irrigated portions of area.
Lawn Area 5: Crested wheat in nonirrigated portions. Kentucky blues and red fescues in irrigated portions of area.
Lawn Area 6: Colonial bent, Kentucky blues, red fescues.
Figure 18-1 Lawn climatic regions.

Table 18-1   GRASS SEED MIXTURES

Situation	Hardiness Zone	Composition
Sunny area	3–7	75% improved bluegrasses + 25% improved red fescues
Shady area	3–7	75% improved red fescues + 25% improved bluegrasses
Play area	4–8	80% improved tall fescues + 20% perennial rye
Quick cover	3–9	75% annual rye + 25% redtop
Rough lawn	3–8	33⅓% Ladino clover + 33⅓% bluegrasses + 33⅓% tall fescues
Heavy traffic	4–8	60% fescues + 20% bluegrasses + 20% perennial rye
Overseeding	7–9	100% redtop

extending along the bottom of regions 1 and 4 in which grasses of neither category perform optimally. Grass seed mixtures of both cool- and warm-season plants are used here. Lawn climatic region 4, which includes much of the Great Plains of the United States and adjacent Canada, tends to have hot and dry summers and lawn irrigation or special attention to watering is required. The mountainous portions of lawn climatic region 5, where irrigation is difficult, will support good lawns of crested wheatgrass.

Establishing a good lawn demands quality seed, appropriate to the particular soil and climatic conditions. Many grass species have been selected and bred for particular characteristics (Table 18-1). Within these, named cultivars have been developed that are generally superior to the unimproved species. The named cultivars have the disadvantage of being almost isogenic (genetically uniform) since some of the seed is obtained by apomixis (nonsexual seed formation). To increase the lawn's survival under adverse conditions, most lawn grasses are sold as mixtures of two or more species. These mixtures are usually keyed to hardiness zones, to environmental conditions in various lawn climatic regions, and to the expected use of the lawn. In southern climates (Hardiness Zones 8 to 10) many lawns are established with a single species of grass, frequently as blends of several cultivars. Lawn grass seed should be labeled with the species and cultivars included, the germination percentage, the percent of weed seed (less than 1 percent is best), the percent of inert materials (less than 5 percent), and the percent of crop seed (less than 0.3 percent). Certified seed labels indicate that the plants were inspected in the field and were found to be true to type.

In most northern regions (Hardiness Zones 4 to 7) the commonly available lawn seed mixtures contain bluegrasses and fescues in varying proportions. Perennial or annual ryegrasses may form a small percentage of the mixture since they germinate quickly. The bentgrasses form superior lawns, but they require more attention and are more fragile than bluegrasses and fescues.

The time of sowing depends on the hardiness zone, the species to be used, and on weather conditions. Best results are obtained with cool-season grasses sown in the fall so that the young seedlings become well established before the ground freezes. At this time of year weed growth and the probability of water stress are reduced. Spring sowings are done as soon as the soil can be prepared because any delay may mean that the seedlings will not yet be established by the time the warmer weather arrives. Special attention is required after spring sowing to remove weeds and to maintain adequate soil moisture.

Sowing seed into a well-prepared seedbed can be done by hand or with mechanical grass seeding equipment. Since the seed is small, hand seeding is made easier if the seed is thoroughly mixed with a carrier such as sand or topsoil. To ensure uniform distribution of seed, half the seed is sown in one direction and the other half at right angles to the first lot. After planting, the seed may be raked with a tooth rake to make sure that the seed is in direct contact with the ground. Rolling or treading the seeded area also ensures good contact. The seed should not be covered by more than 0.2 to 0.3 cm (1/8 in.) of soil for most cool-season grasses. Some varieties, such as the bluegrasses, germinate slowly, requiring over three weeks for full germination. Mulching the sown area conserves moisture, prevents the seed from being washed away by heavy rains, and prevents wide swings in temperature. A weed-free straw or hay cover is excellent when used at the rate of 100 kg/100 m^2 (100 lb/1,000 ft^2). On steep slopes or banks, cheesecloth, sacking, or one of the commercially available mulching cloths can be used. The grass blades will grow through the mulch which usually rots away within a few months.

Moisture control is vitally important during germination and the first few months of lawn development (see Chapter 6). The high humidity resulting from continued saturation of the soil favors the growth of the damping-off fungi including *Pythium, Fusarium, Rhizoctonia,* and species of *Phytophthora.* However, the seedbed and the young seedlings must not be allowed to dry out. As plants develop, root systems penetrate further into the topsoil and the subsoil and less frequent watering is necessary (Figure 18-2).

If the seedbed was properly prepared and adequately fertilized, additional fertilizer may not be needed for the first months of lawn growth. If fall planting was done, a light fertilization in spring when the grass begins to grow may be helpful, particularly if the plants are pale green or yellowish (nitrogen deficient;

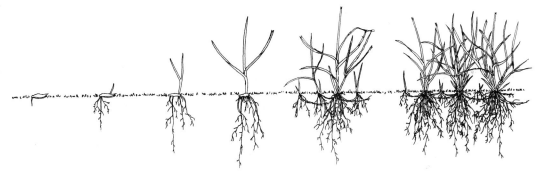

Figure 18-2 Stages in the germination and early development of bluegrass over a five-month period.

see Chapter 7). A phosphorus deficiency is recognized as dark green plants with red stems and reduced growth.

To avoid compaction of the soil, new lawns should not be walked on for the first month following appearance of the seedlings. Mowing can begin at this time with mower height set at 2 in. Chemical weed control is best deferred for another month or can be done the following spring.

Sodding

Sod is pregrown turf consisting of a weed-free mixture of grasses appropriate to the area. It should be purchased locally. Rectangles or strips of a mature turf, 1 to 3 years old, are cut with special equipment to a thickness of 2 to 3 cm (1 in.), with little soil below the mat of roots. Laying sod is expensive, but it is an effective method on slopes subject to erosion or where a fine, mature lawn is to be established in a short time. In many areas sodding provides an excellent turf, usually weed free, that is permanent with proper maintenance.

In Hardiness Zones 4 to 8 sodding is most successful when done in the fall, although spring sodding may be done if adequate moisture and care are provided. In Hardiness Zones 8 to 10, where warm-season grasses are used, summer sodding is best. It is important that the sod is laid as soon as possible after delivery; a delay of even a few days will injure the turf since the root systems are exposed.

Soil preparation is identical to that used for seedbeds except that the soil is graded 2 to 3 cm (1 in.) lower near walkways to adjust for the thickness of the sod. The bed must be well prepared and leveled to allow firm and close contact between the sod and the soil. Rectangles or strips are planted as tightly together as possible, much as flooring tiles are laid. To minimize trampling or compaction of the soil, a board is laid over the soil surface to be sodded. After the sod is installed, the area is top-dressed with a thin layer of good topsoil and topsoil is worked into the cracks between the pieces of sodding. The new lawn is lightly tamped or rolled to ensure good soil-sod contact and is watered immediately. It should be watered frequently for the first growing season to prevent root damage and to encourage good root penetration. A light application of superphosphate will accelerate root penetration.

Some grasses, particularly the warm-season species and the bentgrasses, can also be established from plugs or plantings (Table 18-2). Plug sodding utilizes small rectangles or discs of sodded grasses with adhering soil. These are planted 15 to 30 cm (6 to 12 in.) apart in well-prepared beds. Zoysia and St. Augustine grass are usually introduced as plugs. Bermuda grass, creeping bentgrass, and velvet bentgrass spread rapidly by stolons (horizontal stems that root easily from the nodes) and are planted as individual plants (sprigs) at 10 to 15 cm (4 to 6 in.) intervals. Closer spacing accelerates coverage, but the cost increases proportionally. For large areas, stolon-forming grasses can be shredded and spread mechanically. Plantings, like soddings, must be well watered until the turf is established.

MAINTENANCE

If a fine, thrifty, weed-free lawn is desired, its maintenance becomes a significant part of management and cultivation. Unfortunately, lawns are neither work-free nor trouble-free. Fertilization, liming, watering or irrigation, mowing, and control of animal and plant pests are the basic constituents of lawn management.

Fertilizing

If soil nutrients are brought to an adequate level during site preparation, additional fertilization will be unnecessary for the bulk of the first growing season. Indeed, overfertilization is inadvisable since a young root system is less tolerant of high levels of inorganic salts than is the root system of an established lawn. Excessive nitrogen results in succulent, soft growth that is less disease and insect resistant.

Lawns should not be fertilized when the grass or the soil is wet, but it is good practice to water thoroughly after spreading fertilizer to wash any chemicals off the leaves. This prevents burning and ensures that the fertilizer reaches and enters the soil.

There is some confusion about the amount or rate of fertilizer application. While the phosphorus and potassium components in standard fertilizer formulations are necessary for grass development, lawn grass growth is primarily dependent upon the amount of nitrogen supplied, and it is the nitrogen component that is given primary consideration in determining fertilizer applications. In a 10–5–5 formulation (see Chapter 7), there are 10 lbs of available nitrogen in each 100 lb of fertilizer; a 5–10–5 formulation contains 5 lb of available nitrogen per 100 lbs, and a 20–10–10 formulation has 20 lb of nitrogen per 100 lb. For lawn applications, the amounts needed are usually given as pounds of nitrogen per thousand square feet or kilograms per hundred square meters. To provide 1 lb N/1000 ft^2 (1 kg N/100 m^2) using a 10–10–10 fertilizer, 10 lb (4 kg) of fertilizer would be used.

Fertilizers may contain inorganic nitrogen as ammonium or nitrate ions, organically bound nitrogen, or a mixture of both. Inorganic nitrogen is immediately available to the plants, while organically bound forms release nitrogen slowly (see Chapter 7). When spring applications of fertilizer to cool-season lawns or summer applications to warm-season lawns are made, the combination formulations work well in spite of their high cost. For fall applications, where immediate uptake in cool weather is desired, only inorganic formulations are cost efficient.

Fertilization schedules depend on the region and the grass type (Figure 18-3). Warm-season grasses put on most of their growth during the hot summer months and should be fertilized at the time of maximum growth. Bermuda grass, St. Augustine grass, zoysia, or Bahia grass benefit from high fertilizer applications. Bermuda grass should receive 5 kg N/100 m^2 (5 lb N/1000 ft^2), St. Augustine grass and the zoysias 2 kg N/100 m^2, and Bahia grass 3 kg N/100 m^2.

Table 18-2 SEEDING OR PLANTING OF LAWN GRASSES

Latin name	Common name	Seeds		Plugs or plants		Mowing height (in.)	Remarks
		Time	Rate (lb/1000 ft²)	Time	Rate (number/ 1000 ft²)		
		Cool-season grasses					
Agropyron cristatum	Crested wheatgrass	F	1–2	—	—	2	Dry, cool areas
Agrostis canina	Velvet bentgrass	F	1–2	—	—	1	Humid, cool areas; drought-resistant
A. gigantea	Redtop	F	1–2	—	—	1.5	Quick cover, short-lived
A. stolonifera	Creeping bentgrass	F	1–2	F	1000	1	Humid, cool areas
A. tenuis	Colonial bentgrass	F/S	1–2	—	—	1	Humid, cool areas; finest lawns
Bouteloua gracilis	Blue gramagrass	S	1–2	—	—	1.5	Dry, cool areas; drought-resistant
Festuca rubra	Red fescue	F	3–5	—	—	2	Humid, cool areas; shade-resistant
F. rubra	Fescue, improved	F	2–4	—	—	2	Wear resistant, shade-tolerant
F. rubra heterophylla	Chewings fescue	F	3–5	—	—	1.5	Cool areas, shade-resistant
Lolium multiflorum	Annual ryegrass	F/S	4–6	—	—	2	Quick cover, short-lived
L. perenne	Perennial ryegrass	F/S	3–5	—	—	1.5	Used in mixtures with other grasses

449

Poa pratense	Common bluegrass	F	2–3	—	—	2	Drought-resistant, rough use
P. pratense	Bluegrass, improved	F	1–2	F	1000	2	Most common component in mixtures
Trifolium repens	White clover	F/S	2–4	—	—	1.5	Cool areas, nitrogen-fixing legume
T. r. forma *lodigense*	Ladino clover	F/S	2–4	—	—	—	Dry areas, rough lawns, nitrogen-fixing legume
Warm-season grasses							
Buchloe dactyloides	Buffalograss	S	1–2	S	50	1.5	Drought-resistant, heat-resistant
Cynodon Dactylon	Bermuda grass	S	2–3	S/S	10	.75	Southern areas, tolerates acid soils
Eremochloa ophiuroides	Centipede grass	S	2–3	S/S	10	1	Low maintenance, invasive
Paspalum notatum	Bahia grass	S	2–3	—	—	1	Humid, warm areas; coarse texture
Stenotaphrum secondatum	St. Augustine grass	—	—	S/S	30	1	Shade-tolerant, heat-resistant
Zoysia Matrella	Japanese zoysia	S/S	1–2	S/S	30	1	Wear-resistant, yellows in summer
Z. tenuifolia	Velvet zoysia	S/S	1–2	S/S	30	1	Fine texture, yellows in summer

S = summer; F = fall.

The cool-season grasses grown in Zones 4 to 7, including the bluegrasses, fescues, and ryes, are fertilized at 1 to 2 kg N/100 m² (1 to 2 lb N/1000 ft²). Lawns containing a high proportion of Merion bluegrass benefit from an application of fertilizer at 1.5 times that supplied to lawns in which other cool-season grasses predominate.

There is still some controversy as to the best time or times to fertilize cool-season grasses. If only one application is made, it is best done in the fall, usually in early September. Some schedules call for two applications in the fall, the first soon after the grasses come out of dormancy in August and the second shortly before frost is expected. The total fertilizer nitrogen for a dual fall treatment should be 1 to 2 kg N/100 m² (5 lb N/1,000 ft²). In parts of Hardiness Zones 7 to 8 cool-season grasses are used; in these areas a spring application of half the yearly amount of fertilizer nitrogen can be used with the other half reserved for fall application.

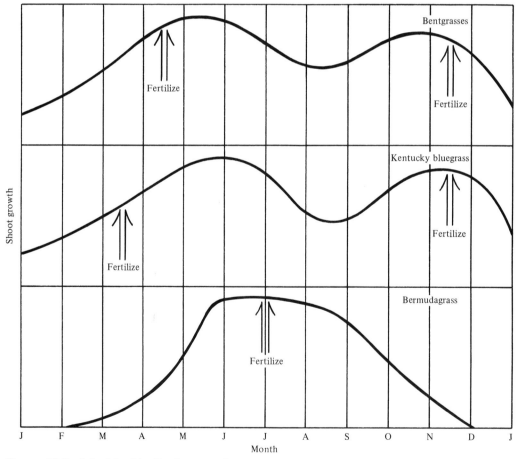

Figure 18-3 Schedule of fertilization according to seasonal growth patterns of lawn grasses.

Liming

It should be obvious that correction of soil pH should be done only when it needs correcting as determined by a soil test. In general, established lawns on sandy soils require liming every two to three years, while those on clay soils need adjustment only every five to six years. The lime is usually supplied in a finely ground or granular form (see Chapter 5) and can be spread at any time of the year, although late fall or very early spring are best. Amounts vary according to need, but are in the range of 10 to 30 kg/100 m² (10 to 30 lb/1000 ft²).

Watering

Watering or irrigation of lawns is, for most areas of North America, a necessity. An acre (0.4 ha) of lawn can transpire 2400 gallons (9600 liters) of water per day in midsummer. Considerable damage will occur if soils dry to their permanent wilting point (−15 bars; see Chapter 6) for any length of time. Many lawn grass roots grow to 30 cm (1 ft) or more into the subsoil and moisture levels at this depth should not fall below −8 bars during the period when the grasses are actively growing. It requires 2 to 5 cm (1 to 2 in.) of water to bring the upper 30 cm (12 in.) of a sandy or silty loam soil from near wilting point to field capacity. This amount of water will be transpired or lost by evaporation in a week under summer conditions. To replace this water, regular waterings are required. In midsummer, when cool-season grasses stop growth and become summer-dormant, less water is needed; if it is desirable to maintain growth during this time, watering must continue at somewhat higher rates than the 2 to 5 cm per week.

A light sprinkling of water several times a week is poor management practice. A good deal of this water is merely evaporated from leaf and soil surfaces and does not enter the soil at all. The water that does enter the soil remains in the upper few centimeters and the grass roots become concentrated in this superficial horizon. The danger of massive root kill by even light droughts or a short period of hot weather is great. Watering should provide the amount needed to bring the upper 30 cm (12 in.) to field capacity and should be repeated when this layer is still above the permanent wilting point—usually once a week or more frequently in very hot, dry weather with moderate to high winds.

A way of making sure that watering is adequate is to bury a small can in the soil up to its top. After watering or a rain, the can should contain 2 to 5 cm of water; when the water has been lost by evaporation, watering should be repeated. Sprinklers should be set to deliver water no faster than the soil can take it up immediately. When delivered at too high a rate, much of it can puddle or run off. Watering is best done when evaporation potential is relatively low, but not when the humidity is so high that the plant leaves and stems retain a film of water for any length of time.

Mowing

The fundamental rule on lawn mowing is to use only well-designed, well-maintained, and well-sharpened equipment. A dull blade, whether on a reel or a rotary mower, will shatter rather than cut grass blades cleanly and will increase the number of plants that die or become susceptible to infection. Although reel mowers involve more human effort, they are preferable to rotary mowers because they cut cleaner and are less dangerous to use.

Cool-season grasses should not, except under special circumstances, be mowed closer than 5 cm (2 in.). Close mowing removes too much of the photosynthetic leaf blade tissue and depresses the growth of root systems. It also exposes previously shaded stems to direct sunlight which may result in sun scald. Cool-season grasses should be mowed at frequent intervals during the growing period. It is a good general rule that lawns should be mowed when the grass length has exceeded the recommended height by no more than 1.0 to 1.5 cm (1/2 in.) where mowing shock is minimal. The warm-season grasses are generally cut shorter than the cool-season grasses. Bermuda grass is maintained at heights of 1.5 to 2.0 cm (5/8 in.) and the others at 2.0 to 2.5 cm (3/4 to 1 in.).

If grass clippings are short, they need not be removed. They will filter down between the grass blades where they will decompose, forming an organic layer that provides humus to the soil and recycles nutrients. Longer clippings, resulting from infrequent mowings, should be removed and saved for a compost pile, since they tend to mat and cover the grass. Mowing should be delayed if the grass is wet from rain or heavy dews since injury to the plants and some soil compaction can occur.

Weeds

A bright green, well-trimmed, and weed-free lawn is not only an esthetic pleasure, but adds financial value to a property. Weed control is a necessary cultural practice for most areas. Close to 50 species of weed plants invade lawns and require control if clean turf is to be maintained (Figure 18-4). Weed control starts with the turf itself. A healthy lawn, provided with adequate fertilizer, water, and lime and properly mowed, resists the invasion of the seeds of many weed species. Weed seeds are prevented from reaching the soil in such lawns, particularly if the turf is mowed to at least 3.5 to 5.0 cm (1.5 to 2.0 in.), a cutting height that is also best for lawn development.

Weedy species in lawns are separated into persistent (perennial) and nonpersistent (annual) types and each type includes monocots and dicots. Two of the more troublesome weedy plants are the crabgrasses (*Digitaria* spp.) and the nimblewills (*Mulhenbergia* spp.). Both are monocots related to the lawn grasses; the crabgrasses are annuals, and nimblewill is a persistent perennial. The crabgrasses are vigorous C_4 photosynthetic plants (see Chapter 11) and are particularly difficult to eliminate once they have become established. Other grass species that are problems for lawns are the creeping bentgrasses (*Agrostis* spp.),

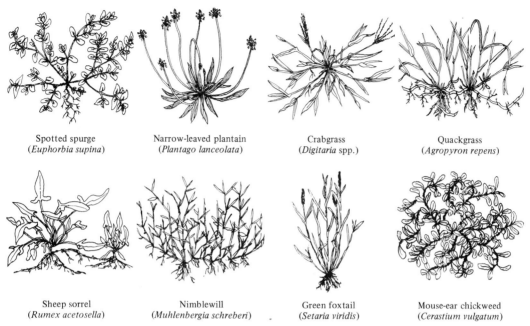

Spotted spurge
(*Euphorbia supina*)

Narrow-leaved plantain
(*Plantago lanceolata*)

Crabgrass
(*Digitaria* spp.)

Quackgrass
(*Agropyron repens*)

Sheep sorrel
(*Rumex acetosella*)

Nimblewill
(*Muhlenbergia schreberi*)

Green foxtail
(*Setaria viridis*)

Mouse-ear chickweed
(*Cerastium vulgatum*)

Figure 18-4 Major weed species in lawns.

foxtails (*Setaria* spp.), Dallisgrass (*Paspalum* spp.), and quackgrass (*Agropyron* spp.).

Since the desired lawn grasses are usually as sensitive to herbicides as are the weedy species, special control measures are required in an established lawn. When lawns contain few weeds, hand removal is the least damaging method of control. Removal is best done after a rain or thorough irrigation since many weeds have relatively superficial root systems and it is easier to pluck out the entire plant when the soil is damp. Many weeds reproduce easily from rootstocks and failure to remove the entire plant results in spread of the weed. This is particularly true for dandelion (*Taraxacum*), cinquefoil (*Potentilla canadensis*), and the plantains (*Plantago* spp.).

Both preemergence and postemergence herbicides are used in any thorough weed control program. The preemergence herbicides inhibit weed seed germination and early seedling growth, but have virtually no effect beyond that stage. They are effective in treating established lawns to eliminate crabgrasses, goosegrass (*Eleusine indica*), and creeping bentgrass (*Agrostis palustrus*), all of which are resistant to most other herbicides. They may also be effective against seedlings of broad-leaved weeds, although postemergence herbicides are usually used for these plants. Preemergence herbicides are available as granules that are spread in early spring. They should not be used on new lawns since they can kill lawn grass seedlings.

The postemergence herbicides include 2, 4-dichlorophenoxyacetic acid (2, 4-D) and its derivatives plus a variety of other chemicals that interfere with a number of physiological activities including photosynthesis, respiration, and synthesis of various compounds. Many are available as spreadable granules or as liquid formulations used as sprays. With few exceptions, spray formulations are most effective against young plants; as many weeds age, their tolerance to herbicides increases.

Herbicides are human and animal toxins, and as with all chemicals, package directions should be followed exactly. They can injure or kill desirable plantings and should not be used in very hot weather where they volatilize or in wind conditions where they may be carried to other plantings. Spot applications can be made by tipping a stick with a paint brush or a piece of plastic foam and touching individual weeds with the herbicide. Although formulations of fertilizer plus herbicides are available for dual treatment of lawns, they are more expensive than purchasing and applying each separately, and the timing for optimum effectiveness of each may be different.

Weed control in new lawns requires somewhat different procedures. Crabgrass seed is rarely found in commercial seed blends because this annual weed matures after the seed of the desirable grasses and the lawn grass seed heads stripped from the plants are above the flowering heads of crabgrasses. Weed seedlings, given half a chance, will outgrow and outcompete lawn grasses. Herbicide treatments should not be used, except as spot treatments, for the first half of the first growing season since seedling grasses are somewhat sensitive to the chemicals. It is better to allow the weeds to develop to a height of 4 to 6 cm above the lawn and then hand remove or mow. The young grass plants will not be severely set back in their development, while many of the young weeds will be killed or weakened by being topped. Repeated mowings will aid grass development until they are herbicide-resistant and then the chemicals for effective weed control are used.

Pests and Diseases

Three insect types are responsible for most lawn problems. Those that suck cell sap include the chinchbugs, some aphids, and scale insects. Plants of St. Augustine grass in the south are particularly plagued by chinchbugs. The sod webworms, occasionally called tobacco crambids, are larvae of moths that cause damage by feeding on grass leaves and stems. Army worms, the larval stage of another moth, are leaf feeders. By far the most serious pests are grubs, the larval hatchlings of the Japanese beetle, May or June beetles, and the billbugs. Beetle grub damage is evidenced by death of patches of grass in June through early August and by observations of white grubs directly beneath the sod. These insects feed on the roots of grass plants just below sod level and can destroy a large lawn area within a week.

The sap sucking insects and leaf feeders are controlled with appropriate insecticide sprays, usually applied in midsummer in the south and a few weeks earlier in more northerly climates. Grubs can be controlled by prevention through sound cultivation practices, trapping or killing adults, use of biological control (see Chapter 10), and soil treatments with appropriate pesticides.

Other animal pests rarely present major problems. Termites damage the roots of some grass species in the Ohio River basin, wireworms occasionally attack grass rhizomes near potato fields, ants are more of a nuisance than a pest. Land crabs dig holes in southern lawns and are controlled with a rotenone solution poured into each burrow. Mole burrows are unsightly and can result in uprooted plants. Moles feed on grubs, so that grub control almost invariably resolves the mole problem. No one has successfully dealt with neighborhood dogs, cats, and squirrels.

A well-managed lawn is the best disease control. Among the worst management practices in terms of disease development is overfertilization with high nitrogen formulations. Hot, wet summers are unavoidable, but they should alert the gardener that special care must be exercised if serious fungal diseases are to be avoided. Among the most common diseases of lawn grasses are the mildews, rusts, and smuts. Mildew infections look as if the grass had been dusted with a white powder and are controlled with fungicides. Rusts and smuts rarely kill thrifty, deep-rooted grass plants and can usually be controlled by fungicides. Smuts attack tender leaves forming black, powdery spore masses on curled leaves. In northern regions snow molds are a recurrent problem. The snow mold fungi attack overwintering leaves, and the results of their activity, dead circles or patches of grass, are seen when the snow melts. Unless the disease is far advanced, fungicidal treatments are effective.

Several leaf spot diseases are evidenced by small, purplish to deep brown spots on leaf blades. Bluegrasses are susceptible to leaf spot fungi, particularly in midsummer when these grasses are entering summer dormancy. When growth resumes in cooler weather, leaf spotting becomes less of a problem unless the fungi had moved into the leaf sheath or the crown in very humid weather. Systemic fungicides are used to prevent spread and overwintering of the fungi.

REPAIR, RESTORATION, AND RENOVATION

Even with reasonable maintenance, lawn repair, restoration, or renovation becomes necessary. Soil compaction in traveled areas, the growth of shade trees, diseases, and neglect can individually or collectively create problems that must be corrected. These operations should be distinguished from routine maintenance.

Older lawns that show minor wear and tear can be repaired by relatively simple procedures. Chemical and hand removal of weeds is best done prior to mowing the lawn to 2.5 cm (1.0 in.). Clippings should not be added to a compost heap, but collected and discarded. Treatments for pests, especially grubs, and any necessary disease control measures are important parts of a repair process. Fertilization to correct nutrient deficiencies, liming as indicated by soil tests, and accelerated maintenance techniques should be included. Repair work can be done at any time of year, but spring and fall are best.

Much has been written about the horrors of thatch buildup as a factor in lawn decline and most of it is probably overstated. The stolons of lawn grasses such as the bents and Bermuda grass are horizontal stems that extend along the ground and become intertwined. As stolons die, they can form a thick layer of organic material that decomposes slowly, sheds water, causes soils to dry out, and harbors earwigs and other pests. True thatch is a fluffy, matted blanket of these stolons above the soil. The organic layer that forms a thatch may contain grass roots which, since they are superficial, are easily killed by even brief droughts. Grasses that spread by tillering, including most species used in hardiness zones colder than 7, do not form extensive thatch layers and drastic treatments are not required for well-maintained lawns. In spring before growth begins, a simple raking with a broom rake is adequate to remove dead stems and leaves. Where true thatch exists, dethatching is done when the lawn is growing vigorously and recovery of the turf will be rapid. Power attachments are convenient and special dethatching rakes with sharp teeth can be obtained. Dethatching is not required annually unless southern area lawns are overseeded with annual rye (*Lolium multiflorum*) to relieve the brown appearance of dormant warm-season grasses.

The need for restoration is indicated by obvious spaces between individual grass clumps. Such work is best done in the fall. All dead plants in the area are removed by combined broom and tooth raking, soil is appropriately fertilized and limed, and a good seed bed is established by scarifying the soil with a sharp tooth rake. This loosens the top layer of soil and ensures that the seed will fall directly on the soil. Care of the newly seeded area is the same as care of a new lawn. Where the area for restoration is small, plugs of turf can be removed from sections of established lawns and planted in the area being restored. Plug planting is most effective in lawns of warm-season grasses. Sodding can be used for restoration as long as the species composition of the sod matches that of the rest of the lawn.

Where soil has become compacted, it is sometimes possible to restore lawns by cleaning up the planting and then overlaying a 2- to 3-cm (1- to 1.5-in.) layer of fine topsoil. The plants will grow through this layer and should tiller to recover the area.

Renovation is needed when spots of lawn are dead or when a portion of the lawn is doing poorly relative to the rest of the planting. The first step is to determine the cause of lawn failure and institute corrective measures before any renovation work is begun. Aside from disease, infestation, shading, and problems of soil composition, the most common cause of localized lawn failure is compaction. Localized compaction is seen as paths through the lawn, or as pools of standing water after rains or watering. Damaged plants grow slowly and show drought symptoms before the rest of the lawn. Heavy clay loams are particularly prone to compaction by foot traffic or power equipment. Where riding mowers are used, it is good practice to alter the pattern of mowing several times during a growing season. Habitual foot travel routes should also be changed. As soil becomes compacted, water penetrates slowly, root systems are poorly aerated, and root growth is restricted.

Where traffic is severe and the area has high value (golf courses, tennis courts), clay soils can be replaced by sandy loams that do not compact as easily. Small areas of compaction are relieved by loosening the turf with a garden fork to fracture the underlying soil. Special spading forks with hollow tines can be used to open up the soil. For larger areas coring spikers are available that will lift out small cores of soil that can then be gently raked into the turf. Compaction work should be done in the spring, with fall being a less satisfactory time.

Where these methods are inadequate, reconstruction may be necessary. Reconstruction involves the removal of the entire lawn or large areas of the lawn and the establishment of a new lawn. This is usually required when less than half of the lawn contains desirable grasses or where growth is so poor that half or more of the lawn is bare. Rototilling or spading to remove all cover is followed by the methods discussed in the first section of this chapter.

GROUND COVERS

In many situations grass lawns are neither practical nor desirable. Heavily shaded areas including those on the north sides of structures, under mature trees, and behind hedges and tall fences rarely receive enough light to allow a good lawn to develop. Areas immediately adjacent to woodlots also rarely form good lawns. Steep banks are difficult to mow, are frequently dry and infertile, and rarely can be successfully seeded because of runoff and erosion. All of these situations are best handled by planting ground cover plants. These should not be considered as second choices or compromise plantings; many ground covers are handsome and colorful additions to the landscape (Table 18-3). Contrasting textures, foliage colors, and splashes of flower color add greatly to the total view of a garden.

Most effective ground covers are herbaceous perennials or small woody shrubs. They may trail along the ground or spread by rhizomes so that bare areas are quickly covered. Some ground covers are essentially care-free, requiring only minimal fertilizing and watering, while others need as much or more attention as lawn grasses. Because of the large number of possible ground covers, selection is based not only on prevailing environmental conditions, but also on considerations of hardiness, foliage and flower interest, and the landscaping plan.

Many low-growing perennial flowering plants can be used as ground covers. Baby's breath (*Gypsophila repens*), turfing daisy (*Matricaria tchihatchewe*), some saxifrages, lily of the valley (*Convallaria majolis*), and others can fill in shaded areas. For southern areas (Hardiness Zones 9 to 10), gopher apple (*Geobalanus* spp.), peperomia, creeping charley (*Pilea hummulariaefolia*), inch plant (*Zebrina pendula*), and several species of veronica are excellent shade-tolerant ground covers. Although not usually considered as ground covers, there are herbs to suit most conditions and locations. Included among those that are often used as ground covers are catnip, tarragon, mint, pennyroyal, burnet, germander, lovage, chamomile, and sweet woodruff.

Few ground covers can tolerate foot traffic. Bugleplant (*Ajuga* sp.) and the creeping thymes (*Thymus* spp.) can withstand some traffic. Creeping dichondra (*Dichondra micrantha*) is the only ground cover that can withstand regular traffic and is a lawn grass substitute. It can be grown only in Hardiness Zones 9 to 10 since it is killed when temperatures reach −4° C (25° F). Dichondra can be started from seed or from plugs in fall. It has high fertilizer requirements (0.5 kg

Table 18-3   SOME GROUND COVER PLANTS

Latin name	Common name	Mature height (cm)	Light	Soil	Flowers	Hardiness zone
Acaena microphylla	Sheepbur	0.5	FS	N	−	7
Achillea spp.	Yarrow	30	FS	N	−	3
Aegopodium spp.	Goutweed	35	FS	N	−	4
Ajuga repens	Bugleweed	20	FS	N	+	4
Akebia quinata	Akebia	Vine	Sh	N	−	5
Aloe spp.	Aloe	10	FS	N	+	9
Andromeda polifolia	Bog rosemary	30	FS	Wet	+	3
Arabis alpina	Rock cress	20	FS	N	+	4
Arctostaphylos spp.	Bearberry	30	FS	Wet	−	3
Arenaria verna	Sandwort	8	FS	N	+	3
Armeria maritima	Thrift	30	FS	Wet	−	3
Cerastium spp.	Snow-in-summer	20	Sh	N	+	3
Chamaemelum nobile	Chamomile	15	FS	N	+	4
Convallaria majalis	Lily-of-the-valley	20	Sh	N	+	3
Cornus canadensis	Bunchberry	18	FS	Wet	+	3
Coronilla varia	Crown vetch	60	FS	N	+	4
Dichondra micrantha	Dichondra	8	Sh	N	−	9
Duchesnea indica	Indian strawberry	5	Sh	Wet	−	6
Erica carnea	Heath	25	FS	Acid	+	6
Euonymus fortunei	Wintercreeper	15	FS	Wet	−	5
Fragaria chiloensis	Wild strawberry	12	FS	N	+	5
Galax urceolata	Wandflower	15	Sh	N	+	4
Gaultheria procumbens	Wintergreen	1	Sh	N	+	4
Glechoma hederacea	Ground ivy	2	FS	N	−	4
Hedera helix	English ivy	Vine	Sh	N	−	6
Juniperis cvs.	Creeping juniper	35	FS	Acid	−	4
Liriope spicata	Lilyturf	20	FS	N	+	7
Mitchella repens	Partridgeberry	3	Sh	N	+	4
Mazus reptans	Mazus	3	Sh	Wet	+	4
Ophiopogon japonicus	Dwarf lilyturf	15	Sh	N	+	6
Pachysandra spp.	Pachysandra	30	Sh	N	−	5
Phlox subulata	Moss pink	15	FS	Wet	+	4
Phyla nodiflora	Lippia	10	FS	N	−	6
Potentilla spp.	Cinquefoil	10	FS	N	+	5
Prunella vulgaris	Self-heal	5	FS	Wet	+	3
Sagina subulata	Pearlwort	10	FS	N	+	5
Sedum spp.	Stonecrop	10	FS	N	+	4
Teucrium chamaedrys	Germander	30	Sh	N	+	6
Thymus spp.	Thyme	4	FS	N	+	4
Veronica spp.	Speedwell	10	FS	N	+	4
Vinca minor	Periwinkle	15	Sh	N	+	5
Viola spp.	Violet	10	Sh	N	+	3

FS = full sun; Sh = partial shade; N = normal soil; Wet = can withstand wet soils; Acid = requires pH below 5.

N/100 m² every two to four weeks) and must be watered more frequently than grass lawns.

Raw banks and steep slopes are among the most difficult areas to cover and few of the usual ground covers can withstand the dry, infertile, hot, and erosion-prone conditions. The best available cover for such areas is crown vetch

(*Coronilla varia*). It is a spreading perennial in the legume family with the ability to fix nitrogen. Originally European, it has naturalized in North America. The widely dispersed root system and its tolerance to dry, hot, and infertile situations makes it a prime candidate for holding banks. The bright pink flowers topping 40- to 50-cm (15- to 20-in.) plants are attractive. Once established, weed competition is minimal in its growing range (Hardiness Zones 3 to 10). Crown vetch is usually started from crowns that are planted 0.6 m (2 ft) apart and set deeply in the soil with most of the crown just below soil level. In order for nodulation and nitrogen fixation to occur, the soil pH must be near or slightly above neutrality (pH 7) and liming may be necessary. A low nitrogen, granular formulation (20 lb of 5-10-5/1000 ft^2) may be applied prior to planting; it need not be repeated until the second or third year. Mulching fall plantings with straw is useful, and spring plantings are greatly benefited by a mulch where the erosion potential is high. Where possible, the planting should be watered during the first season; after the plants are established, they are very drought-tolerant. Crown vetch crowns for planting will usually have few leaves and leaf formation and stem growth is slow; little observable growth is made until the second year after planting.

SUPPLEMENTARY READINGS

All About Groundcovers. 1980. Ortho, San Francisco.

All About Lawns. 1979. Ortho, San Francisco (separate volumes for the south, the west, and the northeast-midwest).

Beard, J. B. 1973. *Turfgrass: Science and Culture.* Prentice-Hall, Englewood Cliffs, N.J.

Cassidy, B. 1976. *Home Guide to Lawns and Landscaping.* Times-Mirror Magazines, New York.

Couch, H. B. 1972. *Diseases of Turfgrass.* Krieger, Huntington, N.Y.

Crockett, J. U. 1971. *Lawns and Groundcovers.* Time-Life Books, Alexandria, Va.

Horticultural Research Service. 1968. *Better Lawns.* Home and Garden Bulletin 512. U.S. Government Printing Office, Washington, D.C.

Langer, R. H. M. 1972. *How Grasses Grow.* Studies in Biology No. 34. University Park Press, Baltimore, Md.

Madison, J. H. 1971. *Practical Turfgrass Management.* Van Nostrand Reinhold, New York.

————. 1981. *Principles of Turfgrass Culture.* Van Nostrand Reinhold, New York.

Smiley, R. W. (ed.). 1983. *Compendium of Turfgrass Diseases.* American Phytopathological Society, St. Paul, Minn.

Sprague, H. B. *Turf Management Handbook.* 3rd ed. Interstate, Danville, Ill.

U.S. Department of Agriculture. 1978. *Lawn Diseases: How to Control Them.* U.S. Government Printing Office, Washington, D.C.

Vance, A. M., and B. A. App. 1968. *Lawn Insects: How to Control Them.* U.S. Government Printing Office, Washington, D.C.

Vengris, J., and W. A. Torello. 1986. *Lawns: Basic Factors, Construction, and Maintenance of Fine Turf Areas.* 4th ed. Thomson, Indianapolis, Ind.

CHAPTER 19

SMALL FRUITS

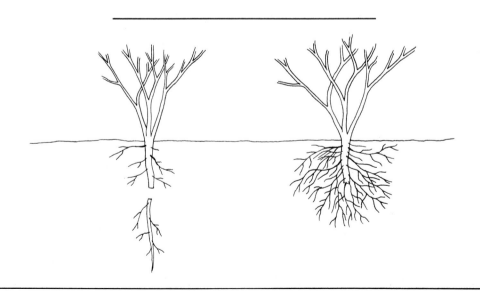

Small fruits is a collective name for plants that bear edible fruits and are not trees (Table 19-1). They are important crops in home gardens and in commercial production. The two most important small fruits in the agricultural sector of the economy are grapes and strawberries.

Small fruits, with the exception of strawberries, are woody perennials, and their cultivation follows the rules noted for such plants. Planting, cultivation, and pruning practices are much the same as for shrubs (Chapter 20). Horticultural practices employed are designed to maximize the production of large, well-formed, disease-free, and tasty fruit. (Fruit trees are discussed in Chapter 20.)

GRAPES

Grapes have been cultivated since the dawn of recorded history. The wine grape (*Vitis vinifera*) originated in the region between the Caspian and Black seas as a monoecious mutant of the normally dioecious *V. silvestris* and was domesticated 7000 years B.P. It was grown in Greece by 5000 years B.P. and was known in Egypt by 4000 years B.P. The grape is the largest and most widely cultivated fruit crop in the world. The bulk of the crop (77 percent) is used for wine and brandy, raisins account for another 18 percent, table grapes for 5 percent, and juice and jelly for a small, but important segment of the industry. There are close to 500 species in the genus with the wine grape alone having over 8000 named cultivars or clones, excluding recent hybrids with other species. *Vitis vinifera* is characterized by forming fruits with thick skins that adhere firmly to the pulpy mesoderm. The fruit is a true berry.

There are three major cultivated North American species. The fox grape, *V. labrusca,* was discovered by Norse explorers of Vineland. The thin skin slips easily from the pulp. 'Catawba' is the most widely known of the labrusca grapes. The renowned 'Concord,' used for sweet wines, juice, and jelly, may be a hybrid between *vinifera* and *labrusca.* The muscadine grape, *V. rotundifolia,* is widely planted in southern regions; 'Scuppernong' is an important cultivar. The

Table 19-1 PLANTING AND FRUITING INFORMATION FOR SMALL FRUITS

Fruit	Planting distance in rows (ft)	Mature height (ft)	Maturity (years)	Number of plants per acre	Yield per plant
Blackberry	4–6	2–4	2	1,800	2 qt
Blueberry	4	3–5	1–2	2,000	3 qt
Boysenberry	4–6	2–4	2	2,500	3 qt
Currant	4	3–5	2–3	2,700	2 qt
Elderberry	6–8	4–6	2–3	750	2 qt
Grape	6–8	—	2–3	800	14 lb
Raspberry	3–4	4–6	1–2	2,400	1 qt
Strawberry	1–2	—	1	20,000	1 qt

riverbank grape, *V. riparia,* is very cold hardy and has been used as breeding material for crosses with other species.

The wine industry in France was virtually destroyed in the middle of the nineteenth century when North American vines were imported as breeding stock. The roots of *V. riparia* and *V. labrusca* were infected with the phylloxera root aphid (*Dactylasphaera vitifolia*) which, although relatively benign on these species, devastated the susceptible wine grape. Since the beginning of the twentieth century, almost all wine grapes have been grafted to North American rootstocks.

In general, grape cultivars are restricted to Hardiness Zones 5 to 8 (Figure 8-4) since blossoms and many vines are killed at $-18°$ C ($0°$ F). Some cultivars of labrusca grapes can be grown in Zone 4, but are frequently killed back by severe winters even in Zone 5. Muscadine grapes can be grown in Zones 7 to 9. Most grape cultivars require from 160 to 175 frost-free days for good plant development and fruit maturation.

For home and commercial plantings, sandy, highly organic soils at pH 5.7 to 7.5 are most suitable. Good drainage is necessary. Stony soils of low fertility are selected in Europe for wine grapes. Planting holes should be large enough to accommodate the root system without any crowding. Granular fertilizers should not be used at planting time. The crown of the plant should be at soil level and any graft union should be above the soil level. Vines are planted 2 to 3 m (6 to 9 ft) apart, although plantings for arbors may be half this distance. Vigorous muscadine cultivars should have somewhat more space between plants. Grapes must be supported by trellises or arbors.

Pruning is the most important cultural practice in fruit production. At the end of the first growing season, the main stem is pruned to leave no more than two or three branch stubs, each containing a single bud (see Figure 14-31). As these buds break in the following spring, the shoots are tied to the trellis. Fruit production during the second growing season is restricted by rubbing off blossoms. The second pruning is done at the end of this second year's growth period. No more than five to seven single-bud shoots are kept for the third year's growth. Grape fruits form from inconspicuous flowers developed on current year's growth. For trellised grapes, subsequent training utilizes the pruning systems discussed in Chapter 14.

Cultivation must be no deeper than 10 cm (4 in.). Weed control by mulching with a 2 m (6 ft) circle about each plant is preferable for home gardens, but is not usually practiced in commercial grape production. Fertilization is restricted to spring applications of 10-10-10 formulation at the rate of 250 to 300 g (1/2 to 3/4 lb) per plant (see Chapter 7). Less fertilizer is used on young plants. Since grape roots extend to 3 m (9 ft) from the base of the plant, the fertilizer should be spread widely.

Grapes are propagated by hardwood cuttings taken from late summer shoots. Tip layering may be used to fill in rows or gaps in arbors (see Chapter 15). Plants in commercial vineyards and in some home gardens may last for many years with proper care.

STRAWBERRIES

Although the small, wild strawberry has been gathered for centuries, commercial berries have been available only since 1800. They originated as a cross between *Fragaria chiloensis* of the western North American and Andean mountains and *F. virginiana* from eastern North America. The plant and its cultivars are usually designated as *F. XAnanassa.* The European everbearing woodland strawberry *F. vesca* is one of the parents of everbearing cultivars. Total commercial and home strawberry production is second only to the grape among small fruits.

The inflorescence is produced terminally on the short compressed stem (crown), but is displaced laterally as a new meristem develops. The edible "berry" is not a true fruit. It is an aggregate fruit formed by the fusion of many ovaries that mature on a common, enlarged receptacle. The true strawberry fruit is an achene, a single seeded fruit (Chapter 3).

There are two major groups of cultivated strawberry. The June- or spring-bearing cultivars form flower buds in the short days of late summer and early fall and bear fruit the following spring. The runners (stolons or horizontal stems) are initiated in the long days of midsummer. In some cultivars additional flowers are initiated in the short days of spring that mature in midsummer. Everbearing cultivars form flower buds throughout the growing season and hence the plant is day neutral. A group of cultivars that appear to be long-day plants, initiating flower buds in midsummer and maturing in the fall, has been developed for regions with long growing seasons.

Most garden soils can support strawberries, although well-drained, sandy soils amended with organic matter such as manure, compost, or peat moss are best. The optimum soil pH is 5.8 to 6.5 and liming is rarely needed except on the less satisfactory clay soils. Full sun is best; light shade for a few hours each day can be tolerated. For both spring and everbearing types, a large number of cultivars and clones are available, spanning a wide range of maturation dates in different hardiness zones from Zone 4 through Zone 9. Since open flowers are killed at 0° C (32° F), colder parts of Zone 5 and much of Zone 4 may not mature a crop in some years. Adequate winter protection is advisable in Zone 6 and is absolutely necessary in colder regions.

To minimize damage from grubs, strawberries should not be planted in soils previously used for sod, pea, tomato, potato, or beet; these soils can be planted to a cover crop for several years before setting strawberries. Soil treatments for grubs, aphids, and wireworms should be done the summer preceding fall or spring planting. Corn aphids can also be a serious pest.

If strawberry plants cannot be set out immediately due to cold, wet soils, they may be stored in plastic bags in a refrigerator for up to a week. In Hardiness Zones 7 to 9 the plants are set out in fall; they are treated as annuals and replaced the next fall. Either spring or fall planting can be done in the Pacific Northwest. In Zones 5 to 6 strawberries can be handled as short-lived (two to four years) perennials, but they tend to run out because of competition from weeds and damage caused by viruses and nematodes. In northern and midwestern regions strawberries are usually planted in early spring; fall plantings are advisable only where winters are mild or the plants can be heavily mulched.

Most strawberries have a chilling requirement (see Chapter 8). Selection and breeding has resulted in cultivars with very low chilling requirements that are suitable for southern climates. In Zones 7 to 9 everbearing types may be effectively June bearing.

Before planting, a third of the root length and all dead leaves are trimmed off. The holes should be large enough so that the roots can be spread out laterally. The crown or bud is planted at ground level; too shallow or too deep planting results in weak plants and encourages excessive runner formation. Mulching with straw, hay, or biodegradable black plastic under each plant conserves moisture and protects the fruit from contact with the soil. If the plants are to be grown as perennials, blossoms on the planting stock are pinched out to reduce nutrient drains on the young plants and to promote early runner formation. Blossoms are allowed to remain and fruit is harvested in the second growing season.

Three methods are used for planting strawberries, each adapted to climate and cultivar type. The hill method is effective for perennial plantings. Plants are set out 30 cm (1 ft) apart in rows 1 m (3 ft) apart. Stolons are removed as they form so that only the parent plant produces a crop.

In matted row plantings, the plants are set 0.5 to 1 m (1.5 to 3 ft) apart and the runners are allowed to develop, resulting in a solid bed of plants in the row. Excess competition is prevented by removal of daughter plants that are too close together; this is only practical in small plantings and is not usually practiced in commercial plantings. Rows are narrow, usually no more than 50 cm (1.5 ft) wide with 1 m (3 ft) between rows. Matted rows are most efficient for June-bearing cultivars, particularly in northern and midwestern regions. The matted row method produces more fruit per unit area than the hill planting.

Space row plantings are essentially a blend of the hill and matted row methods with some daughter plants filling in spaces between mother plants. For all methods, netting over the plants minimizes losses from squirrels, birds, and other pests. Fruit is picked when the pointed tip turns red.

BLUEBERRIES

There are over 100 species in the genus *Vaccinium*, many of them wild plants of North America. The northern lowbush blueberry consists of three species: *V. myrtilloides*, the velvet-leaved blueberry or whortleberry; *V. angustifolium*, the low, sweet blueberry; and *V. vacillans*, the low bilberry. These species, plus *V. lamarckii*, hybridized to form the wild blueberry of Maine and the Canadian Maritime Provinces. The cultivated highbush blueberry is a twentieth-century plant derived from *V. corymbosum*, *V. australe*, and other species. *V. ashei* has been selected for more southerly regions. The rabbit-eye blueberry or huckleberry, cultivated in the south, is in the genus *Gaylussacia* and is distinguished from the blueberry by its large seeds and its ability to grow to over 3 m (10 ft).

Huckleberry cultivation is the same as for the blueberries. For all these plants, the fruit is a true berry.

Highbush blueberries are usually considered to be as hardy as peach (Zone 5) and cannot be grown in areas without a number of days below 8° C (45° F). Best results are obtained in areas with at least 120 frost-free days. Twigs may be killed at −35° C (−31° F) and flower buds are killed at −28° C (−20° F). Spring frosts can kill open blossoms and temperatures below 10° C (50° F) may prevent the necessary pollination by bees and particularly, bumblebees. Flower bud induction is a long-day phenomenon and occurs in late summer and early fall.

Blueberries have fairly exacting requirements. They do best in full or almost full sun. The soil must be acid, between pH 4.0 and 4.8. Poor vegetative growth and leaf yellowing due to iron deficiency become evident at higher pH values. Extremely acid soils may require liming. Treatment prior to planting with sulfur at 1 lb per 100 ft^2 or aluminum sulfate (1/2 cup per plant) will usually bring most loam soils down to acceptable pH values. To maintain the required acidic soils, sulfur or aluminum sulfate treatments may be needed yearly. Moist, well-drained soils with high organic matter are best. Humus formation and maintenance of acidity are also promoted by working peat moss into the soil at the time of planting.

Two- to three-year old, bare-root or container-grown planting stock is usually available for spring planting. The plants can be set out in spring as soon as the soil can be worked (Zones 5 to 6) or in late fall (Zones 6 to 7). For bare-root stock an overnight soaking in a dilute, acidic, water-soluble fertilizer solution just before planting provides the root system with an immediately available supply of nutrients. Plants should be set 1 m (3 ft) apart in rows 1 m apart. The holes should be wide and shallow, and soil can be amended with peat or compost to increase organic matter. It is preferable to remove all flower buds at the time of planting since fruit development drains nutrients from the small root system. Since the plants have very shallow roots, heavy mulching to prevent weed competition and conserve moisture is important. Acidic peat mulches, cotton-seed meal, or hardwood sawdust to a 15-cm (6-in.) depth is generally recommended. Although blueberry is self-fertile, fruit set and berry development are poor and planting at least two cultivars is standard practice. By proper selection of early and late maturing cultivars, the season can be extended over a month or more. Fruit ripening is slow and irregular. Fruit is picked when a light waxy bloom has formed on deep blue to purple berries.

Flower buds form on one- to two-year-old shoots and plants should not be pruned for the first two or three years. Three- and four-year-old stems are pruned out during the dormant period to keep the plants vigorous and to establish good bush form. Maintaining open-centered bushes permits light penetration and facilitates air movement through the planting (see Chapter 14).

Ammonium is a better source of nitrogen than is nitrate or the slow-release formulations and may be applied in spring at the rate of 0.5 lb per 100 ft^2. A 10-10-10 fertilizer will meet the requirements of the plantings.

Blueberries are propagated from hardwood cuttings taken in fall from two-year-old shoots. Softwood cuttings and mound layering can be done with vigorous plants in Hardiness Zones 6 and 7 (see Chapter 15).

BRAMBLE FRUITS

There are close to 100 species in the genus *Rubus,* of which fewer than a dozen have any commercial value or garden interest. All are prickly shrubs, although some almost thornless cultivars have been developed. The fruit is an aggregate consisting of individual drupelets around a core (receptacle). In raspberry the core separates from the attached drupelets when mature fruit is picked, while the core remains with the aggregate blackberry fruit. Canes are biennial, flowering and fruiting the second year. Canes are formed from the vigorous rootstock in the summer.

The red and yellow raspberry is the European *Rubus idaeus* and the North American *R. i. strigosus.* There are two black raspberry species, the more common *R. occidentalis* and the semitropical southern species *R. albescans.* The purple raspberry is a hybrid between *R. idaeus* and *R. occidentalis.* Red raspberries do best in "apple country" and black raspberries develop optimally in "peach country." Several other species have been grown as flowering ornamentals or have occasionally been cultivated. All are hardy to Zone 3 and all but *R. albescans* have an absolute requirement for a cold period. Most cultivars are summer bearing, although the everbearing types have a second flower flush in the long days of midsummer and will mature a second fruit crop in the fall.

Blackberries are genetically highly variable plants embracing at least six species that hybridize freely; the taxonomic arrangement of these species is not well worked out. Most are either upright shrubs or trailing vines and include boysenberry, loganberry, youngberry, and dewberry. All are drought-resistant, deeply rooted plants, but none are as cold hardy as the raspberries. The shrub forms are more cold hardy than the trailing forms, but the trailing types bear better fruit. Because of their high heat tolerance and low chill requirements, blackberries can be successfully cultivated as far south as Zone 8.

Both raspberries and blackberries do best in well-drained soils with pH values between 5.7 and 7.0 that have been supplemented with compost or manure. They should not be planted in land used in the previous 4 or 5 years for any of the solanaceous plants (potato, tomato, pepper, eggplant) because any residual wilt disease fungi will attack the brambles. Because the plants are very susceptible to virus disease, only certified virus-free stock should be planted. Because of the possibility of virus infection, plant far away from any wild ones and not where cultivated varieties had been grown within several years. Spring planting is recommended for Zones 4 to 6 and fall planting (October or November) for Zones 7 to 9. If soils are wet, plants can be stored in a cool, shaded place and the roots kept damp. New plants are spaced 1 m (3 ft) apart with 1 m between rows. Plants should be set 2 cm (1 in.) deeper than they grew in the nursery. After planting, they are cut back to 15 cm (6 in.) above ground level.

When the new growth reaches 0.5 cm (2 ft), the growing tips should be pinched back to release apical dominance and encourage branching. Black raspberries should be planted at least 8 m (25 ft) from red raspberries to prevent cross-pollination which results in poor fruit development.

Trailing blackberries are set out in spring (Zones 4 to 5) or in fall (Zones 6 to 8) as hedges with plants 2 m (6 ft) apart. Side branches are tipped to a length of 30 cm (1 ft). These plants produce best and accumulate fewer pests and diseases when trellised like grapes. The crowns should be set 8 to 10 cm (3 to 4 in.) below the soil surface.

There is no substitute for a deep (8 to 10 cm) mulch for all brambles. Straw, hay, peat, sawdust, or bark mulches are all suitable. Fertilize in spring with 10-10-10 granular formulations at the rate of 1 lb/10 ft (0.45 kg/3 m) of row for raspberries and 1 lb/30 ft of row for blackberries. Raspberries require little cultivation. When heavily mulched, weed competition is minimal. Irrigation is necessary in dry weather and after fertilization. Rodent damage may occur if these pests build their nests in the mulch.

The brambles flower and fruit only on canes produced the previous growing season. Canes that have borne fruit must be removed and burned after the berry crop has been harvested. New canes are formed during the growing season among the canes that are flowering and fruiting (see Figure 14-30). The new canes may be topped to 0.6 m (2 ft) in midsummer or may be allowed to grow to mature height. After the spent canes have been removed, the prospective bearing canes are topped (late fall or early spring) to 1 to 1.5 m (3 to 5 ft). Each stool of canes should be thinned to no more than six to eight canes, removing all weak, thin, or diseased canes. Everbearing cultivars can be handled the same as summer-bearing raspberries or can be pruned back to 1 m (3 ft) while still dormant. This prevents the development of a midsummer crop and increases the size of the fall crop. This method is most effective when separate plantings of everbearing and summer-bearing plants are grown in the same garden. The everbearing plants will be only summer bearing in colder areas (Zones 3 to 4), since the frost-free season is always too short for maturation of a fall crop. Since the summer crop on everbearers is frequently earlier than the crop of summer bearers, an extended picking season can be developed. For everbearing cultivars in which the two crops are feasible, the canes should be topped to 0.8 m (2.5 ft) in early spring while still dormant.

Blackberry canes should be headed back to 1 m (3 ft) in early spring at the time spent and weak canes are removed. Five to eight fruiting canes are left per hill and any plants that come up between rows are removed. For trailing and even for upright cultivars wire supports for the canes are useful, particularly when tall shoots and heavy fruit loads cause bending and breaking of the canes.

The brambles are propagated primarily from root suckers collected in late summer. Cuttings are difficult to root. Trailing blackberries are frequently multiplied by tip layering, either natural or induced. It is strongly advisable to replant after eight to ten years in a fresh location with certified virus-free stock. It is almost impossible to rejuvenate an old planting.

SUPPLEMENTARY READINGS

All About Fruits and Berries. 1980. Ortho, San Francisco.

Childers, N. F. 1983. *Modern Fruit Science.* 9th ed. Horticultural Publications, New Brunswick, N.J.

Coombe, B. G. 1976. The development of fleshy fruits. *Annu. Rev. Plant Physiol.* 26:207–228.

Hedrick, V. P. 1972. *Sturdevant's Edible Plants of the World.* Reprint ed. Dover, New York.

Hill, L. 1977. *Fruits and Berries for the Home Garden.* Knopf, New York.

Hulme, A. C. 1970. *The Biochemistry of Fruits and Their Products.* Academic Press, New York.

Maas, J. L. (ed.). 1984. *Compendium of Strawberry Diseases.* American Phytopathological Society, St. Paul, Minn.

Schery, R. W. 1972. *Plants for Man.* 2nd ed. Prentice-Hall, Englewood Cliffs, N.J.

Shoemaker, J. S. 1975. *Small Fruit Culture.* 5th ed. Avi, Westport, Conn.

Weaver, R. J. 1976. *Grape Growing.* Wiley, New York.

Winkler, A. J., J. A. Cook, W. M. Kliewer, and L. A. Lider. 1974. *General Vitaculture.* 2nd ed. University of California Press, Berkeley.

C H A P T E R   2 0

ORNAMENTAL AND FRUIT TREES AND SHRUBS

ARBORICULTURE

Arboriculture is the planting and care of trees, shrubs, and woody vines. A specialized related field is pomology—the cultivation of woody perennials that bear edible fruits including nuts. Arboriculture differs from forestry which is primarily concerned with the commercial production of timber. There is, however, an association between arboriculture and the recently developed field of urban forestry in which management of extensive plantings of ornamentals has assumed considerable importance. Arboriculture forms the base for landscape design as well as for the management of recreational areas such as parks.

Increased urbanization of North America and Europe has intensified the importance of arboriculture. Trees and shrubs have physical, esthetic, and economic value. They modify the environment, reduce soil erosion, provide valuable crops, and beautify the landscape. Not incidentally, they increase property values for landowners.

Although urban environments tend to be almost 2° C warmer in winter than rural areas, this same temperature differential exists in summer due to the absorption of heat by structures. Trees, shrubs, and other plants ameliorate temperature extremes by controlling solar radiation through reflection, interception, absorption, and transmission. The transpiration of water by a single tree may exceed 400 liters (80 gallons) per day, providing a small cooling effect (see Chapter 6), but the creation of shade is more important in decreasing summer heat. In winter the reduction of wind velocity creates sheltered areas around buildings that can reduce heating costs. Appropriately arranged foundation plants around buildings can create dead air spaces that reduce heat losses. Lines of trees paralleling roads form a sound barrier, ensure privacy, and trap snow to keep sidewalks and roadways free of snow. The texture of foliage, the form of various trees and shrubs, the changes over the seasons, and the ability of trees to attract birds make properly landscaped sites an esthetic pleasure.

MATCHING SITE AND SPECIES

Trees and shrubs are permanent plantings that cannot be moved or changed simply and inexpensively. Decisions about what to plant and where to plant it should be made only after considerable thought and design. A rapidly growing tree planted under the eaves of a building or beneath overhead wires is an invitation to disaster. If in planning the mature specimen is not visualized, it may effectively destroy the balance of an entire landscape, may shade or otherwise interfere with other plants, and may turn out to be in a less than optimal location for its own growth.

For most areas the potential range of species or cultivars that can be used is quite broad. The important characteristics of plant size, branching pattern, foliage texture, growth habit, and reproductive characteristics can be matched with structures, site layouts, and other landscaping factors. By proper selection a group of woody perennials showing seasonal progressions of interest can increase the utility and beauty of a planting. Special consideration should be given to trees

Table 20-1   SOME TREES AND SHRUBS TOLERANT OF CITY CONDITIONS

Latin name	Common name	Zone
Trees		
Aesculus Hippocastanum	Horsechestnut	3–7
Acer palmatum	Japanese maple	6–8
A. platanoides	Norway maple	5–8
Albizia Julibrissin	Silk tree	7–10
Amelanchier canadensis	Serviceberry	5–8
Carpinus Betulus	European hornbeam	4–7
Casuarina stricta	She-oak	9–10
Celtis occidentalis	Hackberry	3–9
Cornus alba	Dogwood	5–8
Crataegus mollis	Downy hawthorn	4–9
Elaeagnus angustifolia	Russian olive	3–7
Eucalyptus spp.	Eucalyptus	7–10
Fraxinus Uhdei	Shamel ash	9–10
Ginkgo biloba	Maidenhair	5–9
Gleditsia spp.	Honey-locust	4–8
Ilex spp.	Holly	5–9
Jacaranda spp.	Jacaranda	9–10
Juniperus spp.	Juniper	3–9
Lagerstroemia indica	Crape-myrtle	7–9
Laurus nobilis	Sweet bay	7–10
Magnolia spp.	Magnolia	7–9
Malus spp.	Crabapple	3–8
Morus alba	White mulberry	5–8
Phoenix canariensis	Canary palm	9–10
Picea abies	Norway spruce	2–6
Pieris japonica	Andromeda	6–9
Pinus nigra	Austrian pine	4–7
P. strobus	Eastern white pine	4–7
P. sylvestris	Scotch pine	3–7
Platanus Xacerifolia	London plane tree	5–8
P. occidentalis	American sycamore	5–10
Quercus palustris	Pin oak	5–7
Q. rubra	Red oak	5–8
Q. Suber	Cork oak	8–10
Schinus Molle	Pepper tree	9–10
Sophora japonica	Pagoda tree	5–10
Tilia cordata	Little-leaf linden	4–7
Shrubs		
Berberis spp.	Barberry	3–7
Deutzia spp.	Deutzia	5–9
Forsythia spp.	Forsythia	4 9
Hibiscus syriacus	Rose-of-Sharon	4–9
Hydrangea spp.	Hydrangea	5–9
Ligustrum spp.	Privet	4–8
Lonicera spp.	Honeysuckle	5–9
Mahonia aquifolium	Grape holly	6–9
Myrica pennsylvanica	Bayberry	3–8
Philadelphus coronarius	Mock-orange	4–10
Potentilla fructicosa	Cinquefoil	3–9
Pyracantha spp.	Firethorn	5–8
Rhododendron spp.	Rhododendron, azalea	5–9
Rosa rugosa	Rugosa rose	3–9
Spiraea vanhouttei	White spirea	4–10
Taxus spp.	Yew	3–8
Weigela spp.	Weigela	5–9

**Table 20-2 SOME TREES AND SHRUBS TOLERANT OF
SEASHORE CONDITIONS**

Latin name	Common name	Zone
Trees		
Aesculus Hippocastanum	Horsechestnut	3–9
Acer platanoides	Norway maple	5–8
Betula spp.	Birch	3–8
Camellia japonica	Camellia	7–10
Cercis canadensis	Redbud	5–8
Chamaecyparis spp.	Cypress	4–8
Crataegus spp.	Hawthorn	4–9
Cryptomeria japonica	Cryptomeria	6–8
Elaeagnus angustifolia	Russian olive	3–8
Gleditsia triacanthos	Honey-locust	5–9
Ilex opaca	American holly	4–7
Juniperus spp.	Juniper	3–9
Magnolia grandiflora	Southern magnolia	6–9
Picea spp.	Spruce	3–6
Pieris japonica	Andromeda	6–9
Pinus nigra	Austrian pine	4–7
P. sylvestris	Scotch pine	3–7
P. thunbergii	Black pine	5–7
Populus spp.	Aspen, poplar	4–9
Prunus serotina	Black cherry	3–7
Tilia cordata	Little-leaf linden	4–7
Shrubs		
Abelia grandiflora	Glossy abelia	6–10
Amelanchier stolonifera	Serviceberry	4–7
Calluna vulgaris	Heather	4–9
Celastrus spp.	Bittersweet	4–8
Clethra alnifolia	Summersweet	3–10
C. carnea	Pepperbush	5–9
Cotoneaster spp.	Cotoneaster	5–7
Cytisus scoparius	Scotch broom	5–9
Erica carnea	Heath	5–9
Eriobotrya japonica	Loquat	8–10
Hibiscus syriacus	Rose-of-Sharon	4–9
Hydrangea spp.	Hydrangea	5–10
Ligustrum amurense	Amur privet	4–7
Lonicera spp.	Honeysuckle	5–8
Myrica pennsylvanica	Bayberry	3–8
Nerium oleander	Oleander	8–10
Pinus mugho	Mugo pine	3–6
Potentilla fruticosa	Cinquefoil	3–8
Prunus maritima	Beach plum	5–7
Rosa multiflora	Multiflora rose	4–8
R. rugosa	Rugosa rose	2–9
Sambucus canadensis	Elderberry	4–9
Spiraea spp.	Spirea	4–10
Tamarix spp.	Tamarix	2–10
Taxus spp.	Yew	3–8

and shrubs that provide multiseason interest. Maples (*Acer* spp.), for example, have delicate spring foliage and bright autumnal coloration. Flowering and fruiting species can be cultivated as ornamental specimens.

As with other plants, the successful cultivation of trees and shrubs must take climatic factors into consideration. The introduction of a nonnative tree or shrub should be done only after determining the hardiness limits of the plant, a simple procedure that is too often neglected. A native species may be growing in a protected site particularly at the limits of its natural range, and introduction into less protected areas will not be successful. Cultivated ornamental or fruiting trees and shrubs should, where possible, be grown to planting size in the area where they are to be permanently established; stock obtained from warmer or colder regions may not adapt readily. Although flowering and fruiting species may survive under inadequate climatic conditions, the more sensitive flower buds may be killed in winter or may not be induced in too mild winters or in very warm summer weather. Even within an adequate hardiness zone, local variations

Table 20-3   SOME TREES AND SHRUBS USED AS WINDBREAKS AND IN WINDSWEPT AREAS

Latin name	Common name	Zone
Trees		
Acer Ginnala	Amur maple	4–7
Cornus mas	Cornelian cherry	5–7
Crataegus spp.	Hawthorn	4–8
Cupressus glabra	Arizona cypress	7–9
C. sempervivens	Italian cypress	8–10
Elaeagnus angustifolia	Russian olive	3–7
Eucalyptus sideroxylon	Ironbark	9–10
Eucalyptus spp.	Eucalyptus	6–10
Juniperus spp.	Juniper	3–9
Laurus nobilis	Sweet bay	7–10
Photinia serrulata	Photinia	7–10
Pinus nigra	Austrian pine	4–6
P. ponderosa	Ponderosa pine	5–8
Populus deltoides	Eastern cottonwood	4–8
P. nigra 'Italica'	Lombardy poplar	4–9
Quercus macrocarpa	Bur oak	4–6
Rhamnus spp.	Buckthorn	7–10
Thuja occidentalis	White cedar, Arbor vitae	3–7
Shrubs		
Berberis spp.	Barberry	3–7
Celtis occidentalis	Hackberry	5–10
Forsythia spp.	Forsythia	4–9
Kolkwitzia amabilis	Beautybush	4–9
Ligustrum spp.	Privet	4–8
Lonicera spp.	Honeysuckle	5–8
Philadelphus coronarius	Mock-orange	4–9
Rosa rugosa	Rugosa rose	3–9
Syringa vulgaris	Lilac	4–8
Taxus spp.	Yew	4–8
Viburnum spp.	Viburnum	3–8

Table 20-4 SOME TREES AND SHRUBS FOR SHADED AREAS

Latin name	Common name	Zone
Trees		
Acer dissectum	Lace maple	6–8
A. Ginnala	Amur maple	4–7
A. saccharinum	Silver maple	4–9
Amelanchier canadensis	Serviceberry	5–8
Camellia japonica	Camellia	6–9
Carya illinoensis	Pecan	6–9
Catalpa bignonioides	Southern catalpa	4–9
Cercidiphyllum aponicum	Katsura tree	6–9
Cercis canadensis	Redbud	5–8
Chionanthus virginicus	Fringe tree	4–10
Cinnamomum camphora	Camphor tree	9–10
Cornus mas	Cornelian cherry	4–8
Laurus nobilis	Sweet bay	7–10
Liquidambar spp.	Sweet-gum	7–9
Sequoia spp.	Redwood	7–8
Sorbus americana	American mountain-ash	3–6
Tsuga	Hemlock	3–7
Shrubs		
Andromeda Polifolia	Bog rosemary	5–8
Berberis spp.	Barberry	3–7
Buxus spp.	Box	6–8
Celtis occidentalis	Hackberry	5–10
Chaenomeles speciosa	Flowering quince	5–9
Clethra alnifolia	Summersweet	3–9
Cotoneaster spp.	Cotoneaster	5–9
Forsythia spp.	Forsythia	4–9
Hamamelis virginiana	Witchhazel	4–8
Hydrangea spp.	Hydrangea	4–9
Ilex glabra	Inkberry	3–6
Philadelphus coronarius	Mock-orange	4–9
Pyracantha spp.	Firethorn	5–8
Rhododendron spp.	Rhododendron	4–8
Skimmia japonica	Skimmia	6–9
Symphoricarpos albus	Waxberry	3–10
Viburnum dendatum	Arrowwood	2–8

in altitude, slope, soil conditions, or other factors may preclude successful establishment. North-facing, elevated slopes with poor soils are far from the equivalent of a protected valley with deep soils.

Soil conditions play a large role in successful cultivation of trees and shrubs. During construction topsoil may have been removed, compacted, contaminated, or otherwise modified. Good soils can be added or poor soils amended, but compaction and contamination require considerable labor and expense to rectify.

Older commercial orchards composed of large, widely spaced trees are being replaced by plantings of smaller, semidwarf plants that are placed closer together. This allows greater production per unit area and facilitates pruning, pest control, and harvesting. The introduction of compact, highly productive,

Table 20-5 SOME TREES AND SHRUBS FOR DRY AREAS

Latin name	Common name	Zone
Trees		
Celtis occidentalis	Hackberry	3–9
Cornus florida	Flowering dogwood	5–9
Elaeagnus angustifolia	Russian olive	3–7
Fraxinus spp.	Ash	4–7
Gleditsia triacanthos	Honey-locust	4–9
Phelodendron amurense	Cork tree	8–9
Quercus rubra	Red oak	5–7
Robinia pseudoacacia	Black locust	3–8
Ulmus parvifolia	Chinese elm	4–9
Shrubs		
Arctostaphylos uva-ursi	Bearberry	2–5
Artemisia spp.	Artemisia	2–5
Berberis thunbergii	Barberry	4–9
Callistemon spp.	Bottlebrush	8–9
Caragana spp.	Pea shrub	5–8
Cotoneaster spp.	Cotoneaster	5–9
Holodiscus dumosus	Rock spirea	5–8
Hypericum calycinum	Goldflower	4–6
Juniperus spp.	Juniper	3–8
Leucophyllum frutescens	Ceniza	7–9
Ligustrum spp.	Privet	4–8
Lonicera spp.	Honeysuckle	5–8
Nerium oleander	Oleander	8–10
Potentilla fructicosa	Cinquefoil	3–8
Symphoricarpos orbiculatus	Coralberry	3–10

spur-type grafted trees has also intensified orchard practice. For home gardens, fruit trees grafted with several cultivars, each as a scaffolding branch, are readily cross-pollinated and produce several cultivars on a single tree. Pome fruits (apple, pear, crabapple) and stone fruits (peach, nectarine, cherry, plum, apricot) are excellent specimen trees with multiseason interest. Some plums, cherries, pears, and apricot cultivars do not bear fruit, but are grown for shade and for their fine displays of flowers.

Where soil, water, or shade conditions are impossible to change, species must be selected that are capable of withstanding or adapting to them. Tables 20-1 and 20-2 list trees and shrubs tolerant of difficult sites. Tables 20-3 to 20-7 list trees and shrubs tolerant of a variety of environmental conditions. This does not imply that other species cannot be used, but they may not do as well as they might under more optimum conditions.

PLANTING

Trees, shrubs, and woody, perennial vines can be started from seed or from rooted cuttings, although these usually require a number of years before a mature plant is obtained. Liners are small plants started from seed or from cuttings

Table 20-6   SOME TREES AND SHRUBS FOR WET SOILS

Latin name	Common name	Zone
Trees		
Acer rubrum	Red maple	4–9
A. saccharinum	Silver maple	4–9
Carya ovata	Shagbark hickory	4–8
C. illinoensis	Pecan	5–7
Crataegus mollis	Downy hawthorn	4–9
Eucalyptus spp.	Eucalyptus	8–10
Fraxinus pennsylvanica	Green ash	5–9
Gleditsia triacanthos	Honey-locust	5–9
Ilex spp.	Holly	6–9
Larix spp.	Larch	4–8
Liquidambar styraciflua	Sweet-gum	7–9
Nyssa aquatica	Tupelo	6–9
Platanus Xacerifolia	London plane tree	5–9
P. occidentalis	American sycamore	5–10
Populus deltoides	Eastern cottonwood	4–8
P. nigra 'Italica'	Lombardy poplar	4–9
Quercus bicolor	Swamp white oak	5–8
Quercus palustris	Pin oak	5–8
Salix spp.	Willow	2–9
Taxodium distichum	Bald cypress	6–9
Tilia americana	American linden	3–8
Tsuga canadensis	Canada hemlock	3–7
Ulmus americana	American elm	3–9
Washingtonia robusta	Mexican Washington palm	9–10
Shrubs		
Acer Negundo	Box elder	3–9
Calluna vulgaris	Heather	4–9
Chionanthus virginicus	Fringe tree	2–9
Clethra alnifolia	Summersweet	3–10
Cornus alba	Tatarian dogwood	3–8
C. alba 'Sibirica'	Siberian dogwood	3–8
Cytisus spp.	Broom	5–10
Euonymus japonica	Euonymus	4–8
Juniperus spp.	Juniper	3–8
Kalmia angustifolia	Sheep laural	5–7
Kolkwitzia amabilis	Beautybush	4–8
Myrica spp.	Bayberry	3–8
Rhododendron nudiflora	Rhododendron	5–8
Rosa rugosa	Rose	2–9
Sambucus canadensis	Elderberry	4–9
Viburnum spp.	Viburnum	3–8

available from commercial nurseries and are sometimes used when large numbers of young plants are needed at low cost.

Most trees and shrubs are available in one of three forms. Bare-root plants are usually two- to four-year-old deciduous trees or shrubs with stems rarely exceeding 2 to 4 cm (1 to 1.5 in.) in diameter. They are usually dug in late fall or early winter when dormant, are root pruned, and winter-protected for spring

Table 20-7 SOME TREES AND SHRUBS FOR ACIDIC SOILS

Latin name	Common name	Zone
Trees		
Ailanthus altissima	Tree of heaven	5–8
Abies spp.	Fir	3–8
Betula spp.	Birch	3–8
Camellia japonica	Camellia	6–9
Chamaecyparis spp.	Cypress	4–7
Citrus spp.	Citrus	9–10
Cornus florida	Flowering dogwood	5–9
C. mas	Cornelian cherry	4–8
Coryolopsis spicata	Winter hazel	5–9
Franklinia alatamaha	Franklin tree	6–9
Ilex spp.	Holly	4–9
Jacaranda acutifolia	Jacaranda	9–10
Juniperus spp.	Juniper	3–8
Larix spp.	Larch	4–8
Magnolia soulangiana	Saucer magnolia	6–9
Metasequoia sp.	Dawn redwood	6–9
Oxydendron arboreum	Sourwood	6–10
Pieris japonica	Andromeda	5–10
Picea spp.	Spruce	3–7
Pinus spp.	Pine	4–8
Populus deltoides	Eastern cottonwood	4–8
Populus spp.	Aspen, poplar	3–9
Quercus palustris	Pin oak	5–7
Styrax japonica	Snowbell	7–10
Tsuga spp.	Hemlock	3–7
Shrubs		
Amelanchier stolonifera	Serviceberry	4–8
Calluna vulgaris	Heath	4–9
Chaenomeles speciosa	Flowering quince	4–10
Cytisus spp.	Broom	5–9
Fothergilla major	Witch alder	5–9
Gardenia jasminoides	Gardenia	8–10
Ilex verticillata	Winterberry	4–8
Kalmia latifolia	Mountain laurel	5–8
Leucothoë spp.	Leucothoë	4–9
Myrica pennsylvanica	Bayberry	3–8
Rhododendron spp.	Rhodendron, azalea	4–8
Stewartia spp.	Stewartia	5–9
Vaccinium spp.	Blueberry	3–8

sale. In general, bare-root stock can be planted only in the spring in more northerly climates. Fall planting is sometimes recommended for warm climates where winter soil temperatures do not go below freezing. The American Association of Nurserymen has prepared standards for shade and fruit trees for recommended ratios of caliper (diameter of the trunk 6 in. above ground level) to height of the plant. They also give some standards for height related to bare-root area and diameter of the root ball (Table 20-8).

Balled and burlapped (B & B) plants are usually larger and older than

Table 20-8 **STANDARDS FOR NURSERY-GROWN TREES AS RECOMMENDED BY THE AMERICAN ASSOCIATION OF NURSERYMEN, INC.**

Type of tree	Caliper (diameter in in. 6 in. above ground)	Recommended height (ft)	Root spread for bare-root stock (in.)	Root ball for B & B stock (in.)
Standard shade trees	$1/2-3/4$	5-6	12	—
	$1-1\frac{1}{4}$	7-9	18	—
	$1\frac{1}{2}-1\frac{3}{4}$	10-12	22	20
	$2-2\frac{1}{2}$	12-14	28	24
	$3-3\frac{1}{2}$	14-16	38	32
Small ornamental trees		$1\frac{1}{2}-2$		10
		2-3		12
		3-4		13
		4-5		15
		5-6		16
Fruit trees				
Standard apple and pear	$7/16$	2		
	$11/16$	$4\frac{1}{2}$		
Dwarf apple and pear	$7/16$	2		
	$11/16$	3		
Apricot	$7/16$	2		
	$11/16$	4		
Sweet cherry	$7/16$	2		
	$11/16$	4		
Sour cherry	$7/16$	2		
	$11/16$	3		
Peach, plum, pear	$7/16$	2		
	$11/16$	5		

bare-root stock. They are field-grown plants that have been carefully cut out of the soil and wrapped in cloth (Figure 20-1). Conifers, broad-leaved evergreens, and mature hardwoods lend themselves well to this procedure. Since the root remains covered by soil and roots are not badly injured, B & B stock can be planted at any time of the year, although spring or late fall are best.

Many woody trees and shrubs are now grown from seed or cuttings in plastic or metal containers and then sold when they are one to several years old, depending on the rate of growth of the species. Container-grown stock has become very popular. A wide selection of plants is available throughout the year, the plants are generally kept top-pruned and well-shaped, they are usually healthy, and, because they are easily handled in the nursery, their cost is reasonable.

When selecting plants, there are several important things to look for. All planting stock should be disease-free and show good branching potential with a form typical of the species. Plants should appear healthy with dark green leaves or needles and firm buds on dormant deciduous plants. The area where the plants have been grown (the provenance) is important; plants grown in climates very different from the permanent location may adapt slowly or poorly, and it is frequently better to obtain locally grown plants. Container stock should be

Figure 20-1 Preparing balled and burlapped (B & B) stock.

selected with care. Poor nursery care may result in spindly plants with poor root systems (low root-to-shoot ratio) or, if the plant has been in the container too long, the root system may be deformed and pot-bound with roots encircling the container (Figure 20-2).

A wide range of trees with edible fruits is available. Nut trees are either semitropical (Brazil nut, cashew, palm) or temperate (walnut, pecan, butternut). Most orchard and landscaping trees are grafts or from cuttings (filbert, hazelnut) because these plants are wind-pollinated and seeds do not come true to type. They are excellent long-lived shade and specimen trees. Almond (*Prunus amygdalus*) is more sensitive to frost damage than the closely related peach and nectarine.

When plants cannot be set in the ground immediately after receipt, they should be heeled-in in a cool place and their roots kept damp. Bare-root trees and shrubs should be soaked several hours in water before planting. Container and B & B plants can be kept for some time, but the container or rootball should not be allowed to dry out. Direct sunlight on the root system must be avoided. Roses, foundation stock of evergreens, and hedge shrubs may be received in plastic wrappers packed with wood chips, peat, or compost and are treated as bare-root stock. Many trees and shrubs have been properly pruned before sale and need only to have dead or damaged roots or twigs removed, but some may require top or root pruning before planting.

The size, shape, and physical condition of the planting hole into which trees or shrubs are placed will determine the potential for successful establishment. The sides of a planting hole should be perpendicular and the hole should be at least 25 percent deeper than the desired planting depth. The diameter of the

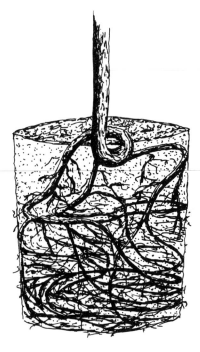

Figure 20-2   Unsatisfactory root of containerized stock.

planting hole should be twice as wide as the spread of the roots or root ball. The sides of the hole should be loosened to allow expansion of the root system. Shade and fruit trees must quickly form an extensive root system; crowded or bent roots will not grow properly and the plant will never develop well.

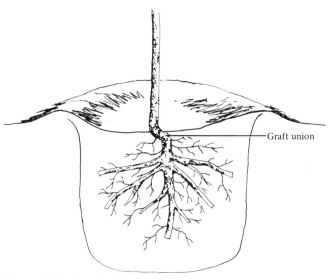

Graft union

Figure 20-3   Planting bare-root stock for standard tree (with graft union just below ground level).

The soil should be amended to develop the structure and texture of a good loam with high tilth (see Chapter 5). Peat, compost, or well-rotted manure plus lime, if required, may be added. Bone meal and slow-release pelleted or stick fertilizer, but not granular fertilizers, are also useful at this time.

When planting bare-root stock, the roots are spread out naturally (Figure 20-3). Amended soil is added slowly and worked carefully under and around the roots. Air pockets are places where infection starts and must be avoided. As the area above the roots is covered, the soil is tamped down firmly. When the hole is half filled and the tree is vertical, water is added to fill the hole completely and allowed to soak in to ensure that the soil will be at field capacity (see Chapter 7). The hole is then filled with soil and watered thoroughly again. At this watering, a dilute solution of a water-soluble fertilizer (half the recommended concentra-

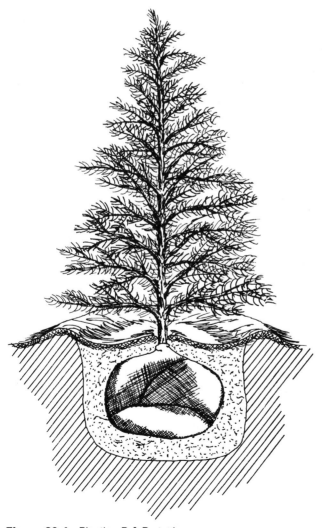

Figure 20-4 Planting B & B stock.

Invert and tap out of tapered container

Cut straight-sided cans

Set plant close to container level

Figure 20-5 Removing and planting containerized stock.

tion) can be used. The surface of the hole should be dished to form a water-retaining basin. A final watering is advisable. The area around the plant should be mulched with 5-cm (2-in.) layer of straw, compost, shredded bark or well-rotted manure.

The same procedure is used to plant container and B & B stock (Figures 20-4 and 20-5). Many foundation evergreens are containerized and larger specimens are usually sold as B & B. If the roots of a container plant are pot-bound, they are loosened and gently pried apart into a more natural growing position to facilitate growth. Container stock should set 2 to 3 cm (1 in.) lower than it was in the container. B & B stock is planted without removing the burlap wrapping, which rots away quickly. The cloth may be slit when the plant is in the hole. Plastic wrap and wires must be removed. Since most conifers and some other plants (heaths and heathers, blueberries, and camellias) require acidic soils (pH 5), the soil used to fill the planting hole is usually amended with milled peat moss and small amounts of ammonium sulfate or an acidic, water-soluble fertilizer.

When planting fruit and nut trees, attention must be paid to the placement of the graft union. Since these species are usually sold as bare-root stock, the graft union, an enlarged area just above the roots, is easily seen. Graft unions are placed just below ground level for standard trees and just above ground level for dwarfed stock. Placing the union above ground level reduces the possibility of sprouts developing from the stock. In standard trees there is less possibility of the development of shoots and roots from the rootstock, while there is a larger tendency for this to occur with the rootstock used for dwarfing.

Shrubs, whether used as specimens or as hedges, are planted in the same manner as trees. When several are to be planted in a row, trenching is more efficient than digging individual holes. Shrubs should be set in the ground 2 to 3 cm (1 in.) deeper than they grew in the nursery with the crown at soil level. The graft knob of roses and other grafted shrubs is placed 5 cm (2 in.) below ground level in cold areas and above ground in warm areas. After they are planted, barberry, forsythia, spirea, honeysuckle, Russian olive, and weigela are severely

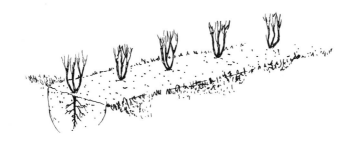

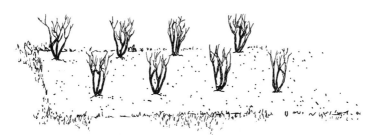

Figure 20-6 Single-row and staggered hedge plantings.

pruned to 30 cm (1 ft) to release apical dominance (see Chapter 14) and increase the number of shoots. Plants used as hedges can be placed in a single row or, for a deeper hedge, in a zigzag pattern (Figure 20-6).

Planting distances vary with environmental conditions and the desired use of the plants (Table 20-9). Climbing roses and other vines should be planted at

Table 20-9 PLANTING DISTANCES FOR PLANTS USED AS HEDGES

Species	Single-row spacing (in.)	Double-row spacing (in.)	Mature height	
			Maximum (ft)	As hedge (ft)
Privet	9	18	10	3–4
Tallhedge	18	48	20	15
Russian olive	24	60	12	3–5
Hardy boxwood	18	24	3	3
Spirea	24	48	15	5–6
Forsythia	24	48	10	4–6
Honeysuckle	24	48	10	3–6
Weigela	36	72	10	3–7
Barberry	12	36	10	4–6
Canada hemlock	18	48	40	6–12
Multiflora rose	18	36	10	6–8
Dwarf honeysuckle	12	24	4	2–4
Blue-leaf	8	12	3	1–2
Tea rose	18	36	4	2–3
Shrub rose	24	60	10	4–6

Table 20-10 PLANTING DISTANCES FOR FRUIT AND NUT TREES IN ORCHARDS OR AS SPECIMENS

Latin name	Common name	Hardiness zone	Height (ft)	Distance between trees (ft)
Carya illinoensis	Pecan	6–9	40	30–40
Citrus limonia	Lemon	9–10	25	25–30
C. paradisi	Grapefruit	9–10	50	30–40
C. reticulta	Tangerine	9–10	25	15–20
C. sinensis	Orange	9–10	40	20–30
Eriobotrya japonica	Loquat	8–10	20	12–15
Fortunella margarita	Kumquat	8–10	20	10–15
Malus pumila	Apple, standard	3–8	35	30–35
	Apple, dwarf	4–8	12	12–15
Olea europaea	Olive	9–10	25	15–20
Prunus Armeniaca	Apricot, standard	6–10	30	18–20
	Apricot, dwarf	6–10	12	10–12
P. avium	Sweet cherry, standard	5–9	45	20–30
	Sweet cherry, dwarf	5–9	12	10–12
P. Cerasus	Cherry, sour pie	3–7	15	10–12
P. domestica	Plum, standard	4–8	25	18–22
	Plum, dwarf	5–9	12	10–12
P. persica	Peach, standard	6–9	25	20–25
	Peach, dwarf	6–9	12	10–12
P. p. nucipersica	Nectarine, standard	6–9	18	20–22
Punica granatum	Pomegranate	7–9	15	12–20
Pyrus communis	Pear, standard	4–8	25	20–25
	Pear, dwarf	4–8	10	10–12

least 1.5 m (4.5 ft) apart. Vines should not be planted closer than 1 m (3 ft) from a wall to allow for good air circulation around the plants. Trellises are needed for vines like wisteria and clematis that climb by tendrils. Those that produce root holdfasts (ivy, Virginia creeper) can be grown directly against brick or stone walls, although the roots can penetrate through the mortar and damage the brick. Specimen shrubs, and particularly roses, should be planted far enough apart so that they will not touch at maturity.

Orchards may be planted in several patterns, depending on the available space, ground conditions, and whether machinery will be used. Spacing depends on the average height of the trees, with dwarf cultivars requiring much less area (Table 20-10). When planted as specimen ornamentals, the same spacing as in orchards is recommended.

The limited root system of a newly planted tree is incapable of performing its varied functions effectively. As broad-leaved plants leaf out or as conifer needles develop, the root system may not encompass enough soil area to supply the tops with water and minerals. For at least the first growing season, the plants must be watered frequently. The occasional addition of water-soluble fertilizer (but not granular fertilizer, which may damage roots) will promote thrifty growth. Adequate mulching retards water loss by evaporation and keeps the soil immediately above the roots cooler. The relatively poor anchoring capacity of young root systems makes newly planted trees susceptible to being windthrown.

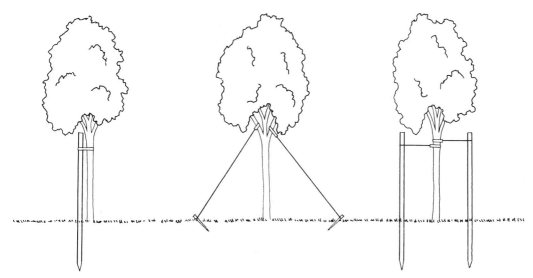

Figure 20-7   Staking newly planted trees.

All bare-root trees over 1.5 m (4.5 ft) should be staked (Figure 20-7). Care must be taken to avoid tying the plant to the stake so tightly that as the stem expands the rope or wires cut into the tender bark.

There is a controversy about wrapping the trunks of young trees. Proponents suggest that the young bark is particularly prone to sun scald, winter splitting, and other injuries and should be wrapped with heavy, treated crepe paper designed for this purpose. Opponents feel that wrapping may constrict growth, delay acclimation and development of heavy bark, and provide a happy home for borers, other pests, and disease organisms. If wrapping is done, it should be done carefully, and wrappings should be removed the second year.

Young trees and shrubs are more susceptible to diseases and to pests than are well-established plants. Partial defoliation or destruction of part of the root system can kill a young plant while an established plant may withstand the loss or damage. Newly planted trees should be examined carefully during the first several years and remedial action taken at the first sign of disease or insect damage. The young bark of such trees is readily eaten by mice and rabbits. Wrapping is only a partial protection and hardware cloth cylinders are necessary in regions where such pests are active. Flexible plastic spirals are inadequate; they do not provide good mouse protection and can allow moisture, disease organisms, and pests to accumulate underneath the coils.

MAINTENANCE OF ESTABLISHED PLANTINGS

It is surprising that people who carefully cultivate vegetable and flower plants and lawns will neglect the proper care of trees and shrubs. Both watering and proper fertilization are frequently ignored; disease and pest problems may be neglected, although they are no less serious than in other plantings. As with other plants, attention to requirements of trees and shrubs is a prerequisite for optimum growth and development.

During the growing season young or established woody perennials should receive 2 to 3 cm (1 in.) of water per week. When rainfall is inadequate, supplementary watering is desirable. Soaking hoses are excellent for these waterings. For larger plantings, like orchards, a permanent irrigation system can reduce plant loss and maintain yields. For smaller trees and for shrubs, an occasional sprinkling of the foliage will wash off accumulated dust and some insect pests.

The fertilization of established trees is accomplished by the introduction of fertilizer into the soil. Except for roses and other shrubs that flower the first year, heavy fertilization should be delayed until the plant is well established and not earlier than the second year after planting. Holes can be dug with a soil auger or with a metal rod to a depth of 15 to 30 cm (6 to 12 in.) for moderate-sized trees

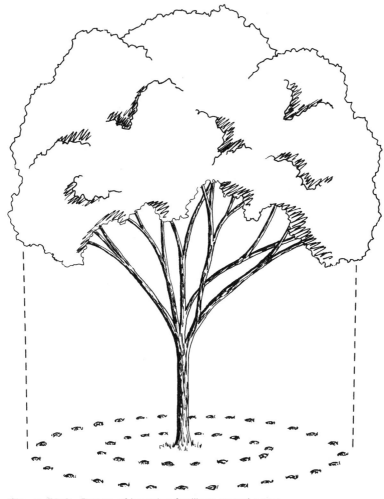

Figure 20-8 Pattern of inserting fertilizer around a tree.

Table 20-11 FERTILIZATION OF TREES

Diameter of trunk[a]		Weight of fertilizer[b]	
cm	in.	kg/tree	lb/tree
2.5	1	0.7	1.5
5.0	2	1.4	3
7.6	3	2.2	5
10.1	4	2.7	6
12.7	5	5.4	12
15.2	6	8.1	18
20.3	8	14.4	32
25.4	10	18.0	40
30.5	12	21.6	48

[a]Usually measured 12 to 18 in. (30 to 45 cm) from soil line.
[b]Based on 5:10:5 granular fertilizer.

and proportionally deeper for older and larger specimens. Several circles of fertilizer holes are needed for large trees with the outermost circle directly under the outermost branches (the drip line) (Figure 20-8). Approximate amounts of a standard 5:10:5 commercial fertilizer are given in Table 20-11. An easier method is to broadcast the fertilizer around the tree and work it into the soil, but it is less efficient because much of the fertilizer will be taken up by herbaceous plants and lawn grasses. Water-soluble fertilizers provide instant nutrition, while slow-release granules or spikes provide nutrients for several years. A 5:10:5 granular fertilizer will last at least one year. Frequent shallow cultivation reduces weeds that compete for nutrients and water. Maintaining a mulch around young trees for several years reduces water loss and competition from weeds, but may result in damage by mice.

Plants that develop best under acid conditions should receive an acidic amendment at least once a year. The most readily available acidifier is ammonium sulfate, which can be used as a side-dressing, incorporated into water, or worked into the soil about the plant. Acid soils in which plants requiring neutral pH values are growing must be limed at regular intervals.

The shape of the tree or shrub will be determined to a large extent by the pruning it receives. While there is a happy balance between too much and too little pruning, it is usually best to err on the side of too much; well-established plants recover quickly from overpruning, but if pruning is too cautious, the time

Board shelter

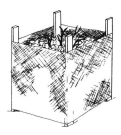

Burlap frame filled with leaves

Mounding with soil

Figure 20-9 Winter protection of shrubs.

for shaping may pass. Apple trees form flowers on wood that is at least two years old, peach flower buds are formed on one-year-old wood, and plum, apricot, and sour cherry form flower buds on the wood formed toward the end of a growing season.

In northerly climates young and even established plantings are subject to winter injury caused by low temperatures and by water losses due to wind. Mulching around young trees and shrubs or soil mounding of shrubs including roses is effective; care must be taken to avoid mouse damage. Frames of burlap placed about the plant will reduce windburn damage (Figure 20-9). Wooden frames above the plants protect them from wind and from branch loss by heavy snow or ice accumulations. Some plants can be wrapped in burlap. Plastic, because it can collect ice inside the wrapping, should not be used. For small conifers and broad-leaved evergreens, antitranspirants applied once or twice during the season can help prevent winter water stress (see Chapter 6).

The age after planting at which fruit trees will flower and bear fruit depends on many factors including cultivar, rootstock, cultivation practices, severity of pruning, and hardiness zone. While it is almost impossible to predict accurately, an estimate of bearing age based on Hardiness Zone 6 is given in Table 20-12 together with an estimate of the expected yields.

Table 20-12 YEARS TO BEARING AND YIELDS OF FRUIT AND NUT TREES IN HARDINESS ZONE 6

Tree	Years to bearing	Yield per plant Hectoliters	Bushels
Fruit trees			
Apple, standard	3–6	1.8–2.9	6–8
Apple, dwarf	2–4	.7–1.1	2–8
Apricot, standard	3–4	1.1–1.8	3–5
Apricot, dwarf	2–4	.4– .7	1–2
Cherry, sweet, standard	3–4	.7–1.1	2–3
Cherry, sour, standard	2–3	.7–1.1	2–3
Cherry, sour, dwarf	2–3	.4– .7	1–2
Citrus, most species	3–5	1.1–1.8	3–5
Nectarine, dwarf	2–3	.7–1.4	2–4
Peach, standard	2–3	.7–1.8	2–5
Peach, dwarf	1–3	.4– .7	1–2
Pear, standard	3–4	.7–1.8	2–5
Pear, dwarf	2–3	.4– .7	1–2
Plum, standard	3–4	.7–1.1	2–3
Plum, dwarf	2–3	.4– .7	1–2
Quince, dwarf	2–3	1.1–1.8	3–5
Nut trees			
Almond	3–5	.4–1.1	1–3
Butternut	4–7	.7–1.4	2–4
Chestnut, Chinese	3–5	.7–1.1	2–3
Filbert	3–4	.4– .7	1–2
Hickory	4–7	.7–1.1	2–3
Pecan	4–7	.7–1.4	2–4
Walnut, black	4–7	1.1–1.4	3–4
Walnut, English	4–7	1.1–1.4	3–4

In spite of adequate care, some fruit trees do not bloom and bear. There can be many reasons for this. Frequently, fruit trees are grown in hardiness zones too cold or too warm for that particular cultivar (see Chapter 8). Flower buds may be killed by cold or may not receive adequate chilling. Cold weather during bloom time may prevent bees and other pollinating insects from "working."

Some fruit trees normally bear well only every other year. This alternate year bearing can sometimes be overcome by early thinning of the crop during the high-yield year. Phloem disruption techniques, while drastic, sometimes increase fruiting (Figure 20-10). Disruption temporarily decreases translocation of carbohydrates formed in the leaves down the stem. This increases the carbohydrate-to-nitrogen ratio and favors flowering. Phloem disruption can be done only at the time flower buds are forming. Scoring the trunk down to the cambium is sometimes effective. Where ringing is done, the cambium is not removed, so that regeneration of new phloem and bark can occur. A more drastic procedure is bark inversion in which a band of bark is removed intact down to the cambium and then replaced upside down (see Figure 20-10).

Early bearing of fruit trees can be promoted in commercial plantings by appropriate use of growth substances formulated especially for this purpose.

The restoration of old and neglected orchards is a long-term project. The first step is removal of dead branches and moderate pruning in late fall or early spring. This is followed by selective pruning the second year, together with fertilization, liming where indicated, and pest control. Over a few years new

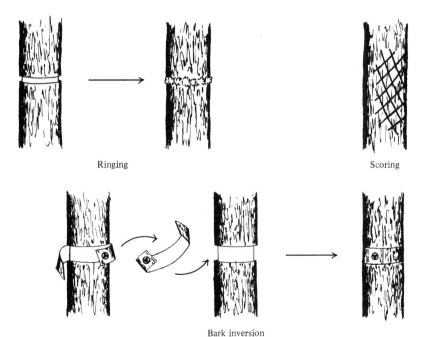

Ringing   Scoring

Bark inversion

Figure 20-10 Phloem disruption to increase fruiting.

scaffold branches will develop and begin to bear within a few years. Orchard renewal by grafting is practical only for home plantings of a few trees and is never practiced in commercial orchards.

SUPPLEMENTARY READINGS

All About Roses. 1984. Ortho, San Francisco.

All About Trees. 1981. Ortho, San Francisco.

Baldwin, I., and J. Stanley. 1984. *The Garden Center Manual.* ISBS/Timber Press, Beaverton, Ore.

Bateson, W. T. 1984. *Landscape Plants for the Southeast.* University of South Carolina Press, Columbia.

Baumgardt, J. P. 1984. *Tree Maintenance.* ISBS/Timber Press, Beaverton, Ore.

Beckett, K. A. 1981. *The Complete Book of Evergreens.* Van Nostrand Reinhold, New York.

Bernatsky, A. 1978. *Tree Ecology and Preservation.* Elsevier, New York.

Blanchard, R., and T. A. Tattar. 1981. *Field and Laboratory Guide to Tree Pathology.* Academic Press, New York.

Bloom, A. 1982. *Alpines for Your Garden.* ISBS/Timber Press, Beaverton, Ore.

Bonnie, F. 1976. *Flowering Trees, Shrubs and Vines.* Oxmoor House, Birmingham, Ala.

Carpenter, P. L., and F. O. Lanphear. 1975. *Plants in the Landscape.* Freeman, San Francisco.

Coutwright, G. 1982. *Trees and Shrubs for Western Gardens.* ISBS/Timber Press, Beaverton, Ore.

Dirr, M. A. 1983. *Manual of Woody Landscape Plants.* 3rd ed. Stipes, Champaign, Ill.

Elias, T. S. 1980. *The Complete Book of Trees of North America.* Van Nostrand Reinhold, New York.

Fiola, J. L. 1984. *Lilacs.* ISBS/Timber Press, Beaverton, Ore.

Flint, H. L. 1983. *Landscape Plants for Eastern North America Exclusive of Florida and the Immediate Gulf Coast.* Wiley, New York.

Forsberg, J. L. 1975. *Diseases of Ornamental Plants.* Special Publ. 3. College of Agriculture, University of Illinois, Champaign.

Garden Club of America. 1984. *Plants That Merit Attention.* I. *Trees.* ISBS/Timber Press, Beaverton, Ore.

Grey, G. W., and F. J. Deneke. 1978. *Urban Forestry.* Wiley, New York.

Harris, R. W. 1983. *Arboriculture: Care of Trees, Shrubs and Vines in the Landscape.* Prentice-Hall, Englewood Cliffs, N.J.

Harrison, C. R. 1975. *Ornamental Conifers.* Macmillan, New York.

Holliwell, R. 1983. *Garden Trees: A Guide to the Siting, Selection and Maintenance of Trees and Shrubs in Small and Medium Sized Gardens.* Wiley, New York.

How to Select and Care for Shrubs and Hedges. 1981. Ortho, San Francisco.

Janick, J., and J. N. Moore. 1975. *Advances in Fruit Breeding.* Purdue University Press, West Lafayette, Ind.

Jaynes, R. A. (ed.). *Nut Tree Culture in North America.* Northern Nut Growers, Hamden, Conn.

Johnson, W. T., and H. H. Lyon. 1976. *Insects That Feed on Trees and Shrubs.* Cornell University Press, Ithaca, N.Y.

Kramer, P. J., and T. T. Kozlowski. 1979. *Physiology of Woody Plants.* Academic Press, New York.

Krussmann, G. 1983. *Handbook of Broad-leaved Trees and Shrubs.* 3 vols. ISBS/Timber Press, Beaverton, Ore.

———. 1983. *Manual of Cultivated Conifers.* ISBS/Timber Press, Beaverton, Ore.

Loewer, H. P. 1983. *A Guide for Landscape, Lawn and Garden Evergreens.* Walker, New York.

McGourty, F. (ed.). 1983. *Nursery Source Manual.* Brooklyn Botanic Garden, Brooklyn, N.Y.

Martin, E. C. 1983. *Landscape Plants in Design: A Photographic Guide.* Avi, Westport, Conn.

Mechlin, S., and E. Bonnano. 1982. *Without a Thorn: A Guide to Rose Gardening in the Pacific Northwest.* ISBS/Timber Press, Beaverton, Ore.

Menninger, E. A. 1978. *Edible Nuts of the World.* Horticultural Books, Stuart, Fla.

Morey, P. R. 1973. *How Trees Grow.* Studies in Biology No. 39. University Park Press, Baltimore, Md.

Nagy, S., and P. E. Shaw. 1980. *Tropical and Subtropical Fruits.* Avi, Westport, Conn.

Novak, V., F. Hrozinka, and B. Stary. 1976. *Atlas of Insects Harmful to Forest Trees.* Elsevier, Amsterdam.

Ouden, P. den, and B. K. Bloom. 1982. *Manual of Cultivated Conifers.* 3rd ed. Kluwer, Hingham, Mass.

Pirone, P. P. 1978. *Diseases and Pests of Ornamental Plants.* 5th ed. Wiley, New York.

———. 1978. *Tree Maintenance.* 5th ed. Oxford University Press, New York.

Root, J. B. 1985. *Fundamentals of Landscaping and Site Planning.* Avi, Westport, Conn.

Snyder, C. L. 1980. *Trees and Shrubs for Northern Gardens.* University of Minnesota Press, Minneapolis.

Stipes, R. J., and R. J. Campana. 1981. *Compendium of Elm Diseases.* American Phytopathological Society, St. Paul, Minn.

Strom, S., and K. Nathan. 1985. *Site Engineering for Landscape Architects.* Avi, Westport, Conn.

Tattar, T. A. 1978. *Diseases of Shade Trees.* Academic Press, New York.

Teskey, B. J. E., and J. S. Shoemaker. 1978. *Fruit Tree Production.* 3rd ed. Avi, Westport, Conn.

Tukey, H. B. 1978. *Dwarfed Fruit Trees.* Cornell University Press, Ithaca, N.Y.

Westwood, M. N. 1978. *Temperate-Zone Pomology.* Freeman, San Francisco.

Wyman, D. 1975. *Dwarf Shrubs.* Macmillan, New York.

———. 1977. *Shrubs and Vines for American Gardens.* Rev. ed. Macmillan, N.Y.

PART SIX

AGRONOMIC CROPS

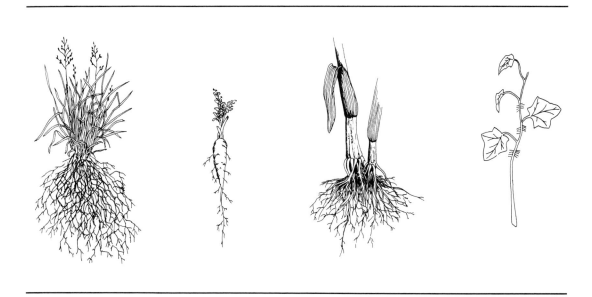

C H A P T E R   2 1

CEREAL GRAINS AND FORAGE GRASSES

In this part we will be concerned with agronomy, the cultivation of grains and food legumes plus the forage plants that are the primary food of our domesticated animals. The scientific study of the cereal grains and grass-family forages is termed agrostology.

Although people have adapted several hundred plant species for use (see Chapter 2), fewer than two dozen cultivated plants account for over 90 percent of their food and stand between health and starvation. Most important for human survival are the cereal grains in the grass family (Gramineae), primarily wheat, rice, maize (corn), and sorghum, but also including the "small grains" such as barley, oats, rye, and the millets. The second important family of primary food crop plants is the Leguminosae containing the peas and beans (the pulses).

The grains together account for over half of the food energy and consumed protein of the world's people (Table 21-1). Cereal grains are the world's major food crops for good reason. Yields are less dependent on energy input than for many other crops, cultivar differences allow crops to be grown and harvested in varied environments, production is relatively reliable, response to fertilizers and pesticides is generally excellent, storage and transportation is efficient, and nutritional values are unsurpassed among the plants.

There is a third category of basic food plants. The root crops are obtained from plants in many botanical families. We in North America are most familar with the white potato *(Solanum tuberosum)*. The yam *(Dioscorea alata)*, sweet potato *(Ipomoea Batatas)*, taros *(Calocasia* spp.), and cassava *(Manihot esculen-*

Table 21-1   WORLD FOOD CONSUMPTION, 1977–1980

	Cereal grains (kg/day/person)	Pulses (kg/day/person)	Root crops (kg/day/person)	Meat (kg/day/person)	Calories Kg/day/person	Calories Percent from plants	Calories Percent produced domestically	Protein g/day/person	Protein Percent from plants
World	1.03	.041	0.342	.088	2590	83	—	69.3	65
Africa	0.55	.030	0.504	.038	2307	93	93	58.6	80
Nigeria	0.48	.036	1.095	.022	2292	96	—	52.7	85
Asia	0.75	.046	0.192	.036	2277	91	96	58.3	79
China	0.82	.077	0.301	.055	2439	90	96	63.4	79
India	0.55	.049	0.082	.011	—	—	100	48.4	87
Europe	1.60	.016	0.684	.208	3410	68	92	96.0	46
United Kingdom	1.09	.008	0.356	.159	3305	62	78	91.6	39
Soviet Union	2.59	.082	0.901	.159	3443	73	92	103.2	50
North America	1.77	.019	0.175	.236	3215	68	130	92.7	39
United States	2.19	.011	0.219	.301	3537	63	134	106.2	32
South America	0.71	.036	0.520	.118	2277	91	108	66.1	56
Brazil	0.75	.049	1.027	.082	2521	83	105	61.2	62
Oceania	1.65	.024	0.309	.334	3202	63	174	95.8	35
Australia	—	—	—	.397	3412	60	192	106.6	32

Source: Data from D. Crabbe, and S. Lawson, *The World Food Book.* Kagen Paul, London, 1978; and Food and Agriculture Organization, United Nations, Rome.

tum) are tropical equivalents of the white potato, supplying excellent levels of carbohydrate, minerals, and vitamins. However, like the white potato, they are notably deficient in the proteins that humans require and that the grains and the legumes provide.

EVOLUTION OF AGRICULTURAL TECHNOLOGY

Domestication of our crop plants provides a record of the coexistence of plants and people extending over many centuries and involving many cultures. Agricultural practices have a history with beginnings shrouded in the mists of time. Once plants were brought under cultivation—by what means we really don't know—there must have been a long period during which selection for useful characteristics resulted in the genera and species that we now use. As plants were moved to different environments, further genetic mixing, selection, and eventually controlled breeding gradually resulted in cultivars adapted to particular sites and to particular cultural needs.

Although we know the time of introduction of plants from the New World into the Old, we can only speculate about the time, the routes, and the peoples who carried other plants around the world. Only in the late nineteenth century did western scientists begin to study the original homes and lineages of economically important food crops. The Swiss botanist Alphonse de Candolle published *Origin of Cultivated Plants* in 1882. The Russian Nicolai Vavilov reactivated the topic in 1951 and his ideas have since been modified as information from cytology, genetics, archeology, and other disciplines became available. The study of plant origins is an important topic in its own right, but it also has immense practical value. By pinpointing the place where a crop plant originated, it is possible to obtain wild progenitors and related species as sources of germ plasm (genetic material) that can be reintroduced into our cultivated plants to enhance disease resistance, physiological attributes, and other characteristics that may allow the production of better crops. This is true not only for our major crops, but also for our vegetables, flowers, and cultivated woody plants. The rapid and almost irreversible destruction of natural ecosystems, particularly in the tropics, has endangered these gene pools and the loss cannot fail to be a serious detriment to future crop improvement.

Civilization, with its legal and political systems, fine arts, religions, cultures, and human interactions, originated with and was dependent upon the domestication of plants, particularly the cereal grains and the pulses. Their cultivation required settled communities with human life regulated by the flow of the seasons. The farmer was rewarded by having an assured, storable, and highly nutritious food supply. Barley and wheat were brought into cultivation in the Fertile Crescent, an arc of land in the Middle East embracing modern Syria, Iraq, Lebanon, and Jordan. Rice came from subtropical China and India. Corn originated in several centers in Central America from which it radiated both north and south. Before the Americas were discovered by Europeans, it was being grown from modern Argentina to Canada. So, too, did the other cereal grains migrate from their centers of origin and domestication. Soybeans are the products of the Far East, two important genera of beans are from the Americas, and other beans and peas are from both the Orient and Europe. Through selection, deliberate breeding, and sometimes by chance, cultivars exist that are reasonably well adapted to most of the climatic conditions in which people live.

Agricultural practices and methods are derived from long human trial and error. From pointed sticks to modern grain drills, from sharpened stone harvesting knives to sickles to modern combines, and from wild gourds to pottery jars to the grain elevators, machinery and facilities have reduced tremendously the human labor that has always been a part of agriculture. Ongoing improvements in cultivation technology include fertilization (see Chapter 7), water control and irrigation (see Chapter 6), and intensive selection, breeding, and genetic engineering (see Chapter 15). These have, since the turn of this century, resulted in greatly enhanced yields. Improved food quality and quantity have allowed the modern farmer to feed over a hundred times more people than had been possible as recently as the middle of the ninteenth century. Today the agricultural population of the United States is less than 4 percent of the total population, while in 1900 it was close to 31 percent. It is only through these modifications in agricultural technology that densely populated cities could have been sustained.

Scientific agricultural research, the basis for successful farming, is usually considered to have started in the eighteenth century. The Danish Agricultural Society was founded in 1769 and the Philadelphia Society for the Promotion of Agriculture was organized in 1785. The Royal Agricultural Society of Great Britain was chartered in 1849, and at the same time German universities were establishing chairs of agricultural chemistry. Of course, perceptive agricultural-ists had been writing and teaching about agriculture for centuries; there are excellent directions for cultivating specific crops in the Judeo-Christian Testa-ments and in books from the Mediterranean basin and from China. But only as the concept of the controlled experiment and methods of investigation became established did scientific agricultural research become important.

In 1862 President Lincoln separated agricultural activities from the U.S. Patent Office and established a Department of Agriculture. In the same year he signed the Homestead Act which allowed individuals to obtain government land for farming. Also in 1862 Lincoln signed a bill introduced by Senator Justin Morrill of Vermont granting each state 30,000 acres of land for each member it had in Congress, with 90 percent of the gross proceeds of the sale of the land to be used for the endowment and maintenance of colleges and universities teaching mechanical and agricultural arts and sciences. The Land Grant College Act made the United States the leader in the scientific study of agriculture. The Hatch Act of 1887 provided a mix of state and federal funds for the activities of the agricultural experiment stations that were part of the agricultural colleges. The facilities, funds, and trained scientists of the state experiment stations were devoted to studying all aspects of the agricultural sector of the nation's economy. When in 1914 the extension services were added to the colleges of agriculture, a direct link was forged between the research scientists and the farmers so that research findings could quickly be transmitted directly to the farm. In the United

States the extension services and the experiment stations have the additional responsibility for the undergraduate and graduate education of future agriculturists and scientists. There is no question that the work of colleges of agriculture is primarily responsible for the enviable productivity of agriculture in North America and throughout the world.

Since the middle of this century agricultural research has been greatly augmented by activities of a diverse group of international agencies. The Food and Agriculture Organization of the United Nations and many foundations and international research institutes, both publically and privately funded, have a role in agricultural improvements. Many groups have focused their attention on underdeveloped nations. Some institutes have taken the responsibility for research on a particular crop (wheat, rice, potato, sugar cane) and for improving the living conditions and agricultural productivity of a country. The Green Revolution was sparked by the efforts of people working in international institutes. Even more recently, industry has become a vital factor in agriculture. Sponsored research in pesticides, fertilizers, genetics, and other technical topics now accounts for about 50 percent of all U.S. agricultural research as governmental roles and fundings are reduced.

Crop forecasting has, in the United States, traditionally been assigned to the Department of Agriculture utilizing the expertise of agricultural economists. This is a difficult job, made more complex by unpredictabilities in weather patterns, complex national and international controls on areas to be planted, costs of production, and predictions of need and ability to pay for the crops. Nevertheless, crop forecasting is vital to national and international agricultural health. The concept and many of the methods are not new; the ancient Chinese had a well-organized system of forecasting and resource allocation well over 2000 years ago.

In the not-too-distant past cereals, pulses, root crops, and horticultural and pomological crops were consumed near the places where they had been grown. The Romans imported wheat from North Africa and the Chinese shipped rice along the coast from the south to the north. Spices and seasonings, a few medicinal plants, and hallucinogenic drugs moved across oceans or across mountains and deserts, but most food crops rarely moved long distances. In North America early settlers could ship only a few high value crops back to Europe. Sugar, tobacco, hemp for cordage, and a few other products were exchanged for manufactured goods. Long distance transport of grains became possible only as roads, canals, and river navigation systems were built in the early nineteenth century. Even then, shipments were limited by weather and by the capacity of the carriers. International transport of basic foods is primarily a development of this century, involving massive grain-carrying ships and a large infrastructure of docking and transport facilities.

Concomitant with the development of shipping and storage facilities was the need for an equally complex financial network involving both political and economic agencies. Matters of balance of payments, trade commissions, and regulatory groups up to and including the highest levels of government are now a significant influence on agricultural productivity. The economic significance of

Table 21-2 EXPORT MARKETS FOR AGRICULTURAL PRODUCTS OF THE UNITED STATES, 1984

Crop	Metric tons (thousands)			Value (thousands of dollars)
Wheat and flour (flour-grain equivalent)				6,783,170
Americas	15,389.0			
Europe and Soviet Union	19,730.5			
Other	4,340.4			
Rice				896,900
Americas	165.7			
Europe	373.1			
Africa	2,271.7			
Middle East	796.7			
Maize (grain)				7,021,957
Americas	5,419.2			
Europe	8,159.2			
Soviet Union	6,985.8			
Asia	19,591.6			
Africa	4,997.5			
Barley				273,551
Total grain	2,047.6			
Total malt	74.6			
Rye				866
Oats				2,117
Americas	1.3			
Soviet Union	3.6			
Sorghum (grain)				829,235
Americas	2,987.1			
Europe	600.5			
Asia	2,296.8			
Africa	6,226.0			
Soy	*Oil*	*Meal*	*Beans*	7,415,523
North America	177.9	623.4	1,795.6	
South America	143.4	564.2	244.4	
Europe	11.3	2,919.8	10,159.9	
Soviet Union	66.9	17.8	40.5	
Africa	66.9	17.1	40.0	
Asia	426.6	703.4	7,317.6	
Oceania	1.2	21.4	13.1	

Source: U.S. Department of Agriculture, *Agricultural Statistics,* Washington, D.C., 1985.

major-crop agriculture to the United States is very great. Exports of the United States include technology (an increasing component), the products of heavy industry (a decreasing component), products of light industry (a fairly stable component), and agricultural products. Table 21-2 gives the value of United States exports of some cereal and legume foodstuffs. Without such exports this nation would be at serious financial risk. As other nations, using intensive cultivation techniques, enter the export markets, competition will continue to affect the financial health of agricultural sectors of all countries. Intensive international competition depresses prices, sometimes to the point where the grower, unless subsidized, receives less than the costs of production. Such considerations become matters of national and international concern; political and economic factors exist now in all countries and sometimes dominate the more immediate matters of the production of food for human well-being.

Agriculture is currently a troubled sector of the world's economy. In many advanced countries sophisticated agricultural technology has resulted in surpluses that depress prices of agricultural commodities. This has resulted in the forced sale of prime producing lands, the disruption of supporting industries, and the dislocation of experienced farm families. Huge agribusiness conglomerates, taking full advantage of economies of scale, have further modified the agricultural economy of the United States and other nations.

POPULATION AND PRODUCTIVITY

Agricultural productivity can be evaluated using many different criteria; yields per hectare, monetary values, farm income, and other measures are useful in specific contexts. Ultimately, however, productivity must be referable to the ability of agriculture to feed people. As seen in Figure 21-1, the world's population has increased exponentially; between 1985 and 2100 the earth's population will have doubled. These increases are not uniformly distributed

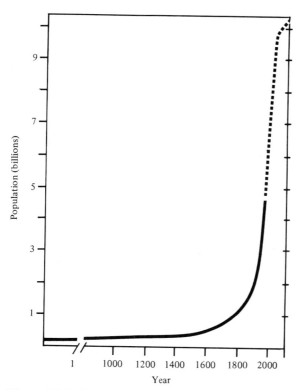

Figure 21-1 Past and projected world population

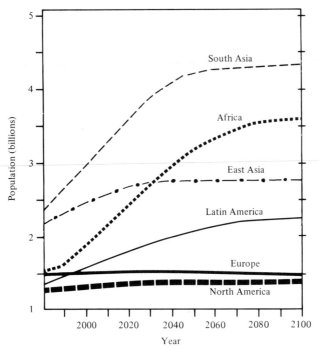

Figure 21-2 Projected population of areas of the world

(Figure 21-2); the bulk of the increase is occurring in the underdeveloped countries of Asia, Africa, and Central and South America.

Two measures of population growth in addition to numbers and distribution have proved to be valuable. The first is the annual population growth rate (Table 21-3). A rate of 2 percent means that a population will double in 35 years, 3 percent in 23 years, and 4 percent in 17.5 years. In most developed countries the rate is 1.3 or below; this is essentially a replacement level rather than providing for population increases without immigration.

The average population growth percentage for a country does not reflect the distribution of people within that country. Almost without exception, rural populations are at or below replacement levels, while the major burst of population growth is occurring in urban areas, which are projected to more than double in size between 1985 and 2000 (Table 21-4). This urban population rarely includes food producers. Urbanization is also accompanied by loss of productive agricultural land, a diversion of water and energy to the cities, and a concentration of wealth that is less available for agricultural uses. Because of the law of supply and demand, costs of feeding people are continually rising. In developed countries less than 25 percent of family income goes for food, as contrasted with 70 percent in the poor nations. This high proportional cost for survival limits the accumulation of capital for development and, equally important, precludes the possibility of securing funds for human advancement, education, and a more

Table 21-3 ANNUAL POPULATION GROWTH RATES, 1980–1985

	Percent Population Growth			Life expectancy[a]	Fertility rate[b]
	Urban	Average	Rural		
World	2.5	1.67	1.1	64.6	3.55
Africa	5.2	3.01	2.0	49.7	6.43
Kenya	7.4	4.12	2.3	52.9	8.12
Cameroon	6.6	1.36	0.0	48.0	5.79
Asia	2.9	1.73	1.3	57.9	3.56
Pakistan	4.3	3.08	2.6	50.0	5.84
Japan	0.6	0.57	−1.7	76.6	1.71
Europe	0.9	0.33	−1.3	73.2	1.90
Albania	3.5	2.21	1.4	70.9	3.60
Switzerland	0.3	−0.56	−1.7	75.9	1.33
Middle East	—	2.10	—	68.1	—
Bahrain	4.6	4.32	3.1	68.2	4.63
Lebanon	1.2	−0.01	−4.5	65.0	3.79
North America	1.8	1.38	0.7	71.7	2.69
Honduras	5.4	3.39	2.6	59.9	6.50
Canada	1.2	1.21	1.2	74.9	1.81
Cuba	1.7	0.62	0.9	73.4	1.97
United States	1.0	0.86	0.5	74.0	1.85
South America	3.3	2.24	−0.3	64.0	4.00
Ecuador	4.4	2.24	2.1	62.6	6.00
Uruguay	0.9	0.70	−0.06	70.3	2.76
Oceania	1.5	1.50	1.4	70.9	2.71
Solomon Islands	—	3.60	—	—	—
New Zealand	0.8	0.75	0.3	73.4	1.85

[a]Life expectancy at birth, 1980–1985.
[b]Fertility rate (average number of children a woman might have during her reproductive years), 1984.
Source: Department of International Economic and Social Affairs, United Nations, New York.

Table 21-4 POPULATION TRENDS IN SOME MAJOR URBAN AREAS OF THE WORLD

Urban area	Rank	Annual change[a] (percent)	Population (millions)	Total change[b] (percent)
Mexico City, Mexico	1	3.8	18.1	484
Tokyo-Yokohama, Japan	2	0.2	17.2	157
São Paulo, Brazil	3	4.4	15.9	468
New York-New Jersey, United States	4	−0.4	15.3	23
Shanghai, China	5	0.0	11.8	15
Seoul, Korea	9	3.7	10.2	827
Bombay, India	10	3.5	10.1	248
Paris, France	15	0.2	8.9	62
Jakarta, Indonesia	19	4.1	7.9	339
Milan, Italy	25	1.2	7.0	94

[a]Annual change, 1985.
[b]Total change, 1950–1985.
Source: Department of International Economic and Social Affairs, United Nations, New York.

secure and pleasant life. Asking the agricultural sector to do much more with much less is a challenge for the entire world.

A second measure of population growth is the fertility rate, an assumption of the number of children a woman may bear during her fertile period (see Table 21-3). The fertility rates of the developed countries are, as expected from the growth percentage data, under 2.0; a replacement fertility rate is 2.1, to account for child mortality. Kenya, a nation with an annual percentage growth rate of 7.4, has a fertility rate of over 8.0, while Japan, whose population growth rate is 0.57, has a fertility rate of 1.71.

The land area of the world is finite; few nations are capable of reclaiming the sea as has Holland. One consequence of unequal population growth is unequal population density. Europe has the greatest percentage of its lands in arable crops, followed by the United States, while much of the land in underdeveloped countries with increasing populations is in tropical forests whose potential for agricultural production is severely limited. Pasture and range-lands, used primarily for domestic animals, are most available in Oceania where Australia and New Zealand graze cattle and sheep very efficiently (Table 21-5). African pasture and range-lands are, because of insect-borne diseases of humans and animals, only marginally available. A good deal of the Asian pasture and range is mountainous and suitable for grazing only limited numbers of domestic animals.

It is now abundantly clear that agricultural productivity must continue to increase at a rapid and sustained rate. Grain production will have to increase 2.2 percent yearly and, while this has been achieved since 1965, continued increases cannot be assured. Some idea of the success of agriculture can be seen in the United States, a useful although not perfect model since energy inputs into crop

Table 21-5 DISTRIBUTION OF LAND AREA AND USES OF AVAILABLE LAND, 1983–1985

	Land area (millions of ha)	Population density (people/ha)	Cropland (percent of total)	Meadow/pasture (percent of total)	Forest/woodland (percent of total)
World	14,474	0.36	11	24	31
Africa	2,966	0.50	6	26	23
Asia	2,679	0.20	17	24	21
Europe	473	0.30	30	18	33
Soviet Union	2,227	0.90	10	17	41
North America	2,136	0.76	13	17	32
Canada	922	0.02	5	3	35
United States	918	0.25	21	26	30
South America	1,754	0.48	8	26	53
Oceania	843	2.31	6	55	18

Source: Food and Agriculture Organization, United Nations, Rome.

production are among the highest in the world. In the United States average crop production increased by 40 percent since 1967, a period in which the population increased by 18 percent. On a per capita basis 700 kg (1543 lb) of cereal grain is used within the country each year including the 85 percent of total available grain (mostly maize) fed to animals for meat production. This pattern of cereal and pulse utilization is matched in Europe, Oceania, and Argentina. In most other areas of the world direct human consumption is the major use of the crops. In affluent countries a significant amount of maize and sorghum is also grown for silage. Thus, 104,056 thousand metric tons of maize and 6,472 thousand metric tons of sorghum are grown annually and are not usually calculated in grain/people ratios, although they use productive land and ultimately feed people.

In spite of the signal advances in agricultural technology, some portions of the world are experiencing food shortages sufficiently severe to cause malnutrition, forced migrations, and famine. In part, these result from changes in weather patterns about which little can be done, at least in the short term, although technologies, frequently too costly to be implemented in less developed countries, exist to ameliorate the situation somewhat. There is, now, sufficient agricultural productivity worldwide to feed adequately the present population. Surpluses and hunger exist because food is not distributed on the basis of need and the basic costs of production and distribution cannot be covered by funds available in the needy countries. Almost as serious, overuse and improper cultivation methods have, over centuries, so injured many lands that productivity is drastically reduced. Restoration of the fertility of land is a major problem whose solution, like that of population, is not clearly visible.

Agricultural productivity varies tremendously in time and space. Most of the factors that control productivity are fairly obvious and are almost equally divided between those that are under human control and those that are not. Human intervention to affect conditions caused by weather is very limited. Too little water (drought) and too much water (floods) have been a constant theme in the history of agriculture. Short-term alterations in weather patterns resulting in poor growing conditions are unpredictable, but long-term cycling of weather patterns can be predicted, even if only on a probability basis. Thus, the agriculturist can expect that in the North American southwest, North Africa, and Southeast Asia, drought conditions will occur at fairly regular intervals. This situation of unsatisfactory water supplies has, for centuries, been relieved by irrigation and flood control which, themselves, may have undesirable consequences.

The perils to which crops are exposed seem almost endless (see Chapter 10). Insects and other animals consume planted seed, growing plants, mature fruits, and plant products in storage. Competition from weeds reduces yields. Diseases caused by viruses, bacteria, fungi, and a few flowering plants reduce yields and kill plants. Where funds and knowledge are available, these biotic perils can be controlled if not completely eliminated. The pesticide and fertilizer industries are a vital part of modern agriculture in spite of almost criminal misuse of these chemicals by many people. There is no doubt that without the products of these industries, there would not be enough food produced to feed the present population of the world, much less those soon to be born.

Although grossly oversimplified, total world production of major food crops can be increased by three major routes: increases in good quality arable land, greater efficiency of crop production, and development of new or improved food plants. Virtually all areas of scientific research can, and indeed must, be involved in solving the problems which the seemingly inexorable increases in population have caused. To do so will require massive funding, the education of many additional scientists and support personnel, and the close collaboration of governments. Agricultural productivity also has human components. There is an understandable reluctance of people to alter time-honored techniques and ways of doing things. There will have to be a decision to slow and ultimately to stop the increases in population. And no one thinks that these personal and cultural components can easily be modified.

The matter of increasing good quality arable lands has both political and agronomic aspects. In many countries land is owned or controlled by an oligarchy of wealthy families who desire to obtain as much income as possible with, in some cases, little regard for the land or for the people who work the land. Where expedient and financially advantageous, productive land is removed from cultivation or is diverted into the production of luxury crops. Tenants or sharecroppers have little incentive to improve production or to husband the land and are frequently unable to secure funds to make changes. Land tenure and land reform are political and social aspects of the problem of increasing arable land.

There are many developed and emerging technologies available to improve land quality. Some reclamation practices, including draining swamps, reducing the amount of severely eroded land, and restoring cover and adjacent forests to limit erosion, are being practiced in countries like China and India. Nevertheless, the supply of arable land is and will remain relatively inelastic and a major effort will have to be made to improve the quality of the land now in production. Irrigation of semiarid lands, an ancient practice, has great potential in some areas of the world. Many of the effective techniques have been used by thrifty agriculturists for centuries and some modern methods have simply built upon these ancient ones. Soil and water conservation practices and techniques to reduce nutrient leaching and to restore water-holding capacity have the potential to provide better quality land and to restore poor quality land. Fertilization, greatly improved by recent research, is vital for land improvement.

Enhancing the quality of arable land is, however, not without dangers. Salinization of irrigated lands (see Chapter 5) has increased over time and attempts to reverse it have so far failed. Improperly applied fertilizers and pesticides pollute water courses and are a clear damage to human and animal health. Many of the techniques initially developed for maintaining land quality in temperate climates simply do not work in subtropical and tropical regions and unthinking application of such procedures can do more harm than good.

The second aspect of increasing agricultural productivity is the improvement of the efficiency of crop growth and development. At least part of such improvement is directly related to obtaining and conserving the quality of arable land, but a major consideration in increased efficiency is in the technology used to raise crops. Table 21-6 demonstrates the effect of increasing the technological base of agriculture. Emphasis here is on only one technological unit, the tractor, and two chemical treatments, fertilizers and pesticides. In nations where machinery has not replaced human toil, efficiency is low. Pesticides and fertilizers are most economical and effective when mechanically distributed. Sowing, tilling, and harvesting are all enhanced by efficient machinery designed for particular agricultural situations. Saudi Arabia, a desert nation, can cover the costs of importing most of its food because of its reserves of oil, but this is not true for poor countries. Where new methods such as no-till agriculture are used

Table 21-6 USE OF AGRICULTURAL TECHNOLOGY, 1981–1983

	Irrigated land (percent of cropland)	Fertilizer use (kg/ha cropland)	Pesticide use (ml/ha cropland)	Tractors (no./thousand ha)
World	14	78		15.3
Africa	4	19	130	2.7
Algeria	5	19		8.6
Kenya	0	15		5.0
South Africa	8	87		13.3
Asia	29	71		8.5
China	45	155		8.1
India	23	34	175	2.7
Japan	67	400	12000	6.1
Europe	11	223	2200	63.1
West Germany	4	427		196.7
United Kingdom	2	347		74.7
Soviet Union	8	85		11.4
Middle East	—	—		—
Israel	49	179		63.4
Saudi Arabia	35	72		1.2
Turkey	8	50		17.8
North America	10	83		20.2
Canada	1	43		14.2
Mexico	22	72		6.7
United States	11	94	2200	24.2
South America	6	27	350	4.9
Argentina	5	3		4.3
Brazil	3	37		4.6
Oceania	4	35		9.2
Australia	4	25		7.3
New Zealand	43	1014		207.2

Source: Food and Agriculture Organization, United Nations, Rome.

to conserve water, reduce erosion, and maintain humus levels, there is need for extensive use of herbicides, which are also most efficiently handled mechanically. Agricultural efficiency doesn't end when a crop is harvested. Its storage, transportation, and distribution can be as important as yields. The technology in developed countries may not be effective elsewhere; in many cases the infrastructure of roads and facilities and the whole economic structure of a country become of great significance in determining agricultural efficiency.

Cultivation practices are the focus of a good deal of research. Under certain conditions no-till techniques have been dramatically effective. Modifications in plowing, harrowing, and harvesting have also been shown to enhance growth and raise yields. The advances in knowledge of the metabolic roles of plant growth-regulating chemicals—initially a pure science research area—have been transferred to the field to allow precise regulation of various stages in crop development. Some growth regulators have proved to be virtually irreplaceable for certain crops. The interactions of organic chemists, plant physiologists, and practicing agronomists will continue to benefit agriculture.

For centuries cereal grains were grown from seed whose genetic composition was necessarily varied. Possessing different genotypic and phenotypic attributes and capacities, individual plants might do well or poorly in a given year. Nevertheless, while yields might be reduced, the farmer had a fair chance of bringing in a crop even under adverse conditions. As pure lines with high-yield potential were developed, they became the primary ones used. While this has been generally successful, unexpected climatic or biological stresses can cause devastating losses. There has, consequently, been a trend away from the sole use of highly inbred lines. There has also been deliberate planting of seed with different genotypes in the same field. This heterogeneous cropping technique is effective both in countries where herbicide and insecticide use is high, and in countries where the costs of complete pesticide use are prohibitive.

Another recent innovation is the planting of species mixtures, notably barley and oats, when the cereals are used as animal feed. Costs of production are reduced and the animals seem to grow better with the mixed feed. Alternating rows of different plants—maize and beans or maize and squashes, for example—has an ancient history in the Americas and similar intercropping has been used elsewhere for a variety of crops. This technique is of considerable current research interest.

There are drawbacks to the immediate application of efficient methods of production. Most critical are the start-up costs for machinery, the costs of fuel and maintenance, and the costs and time required to train people to use the equipment and agricultural chemicals. Many countries do not have the financial reserves needed for mechanization. In some areas the land is unsuitable for conventional types of machinery and there is frequently little incentive to produce special machinery when projected sales will be low. Introduction of machinery also has social and cultural implications that must be evaluated not only by trained agricultural people, but also by anthropologists, sociologists, and psychologists who can determine the impact of technology on cultural beliefs and practices. The agricultural economist also has an important role to play.

The third method for increasing food production is developing new or improved food plants. Classical breeding techniques, using germ plasm from related wild plants, as well as newer genetic engineering methods are being used (see Chapter 15). The time needed to develop a new cultivar has been shortened and the ability to obtain a plant with precisely the desired characteristics has been increased. Special care has been given to retaining older cultivars to broaden the base for genetic work. Gene banks have been established for most of our important food plants. Lines of rice, wheat, maize, and the pulses are maintained by international institutes and departments of agriculture throughout the world. The International Rice Institute in the Philippines and the agriculture department of China together maintain many thousands of genetic lines of this cereal.

There has been increasing interest in bringing new plants into cultivation. To a large extent, these are not new agricultural plants, but plants that have been cultivated by isolated groups of people or have fallen out of favor. Grain amaranth *(Amaranthus* spp.) was grown extensively in Mesoamerica over 3000 years ago. Although amaranth is a dicot rather than a cereal, it has considerable potential as a high-protein seed for humans and domestic animals. Similarly, some of the lesser known beans are being evaluated as potentially valuable food sources. Search for grass and legume forage plants has, to date, turned up several that have great potential in subtropical and tropical areas.

CEREAL GRAINS

Wheat

Wheat, a member of the grass family, Gramineae, has been grown as a crop for at least 10,000 years (Chapter 2). Its continued importance to humans as a source of calories and specific nutrients cannot be overemphasized. The earliest wheat was probably einkorn *(Triticum aegilopoides),* a wild wheat with seven pairs of chromosomes. Wild ancestors possessed a brittle rachis, the terminal part of the stem to which the flower-containing structures, spikelets, are attached. This characteristic, an advantage for the natural dispersal of seed, has been bred out of modern wheats to allow efficient harvesting and to minimize loss of grain. Modern wheats, thus, are no longer self-sowing. Through chance as well as deliberate hybridization, there are recognized today several species of wheat based on their chromosome number, number of florets at each node, and other heritable characteristics (see Figure 2-2, Table 21-7). Three species are of commercial importance: *T. aestivum,* common bread wheats; *T. durum,* pasta product wheats; and *T. compactum,* pastry flour wheats. The other species are grown for livestock feed.

The increase in chromosome number from 7 pairs (14 chromosomes) in the diploid group to 21 pairs (42 chromosomes) in the hexaploid wheats has led also to increases in leaf and in grain sizes. New cultivars are continually being

Table 21-7 CHARACTERISTICS OF MAJOR WHEAT (*TRITICUM*) SPECIES

Latin name	Common name	Cultural types	Number of chromosomes	Number of florets at each rachis node	Kernel color
T. monococcum	Einkorn wheat	Winter, spring	14 (diploid)	1	Pale red
T. dicoccum	Emmer wheat	Winter, spring	28 (tetraploid)	2	Red, white
T. durum	Durum wheat	Spring	28 (tetraploid)	3-6	Red, white
T. turgidum	Poulard wheat	Winter, spring	28 (tetraploid)	3-6	Red, white
T. polonicum	Polish wheat	Spring	28 (tetraploid)	3-4	Red, white, amber
T. spelta	Spelt	Winter, spring	42 (hexaploid)	3-5	Pale red
T. compactum	Club wheat	Winter, spring	42 (hexaploid)	5-6	Red, white
T. sphaerococcum	Shot wheat	Spring	42 (hexaploid)	6-7	Red, white
T. aestivum	Bread wheat	Winter, spring	42 (hexaploid)	3-6	Red, white

Soft red winter wheat

Hard red spring wheat

Hard red winter wheat

Durum wheat

Soft white winter wheat

Figure 21-3 Growing areas in the United States of the five market classes of wheat

introduced—there are over 1000 bread wheats alone—that have greater winter hardiness, increased yields, increased resistance to disease, and other desired characteristics to fit particular climatic conditions.

Wheat is produced worldwide. There are cultivars that can be grown in a

Table 21-8 PRODUCTION OF WHEAT, 1984

	Area (thousands of ha)	Yield (kg/ha)	Production (thousands of metric tons)
World	231,869	2,250	521,860
Africa	8,244	1,124	9,267
South Africa	1,820	1,181	2,150
Morocco	1,856	1,072	1,989
Asia	81,762	2,129	176,219
China	29,468	2,975	87,682
India	24,395	1,851	45,148
Europe	27,243	4,719	128,565
France	5,095	6,454	32,884
United Kingdom	1,939	7,715	14,960
Soviet Union	51,061	1,488	76,000
North America	41,369	2,324	96,131
Canada	13,158	1,611	21,199
United States (41 states)	26,771	2,638	70,684
Winter wheat	20,605	2,747	56,050
Spring wheat	4,878	2,407	11,820
Durum wheat	1,288	2,138	2,814
Kansas	2,800	2,618	11,729
North Dakota	2,165	2,230	7,730
South America	8,911	1,866	16,625
Argentina	6,120	2,124	13,000
Brazil	1,736	1,054	1,830
Oceania	12,278	1,537	18,875
Australia	12,214	1,521	18,580

Nations selected to provide some idea of variations in production.
Source: Food and Agriculture Organization, United Nations, Rome, 1984; U.S. Department of Agriculture, *Agricultural Statistics,* Washington, D.C., 1985.

wide variety of climatic conditions in latitudes from 30° north or south to 60° north or south. Wheat is not grown in subtropical areas (from the equator to 30° north or south latitude) because of too warm temperatures and sprouting of grains during preharvest rains. Production data show that Asia is the world leader followed by Europe and North America (Table 21-8). It is the major agronomic crop in both the United States and Canada and is the most widely grown of the cereal grains; 22 percent of the cereal grain area is in wheat compared to 13 percent for rice.

Production areas in the United States for the five market classes of wheat are shown in Figure 21-3. The names of these wheats are defined by the hardness of the grain, the color of the grain, and the growth requirements of the plant, particularly the ability to survive low winter temperatures. These classes are hard red spring, hard red winter, soft red winter, durum, and soft white winter.

Hard red spring wheats, used for bread flours, are planted in the spring in the northern areas of the United States and southern areas of Canada where the winters are too severe for plant survival. They can, however, be planted in the fall in the southwest. The two types of winter wheats are grown in the central United

States. Winter wheat cultivars survive overwintering in the four- to six-leaf stage. The young plant becomes dormant during the winter, resumes growth in the early spring, and is harvested in the early summer. This schedule avoids detrimental high temperatures, summer drought, and late summer diseases. Hard red winter is milled for bread flour and soft red winter is used for cake and pastry flour. Durum wheat, grown in a small area in North and South Dakota, is used primarily for pasta products. White wheat, which is milled into flour for pastry and crackers, is produced in scattered areas, predominantly on the west coast. Hard wheat cultivars contain high total protein levels of 11 to 14 percent and high gluten type protein, while soft wheats have lower total protein and gluten levels.

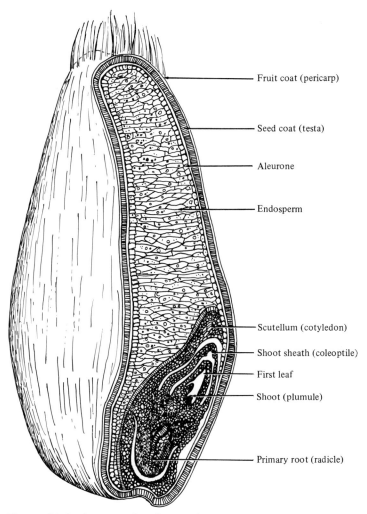

Figure 21-4 Anatomy of a wheat grain

Wheat seed is actually a dry fruit, that is, a grain or caryopsis (Figure 21-4). It germinates between 4° and 37° C (39° to 99° F) with an optimum of 20° to 25° C (68° to 77° F). The large endosperm is a large reserve of nutrients for the growing embryo and seedling and hence permits fast establishment of the plant. The primary root system is capable of penetrating soil to a depth of 2 m (78 in.) if sufficient water is present. The plant may tiller extensively, that is, form new shoots from axillary buds on the main stem. This characteristic is cultivar-dependent and may result in an increase in seed-bearing shoots if each tiller forms an inflorescence (spike). Tillering may also be enhanced by high light intensity and high nitrogen fertilization.

Mature plants vary in height from 0.3 m (12 in.) to 1.5 m (58 in.), but increased fertilization causes the tall cultivars to lodge (to fall over). Dwarf or semidwarf cultivars, in which lodging is less of a problem, are planted more extensively. Since the 1960s the semidwarf cultivar Norin 10 has been planted widely and has also been used as a parent for breeding experiments. Its offspring show an increase in tillering and in the number of fertile flowers in a spike.

Most cultivars of wheat are quantitative long-day plants, flowering sooner the longer the day length (Chapter 9). Winter wheats have an obligatory requirement for vernalization (Chapter 8). Depending upon the cultivar, 42 to 56 days at 3° C (37° F) is most effective. Spring wheats have little or no vernalization requirement, but are more responsive to long days. The number of flowers formed per spike or within a spikelet (individual units on a spike) is under environmental control. High light intensity and high nitrogen levels increase flowering, while shading due to densely tillered stand or high planting density decreases flowering. The individual wheat flower contains three stamens and a pistil and self-pollination is the rule. Cross-pollination is unusual (less than 5 percent) and F_1 hybrids, commonly used in corn cultivation, are difficult to obtain or to maintain.

Wheat is a C_3 plant (Chapter 11). It develops and matures best in cool, moist environments. A day temperature around 26° C (77° F) and a night temperature around 9° C (48° F) are optimum. Other environmental factors that increase grain yields are sufficient moisture, high nitrogen fertilization, and high light intensity. These factors maximize leaf area formed by the plant, particularly the flag leaf (the uppermost leaf on the stem). The longer amount of time available for the photosynthetic process permits increased synthesis of carbohydrate and protein, both of which are eventually translocated to and stored in the maturing grain.

Water, whether from rainfall or irrigation, is required at a level of 25 to 100 cm (10 to 39 in.) annually. The timing of fertilizer application is as important as the amount. Split fertilization gives best results relative to maximum vegetative growth, grain yield, and protein content. Times of application should coincide with leaf expansion, floral initiation, and appearance of the flag leaf.

Wheat is prone to attack by a number of fungi, including the rusts and smuts. Resistant varieties should be planted when available. Unfortunately, mutation of the pathogens is as rapid or more rapid than geneticists can breed for resistance, and genetic modifications for disease resistance are an ongoing requirement for good yields. Seed can be protected against some fungal pathogens by treatment with fungicides, and vegetative plants are sometimes treated during plant development. Insect damage is also a problem. In the eastern United States the Hessian fly can be devastating and wheat is not planted until after the "fly-free" date. Wheat sawfly is a serious pest in the northwestern United States.

Corn (Maize)

Zea Mays—corn, Indian corn, or maize—a plant of New World origin, has been cultivated for at least 7000 years in Mesoamerica (Figure 21-5). North America, particularly the United States, is the leading producer (Table 21-9). Although it is used directly as human food, in North America almost all of the corn is used as a livestock feed crop. Shelled corn, green chop, or silage are of great importance in raising domestic animals.

Corn is a highly productive crop and it is widely grown, but individual cultivars have narrow climatic limits. All are chill sensitive to low temperatures and do not tolerate temperatures below freezing. It responds positively to warmth and high light. Maximum rates of photosynthesis and of development are at 30° to 33° C (86° to 91° F). At 10° C (50° F) both rates are slow. It is the only major cereal possessing the C_4 type of photosynthesis and has a photosynthetic efficiency higher than any C_3 cereal. Corn can be grown in relatively dry climates with 20 to 25 cm (8 to 10 in.) annual rainfall, although it is usually irrigated when natural rainfall is that low.

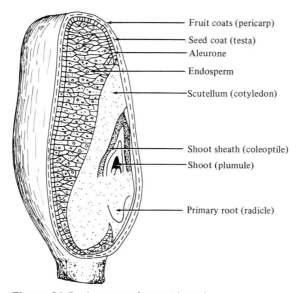

Fruit coats (pericarp)
Seed coat (testa)
Aleurone
Endosperm
Scutellum (cotyledon)
Shoot sheath (coleoptile)
Shoot (plumule)
Primary root (radicle)

Figure 21-5 Anatomy of a corn kernel

Table 21-9   PRODUCTION OF MAIZE, 1984

	Area (thousands of ha)	Yield (kg/ha)	Production (thousands of metric tons)
World	129,627	3,466	449,255
Africa	19,368	1,146	22,201
South Africa	3,953	1,123	4,440
Egypt	760	4,737	3,600
Asia	36,150	2,771	100,157
China	18,901	3,846	72,690
India	6,000	1,292	7,750
Europe	11,429	5,273	60,264
Spain	2,950	4,407	13,000
Yugoslavia	2,360	4,773	11,265
Soviet Union	3,919	3,317	13,000
North America	41,182	5,304	218,437
Canada	1,192	5,894	7,024
United States (41 states)	29,062	6,692	194,475
Maize silage	3,013	7,728	104,000
Iowa	5,160	7,060	29,055
Illinois	4,376	7,240	26,410
South America	17,490	1,990	34,804
Brazil	12,204	1,735	21,174
Argentina	3,025	3,141	9,500
Oceania	98	4,400	392
Australia	63	3,314	210
New Zealand	21	8,309	172

Nations selected to provide some idea of variations in production.
Source: Food and Agriculture Organization, United Nations, Rome, 1984; U.S. Department of Agriculture, *Agricultural Statistics,* Washington, D.C., 1985.

The plant varies in height from 60 cm (24 in.) to 700 cm (264 in.). The stems are thick, but they are not hollow, and relatively lodge-resistant even with high nitrogen fertilizer. Aerial prop roots emerge from stem nodes above ground and if these grow into the soil, they provide extra support for the stem. Tillering has essentially been eliminated through genetic selection and is also inhibited by shading in dense plantings. The total plant population is controlled, therefore, by the seeding rate to establish a specific number of plants per hectare. The total number of plants per hectare reflects the use of the crop, either as silage or grain, and all the environmental parameters that determine final yield.

Unique among the major cereal grains, corn is monoecious. The male flowers form a tassel at the terminal meristem of the stem. The female flowers, the ear or cob, form in a leaf axil midway up the stem and are enclosed by thick leaves called husks. The ovaries form on the central axis of the ear (cob), and the stigma-style apparatus (the silks), emerge from the husks and are wind polli-nated. Cross- or open-pollination occurs naturally and has led to a high degree of genetic variability. More than one ear may form on a stalk, a characteristic that is cultivar-dependent. The ears vary in length from 2.5 cm (1 in.) to almost 1 m (39 in.).

All of the cultivars of corn in current use possess 10 pairs of chromosomes; the diploid number of chromosomes is 20. Until recently, wild lines or species that could be crossed with modern corn were unknown, although there has long been speculation about the ancestors of corn. A breakthrough in the understanding of the genetic background of corn has occurred that can have important consequences for introducing better disease resistance and cold tolerance and even for modifying the annual growth habit of the species. Teosinte *(Z. mexicana),* a tall annual grass species native to Mesoamerica, not only resembles corn, but crosses with it. Teosinte has greater disease resistance than corn. In addition, a perennial teosinte *(Z. diploperennis)* has been discovered that also crosses with corn. These plants have the potential of providing genes that may permit the development of corn capable of high production by allowing more than one crop to be grown in each growing season.

When grown for silage, the stems, leaves, and any ears are chopped. The high carbohydrate level of the plant is readily fermented to give a silage high in organic acids that increase the acidity of the chopped material to pH 3.8 to 4.0. This low pH and high organic acid content are preservatives that allow the silage to be stored for long periods of time.

Modern hybrids, cultivars with greater yields per hectare, greater disease resistance, and higher total protein in the grain, result from controlled pollination. The procedure requires breeding of superior male and female inbred lines. When these are deliberately crossed (controlled pollination), the F_1 progeny are usually more vigorous and higher yielding than the parents, the condition called heterosis or hybrid vigor. Hybrid seed must be produced each year by preventing natural cross-pollination. This is achieved by removal of the male tassel from the plant and pollinating the silks with pollen from the male inbred line. Male sterile lines have been developed which obviates the detasseling step. The maintenance of inbred lines and yearly production of hybrid seed require an expensive infrastructure. Less developed countries cannot usually afford this, and their corn is open-pollinated and usually much less productive.

Corn is classified commercially into seven types: flint, dent, floury, pop, sweet, waxy, and pod (Figure 21-6). Flint cultivars have hard endosperms and the seed stores well. This type was grown by North American Indians when the first Europeans arrived. Dent has both hard and soft endosperm; the soft center of the grain dents as the seed dries. This is the principal type grown for grain and for animal fodder and silage. Floury seed has a soft endosperm which is easily ground into flour. Pop cultivars have a hard endosperm resembling flint, which explodes or pops when heated. Sweet cultivar seeds are wrinkled and glassy, and the endosperm is sweet. Waxy corn is used for food processing. Pod corn is almost exclusively ornamental; each kernel on the cob is covered by a leaf, called the glume, making the ear more similar in appearance to other types of cereal inflorescences.

Sweet corn, the major type of corn eaten directly, is harvested when the kernels are immature—juicy, tender, and sweet. The endosperm is still milky and has not hardened. Standard sweet corn has a gene that inhibits the

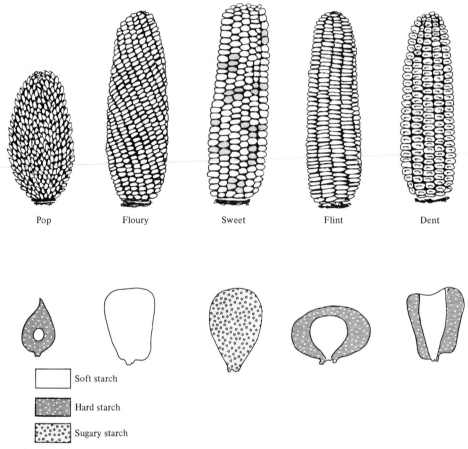

| Pop | Floury | Sweet | Flint | Dent |

☐ Soft starch

▦ Hard starch

⣿ Sugary starch

Figure 21-6 Major corn types and kinds of starch stored in endosperm of kernels

conversion in the endosperm of sucrose sugar to starch. If the ears are refrigerated after harvesting, the corn will be sweet for about 24 hours. Super-sweet cultivars have an additional gene that programs for a higher sugar content than standard as well as a slower rate of sucrose to starch conversion. These ears can be refrigerated for 5 to 10 days before they lose their sweetness.

Rice

The origin of rice is not at all clear. It is known to have been grown in India and China at least 5000 years ago. Rice today is second only to wheat in importance in feeding the earth's hungry human population. Countries of Asia are the leading producers, with South America a distant second (Table 21-10). Of the rice grown worldwide, almost all of it is consumed directly by people.

Rice is the only major crop that is predominantly grown in standing water. These cultivars are referred to as lowland rice. The root system is continuously

Table 21-10   PRODUCTION OF RICE, 1984

	Area (thousands of ha)	Yield (kg/ha)	Production (thousands of metric tons)
World	147,519	3,186	469,959
Africa	5,008	1,713	8,582
Egypt	420	5,310	2,230
Madagascar	1,200	1,777	2,130
Asia	132,572	3,268	433,197
China	34,346	5,271	181,028
India	42,800	2,126	91,000
Europe	378	5,189	1,959
Italy	178	5,770	1,027
Spain	73	5,986	437
Soviet Union	688	3,634	2,500
North America	1,934	4,406	8,121
Mexico	204	3,106	635
United States (6 states)[a]	1,126	5,520	6,216
California	172	7,920	2,404
Arkansas	108	5,175	1,376
South America	6,815	2,134	14,542
Brazil	5,356	1,685	9,023
Colombia	346	4,658	1,696
Oceania	124	5,305	658
Australia	113	5,596	635

Nations selected to provide some idea of variations in production.
[a]70 percent long grain, 20 percent medium grain, 1 percent short grain.
Source: Food and Agriculture Organization, United Nations, Rome; U.S. Department of Agriculture, *Agricultural Statistics,* Washington, D.C., 1985.

submerged; the oxygen requirement of the roots is met through air-filled tissue between the aerial leafy part of the plant and the roots. Some cultivars, called upland rice, are adapted to dry land cultivation, but their yields are lower than the paddy-grown rices. The fertile river basins and deltas of subtropical, tropical, and warm temperate areas are the major sites of production. Rice is generally adapted to regions of high temperature, although it has a C_3 type of photosynthesis. Cold-tolerant cultivars are becoming available, extending the range of growing areas to cool mountainous regions in the tropics and in temperate zones. Of all the cereals, rice has the greatest genetic potential to adapt to a wider range of environmental conditions.

There are two major rice species, each with 12 pairs of chromosomes. *Oryza glaberrima* is grown now only in West Africa. *O. sativa* has two biotypes. The indica biotyope is cold-intolerant and is the traditional rice grown in the tropics. The more cold-tolerant japonica biotype is more widely grown throughout the world. Japonica cultivars usually produce short grains, while indica are the long grain types. Plant height for rice cultivars varies from 40 to 700 cm (16 to 275 in.) with 100 cm (39 in.) considered optimum for lowland, paddy cultivars.

The inflorescence is a panicle and the self-pollinated individual flowers

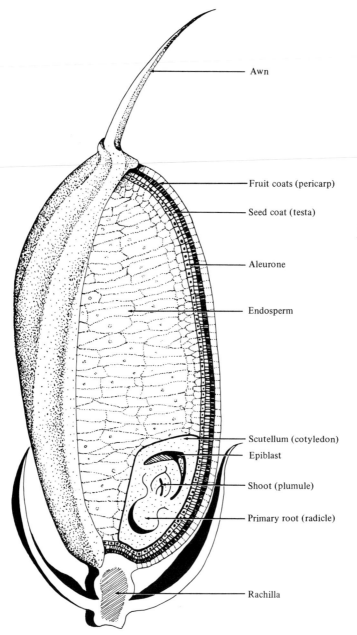

Figure 21-7 Anatomy of a rice grain

contain one pistil and six stamens. Hybrids are not easily obtained. Intensive genetic breeding between indica and japonica biotypes was successfully brought to fruition in 1966 with the introduction of the first of the Green Revolution miracle cereals. The hybrid IR8 combined the best characteristics of the two biotypes. Indica rice, with tall, weak stems that lodge readily, but large numbers of tillers, was hybridized with japonica rice which is resistant to lodging because it is short, responds well to fertilization, has low tillering capacity, and is susceptible to many diseases. The hybrid IR8 is semidwarf, with thick, sturdy, lodge-resistant stems, has upright leaves to maximize light interception for photosynthesis, has high tillering capacity, and yields well if supplied with high levels of nitrogen fertilizer. Most rice cultivars are basically short-day plants, but the new hybrids are day neutral allowing more than one crop per year to be grown. There are now a number of new rice cultivars adapted for various growing and climatic conditions.

In tropical areas rice can be treated as a perennial and ratoon-cropped. (A ratoon is a crop produced on a shoot of a perennial plant or sometimes the shoot itself.) Following the first harvest, basal buds on the stems grow out and flower to yield a second harvest. This eliminates the labor and expense of reseeding. In most parts of the world rice is hand-planted using 3-week-old seedlings. In the United States rice cultivation is totally mechanized from seeding to harvesting.

Kernels of rice are 80 percent starch and 6 to 8 percent protein. It does not contain the gluten proteins and leavened bread cannot be made with rice flour. White rice is white because the brown-colored bran, the fruit coats (pericarp) derived from the ovary wall, and the embryo are removed by milling (Figure 21-7). This results in a lower protein content. Brown rice has less of the bran and embryo removed and retains more of the natural protein.

Sorghum

Although sorghum is usually considered to have first been domesticated in sub-Saharan Africa, including modern Ethiopia, Chad, and the Sudan, there were independent centers of domestication in India and Pakistan. African cultivation occurred some 5000 years ago. There are many wild species and literally thousands of hybrids among the cultivated species. Many cultivated and gathered types are locally developed, well adapted for particular growing conditions. For convenience, and perhaps out of desperation, cultivated sorghums are all placed in the same species, *Sorghum bicolor*. At least two other species, Sudan grass *(S. Sudanese)* and Johnson grass *(S. halepense)* are interfertile with *S. bicolor* and are grown as forage grasses, although they become persistent weeds if given half a chance.

Four types of sorghum are recognized on the basis of their growth habits and their economic uses: grass, broomcorn, sweet, and grain. Grass sorghums, including Sudan and Johnson grasses, are grown as pasture plants and harvested for hay, green chop, and silage. Many lines contain hydrocyanic (prussic) acid and livestock are not allowed to forage until the plants are at least 50 cm (20 in.) tall.

Broomcorn sorghums are harvested before full maturity and the long, fibrous flower panicles are made into stiff whiskbrooms.

Sweet sorghums are sometimes called *S. bicolor* var. *saccharatum.* The stalks, growing to 4 m (13 ft), are succulent and their cell sap is high in sucrose. Stems are crushed and the sugar concentrated with heat. The sugar is usually not crystallized, but is prepared as a syrup or molasses used directly or fermented into a strong beer (see Chapter 10). Sweet sorghums are extensively grown in the American South for forage and silage.

Grain sorghums include a number of well-defined cultivar groups including the kafir grains, milo, hegari, and durra. Within the grain sorghums are a number of races selected for cultivation in different climatic conditions. They interbreed freely so that the plant geneticist has a broad range of genetic characteristics from which to select.

All sorghums share several characteristics of agronomic importance. Like corn, they photosynthesize through the C_4 pathway so that they develop well in hot climates and show high vegetative and reproductive efficiency. Sorghums are usually drought-tolerant. Many are capable of maturing a crop with less than 25 cm (10 in.) of water. Leaf and root characteristics allow this high water-use efficiency. Leaves have a waxy bloom and can roll tightly to conserve water. The wax can be removed and used industrially. Sorghums have extensive fibrous root systems to exploit soil water and nutrient reserves with root-to-shoot ratios strongly skewed toward root biomass. Like corn, sorghums form prop roots and lodging is reduced. All are capable of growth in infertile soils, although they

Table 21-11 PRODUCTION OF SORGHUM, 1984

	Area (thousands of ha)	Yield (kg/ha)	Production (thousands of metric tons)
World	49,004	1,463	71,698
Africa	15,328	587	9,002
Nigeria	6,000	500	3,000
Sudan	3,500	414	1,450
Asia	20,795	1,048	21,787
India	16,500	715	11,800
China	2,703	3,157	8,532
Europe	158	3,486	550
France	58	4,414	256
Italy	22	4,703	105
Soviet Union	152	1,316	200
North America	8,717	3,366	29,345
United States (23 states)	6,211	3,541	21,994
Sorghum silage	244	23,744	14,497
Kansas	1,700	3,238	5,501
Nebraska	760	4,065	3,086
South America	3,115	2,867	8,930
Argentina	2,370	3,101	7,350
Colombia	264	2,282	602
Oceania	740	2,584	1,885
Australia	738	2,584	1,880
Fiji	1	4,000	3

Nations selected to provide some idea of variations in production.
Source: Food and Agriculture Organization, United Nations, Rome, 1984; U.S. Department of Agriculture, *Agricultural Statistics,* Washington, D.C., 1985.

respond well to fertilization. Sorghum productivity in the United States, a home for sorghum only since about 1850, is high (Table 21-11).

As human or animal food, grain sorgums are nutritious, with protein content up to 15 percent and in some new cultivars up to 25 percent, with good ratios of essential amino acids. The elastic gluten proteins are not produced. The grain is boiled into gruels or milled into flour used to bake flat breads. It is sometimes popped like popcorn and covered with sorghum molasses.

The semitropical, arid-land sorghums are very chill sensitive. Germination is best at 23° C (73° F), and flower formation and maturation can occur at temperatures up to 35° C (95° F). The plants tiller readily, but excessive tiller development delays maturation. Most grain sorghums are tall plants, up to 6 m (20 ft) in height; dwarf cultivars are less than half this height and have a more favorable ratio of grain to stover (stalks and leaves). Traditional cultivars, and most of those grown in the United States, are short-day plants with a critical photoperiod of 10 hours. A few semi-long-day lines with greater chill tolerances are grown in the Dakotas and Nebraska.

The inflorescence is a compact panicle containing perfect and imperfect (mostly staminate) spikelets, each bearing a single flower. Although there is no barrier to cross-pollination, and male-sterile lines exist, sorghums are usually self-pollinated. Fruit maturation is rapid; this characteristic is being enhanced by breeding to allow adequate time in northern climates for maturation of the grain.

Agronomists believe that the grain and sweet sorghums have importance for development of food supplies in dry, hot lands with infertile soils. Improvements in growth characteristics obtained to date and the establishment in Mexico of a gene pool bank will undoubtedly permit rapid genetic research on this highly useful species.

SMALL CEREAL GRAINS

Barley

Barley is one of the more ancient of cultivated cereals. It was being grown in the Fertile Crescent 9,000 to 10,000 years ago, some centuries before wheat was domesticated. It fed the slaves who built the pyramids of Egypt and sustained the wandering Israelites. Barley reached the New World in 1554 when the Spanish brought it to Mexico and California and it became established in New England in 1602. The Atlantic coastal region proved to be an unsatisfactory growing region and, as the United States and Canada marched westward, barley was carried to the Great Basin region between Illinois and the foothills of the Rockies where it is now a major cereal grain crop.

There are about 25 closely related species in the genus *Hordeum* of which only one, *H. vulgare,* is grown as a cereal. The primitive barleys were two-rowed forms in which the kernels were borne in two lines on the rachis. Four- and six-rowed types developed later through selection and uncontrolled cross-fertilization. Within each of the row types there are cultivars that are hull-less

Table 21-12 PRODUCTION OF BARLEY, 1984

	Area (thousands of ha)	Yield (kg/ha)	Production (thousands of metric tons)
World	78,581	2,184	171,635
Africa	4,786	766	3,665
Morocco	2,126	661	1,405
Algeria	900	653	588
Asia	10,993	1,453	15,985
Cyprus	1,201	2,499	3,000
United Arab Emirate	3,250	2,000	6,500
Europe	18,696	4,250	79,452
West Germany	2,113	5,463	11,543
Switzerland	53	5,911	311
Soviet Union	30,426	1,380	42,000
North America	9,388	2,543	23,876
Canada	4,546	2,250	10,252
United States (29 states)	4,468	22,910	12,968
North Dakota	1,160	2,875	3,341
Idaho	536	3,598	1,922
South America	475	1,260	599
Argentina	110	1,514	167
Peru	89	1,075	96
Oceania	3,818	1,587	6,059
Australia	3,695	1,480	5,470
New Zealand	123	4,795	589

Nations selected to provide some idea of variations in production.
Sources: Food and Agriculture Organization, United Nations, Rome, 1984; U.S. Department of Agriculture, *Agricultural Statistics,* Washington, D.C., 1985.

and others in which the hulls are either loosely or firmly attached to the grain. Most barleys have long bristles, called awns or beards, although this structure has been eliminated in some lines used as animal feed.

In the United States it is the fourth most important cereal after wheat, corn, and sorghum, and it is second in importance in Canada after wheat (Table 21-12).

In both countries close to half the crop is fed to swine and poultry or used to finish feedlot cattle. Most of the rest of the crop grown in North America is used for malting, but in Europe the proportions for feed and for malt are reversed. Only about 3 percent of the barley is used for human food. Breakfast cereals and malted products account for most of the food barley. In North Africa, the Near East, the Soviet Union, and parts of Asia, pearled barley (freed of hulls and the outer layers of the kernel by milling) is eaten like rice, boiled into gruels, or milled for flour. Since the plant does not synthesize the elastic proteins, the bread is flat; the bannock bread of Scotland and Ireland is an unleavened barley product baked on a griddle. Nutritionally, barley has about the same protein levels as wheat. New cultivars have improved levels of the essential amino acid lysine.

The drought- and salt-tolerances of barley are outstanding, allowing crops to be harvested in semiarid North Africa and in drought-prone regions of Asia. Barley is usually the only successful cereal crop in saline or sodic soils (see Chapter 5) and it can be irrigated with salty water. Irrigation of the lands in the Middle East where wheat originated resulted in saline soils incapable of growing wheat, and barley is now grown there. While capable of developing in infertile soils, it responds well to fertilization. Optimum soil pH is above 6.5; in soils in which aluminum toxicities are common, liming is absolutely necessary to raise the pH of the soil solution above the pH value where aluminum remains in solution.

Both winter and spring barley cultivars are grown. Spring cultivation starts in March through June depending on soil temperatures; grains will germinate at 3° to 5° C (37° to 41° F), but temperatures of 5° to 10° C (41° to 50° F) are needed for good seedling development. Spring barley will mature in two to three months after sowing since it requires fewer heat units (see Chapter 8) than other cereals. Winter barley requires vernalization (see Chapter 8), although it needs shorter periods at low temperature than the more winter-hardy wheats or rye. Because of the lower winter hardiness of barley, it is usually sown several weeks earlier than winter wheat. Winter-hardy barley is frequently rotated with corn or soybean, usually planted when corn is harvested and harvested immediately before soy must be planted.

Barley is photoperiodic. Long days are required and almost all cultivars must mature before frost. The critical photoperiod varies with the cultivar. Fortunately, the time required between flower induction and ripening is short compared with other cereal grains. Tillering, however, is repressed by long-day conditions and tillers tend to be shorter than the primary axis even though the grain heads mature synchronously. Attempts are being made to develop day-neutral cultivars to extend the growing range of the plant, although its limited cold-resistance would prevent it from being grown in far northern regions of Canada.

The barleys grown for malting are genotypically different from those grown for food grain. Lines with hulls are used for malt because the kernels are protected from damage and their sprouting is more regular.

The plant crosses readily within the species and there are several intergeneric hybrids with wheat. Increasing productivity by shortening the time to maturation of winter barley, raising the cold tolerance, and improving nutritional value are all necessary for raising the value of barley as a crop.

Rye

Rye *(Secale cereale)* has been cultivated for about 5000 years, a shorter time than the other major cereal grain crops. It apparently originated in southwestern Asia from *S. montanum* or *S. anatolicum.* Modern rye is a cultivated species and has not been found in the wild. It is likely that for some centuries it was a weed in wheat fields and was grown as a separate crop only when it was carried into Europe. It was known to the Greeks, but attained its greatest importance as a

Table 21-13   PRODUCTION OF RYE, 1984

	Area (thousands of ha)	Yield (kg/ha)	Production (thousands of metric tons)
World	17,357	1,793	31,126
Africa	40	279	11
South Africa	38	273	9
Morocco	2	1,048	2
Asia	933	1,958	1,943
China	700	2,143	1,500
Turkey	250	1,440	360
Europe	5,941	2,866	17,025
Poland	3,545	2,691	9,540
West Germany	700	3,386	2,300
Soviet Union	9,420	1,115	10,500
North America	767	1,938	1,487
United States (26 states)	397	2,073	823
South Dakota	108	2,540	432
Minnesota	70	2,412	266
Canada	370	1,795	664
South America	171	874	150
Argentina	160	875	140
Chile	3	1,294	4
Oceania	26	417	11
Australia	25	400	10
New Zealand	1	2,500	1

Nations selected to provide some idea of variations in production.
Source: Food and Agriculture Organization, United Nations, Rome, 1984; U.S. Department of Agriculture, *Agricultural Statistics,* Washington, D.C., 1985.

grain crop in Russia and northern Europe. North American production is relatively small (Table 21-13).

The kernels contain the elastic proteins that permit leavening, but less than wheat flours. European rye breads are dark, heavy, somewhat bitter, and very nutritious, since rye flour is used alone or with only a small proportion of wheat flour. North American rye breads may contain equal proportions of rye and wheat flours and are much lighter in color and texture. Rye is a feed grain in both Europe and North America. The stalks of rye are long, up to 1 m (39 in.), tough, and fibrous; they are used for thatching or are woven into hats and handbags. Alcoholic fermentation yields both a heavy beer and rye whiskey.

Both spring and winter cultivars are grown, although almost all of the rye is now from winter cultivars; spring cultivars have lower yields and are less cold-tolerant than winter lines. Winter rye is among the most cold hardy of the cereals. It germinates at 1° C (33° F) and can mature at 12° C (55° F). It is grown above 53° north latitude and at 4,300 m (14,400 ft) above sea level in the Himalayan Mountains. Rye can produce a crop in poor soils, although it responds well to fertilization. Its optimum pH is close to 6.0, but it will mature in soils with pH values as low as 4.5 or as high as 8.0.

Like winter wheats and barleys, winter rye requires vernalization for 40 to

55 days at 4° C (40° F). It is a long-day plant with a 14-hour critical photoperiod, but since it matures quickly after pollination and fertilization, seed filling usually occurs before killing frosts. Flowers are almost entirely cross-pollinated; the plant is effectively self-sterile and few pure line cultivars are available. The fruiting head is an elongated spike with three-flowered spikelets.

Rye is very susceptible to infection by *Claviceps purpurea,* the fungus whose reproductive structure, a sclerotium, causes ergotism in humans and animals.

The high cold tolerance, ability to grow in poor soils, drought resistance, and good nutritional qualities suggest that improvements in growth characteristics related to yields and disease resistance can significantly increase the economic potential of rye.

Triticale

It is almost unprecedented to be able to follow with precision the invention of a new economic plant. Although it was known in 1875 that rye and wheat would occasionally interbreed, it was not until 1918 that Soviet agronomists obtained fertile hybrids from crosses of these two genera. Studies were continued in Germany and Sweden between 1935 and 1937, and in 1945 a breeding project was initiated at the University of Manitoba. The new cereal, named triticale *(XTriticosecale),* has either the genetic complements of both tetraploid wheat and diploid rye to form the hexaploid or modified genomes of hexaploid wheat and hexaploid rye to form the octaploid.

The ideal cross between wheat and rye should combine the valuable characteristics of both including high yields, the cold hardiness of rye, the tillering ability of wheat, high disease resistance, high nutritional levels, and the leavening ability of wheat. To date, however, these hopes have not been completely realized in triticale. While protein levels can be up to 22 percent and there are genetic lines with broad ranges of adaptability to temperature extremes, triticale has a high water requirement, a need for high amounts of fertilizer, and, with fewer kernels per head, relatively low yields. It is being grown in eastern Europe and the Soviet Union, but has not achieved significant economic importance in North America. Among major problems that still have to be solved are the tendency to lodge, poor seed set, spike shattering, grain wrinkling, and disease susceptibility. At present triticale finds its greatest use as a minor feed grain.

Oats

Oats was probably the last of the cereal grains to be domesticated in the eastern Mediterranean region. Most botanists date this domestication to 3000 years ago. The Greeks knew it as a weed in wheat fields and it entered central Europe as a contaminant in harvested wheat. Romans grew it as feed for military horses and scorned the Germans and the Celts for eating it. It was grown in northern Europe as food for domestic animals and, in times of necessity, it was eaten by people.

Table 21-14 PRODUCTION OF OATS, 1984

	Area (thousands of ha)	Yield (kg/ha)	Production (thousands of metric tons)
World	25,526	1,698	43,355
Africa	647	391	253
South Africa	400	193	77
Algeria	115	600	69
Asia	754	1,480	1,116
China	430	1,279	550
Turkey	172	1,837	316
Europe	4,675	3,188	14,903
Poland	934	2,787	2,604
Greece	550	3,753	2,083
Soviet Union	12,806	1,171	15,000
North America	4,794	2,007	9,620
United States (36 states)	3,287	2,084	6,850
North Dakota	1,160	2,875	3,341
Idaho	536	3,598	1,922
Canada	1,406	1,899	2,670
South America	692	1,354	937
Argentina	414	1,427	591
Chile	96	1,694	163
Oceania	1,168	1,317	1,525
Australia	1,145	1,284	1,470
New Zealand	13	4,129	55

Nations selected to provide some idea of variations in production.
Source: Food and Agriculture Organization, United Nations, Rome, 1984; U.S. Department of Agriculture, *Agricultural Statistics,* Washington, D.C., 1985.

Few contemporary cultures use it as a primary cereal grain, although it has a minor role as a cooked breakfast cereal. Oats was introduced into North America in 1602 as horse feed, but as American farms became mechanized, the use of oats decreased and the plant is now a minor component of the cereal markets of the world (Table 21-14).

The origin of cultivated oats, *Avena sativa,* is something of a mystery. It has been postulated that it is a mutant of wild oats, *A. fatua,* still present in Asia Minor, but cytogenetic studies have indicated that cultivated oats is polyphyletic (derived from more than one wild progenitor) with several species in the genus contributing to the cultivated plant.

Both winter and spring types are available. Winter-planted oats is grown in the American South at latitudes below that of Missouri. Most of the North American oats are spring-planted cultivars. Because of its hollow stem, it is more prone to lodging than some other cereals. The plant is induced to flower by short days, but there is some possibility of obtaining day-neutral lines that would be useful in extending its growing range. Oats is self-pollinated and the branched panicle may either have all spikelets on the same side of the panicle or spreading toward all sides. The grain has the protein level of barley. Oats is less tolerant to temperature variations, poor or saline soils, and low water supplies than barley, and it seems likely that barley will continue to replace oats as a feed grain.

Table 21-15 SOME OF THE MORE COMMON CULTIVATED MILLETS

Latin name	Common name	Uses
Echinochloa crus-galli	Japanese barnyard millet	Food
E. colona	Shama millet	Food
Eleusine coracana	Finger millet, ragi	Food
Eragrostis Tef	Teff	Food
E. lehmanniana	Lovegrass	Forage
Panicum miliaceum	Broomcorn millet, proso, hog millet	Food, forage
P. maximum	Guineagrass	Pasture
P. obtusum	Vine mesquite	Pasture
P. purpurascens	Paragrass	Pasture
P. ramosum	Brown-top millet	Forage
P. texanum	Texas millet	Pasture
P. virgatum	Switchgrass	Pasture
Paspalum dilatatum	Dallisgrass	Forage, lawns
P. notatum	Bahia grass	Pasture, lawns
Pennisetum americanum	Pearl millet, bajra, cattail millet	Food
P. clandestinum	Kikuyu grass	Forage
P. purpureum	Elephant grass	Forage
Setaria italica	Foxtail millet	Food

Millets

The millets, including species in 8 to 10 genera with over 25 cultivated species (Table 21-15), are of great agronomic importance in semiarid, subtropical to tropical areas of the world. In agricultural commerce they are considered to be minor cereal and forage crops (Table 21-16), but such statistics conceal their importance. In underdeveloped countries the food millets are frequently all that

Table 21-16 PRODUCTION OF MILLETS, 1984

	Area (thousands of ha)	Yield (kg/ha)	Production (thousands of metric tons)
World	42,351	729	30,869
Africa	15,731	566	8,907
Nigeria	5,000	600	3,000
Mali	1,250	640	800
Asia	23,814	822	19,566
India	18,500	638	11,800
China	3,902	1,692	6,604
Europe	16	1,922	30
Portugal	6	1,613	10
France	1	4,354	6
Soviet Union	2,640	833	2,200
North America	—	—	—
South America	114	1,196	136
Argentina	114	1,196	136
Oceania	36	836	30
Australia	36	836	30

Nations selected to provide some idea of variations in production.
Source: Food and Agriculture Organization, United Nations, Rome, 1984; U.S. Department of Agriculture, *Agricultural Statistics,* Washington, D.C., 1985.

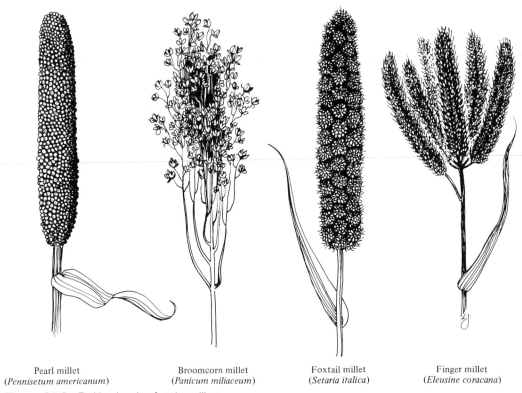

Pearl millet   Broomcorn millet   Foxtail millet   Finger millet
(*Pennisetum americanum*)   (*Panicum miliaceum*)   (*Setaria italica*)   (*Eleusine coracana*)

Figure 21-8 Fruiting heads of major millets

stands between a reasonable diet and starvation, particularly in drought years. In North America and Europe they are grown primarily as forage crops.

There is little consensus on the places of domestication of most of the millets or on the routes and dates of their intercontinental dispersions. Some species may be of worldwide natural distribution, domesticated independently by different human societies. Analysis is complicated by their ability to hybridize readily with related species. Both natural hybrids and hybrids within cultivated lines have been found (Figure 21-8). *Pennisetum americanum,* pearl millet, has been found in archeological sites in the Tehuacan Valley of Mexico dated from 5000 years B.P., but its cultivation declined as corn became the predominant cereal grain. *Panicum miliaceum,* the broomcorn millet, may have been one of the five sacred grains (wheat, rice, common millet, glutinous millet, and soy) of ancient China where it is still cultivated. *Setaria italica,* the foxtail millet, is from sub-Saharan Africa and is also known as a prehistoric cultivated plant of the Middle East and the Mediterranean basin where it may have predated wheat. *Eleusine coracana,* finger millet, is an East African native that was first cultivated in tropical, dry highlands.

There are several reasons for the success of millets in dry, hot regions. They utilize the C_4 pathway for carbon fixation in photosynthesis. *Panicum* is particularly noteworthy because it has both the C_3 and the C_4 routes. Linked with

C_4 metabolism are a reduction in photorespiration, which allows the accumulation of biomass, and well-developed structural and functional mechanisms for water conservation. Pearl millet can mature in India or central Africa with less than 30 cm (13 in.) of water. While adapted for growth with minimal water, millets develop more quickly, grow larger, and mature more rapidly with water supplies closer to those used by sorghum, but less than those needed for corn.

Where available, fertilizers dramatically increase grain and forage yields. Nitrogen fertilization can more than triple grain yields. Even without added nitrogen, root-associated, free-living bacteria are capable of fixing up to 40 kg nitrogen/ha (38 lb nitrogen/acre), almost a tenth of the optimum nitrogen requirements of the plant. Root systems are fibrous and are capable of deep penetration into well-watered loams or sandy soils.

Considerable differences are found in the patterns of vegetative and reproductive growth of various millets. Tillering is common, but it is not usually extensive, and when grown for grain, several harvestings are needed because the tillers do not mature synchronously. Growth rates also vary. Several lines have been isolated that will grow to only 1 or 1.5 m (39 to 60 in.) instead of over 3 m (11 ft). These offer promise for breeding millets that might be counterparts of the Green Revolution rices and wheats. Many millets can be crossed with other species in the same genus or, occasionally, with related genera to form triploid plants with greatly increased seed production. There are now several F_1 hybrid lines of pearl millet that produce up to 10,000 kg/ha (9,000 lb/acre).

Many millets are photoperiodic. Pearl millets are short-day plants with a critical photoperiod of 12 hours, but a few other millets are facultative short-day plants, and one line is reported to be day neutral. The short-day cultivars are best for forage. In North America they usually fail to mature fruit heads because final grain ripening is slow after flower induction and the chill-sensitive plants are killed back by even light frosts.

Nutritionally, grain millets have a fairly uniform food value. All have moderate protein levels, about those of rice. Lacking the elastic proteins, millets are eaten like rice or the flour is baked into flat breads. Today, grain millet production is mostly in central Africa and India, with some cultivation in China. The forage millets are grown as annual plants harvested as hay or for silage. They do well in association with forage legumes or other forage grasses. They have been planted in many areas of southern North America.

Grain millets have just begun to receive the research interest of agronomists and plant breeders and the potential for their improvement is great. Their drought and heat resistance, good yields with minimum fertilization, acceptance by people in many cultures, and relative ease of cultivation suggest that they will become increasingly important as food and forage plants.

Wild Rice

Compared with other cereal crops, wild rice is economically insignificant. It may well be an epicurean delight for gourmets with considerable discretionary income, but its inclusion here reflects the interest in following the domestication of a wild plant. For about 6000 years the American Indians of Minnesota and adjacent Canada gathered wild rice, but did not cultivate it.

Wild rice is usually classified as *Zizania aquatica,* although it is sometimes classified as *Z. palustris.* Three subspecies are recognized. The food grain subspecies is *Z. a. angustifolia.* Two other subspecies, *Z. a. interior* and *Z. a. brevis,* grow in tidal waters, tributary streams, and marshes along the Atlantic coast and inland waters, but are not used for human food. They are, however, important food chain components of aquatic ecosystems.

Wild rice is not closely related to common rice, although it shares many characteristics common to most members of the grass family. Like common rice, it grows in aquatic habitats. It is an annual reaching 150 to 300 cm (10 to 15 ft) with fibrous root systems deeply imbedded in the mud at the bottom of ponds and lakes. Stems are weak because they contain many air spaces to keep the plant buoyant; lodging is a serious problem. The plant is monoecious, flowering in July through August, and it can be either self- or cross-pollinated. The grain, a caryopsis like other cereals, sinks to the bottom of the lake where it remains dormant during the six- to eight-month winter period. There is some evidence that vernalization may be required.

On Indian reservations in Minnesota and Ontario, the Chippewa people traditionally, and now by law, harvest wild rice by poling a canoe into stands of the plant and knocking the ripe heads into the boat. The process is very inefficient; yields rarely exceed 60 to 80 kg/ha (55 to 75 lb/acre) and much of the grain falls back into the lake. Most of the wild rice sold today is harvested by this method, although modern machinery has replaced the crude cleaning processes.

Since 1950 attempts have been made to use paddy cultivation techniques so successful with true rice. Ultimately, it is hoped to grow wild rice under controlled conditions so that at maturity paddies can be drained to allow efficient mechanical harvesting. Growers face several difficulties that limit production of paddy-grown wild rice. Mature heads are prone to shattering, but one strain shows reduced shattering. Under natural conditions maturation is not synchronous and the traditional harvester has to harvest several times during a growing season. Considerable variation in productivity is found under natural conditions. In addition to a broad array of insect pests and fungal disease that limit production, red-winged blackbirds apparently share the gourmet's liking for the grain, a freshwater shrimp eats submerged seedlings, and both carp and muskrats eat the roots. Anthropogenic acidification of lakes has already reduced yields, since *Zizania* flourishes only at water pH values of 7.5 to 8.5. Nevertheless, a few growers have obtained yields exceeding 1200 kg/ha (1000 lb/acre).

FORAGE GRASSES

"Black and white cows eat green grass, give white milk and yellow butter, and provide red meat." So do goats, sheep, camels, and giraffes. These animals are all ruminants with complex stomachs in which microorganisms break down (hydrolyze) the complex carbohydrates in forage grasses into metabolically useful sugars. Horses and zebras, rabbits and other rodents, and the other grass-eating animals have simpler stomachs and associated gut structures in which the same microbial-assisted hydrolyses occur.

The word forage is usually restricted to those plants, almost exclusively members of the grass or the legume families, growing in pastures, in meadows, or on open ranges and browsed or grazed or harvested for animal food. The importance of forage crops cannot be overemphasized. More land is in permanent pasture or meadow than is devoted to any other crop. In addition to their importance as forage, the grasses and legumes are vital for land conservation, used as cover to prevent wind or water erosion, to provide organic matter for soil building (see Chapter 5), and to utilize lands that are otherwise unsuitable for agriculture. Estimates of forage acreage, production, and value are low since much of the forage is grown and consumed locally. Worldwide at least 3 billion hectares (7 to 8 billion acres) are in permanent pasture, range, or meadow. The economic value of the domestic animals raised entirely or partly on forage in the United States alone exceeds $30 billion annually. In North America over half the protein consumed by people is from animal products and about 60 percent of the total feed for these animals is derived from forage.

Historically, grazing lands were unmanaged. The rangelands in North America are an excellent example. In much of Africa and Asia as well as in parts of North and South America, forage still consists entirely of native plants. Grazing is seasonal, and nomadic people moved themselves and their animals long distances to secure food. As agriculture spread to the colder temperate zones and settled communities developed, both native and planted forage species were harvested to provide feed over the winter or the dry season. Haying and curing of forage plants has been practiced for over 4000 years. A good deal of the ingenious agricultural machinery was invented to collect, cure, and store forage plants.

The growth habits of grasses are admirably suited for use in permanent pastures and meadows as well as for open range grazing. Root systems are fibrous, extending laterally and vertically to obtain water and minerals from the soil. Leaves grow from a meristematic zone at the base of each leaf so that removal of most of the leaf blade does not prevent further leaf growth (Figure 21-9). Forage grasses have two major growth habits (Figure 21-10). Sod-forming grasses have low growing leaves and stems and tend to reproduce vegetatively by rhizomes or stolons. Since they do not grow tall, they are less easily grazed. Bunch grasses tend to have fibrous roots systems and grow taller.

Forage grasses are perennial and disease-resistant; many are drought-tolerant and winter-hardy. Protein contents are close to 8 percent. Sufficient genetic plasticity exists in many species to allow these plants to grow in a variety of climatic conditions. Some genera of forage grasses contain species with C_4 photosynthesis and have high levels of productivity. When properly managed, yields are high. Since they are monocots, many are resistant to herbicides that kill broad-leaved weeds so that fields can be kept clear of competitors. The production by grasses of apomictic seed (see Chapter 15) and their ability to

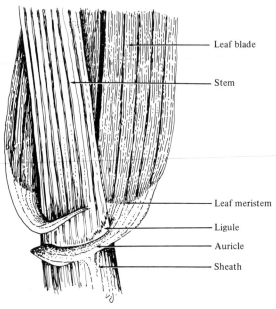

Figure 21-9   Stem node and sheathing leaf of grasses

produce new plants from rhizomes (see Chapter 14) facilitate the development of
genetically uniform stands that extend over considerable distances.

Forage grasses are consumed directly by browsing animals and are also
harvested for future use. Hay is cut grass, dried to about 15 percent moisture
content and stored loose or bailed into rectangular or rolled bales. Straw is dried

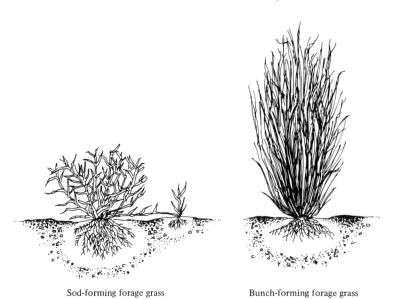

Sod-forming forage grass   Bunch-forming forage grass
Figure 21-10   Growth habits of forage grasses

Table 21-17 SOME MAJOR COOL-SEASON PERENNIAL FORAGE GRASSES

Latin name	Common name	Origin	Imported to North America	Cultivars	Bunch or sod	Rhizomaceous or fibrous	Tillering ability	Grazing potential	Winter injury	Drought resistance	Disease resistance	Insect resistance
Agropyron spp.	Wheatgrasses	Native, Eurasia	1800	Many	B, S	R	+	M	M	H	M	M
Bromus spp.	Bromegrasses	Native, Europe	1890	Many	S	R	+	M	M	H	H	H
Dactylis spp.	Orchardgrasses	Europe	1750	Many	S	R	+	M	M	M	L	M
Festuca arundinacea	Tall fescue	Europe	1700	Many	B	R	+	H	L	H	M	M
Phalaris spp.	Reed canarygrasses	Europe	1880	Few	S	F	+	M	M	M	H	H
Phleum pratense	Timothy	Europe	1750	Many	B	R	+	M	H	L	M	H
Poa spp.	Bluegrasses	Native, Europe	1650	Many	S	R	+	H	M	M	M	M

H = high, M = moderate, L = low.

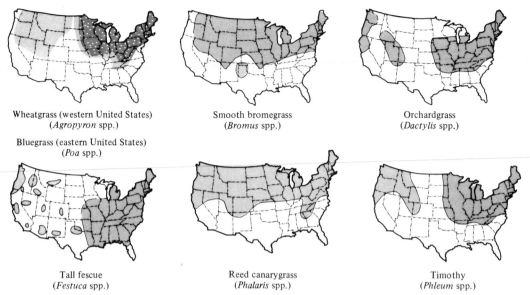

Wheatgrass (western United States)
(*Agropyron* spp.)

Bluegrass (eastern United States)
(*Poa* spp.)

Smooth bromegrass
(*Bromus* spp.)

Orchardgrass
(*Dactylis* spp.)

Tall fescue
(*Festuca* spp.)

Reed canarygrass
(*Phalaris* spp.)

Timothy
(*Phleum* spp.)

Figure 21-11   Distribution of some cool-season perennial forage grasses. (Modified from *Forages: The Science of Grassland Agriculture.* 3rd ed. Edited by M. E. Heath, D. S. Metcalf, and R. F. Barnes. (c) 1973 by the Iowa State University Press, Ames, Iowa 50010.)

cereal grain plants. Some hay is chopped or pelletized. Hay may be converted into silage by a controlled anaerobic fermentation process. Stalks and leaves of corn, sorghum, and sugar cane are used as dry fodder or are made into silage. During the fermentation total acidity of the silage increases from less than 1 percent to 8 to 10 percent, which aids in prolonging storage and assists in its digestion by domestic animals.

There are close to 5000 species in the grass family, many of them capable of being used as forage plants. Many are used only in their native areas and, in some cases, there are no cultivated replacements available. This is particularly true in tropical lands. Unfortunately, native rangelands on all continents are severely overgrazed, a major consideration in our efforts to conserve natural resources and to provide meat and dairy products for a rapidly expanding population.

In regions of intensive agriculture a small percentage of the total number of potential forage grasses has been selected and bred to specifications imposed by climate, soil, available water, and type of domestic animal to be fed. There are 12 to 15 ecological groups of forage grasses that are widely cultivated in North America and several other groups have become dominant in permanent pastures of tropical areas. Because of their importance, the agronomic literature is extensive. Techniques for cultivation and handling vary with location, local needs, and local conditions.

The forage grasses are usually separated into several major categories. There are cool-season perennials whose growth is best in more temperate to cold parts of North America (Table 21-17, Figure 21-11) and warm-season grasses

Table 21-18 SOME MAJOR WARM-SEASON PERENNIAL FORAGE GRASSES

Latin name	Common name	Origin	Imported to North America	Cultivars	Bunch or sod	Rhizomaceous or fibrous	Grazing potential	Winter injury	Drought resistance	Disease resistance	Insect resistance
Cynodon dactylon	Bermuda grass	South Asia	1750	Few	S	F	H	H	H	M	M
Paspalum dilatatum	Dallisgrass	South America	1850	Few	S	R	L	H	H	M	M
P. notatum	Bahia grass	South America	1850	Many	S	R	M	H	M	M	M
Lolium multiflorum	Ryegrass	Asia Minor	1850	Many	S	F	M	H	M	M	M

H = high, M = moderate, L = low.

Bermudagrass
(*Cynodon dactylon*)

Bahiagrass
(*Paspalum notatum*)

Ryegrass
(*Lolium multiflorum*)

Figure 21-12 Distribution of some warm-season perennial forage grasses. (Modified from *Forages: The Science of Grassland Agriculture.* 3rd ed. Edited by M. E. Heath, D. S. Metcalf, and R. F. Barnes. (c) 1973 by the Iowa State University Press, Ames, Iowa 50010.)

that flourish only in warmer to subtropical regions (Table 21-18, Figure 21-12). There is some overlap in the distribution of the cool- and warm-season forage grasses. Many of the important forage grasses are imports to North America, some having been introduced during the past 100 years as North America became an international supplier of beef, dairy products, and sheep. Soil types, climatic conditions, temperature regimes, and photoperiods vary even within the cool- and warm-season areas and both native and introduced forage grasses show considerable ecotypic and genotypic adaptive responses.

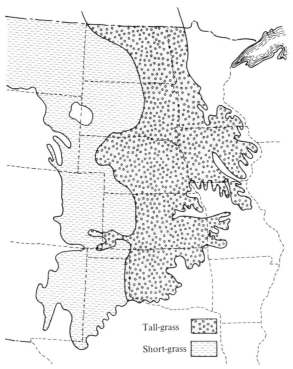

Tall-grass

Short-grass

Figure 21-13 Location of tall-grass and short-grass range grasses

A third category of forage grasses, which includes both cool- and warm-season species, is the range grasses. Mostly native, they formed the oceans of grass that nourished buffalo and later long-horned cattle. The area of land covered by the native range grasses was and still is very large (Figures 21-13 and 21-14, Table 21-19). Ecologically, two growth regions have been delimited. The tall-grass prairies extend from about 95° west longitude (the border between Manitoba and Ontario to the north and eastern Oklahoma to the south) to 101° west longitude (the border between Saskatchewan and Manitoba to the north and central Texas to the south). The short-grass prairies extend westward from the tall-grass region to the foothills of the Rocky Mountains. The tall-grass lands are dominated by big and little bluestem grasses *(Andropogon* spp.), while the gramagrasses *(Bouteloua* spp.) and buffalograsses *(Buchloe* spp.) dominate the short-grass Great Plains and are still the major forage grasses in these areas.

The topsoil of the original range grasslands was deep, fertile, and high in the humus formed from leaves and root systems of the grasses. These areas, as the North American pioneers discovered, were potentially among the richest agronomic lands on the continent. They became the setting for a series of major conflicts during the European expansion into the area: Indians versus buffalo hunters, sheepmen versus cattlemen, ranchers versus "sodbusters." Transformation of these lands into cereal grain fields is another chapter in North American history. And so is the damage done by unthinking removal of the grass that led to the erosions we call the dust bowls.

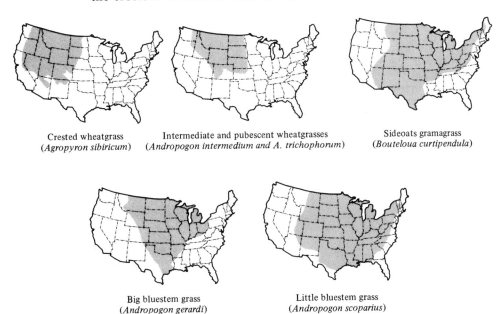

Crested wheatgrass
(Agropyron sibiricum)

Intermediate and pubescent wheatgrasses
(Andropogon intermedium and A. trichophorum)

Sideoats gramagrass
(Bouteloua curtipendula)

Big bluestem grass
(Andropogon gerardi)

Little bluestem grass
(Andropogon scoparius)

Figure 21-14 Distribution of some major range, prairie, and dryland perennial forage grasses. (Modified from *Forages: The Science of Grassland Agriculture.* 3rd ed. Edited by M. E. Heath, D. S. Metcalf, and R. F. Barnes. (c) 1973 by the Iowa State University Press, Ames, Iowa 50010.)

Table 21-19 SOME MAJOR RANGE, PRAIRIE, AND DRYLAND PERENNIAL FORAGE GRASSES

Latin name	Common name	Origin	Imported to North America	Cool or warm season	Cultivars	Bunch or sod	Rhizomaceous or fibrous	Grazing potential	Winter injury	Drought resistance
Agropyron sibiricum	Crested wheatgrass	Siberia	1910	Cool	Many	B	F	H	L	H
A. intermedium	Intermediate wheatgrass	Russia	1932	Cool	Many	S	R	H	L	M
Buchloe dactyloides	Buffalograss	Native		Warm	Few	S	R	H	H	H
Bouteloua curtipendula	Sideoats gramagrass	Native		Warm	Many	B	R	M	M	M
B. gracilis	Blue gramagrass	Native		Warm	Some	B	F	H	M	H
Andropogon gerardi	Big bluestem	Native		Warm	Many	S	R	H	M	H
A. scoparius	Little bluestem	Native		Warm	Many	B	F	M	M	H

H = high, M = moderate, L = low.

SUPPLEMENTARY READINGS

Aldrich, R. S., W. O. Scott, and E. R. Leng. 1976. *Modern Corn Production.* A & L, Champaign, Ill.

Austin, R. B., and R. B. Jones. 1976. The physiology of wheat. *Cambridge Plant Breeding Institute Report.* 1975: 20–73.

Carlson, P. S. (ed.). 1980. *The Biology of Crop Production.* Academic Press, New York.

Evans, L. T. (ed.). 1975. *Crop Physiology: Some Case Histories.* Cambridge University Press, Cambridge.

Francis, C. A. (ed.). 1986. *Multiple Cropping Systems.* Macmillan, New York.

Gallagher, E. J. (ed.). 1984. *Cereal Production.* Butterworth, London.

Gras, N. S. B. 1940. *A History of Agriculture.* 2nd ed. Crofts, New York.

Grigg, D. 1986. *The World Food Problem: 1950–1980.* Basil Blackwell, London.

Harlan, J. R. 1971. Agricultural origins: Centers and non-centers. *Science* 174:468–474.

Heath, M. E., D. S. Metcalf, and R. F. Barnes (eds.). 1985. *Forages: The Sciences of Grassland Agriculture.* 4th ed. Iowa State University Press, Ames.

Hebblethwait, P. D. (ed.). 1978. *Seed Production.* Butterworth, London.

Ishikuza, Y. 1971. Physiology of the rice plant. *Agronomy* 23:241–315.

Janick, J., R. W. Schery, F. W. Woods, and V. W. Ruttan. 1981. *Plant Science: An Introduction to World Crops.* 3rd ed. Freeman, San Francisco.

Klein, R. M. 1987. *The Green World.* 2nd ed. Harper & Row, New York.

Martin, F. W. (ed.). 1984. *CRC Handbook of Tropical Food Crops.* CRC Press, Boca Raton, Fla.

Mathre, D. E. 1982. *Compendium of Barley Diseases.* American Phytopathological Society, St. Paul, Minn.

Metcalf, D. S., and D. M. Elkins. 1980. *Crop Production: Principles and Practice.* 4th ed. Macmillan, New York.

Needham, J., and F. Bray. 1984. *Science and Civilization in China.* Vol. 6. *Biology and Biological Technology.* Part 2. *Agriculture.* Cambridge University Press, Cambridge.

Peterson, R. H. 1965. *Wheat: Botany, Cultivation and Utilization.* Wiley-Interscience, New York.

Pimentel, D., and C. W. Hall. 1984. *Food and Energy Resources.* Academic Press, Orlando, Fla.

Poelman, J. M. 1979. *Breeding Field Crops.* 2nd ed. Avi Books, Westport, Conn.

Poincelot, R. P. 1986. *Towards a More Sustainable Agriculture.* Avi Books, Westport, Conn.

Rachie, K. O., and J. V. Majmudar. 1980. *Pearl Millet.* Pennsylvania State University Press, University Press.

Rasmussen, D. C. (ed.). 1985. *Barley.* American Society of Agronomy, Madison, Wis.

Richardson, W. N., and T. Stubbs. 1978. *Plants, Agriculture and Human Society.* W. A. Benjamin, Reading, Mass.

Scientific American Board of Editors. 1976. *Food and Agriculture.* Freeman, San Francisco, Calif.

Schery, R. W. 1972. *Plants for Man.* 2nd ed. Prentice-Hall, Englewood Cliffs, N. J.

Shurtleff, M. C. (ed.). 1982. *Compendium of Corn Diseases.* American Phytopathological Society, St. Paul, Minn.

Simpson, B. B., and M. Conner-Ogorzaly. 1986. *Economic Botany.* McGraw-Hill, New York.

Singer, C., E. J. Holmyard, and A. R. Hall (eds.). 1958. *A History of Technology.* 5 vols. Oxford University Press, Oxford.

Spiertz, J. H. J., and T. H. Kramer (eds). *Crop Physiology and Cereal Breeding.* Poduc, Wageningen, Netherlands.

Stoskopf, N. C. 1985. *Cereal Grain Crops.* Reston, Reston, Va.

Streuver, S. (ed.). 1971. *Prehistoric Agriculture.* Natural History Press, Garden City, N. Y.

Weise, M. V. 1977. *Compendium of Wheat Diseases.* American Phytopathological Society, St. Paul, Minn.

CHAPTER 22

FOOD LEGUMES AND FORAGE LEGUMES

FOOD LEGUMES

Seeds of the food legumes, sometimes called the grain legumes or the seed legumes, are almost as important in human and animal nutrition as the cereal grains. Protein levels in some legume seeds may exceed 35 percent compared with 12 percent in wheat flour and 18 percent in nuts, and their amino acid ratios are closer to those in animal proteins than the amino acid ratios in any other edible plant product. Some legume seeds have 20 to 45 percent by weight of lipids (oils and fats) that are recoverable for nutritional and industrial purposes. The meal cake residues remaining after extraction of oils are widely used for feeding poultry and other domestic animals.

Seed legumes have been primary human food for centuries. Domestication, dispersion, and diversification have resulted in large numbers of cultivars in most legume crop species. It is, however, only recently that seed legumes have become a major component of world agricultural trade and many species are still of only local importance. Some of these local species are being evaluated as potentially important new agronomic crops in North America and Europe and to improve the diets of peoples in poor countries.

General characteristics of the legume family (Leguminosae) were covered in Chapter 1. The seeds possess two large cotyledons enclosing the embryo. Cotyledonary cells contain the proteins, carbohydrates, and lipids. When harvested and cured, legume seeds contain 10 to 12 percent water by weight and are storable under dry and cool conditions for a number of years while retaining their nutritive values and their viability. Most legume seeds do not require any postharvest treatment for germination (see Chapter 14).

The agronomic and horticultural species of seed and forage legumes are all nitrogen fixers, each utilizing specific species or strains of the associative *Rhizobium* bacteria (see Chapter 7). The agronomic importance of nitrogen fixation cannot be overemphasized. Fixation may exceed 200 kg nitrogen/ha/year for annual legumes and somewhat more in the perennials used as forage. In general, about 75 percent of the nitrogen fixed is incorporated into the plant and, at maturity, a significant fraction accumulates in the fruit and seeds. During harvest the stems and leaves are frequently discarded, resulting in losses of fixed nitrogen, and there is growing realization that mulching or composting these residues is economically valuable. Of the nitrogen remaining in the root system, about a third is returned to the soil the following year. This represents close to 20 percent of the nitrogen fixed by the plant and can reduce the cost of fertilization for crops grown in fields previously planted to legumes. In some situations legume cover crops are used as green manures and are incorporated into the soil before the new crop is planted.

The efficiency of the nodulation process and of subsequent nitrogen fixation varies with the legume species or cultivar, the *Rhizobium* species or strain, and the technique used to inoculate the roots. New methods of obtaining good nodule development are still being worked out. The amount of nitrogen fixed over a growing season also depends on many soil, weather, and cultivation factors.

Soybeans

The soybean, *Glycine max,* is native to the north China plains where it has been cultivated for 7000 years as one of the five sacred grains. Known as *ta tou* or *jung shu,* the ability of soybean to prepare the soil for subsequent cultivation of other crops was recorded 3000 years ago. Soybeans were grown in Japan and Korea 2500 years ago, but did not reach the West until 1690 when they were introduced into the botanical gardens of Paris. Benjamin Franklin brought seeds to the United States from France in 1785 and Japanese cultivars were introduced by Commodore Matthew C. Perry in 1854. Some minor agricultural plantings, primarily for forage, were made before 1920, but it was only in the 1930s that large-scale soybean cultivation began.

In terms of world production soybeans are exceeded only by maize and rice, and in terms of value soybeans are only a bit behind wheat. In the United States, the world's leader in soybean production (Table 22-1), essentially the same amount of land is used as for wheat or maize. This is not true worldwide, since the area sown to wheat is considerably greater. The United States is also the major exporter of soybeans and soy products and they form a significant part of the nation's agricultural economy.

For many growth and reproductive processes the soil and climatic conditions for optimum soybean cultivation are virtually identical to those of maize. As cultivars adapted for different photoperiodic and temperature regimes have

Table 22-1 PRODUCTION OF SOYBEANS, 1984

	Area (thousands of ha)	Yield (kg/ha)	Production (thousands of metric tons)
World	52,056	1,727	89,893
Africa	397	953	378
Egypt	62	2,339	145
Nigeria	200	300	60
Asia	10,140	1,231	12,482
China	7,507	1,293	9,710
India	850	941	800
Europe	577	1,693	946
Romania	300	1,357	407
Yugoslavia	115	1,974	227
Soviet Union	772	699	540
North America	27,628	1,896	52,368
Canada	417	2,240	934
United States (29 states)	26,746	1,893	50,643
Illinois	3,608	2,175	7,865
Iowa	3,360	2,142	7,210
South America	12,496	1,848	23,095
Brazil	9,416	1,650	15,537
Argentina	2,576	2,601	6,700
Oceania	47	1,798	84
Australia	47	1,798	84

Nations selected to provide some idea of variations in production.
Source: Food and Agriculture Organization, United Nations, Rome, 1984; U.S. Department of Agriculture, *Agricultural Statistics,* Washington, D.C., 1985.

been developed, regions available for soybean cultivation have been extended and now include southern Canada to the southern United States. Brazil, with the Southern Hemisphere equivalent of the temperate zone of mid-North America, has recently become a major Western Hemisphere producer.

The self-fertile soybeans have been placed into groups based on the time neded to reach maturity. Cultivars are available with maturation times ranging from 90 to 180 days. This variation allows them to be grown in different latitudes but still obtain the critical photoperiod for flower induction in time for fruit to form before killing frosts. Those cultivars requiring long-day conditions are grown in northern latitudinal zones, while the short-day cultivars can be induced to flower in southern areas that have a longer growing period in early fall. The soybean growing area has been divided into bands with Zone 00 in southern Canada and Zone VIII at the Gulf of Mexico.

Cultivars are also classified as determinate, with vegetative growth stopping before flowering, or indeterminate, where vegetative growth continues for several weeks after flower initiation. Under particular growing conditions one or the other growth type may be desirable.

Soil requirements are fairly broad, although best growth is obtained in fertile soils with good drainage. Soybeans do poorly in saline soils. Both growth and nodule activity are depressed at soil pH values below 6.5. Liming is usually necessary and molybdenum applications are used where acidity is a problem. Seed properly inoculated with effective strains of the nitrogen-fixing bacteria show good nodulation, and nitrogen fertilization is usually not needed and may repress nitrogen fixation. Phosphorus and potassium are supplied where analyses indicate. Soybeans require abundant moisture for best development, and drought can drastically reduce yields. Up to 600 grams of water are used to produce each gram of dry matter. Irrigation is rarely used for soybean production, although otherwise suitable areas in the southwest are sometimes irrigated. Weed control is necessary. Weeds are reduced by careful seedbed preparation, early cultivation, and the use of preplant and preemergence herbicides. Disease-resistant cultivars have reduced the need for massive applications of pesticides; insects are usually not a serious problem and are controllable by appropriate insecticides.

In Zones 00 to 2 and 3 seeds are sown as soon as possible in early spring when soil temperatures reach 15° C (60° F). In those zones where corn is the other major crop (Illinois and Iowa), soybeans are planted at the same time as the corn or immediately afterwards. Early-maturing cultivars are used where weather conditions delay planting as much as a week or two, but yields are usually lowered. In southerly zones soybeans are rarely planted beyond early midsummer even when soils have warmed up sufficiently for good germination and nodulation.

Beans

There are a number of genera of beans native to different parts of the world. The common beans in the genus *Phaseolus* are all New World contributions to human

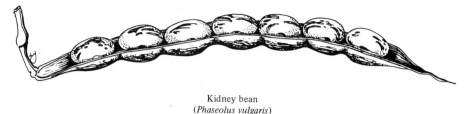

Kidney bean
(*Phaseolus vulgaris*)

Figure 22-1 Kidney bean fruit

nutrition. They were brought to Europe after they were recorded by Columbus. They, along with corn and squash, were staples of the diet in both Americas for 7000 years. *P. vulgaris* includes kidney (Figure 22-1), pinto, soldier, and many other cultivars and the string, wax, snap, and haricot beans eaten as green, immature fruits. Bush (determinate) and pole (indeterminate) cultivars are extensively grown in home gardens and under field conditions. The lima or butterbean *(P. lunatus),* native to the Andean region, was named after the city of Lima, Peru (Figure 22-2). Scarlet runner beans *(P. coccineus)* are also from South America where both seeds and the thickened, tuberous root are eaten. The major bean of northern Mexico *(P. acutifolius),* the tepary bean, has also been cultivated for thousands of years.

All of the *Phaseolus* beans are warm-season plants, usually grown as annuals. All require warm to hot weather conditions for vegetative and reproductive growth. Germination is best at 20° to 25° C (68° to 76° F). None are particularly drought-resistant. Well-drained, nearly neutral loamy soils (pH 6.5 to 7.5) with adequate lime potential are preferable. Maturity ranges from 50 to 65 days for pod development to the green stage suitable for eating and at least another 10 days for formation of mature seed. Disease tolerances are high because many disease-resistant cultivars are available. The market cultivars are usually determinate types to allow harvesting by machine at one time. Common beans are a major component of the dry bean production in North America (Table 22-2).

Beans in the genus *Vicia* are the most important ones grown in Europe and the Orient (Table 22-3). The most widely produced is *V. Faba,* variously called fava bean, Windsor bean, horse bean, and broad bean (Figure 22-3). Broad beans have been cultivated for well over 6000 years, having been domesticated in North

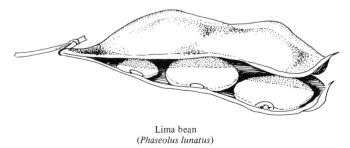

Lima bean
(*Phaseolus lunatus*)

Figure 22-2 Lima bean fruit

Table 22-2   PRODUCTION OF DRY BEANS, 1984

	Area (thousands of ha)	Yield (kg/ha)	Production (thousands of metric tons)
World	20,642	594	15,469
Africa	2,510	654	1,642
Uganda	380	947	360
Burundi	290	897	260
Asia	12,819	549	7,038
India	9,200	380	3,500
China	1,562	1,183	1,848
Europe	1,317	632	832
Romania	550	345	190
Yugoslavia	160	988	158
Soviet Union	75	1,040	78
North America	3,347	798	2,670
Mexico	2,158	589	1,270
United States (31 states)	589	1,597	941
Michigan	156	1,205	199
Nebraska	68	2,138	154
South America	5,970	537	3,206
Brazil	5,306	494	2,621
Argentina	210	1,119	235
Oceania	4	750	3
Australia	4	750	3

Nations selected to provide some idea of variations in production.
Source: Food and Agriculture Organization, United Nations, Rome, 1984; U.S. Department of Agriculture, *Agricultural Statistics,* Washington, D.C., 1985.

Africa and possibly in southwestern Asia. They reached Europe in Neolithic times and the Far East by 500 via the trade and spice routes. Broad beans were being grown in North America by 1602. The species, like the other edible legumes, is self-fertile and annual, and the pods are borne on racemes that develop in the axils of leaves. Most cultivars bear tendrils and are usually staked. They are cool-season plants with optimum growth temperatures of 16° to 18° C (60° to 65° F). Maturation requires 110 to 120 days. Because of this long growing period, the cooler parts of the mid-South are usually the better areas for commercial production.

Some humans, particularly those from the Mediterranean region, are genetically predisposed to allergic reactions to broad beans. In this condition, known as favism, red blood cells are broken down resulting in anemia or in shock reactions.

Two other members of the genus, *V. angustifolia* and *V. Cracca,* are of European origin and are of local interest, although they are not commercially cultivated in North America. Other species in the genus are forage plants of cooler regions and the vetches *(Vicia* spp.) are extensively planted on road cuts and on land being reclaimed.

Many other genera and species of bean have been cultivated for centuries. The lentil *(Lens culinaris)* originated in southwestern Asia and spread to the Mediterranean 5000 years ago (Figure 22-4). It was introduced into North

Table 22-3 PRODUCTION OF LENTILS, CHICK-PEAS, AND BROAD BEANS, 1984

	Area (thousands of ha)			Yield (kg/ha)			Production (thousands of metric tons)		
	Lentils	Chick-peas	Broad beans	Lentils	Chick-peas	Broad beans	Lentils	Chick-peas	Broad beans
World	2,320	9,839	2,394	633	663	1,226	1,538	6,526	4,039
Africa	142	355	802	512	721	1,189	73	256	954
Libya	50			640			32		
Ethiopia		121			736			89	
Morocco			200			610			122
Asia	1,915	9,140	1,858	658	654	1,265	1,260	5,980	2,350
Turkey	620			919			570		
India		7,308			651			4,755	
China			1,800			1,250			2,250
Europe	101	141	340	855	711	1,638	86	101	556
Spain	64			688			44		
Spain		88			682			60	
West Germany			67			1,241			183
Soviet Union	17		14	647		2,059	11		40
North America	94	160	83	829	1,031	923	78	165	77
Canada	55			702			39		
Mexico		160			1,031			165	
Mexico			30			1,333			40
South America	52	41	195	597	572	474	31	24	93
Chile	24			675			16		
Colombia		23			478			11	
Brazil			142			246			35
Oceania			16			625			10
Australia			16			625			10

Nations selected are leading producers of each legume.
Source: Food and Agriculture Organization, United Nations, Rome, 1984.

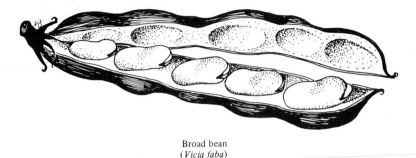

Broad bean
(*Vicia faba*)

Figure 22-3   Broad bean fruit

America by 1700, and today almost all commercial plantings of lentils are made in the Palouse Hills of northern Idaho and eastern Washington states. A cool-season annual with moderate drought resistance, lentils were the "meat" of Roman Catholics during Lent and meatless fast days. They are used for soups and porridges.

The chick-pea or garbanzo *(Cicer arientinum)* is a small annual native to western Asia where it has been grown for 6000 to 7000 years (Figure 22-5). It is used as a vegetable and is also ground into a flour. India is the major producer. Mexico is the primary source of chick-peas in North America (Table 22-3). The plant is a warm-season annual, does not require extensive fertilization or cultivation, and has excellent drought resistance. The pigeon pea *(Cajanus cajan)* is still important in its native home in Egypt's Nile Valley as well as in equatorial Africa (Figure 22-6). It grows well on marginal lands that receive only scant rainfall. Pigeon peas are almost unknown in North America, although they were a staple of the diet of black slaves in the American South.

The genus *Vigna* contains the Adzuki bean *(V. angularis)* of Asia, the snail bean *(V. Caracalla)* of tropical South America, the black gram *(V. mungo),* and the green gram *(V. radiata)* of southeast Asia (Figure 22-7). The gram beans are important staples of oriental diets. The early germination stage of the green gram is the oriental bean sprout. A familiar bean is the cowpea or black-eyed pea *(V.*

Lentil
(*Lens culinaris*)

Figure 22-4   Lentil fruit

Chick-pea
(*Cicer arientinum*)

Figure 22-5   Chick-pea fruit

Pigeon pea
(*Cajanus cajan*)

Figure 22-6   Pigeon pea fruit

unguiculata) (Figure 22-8). A native of southern Asia, it was cultivated in Africa and brought to North America by black slaves about 1600. A warm- to hot-season plant, it is a minor agricultural crop and is grown in southern home gardens.

Peas

Closely following tomatoes, peas are among the most ubiquitous table vegetables in North America and Europe (Figure 22-9). The species, *Pisum sativum,* originated in western Asia. Dried peas have been unearthed by archeologists working in Egypt, central Africa, the Middle East, India, and the Far East, indicating that the plant was widely cultivated thousands of years ago. Until the popularization of fresh green peas by the court of Louis XVI in France during the eighteenth century, most of the world's pea crop was dried for soups, gruels, and porridges. Even today, the bulk of the pea crop is in the dry state (Table 22-4).

Over the centuries thousands of cultivars have been obtained to meet production and marketing requirements. Bush and pole, determinate and indeterminate, vining types and sprawling lines suitable for mechanical harvesting are available. Edible podded cultivars, developed in Ming dynasty China, now include the sugar snap types developed in North America. Lighter green-seeded types are preferred for canning, while darker skinned peas are more commonly grown for fresh or frozen table use. The species is genetically plastic, a fact that was used by Fr. Gregor Mendel in his pioneering genetic studies on the inheritance patterns of green versus yellow and smooth versus wrinkled lines.

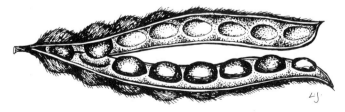

Green gram
(*Vigna radiata*)

Figure 22-7   Green gram fruit

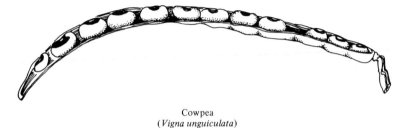

Cowpea
(*Vigna unguiculata*)

Figure 22-8   Cowpea fruit

Peas are cool-season annual plants that rarely show good germination at soil temperatures below 15° C (55° F) and fail to germinate above 30° C (86° F). Young seedlings have moderate resistance to chilling (5° C) injury. Soil moisture is frequently a limiting factor in germination and early growth since peas will rot in wet soils and germinate poorly in dry soils. Optimum vegetative development is at 16° to 21° C (60° to 70° F) and decline occurs above 27° C (80° F). Depending on cultivar and growing conditions, peas will reach market maturity in 56 to 75 days for fresh peas and about 10 to 14 days longer for mature peas. Dry seed at 7 percent moisture content can be stored with little loss for up to three years under cool conditions.

Peas are relatively tolerant to diverse soil types. Optimum soil pH values are close to 6.8, although the plant will grow and mature at pH 5.5 if supplied with nitrogen fertilizer to replace nodular nitrogen fixation. Moderately high phosphorus and potassium fertilization is usually recommended several weeks before flower induction. Manganese (see Chapter 7) is supplied where soils are deficient. Peas are susceptible to boron injury which can be relieved by lime applications. The flowers are self-fertile and the resulting seeds are "like two peas in a pod." Although host to a wide range of diseases, resistant cultivars are available against major fungal and bacterial pathogens.

Peanuts

Arachis hypogaea, the peanut, groundnut, goober, or pinderbean, was domesticated in eastern Peru and Brazil 5000 years ago, was transported to Europe by

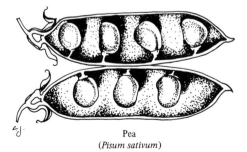

Pea
(*Pisum sativum*)

Figure 22-9   Pea fruit

Table 22-4 PRODUCTION OF PEAS, 1984

	Area (thousands of ha)		Yield (kg/ha)		Production (thousands of metric tons)	
	Green	Dry	Green	Dry	Green	Dry
World	750	8,612	6,134	1,234	4,603	10,627
Africa	22	407	5,734	689	126	280
Morocco	8		4,133		31	
South Africa	4		5,500		22	
Ethiopia		144		785		113
Zaire		74		649		48
Asia	160		4,092		655	
China	49	1,400	5,588	1,500	271	2,100
India	91	437	2,833	835	258	365
Europe	266	469	7,671	3,406	2,041	1,598
United Kingdom	44		12,226		533	
France	47	129	10,257	4,806	480	620
Denmark		44		5,659		249
Soviet Union	74	5,400	3,514	1,037	260	5,600
North America	164	169	7,451	1,963	1,218	333
United States	134	89	8,396	2,202	1,125	196
Canada	19	72	2,881	1,814	53	131
South America	40	124	2,796	723	111	89
Argentina	11		3,182		35	
Colombia		57		614		35
Peru	12	25	2,906	840	34	21
Oceania	25	122	7,649	1,607	192	196
Australia	16	104	9,375	1,308	150	136
New Zealand	9	18	4,615	3,333	42	60

Nations selected to provide some idea of variations in production.
Source: Food and Agriculture Organization, United Nations, Rome, 1984.

the Spanish in the early sixteenth century, was carried to China and Africa by Catholic missionaries in the closing decades of the sixteenth century, and was returned to North and Central America by African slaves by 1700. Today over half the peanuts grown in the world are produced in India and China where they, like other leguminous seeds, are basic components of the diet (Table 22-5). Whole, shelled peanuts are eaten as a vegetable or snack and are used in soups and stews. Peanut butter is a primary food of the youth of North America. The peanut seed is an excellent protein source (25 percent by weight) and, like soybeans, is an outstanding source of polyunsaturated oils (45 percent by weight). The purified oil is used for food as a liquid or is hydrogenated into cooking fats. It has many industrial uses. The meal remaining after expression of the oil is used as animal feed, and the vegetative residues are a useful fodder for hogs.

The peanut is unusual in its fruit maturation. Following self-fertilization of the flowers, the flower stalk (the pedicel or "peg") curves down, elongates, and pushes the developing fruit into the soil where maturation of the pod and seeds occur.

There are two major subspecies of the peanut. The Virginia type has a

Table 22-5   PRODUCTION OF PEANUTS IN SHELL, 1984

	Area (thousands of ha)	Yield (kg/ha)	Production (thousands of metric tons)
World	18,353	1,123	20,611
Africa	5,812	659	3,832
Senegal	873	782	682
Zaire	525	724	380
Asia	12,342	1,220	13,840
India	7,250	952	6,900
China	2,442	2,007	4,900
Europe	11	2,188	24
Greece	3	3,333	10
Bulgaria	5	1,333	6
Soviet Union	5	1,400	8
North America	774	2,839	2,196
United States (9 states)	614	3,270	2,008
Georgia	26	3,797	1,029
Alabama	88	3,330	541
South America	368	1,789	658
Argentina	146	2,255	329
Colombia	150	1,653	248

Nations selected to provide some idea of variations in production.
Source: Food and Agriculture Organization, United Nations, Rome, 1984; U.S. Department of Agriculture, *Agricultural Statistics,* Washington, D.C., 1985.

spreading growth habit, forms runners (stolons), and usually has two large seeds per pod. Maturation requires 120 to 180 days. The Spanish type shows a more upright or bunching growth form, and the pod contains two to four smaller seeds. Maturation is earlier, usually requiring 90 to 100 days. The seed coats (testa) of the Spanish peanuts are darker brown than those of the Virginia cultivars. Virginia peanuts are grown extensively in Virginia and the Carolinas, while the Spanish peanuts are usually grown in Georgia and Alabama.

In addition to requirements for warm temperatures, soil characteristics are of great importance in peanut cultivation. Light, sandy loam soils are best, facilitating the forcing of the developing fruit into the soil. Spanish cultivars are planted in early spring and Virginia peanuts usually in mid- or late spring. Irrigation is useful, particularly when the soil is water-deficient at planting time or during the period of rapid vegetative growth. Heavy, late summer rains can seriously reduce yields. Peanut plants have high requirements for nitrogen even when adequately nodulated; up to 100 kg nitrogen/ha (95 lb/acre) are supplied as side-dressings. Phosphorus is usually also supplied, but potassium is rarely needed. Micronutrients are given as indicated by soil analyses. Although disease-resistant lines have been obtained, rusts are a major problem. Insect pests are controlled with appropriate pesticides.

Peanuts do not store well for long periods of time and the crop is moved to market as soon as possible, usually in less than a year after harvesting. Peanuts in storage and processed peanut products are susceptible to infection by *Aspergillis flavus,* a fungus that produces highly carcinogenic and liver-damaging aflatoxins.

FORAGE LEGUMES

The major forage legumes grown in North America are introductions from Europe, although some originated in Asia. In general, they tend to be more demanding than many forage grasses and usually have somewhat smaller ranges of adaptability to suboptimum climatic, soil, and other conditions (Table 22-6, Figure 22-10). Most are less winter hardy than grasses and have higher water requirements for survival and high yields. These disadvantages are frequently more than balanced by high productivity and the excellent nutritional quality of legume hays and silages. In addition, the nitrogen-fixing ability of legumes reduces the expenses of fertilization and greatly improves the soils.

There is increasing evidence that pasturage is greatly benefited when appropriate mixtures of forage legumes and forage grasses are planted together. There are higher total hay and silage yields than with either plant type alone and the survival of both is enhanced, especially under variable and harsh environmental conditions. Winter injury to the less tolerant legumes is reduced, weed competition is less of a problem because the soil surface is uniformly covered with plants that crowd out weeds, and there is less lodging of the legumes. The nitrogen fixed by the legumes becomes available to the grasses as the legume

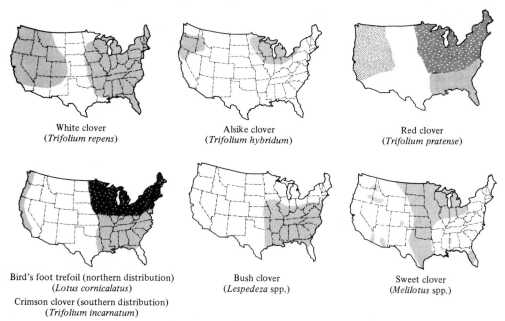

White clover
(*Trifolium repens*)

Alsike clover
(*Trifolium hybridum*)

Red clover
(*Trifolium pratense*)

Bird's foot trefoil (northern distribution)
(*Lotus cornicalatus*)

Crimson clover (southern distribution)
(*Trifolium incarnatum*)

Bush clover
(*Lespedeza* spp.)

Sweet clover
(*Melilotus* spp.)

Figure 22-10   Distribution of perennial forage legumes. Alfalfa is grown in all states. Red clover is grown in all northern states as a perennial, under irrigation in western states, and as a winter annual in southern states. White clover is grown under irrigation in western states. (Modified from *Forages: The Science of Grassland Agriculture.* 3rd ed. Edited by M. E. Heath, D. S. Metcalf, and R. F. Barnes. (c) 1973 by the Iowa State University Press, Ames, Iowa 50010.)

Table 22-6   SOME CHARACTERISTICS OF THE MAJOR FORAGE LEGUMES

Latin name	Common name	Origin	Imported to North America	Hectares planted (millions)
Medicago sativa	Alfalfa, lucerne	Middle East	1850	13
Trifolium repens	Ladino clover, white clover	South Europe	1700	2
T. hybridum	Italian clover, Alsike clover	Asia Minor	1840	—
T. pratense	Red clover	Southwest Asia	1650	4
T. incarnatum	Crimson clover	Southeast Europe	1819	—
Lotus cornicalatus	Bird's foot trefoil	Eurasia	1920	0.4
Lespedeza spp.	Bush clover, lespedeza	East Asia	1900	3
Melilotus spp.	Sweet clover	West Asia	1750	4

H = high, M = moderate, L = low.
LD = long day, SD = short day.

plants decay. Feeding with mixed legume-grass hay or silage permits better growth of domestic animals, probably because the mixed forage has a better balance of amino acids. Livestock bloat, a serious problem, occurs when cattle receive too much legume protein along with inadequate carbohydrate. This danger is reduced by providing mixed grass-legume feed. Clover hays and silages may, if they become infected with certain fungi that transform coumarin into dicoumarol, cause a serious "bleeds" disease, but this potentially fatal condition can be cured if diagnosed early.

SUPPLEMENTARY READINGS

Duke, J. A. 1981. *Handbook of Legumes of World Economic Importance.* Plenum, New York.

Evans, L. T. (ed.). 1975. *Crop Physiology. Some Case Histories.* Cambridge University Press, Cambridge.

Fredericksen, R. A. 1986. *Compendium of Soybean Diseases.* American Phytopathological Society, St. Paul, Minn.

Graham, J. H. 1979. *Compendium of Alfalfa Diseases.* American Phytopathological Society, St. Paul, Minn.

Heath, M. E., D. S. Metcalf, and R. F. Barnes (eds.). 1985. *Forages: The Science of Grassland Agriculture.* 4th ed. Iowa State University Press, Ames.

Hebblethwait, P. D. (ed.). 1984. Vicia Faba: *Agronomy, Physiology and Breeding.* Nijhoff/Junk, Amsterdam.

Cultivars	Climatic factors				Soil factors							
	Winter injury	Drought resistance	Photoperiod	Vernalization	Acid tolerance	Lime requirement	Fertilizer minerals	Grazing potential	Nitrogen fixation (kg/ha/year)	Self-propagation	Disease resistance	Insect resistance
Many	H	H	LD	+	L	H	P, K	L	225	L	M	H
Many	M	M	LD/SD	+	L	H	P, K	M	200	M	L	M
Few	M	L	LD	+	H	M	—	M	135	M	M	M
Many	M	M	LD	+	M	M	P, K	M	130	H	L	M
Few	H	M	LD	+	M	M	—	H	115	L	H	L
Many	L	M	LD	+	L	M	P, K	H	115	H	M	M
Some	L	M	LD	+	L	H	P, K	H	100	L	H	L
Many	M	H	LD	+	L	H	P	M	135	L	H	M

National Academy of Science. 1979. *Tropical Legumes: Resources for the Future.* National Academy Press, Washington, D.C.

Norman, A. G. (ed.). 1978. *Soybean Physiology, Agronomy and Utilization.* Academic Press, New York.

Salunkhe, D. K., and J. K. Chaven. 1985. *Postharvest Biotechnology of Food Legumes.* CRC Press, Boca Raton, Fla.

Taylor, N. L. (ed.). 1985. *Clover Science and Technology.* American Society of Agronomy, Madison, Wis.

Witcombe, J. R., and W. Erskine (eds.). 1984. *Genetic Resources and Their Exploitation—Chick Peas, Fava Beans, and Lentils.* Kluwer, Hingham, Mass.

Woodroof, J. G. 1973. *Peanuts—Production, Processing, Products.* 3rd ed. Avi Books, Westport, Conn.

A P P E N D I X   A

CONVERSION FACTORS

Metric units are used throughout the world and even in those few countries that still use nonmetric units, the scientific community uses the uniform system codified by the International Bureau of Weights and Measures. These are known as SI units, the initials standing for the *Système International d'Unités.* Complete details are provided in *Metric Practice Guide,* published in 1977 by the Canadian Fertilizer Institute, Ottawa, Ontario, Canada, and *The International System of Units (SI),* published in 1977 as Special Publication 330 by the U.S. National Bureau of Standards, Department of Commerce. The *Handbook of Chemistry and Physics,* published by the CRC Press, Boca Raton, Florida, updated at frequent intervals, contains a comprehensive series of conversion factors. Some of the more frequently used factors are provided in the following table. It is common practice to round off the numbers to the nearest whole number unless there is good reason to have additional significant numbers.

To convert SI to U.S. units, multiply by	SI unit Name	SI unit Abbreviation	U.S. unit Name	U.S. unit Abbreviation	To convert U.S. to SI units, multiply by
		Temperature			
$1.8 + 32°$	Celcius	°C	Fahrenheit	°F	$0.55 - 32°$
		Weight			
0.035	gram	g	ounce	oz	28
2.2	kilogram	kg	pound	lb	0.45
1.1	tonne	t	ton	t	0.9
		Length			
0.04	millimeter	mm	inch	in.	0.025
0.39	centimeter	cm	inch	in.	2.54
3.28	meter	m	foot	ft	0.305
1.094	meter	m	yard	yd	0.914
0.62	kilometer	km	mile	mi	1.61

(Continued)

(Continued)

To convert SI to U.S. units, multiply by	SI unit		U.S. unit		To convert U.S. to SI units, multiply by
	Name	**Abbreviation**	**Name**	**Abbreviation**	
			Volume		
0.034	milliliter	ml	ounce	oz	29.6
0.2	milliliter	ml	teaspoon	tsp	4.9
0.067	milliliter	ml	tablespoon	tbl	15
4.17	liter	l[a]	cup	c	0.24
2.1	liter	l	pint	pt	0.47
1.06	liter	l	quart	qt	0.95
0.26	liter	l	gallon	gal	3.8
35	cubic meter	m^3	cubic foot	ft^3	0.03
1.3	cubic meter	m^3	cubic yard	yd^3	0.76
2.84	hectoliter	hl	bushel	bu	0.36
0.28	liter	l	bushel	bu	36
			Area		
2.47	hectare	ha	acre	A	0.405
247	square kilometer	km^2	acre	A	0.004
10.8	square meter	m^2	square foot	ft^2	0.093
0.105	square centimeter	cm^2	square inch	$in.^2$	6.45
2.6	square kilometer	km^2	square mile	mi^2	0.4
			Yield or rate		
0.45	tonne/hectare	t/ha	ton/acre	t/A	2.24
0.89	kilogram/hectare	kg/ha	pound/acre	lb/A	1.12
1.15	hectoliter/hectare	hl/ha	bushel/acre	bu/A	0.89
0.15	kilogram/hectare	kg/ha	bushel/acre	bu/A	67.2
1.07	liter/hectare	liter/ha	gallon/acre	gal/A	9.35
8.35	kilogram/liter	kg/liter	pound/acre	lb/A	0.12

[a]According to some styles (and the one used in this book), liter is not abbreviated.

A P P E N D I X   B

SOURCES OF INFORMATION AND PUBLICATIONS ON HORTICULTURAL TOPICS

A "List of Available Publications" can be obtained from the Office of Governmental and Public Affairs, U.S. Department of Agriculture, Washington, D.C. 20250, and "For Sale Only" publications can be obtained through the Superintendent of Documents, Government Printing Office, Washington, D.C. 20402. Information from Canadian sources can be obtained from Information Services, Agriculture Canada, Ottawa, Ontario, Canada K1A OC7.

For information and publications keyed to more local conditions, requests can be addressed to the Agricultural Extension Service or the Agricultural Experiment Station in a state or province.

State or province	Post office	State or province	Post office
Alabama	Auburn 36830	New York	Ithaca 14853
Alaska	Fairbanks 99701		Geneva 14456
Arizona	Tucson 85721	North Carolina	Raleigh 27607
Arkansas	Fayetteville 72701	North Dakota	Fargo 58102
California	Berkeley 94720	Ohio	Columbus 43210
	Davis 95616		Wooster 44691
	Riverside 92502	Oklahoma	Stillwater 74074

(Continued)

(Continued)

State or province	Post office	State or province	Post office
Colorado	Fort Collins 80521	Oregon	Corvallis 97331
Connecticut	Storrs 06268	Pennsylvania	University Park 16802
	New Haven 06504	Puerto Rico	Mayaguez 00708
Delaware	Newark 19711	Rhode Island	Kingston 02881
Florida	Gainesville 32611	South Carolina	Clemson 29631
Georgia	Athens 30601	South Dakota	Brookings 57006
Hawaii	Honolulu 96822	Tennessee	Knoxville 37901
Idaho	Moscow 83843	Texas	College Station 77843
Illinois	Urbana 61801	Utah	Logan 84321
Indiana	Lafayette 47907	Vermont	Burlington 05405
Iowa	Ames 50010	Virginia	Blacksburg 24061
Kansas	Manhattan 66505		Norfolk 23501
Kentucky	Lexington 40506	Washington	Pullman 99163
Louisiana	Baton Rouge 70803	West Virginia	Morgantown 26506
Maine	Orono 04473	Wisconsin	Madison 53706
Maryland	College Park 20742	Wyoming	Laramie 82070
Massachusetts	Amherst 01003		
Michigan	East Lansing 48823	Alberta	Edmonton
Minnesota	St. Paul 55101	British Columbia	Victoria
Mississippi	State College 39762	Manitoba	Winnipeg
Missouri	Columbia 65201	New Brunswick	Fredericton
Montana	Bozeman 59715	Newfoundland	St. Johns
Nebraska	Lincoln 68503	Nova Scotia	Halifax
Nevada	Reno 89507	Ontario	Toronto
New Hampshire	Durham 03824	Prince Edward Island	Charlottetown
New Jersey	New Brunswick 08903	Quebec	Quebec
New Mexico	State College 88003	Saskatchewan	Regina

GLOSSARY

abscisic acid Growth-inhibiting chemical that induces numerous effects including abscission, dormancy, and inhibition of seed germination.

abscission The dropping of leaves, flowers, fruits, or other plant parts, usually following the formation of an abscission zone.

abscission layer Layer of cells in the abscission zone, the disjunction or breakdown of which separates a plant part, such as leaf, fruit, or flower, from the plant.

abscission zone Zone at the base of a leaf, flower, fruit, or other plant part containing tissues that play a role in the separation of the plant part from the plant.

absorption Uptake of any material by a plant or plant part, such as water by the root system or pesticide through the leaves.

accessory bud Lateral bud occurring at the base of a terminal bud or at the side of an axillary bud.

accessory pigment Pigment that captures light energy and transfers it to chlorophyll *a*. Also called antennae pigment.

achene A simple, dry, one-seeded, indehiscent fruit that is separable from the walls of the ovary, except where it is attached to the pericarp.

acid Substance that upon dissociation releases hydrogen ions (H^+) but not hydroxyl ions (OH^-). Having a pH of less than 7.

acid-forming compound Material that reacts to acidify the soil or acidifies the soil as it decomposes, such as agricultural sulfur and peat moss.

acid-loving Describing plants that grow best in an acidic medium.

acid soil Soil with a pH below 6.

acre-foot The volume of water required to cover 1 acre (0.405 ha) to a 1-ft (15.2 cm) depth; equal to 43,560 ft^3 or 1,233 m^3.

acropetal Produced in succession toward the apex, as applied to cell series, tissues, or organs. The opposite of basipetal.

action spectrum The spectrum of light waves that elicits a particular reaction.

active growth Phase of the plant life cycle characterized by rapid stem lengthening and leaf production.

adhesion The attraction of dissimilar molecules for each other. A sticking together of unlike substances, such as soil and water.

adsorption Accumulation of ions on a solid caused by ion exchange or other reactions.

adventitious bud Bud produced on a part of a plant where a bud is not usually found, such as on a leaf vein or root.

adventitious root   Root produced from tissues other than primary root tissues, as from the stem.

adventitious structure   Structure arising from places other than the usual.

aeration   Penetration and circulation of air in the soil. A method of increasing air penetration into compacted soil by removing slices or cores of soil.

aerobic   Requiring oxygen or occurring only in the presence of oxygen as in aerobic respiration.

after-ripening   Various changes that must occur in some dormant seeds before germination can occur.

aggregate fruit   A fruit developing from the several separate carpels of a single flower.

aggregation   Groups of soil particles clumped together.

air drainage   Flow of cold air downhill.

air-layering   A method of propagation in which root formation from a stem is promoted while the stem is intact on the parent plant; the rooted portion is then detached and potted separately.

aleurone   Proteinaceous material, usually in the form of small granules, found in the outermost cell layer (the aleurone layer) of the endosperm of wheat and other cereal grains.

algae   Photosynthetic eukaryotic organisms not forming multicellular sex organs (except blue-green algae, which are photosynthetic prokaryotes).

alkali   Substance that upon dissociation releases hydroxyl ions (OH−).

alkaline   Having a pH greater than 7.

alkaline soil   Soil with a pH of 7.5 or higher.

alkali soil   Soil with a pH of 8.5 or higher or with high sodium content or both.

allelopathy   Injury, inhibition, or stimulation of growth of one plant by another through excretion of toxic or other substances from roots or other plant parts.

alternate leaf arrangement   An arrangement of leaves on a stem in which there is one leaf per node and the leaves form a spiral along the stem.

amendment   Material added to soil to modify its structure, texture, pH, or other property.

amino acid   An organic acid having one or more amine groups (NH_2^-).

ammonification   Decomposition of amino acids and other nitrogen-containing organic compounds, resulting in the production of ammonia (NH_3) and ammonium (NH_4^-).

amylase   An enzyme that hydrolyzes starch.

amylopectin   A molecular form of starch consisting of a branched polymer of glucose.

amyloplast   A leucoplast in which starch is stored.

amylose   A molecular form of starch consisting of an unbranched polymer of glucose.

anaerobic   Not requiring oxygen or occurring only in the absence of oxygen.

anaphase   Stage in mitosis in which the chromatids of each chromosome separate and move to opposite poles; similar stage in meiosis in which chromatids of paired chromosomes move apart.

anatomy   The study of the internal structure of organisms.

angiosperm   A member of the group of plants (Angiospermae or flowering plants) whose seeds are enclosed in an ovary.

anion   Negatively charged ion.

annual   Flowering plant that completes its entire life cycle of germination, flowering, and seed production in one year and then dies.

annual ring   In woody plants, a growth layer formed during one growing season.

anther   The part of a stamen in which pollen is produced.

anthocyanin   Water-soluble blue, purple, and red pigments found in vacuoles of cells.

antidesiccant   Material applied to plants to reduce the rate of transpiration.

aphid   Small, soft-bodied insect that feeds on young leaves and buds by sucking plant juices, causing curling and distortion of new growth.

apical dominance   Influence exerted by a terminal bud in suppressing the growth of lateral buds.

apical meristem   The growing point, or zone of cell division, at the tip of a root or stem in vascular plants.

apomixis   Form of reproduction in which new individuals are produced without nuclear or cellular fusion, but instead the embryo develops from an unfertilized egg or from tissues that surround the embryo sac.

arboretum   A place where trees are grown, alone or with other plants, for scientific and educational purposes.

arboriculture   The branch of horticulture that deals with the care and maintenance of ornamental trees and shrubs.

artificial medium   A growing medium that does not contain mineral soil.

artificial system   Any classification system of plants devised for convenience and based on arbitrary, variable, and superficial characteristics.

asexual reproduction   Any reproductive process that does not involve the fusion of gametes. The propagation of a whole plant from any cell, tissue, or organ of that plant.

ash content   Amount of mineral matter present in a soil or in plants.

ATP   Adenosine triphosphate, a compound that releases metabolic energy when it gives up its third phosphate group.

autotroph   Organism able to synthesize the nutritive substances it requires from inorganic materials.

auxin   A plant growth-regulating substance involved in cell elongation, dormancy, abscission, rooting, tuber formation, and other activities. Indoleacetic acid (IAA).

available nutrient   Nutrient that is not bound or insoluble and so can be taken up and used for plant growth.

available water   Soil moisture between field capacity and the wilting coefficient (minus one-third to minus 15 bars soil moisture potential).

axil   Angle between a twig or leaf petiole and the stem from which it grows.

axillary   Occurring in the axil of a leaf.

axillary bud   Bud located in a leaf axil.

bactericide   A chemical used to control bacterial diseases by making the bacterium incapable of reproduction.

balanced fertilizer   Fertilizer containing adequate ratios of nitrogen, phosphorus, and potassium.

balled and burlapped (B & B)   A method of preparing plants for transplanting in which the plant is dug with a ball of soil around the roots and the roots and soil are wrapped in burlap or other sheeting.

bare root   A method of preparing plants for transplanting in which dormant plants are dug and held with no soil around the roots.

bark   A nontechnical term applied to all tissues outside the vascular cambium, including phloem and dead outer bark (phellem).

base   A chemical that in solution has a pH greater than 7 and contains hydroxyl ions (OH$^-$).

basipetal   Produced in succession toward the base of the organ.

bast fiber   Phloem fiber.

bearing age   Age at which a tree begins to produce fruit.

bed   Soil area prepared for planting.

berry   Simple, fleshy fruit with a fleshy ovary wall, one or more carpels and seeds.

biennial   A flowering plant that requires two growing seasons to complete its life cycle, with vegetative growth occurring in the first season and then flowering in the second season after a dormant period.

binomial system   The classification system of plants giving each two names, the first a genus and the second a species name or specific epithet. Developed by Carolus Linnaeus.

biological control   The control of plant pests and pathogens by using parasites, predators, and pathogens that naturally affect them.

black frost   A frost severe enough to kill plant tissue and turn it black.

blade   The expanded portion of a leaf. Also called the lamina.

blanch   To make plant tissue pale and succulent by excluding light during the plant's growth. To heat plant tissues in hot water or steam for a brief period to inactivate enzymes.

blight   Any of several bacterial or fungal diseases causing spotting or wilting, frequently resulting in death.

block garden   Type of vegetable gardening in which plants are grown in groups rather than in rows.

bolting   Production of a flower stalk.

borer   Insect that burrows into plant organs.

botanical insecticide   Insecticide, such as pyrethrum, rotenone, and ryania, derived from plants.

bottom watering   Supplying water to pots or flats so that it is absorbed by the soil from the bottom, rather than percolating down from above.

bract   Modified leaf that subtends flowers or inflorescences and may appear to be a petal.

bramble   Plant in the genus *Rubus,* such as raspberry, blackberry, dewberry, and loganberry.

branch   Lateral portion of a plant that originates from the main stem axis.

branch root   Root arising from an older root. Also called lateral or secondary root.

branch spreader   Wood or metal strip inserted between the trunk and branch of a fruit tree to widen the crotch angle.

breaking dormancy   Causing a plant or seed to change from the dormant to the active growth phase.

broad-leaf weed   A dicot weed.

bud   Undeveloped stem containing embryonic leaf, flower, or leaf and flower organs.

budding   Type of grafting in which a vegetative bud (scion) is implanted into a stem or rootstock (stock).

bud sport   Mutation occurring in the apical meristem.

bulb   Underground storage organ composed of an enlarged, fleshy, shortened stem covered with modified leaves (bud scales).

bulbil   Aerial bulblets.

bulblet   Miniature bulb developing from a meristem in the axil of a bulb.

bulliform cell   Enlarged epidermal cell found in the leaf of grasses that functions in rolling and unrolling the leaf.

bundle scar   Place on leaf scar where vascular bundles had been.

bundle sheath   Layer or layers of cells surrounding a vascular bundle.

burn   Browning of plant organ due to water deficit, high temperature, or exposure to a toxic chemical.

burned lime   Limestone heated to drive off carbon dioxide leaving the oxide form CaO.

C₃ plant Plant in which the first product of carbon dioxide fixation is the three-carbon compound phosphoglyceric acid. Most plants are included in this classification.

C₄ plant Plant in which the first product of carbon dioxide fixation is the four-carbon compound oxaloacetic acid. Many tropical grasses, corn, sugarcane, and some dicot weeds are included in this classification.

calcitic lime Calcium carbonate ($CaCO_3$).

callus Undifferentiated tissue composed of large, thin-walled cells usually developing as a result of injury. Term also used in tissue culture, grafting, and wound healing.

Calvin-Benson cycle Series of enzymatic reactions in photosynthesis in which carbon dioxide is fixed (reduced) eventually to form sugar.

calyx All the sepals of a flower considered collectively. The outermost whorl of flower parts.

cambial zone Region in stems and roots consisting of the cambium and its recent derivatives.

cambium A meristem with the products of division usually arranged in rows, as in the vascular cambium.

candle The new growth of a needle-bearing conifer.

cane Long, flexible shoot of grapes and brambles.

canker Disease affecting woody plants that destroys tissues in a localized area.

capillarity Movement of water into soil pores or other small pores.

capillary water Water held in capillary pores of soils that can be used to meet the water needs of a plant.

capsule Simple, dry, dehiscent fruit with two or more locules.

carbohydrate Organic compound consisting of linked carbon atoms to which hydrogen and oxygen are attached in a 2:1 ratio.

carbon cycle Global circulation and utilization of carbon.

carotene Yellow or orange hydrocarbon pigment involved in light reactions of photosynthesis.

carotenoid Red to yellow pigments. Oxidation products of carotene which are called xanthophylls.

carpel Female organ of a flower, the megasporophyll.

caryopsis Simple, dry, one-seeded, indehiscent fruit with firmly attached pericarp. Characteristic fruit of grasses, a grain.

Casparian strip A bandlike wall formation containing lignin and suberin found in endodermal root cells.

catabolism Those parts of metabolism in which energy is released.

cation A positively charged ion, such as Ca^{+2} and Na^+.

cation exchange capacity (CEC) Number of negatively charged sites on soil particle that can hold cations. CEC is low for sand and high for clay and soil organic matter.

catkin Inflorescence of unisexual flowers.

cell Smallest unit of living matter capable of independent existence. Organized unit of protoplasm bounded by membrane and in plants usually surrounded by a wall.

cell differentiation Changes in cells during growth that result in specialization in form and function.

cell division Division of cytoplasm into two or more parts by formation of a cell plate. Also called cytokinesis.

cell sap Water and dissolved substances in plant cell vacuole.

cellulose A polysaccharide carbohydrate consisting of long, straight, and branched chains of anhydrous glucose residues. A principal constituent of plant cell walls.

cell wall Covering around living protoplast in plant cells. In flowering plants, wall consists of cellulose fibrils plus other substances.

central leader   The main shoot of a tree.

central leader form   A training method for fruit trees that leaves the central leader intact.

certified seed   Progeny of registered seed stock.

chelate   Complex organic molecule that can combine with cations and does not ionize. Chelates can supply micronutrients to plants at slow, steady rates.

chemoautotrophic   Organism capable of manufacturing all its required nutrients using energy derived from chemicals.

chewing insect   Insects that can eat plant parts.

chilling injury   Damage to plants resulting from exposure to cold, but above freezing temperatures.

chilling requirements   A cold period required by some plants in order to break rest or physiological dormancy. Usually expressed as hours required to break rest at $7°$ C.

chimera   Combination of tissues with differing genetic constitution.

chlorenchyma   Cells containing chloroplasts including leaf mesophyll and other parenchyma cells.

chlorophyll   Green pigments in chloroplasts, composed of magnesium-porphyrins, that absorb radiant energy and transfers it into chemical energy.

chloroplast   Membrane-bound organelle in which photosynthetic chemicals and structures are contained and photosynthesis occurs.

chlorosis   Symptom of nutrient imbalance or disease expressed by reduction in chlorophyll and development of yellow color.

chromoplast   Plastid containing pigments.

chromosome   Structure in nucleus that bears genetic information and consists of DNA and protein.

circadian rhythm   Regular cycle of cellular activity that occurs on a daily basis.

citric acid cycle   Biochemical pathway that is part of the respiratory process. Also called tricarboxylic acid cycle or Krebs cycle.

cladophyll   A branch that resembles a foliage leaf.

class   A hierachial ranking between order and division; a group of related orders.

clay   One of the three basic soil particles, with sizes less than 0.002 mm in diameter.

clean cultivation   Soil tillage to eliminate all vegetation except for the crop.

climate   The long-term average weather.

clod   Hard lump of soil that is difficult to break.

clone   A population of plants descended from a single individual, possessing the same genetic constitution and propagated entirely by vegetative means.

C:N ratio   Relative proportions of carbon-containing substances and nitrogen compounds in a plant or in soil.

CO_2 compensation point   That concentration of carbon dioxide (CO_2) at which there is no net change in CO_2 in the plant since respiratory loss balances photosynthesis.

coarse aggregate   A material composed of large particles, such as sand, that is added to soil to improve drainage.

coenzyme   A biological catalyst that interacts with a protein to cause an enzymatic alteration in a substrate.

cohesion   The attraction of identical molecules for each other.

cold hardiness   Minimum temperature at which a plant will survive. Also called cold tolerance.

cold storage   Storage of plants or plant parts at a constant low temperature.

cole crop   Any of several related vegetables in the family Cruciferae, including cabbage, broccoli, cauliflower, and mustard.

coleoptile   Sheath in grass seedlings that encloses the apical meristem and the primary leaf.

collenchyma Supporting tissue composed of elongated living cells with unevenly thickened walls.

colloid An insoluble particle small enough to remain suspended in a liquid; generally from 0.001 to 0.1 μm.

compaction Excessive packing or settling of soil caused by rain or traffic.

companion cell Living cell associated with the sieve cell of phloem tissue.

companion planting Planting of insect-repellent plants among other types of plants that are susceptible to insect attack.

compatible In reference to species or other taxa, capable of crossbreeding.

complete fertilizer Fertilizer that contains N, P, and K.

complete flower Flower that has both male and female structures and both sepals and petals.

compost Soil amendment derived from decomposed plant material.

composting Piling of plant material to facilitate its decomposition.

compound leaf Leaf blade that is divided into several leaflets.

compound ovary Ovary with two or more locules.

compression wood Reaction wood in conifers formed on lower sides of branches and characterized by dense structure.

container gardening Growing of crop plants outdoors in containers. Also called pot gardening.

container-grown stock Landscape plants grown from seed or transplants in cans or plastic pots.

controlled atmosphere storage (CAS) Cold storage where atmospheric gas contents are controlled at levels that facilitate extended storage life, usually increased carbon dioxide and reduced oxygen.

cool-season vegetable Cold-tolerant or cold-requiring vegetable that develops best in spring or fall.

cork Cells or tissues (phellum) formed from cork cambium that serve a waterproofing protective function on stems or roots.

cork cambium Generative layer of cells that produces cork or bark.

corm Fleshy, underground stem with few nodes and compressed internodes.

Cornell mixes Potting media developed at Cornell University.

corolla All of the petals of a flower considered collectively.

cortex Parenchyma tissue between the epidermis and vascular cylinder of stems and roots.

corymb Type of raceme inflorescence.

cotyledon Part of the seed embryo composed of one or more simple seed leaves.

cover crop Fast-growing species that is planted when crops are not being grown in an area or between areas of planted crops to reduce soil erosion, inhibit weed growth, conserve nutrients, and provide organic matter.

critical photoperiod The specific light-to-dark ratio required to activate vegetative or reproductive responses.

crop rotation Planting different species in the same area in alternate growing seasons to reduce buildup of disease or insects and depletion of particular nutrients.

cross-pollination Process by which pollen is transferred from one flower to another.

crown Top of a root system where the roots meet the stem. Also the top of a tree.

crusting Soil surface having a smooth, glazed appearance.

cultivar (cv) A horticultural rather than a botanical classification identifying a plant that originated and is maintained under cultivation.

cultivate To loosen the soil to promote tilth and provide aeration. More generally, to work to promote the growth of plants.

cultural control   The control of plant pests and pathogens by using cultivation methods that destroy them, inhibit their growth, or reduce their access to susceptible plants.

cultural requirements   Climatic, soil, light, moisture, and other conditions that influence plant growth processes.

cut flower   Plant grown specifically for the display of its flowers in containers.

cuticle   Waxy covering on leaves or fruit that reduces water loss.

cutin   Waxy chemical complex that forms cuticle.

cutting   A detached plant part that under appropriate cultural conditions can regenerate the complete plant without sexual processes.

cyme   A flat-topped, determinate inflorescence.

cytochrome   Any of several iron-porphyrin compounds involved in energy transfer in both respiration and photosynthesis.

cytokinesis   Cytoplasmic division with or without nuclear division.

cytokinin   Any of several naturally occurring plant growth regulators involved in elongation, division, and differentiation of plant cells.

cytology   The study of the structure and activity of cells.

cytoplasm   Collective term for the protoplasm of a cell exclusive of the nucleus.

daily flow irrigation   Trickle irrigation.

damping-off   A disease caused by soil-borne fungi attacking seedlings at the soil line and killing the stem.

dark reactions   Series of enzymatic reactions in which carbon dioxide is fixed or reduced to form a carbohydrate using energy derived from nonenzymatic light reactions.

dark respiration   Series of enzymatic reactions in which carbohydrates are broken down to yield energy independently of the presence of light.

day-neutral plant   Plant that flowers irrespective of the photoperiod.

deciduous   A plant that drops its leaves at the start of the dormant season. Having parts that are shed seasonally, as a plant that drops its leaves seasonally. The opposite of evergreen.

decline   General decrease in the vigor of a plant.

decomposer   An organism, such as a bacterium or fungus, that breaks down organic materials.

decomposition   Breakdown of plant and animal residues usually caused by microorganisms.

dedifferentiation   Reversion of specialized cells to an undifferentiated condition.

deficiency   Absence or insufficiency of some material needed for normal growth and development.

defoliation   Dropping or abscission of most of the leaves of a plant.

denitrification   Conversion of nitrate to gaseous forms leading to loss of nitrogen from soil.

deoxyribonucleic acid (DNA)   Carrier of genetic information encoded in purine and pyrimidine residues. Capable of self-replication and determines sequences of coded information on RNA.

desucker   To remove undesired shoots from the roots or stem of a plant.

determinate   Having genetically limited growth and reproduction.

dethatch   To remove from a lawn a layer of dead and living roots and stems that has accumulated on the soil surface.

development   Processes of change in a plant or plant part from its inception to maturity.

dew point   The temperature at which water vapor in the air reaches 100 percent relative humidity and condensation on a cooler surface occurs.

dicotyledon, dicot One of the two classes of angiosperms, characterized by two cotyledons and usually net venation of leaves. See monocotyledon.

dictyosome Cell organelle composed of disk-shaped sacs and involved in membrane formation, secretion, and cell wall formation. Also called the Golgi apparatus.

differentially permeable membrane A membrane capable of permitting diffusion of different substances at different rates.

differentiation Process by which unspecialized cells, tissues, or organs become progressively specialized.

diffusion Movement of particles or ions from a region where they are more concentrated to a region of lower concentration.

dichasium A type of inflorescence.

dioecious Unisexual. Having male and female imperfect flowers on separate plants.

diploid Possessing two complete sets of chromosomes. The 2n chromosome number is characteristic of the sporophyte generation.

direct seeding Sowing seed in the area where the plants will grow.

disaccharide A sugar, such as sucrose, composed of two molecules of simple sugars.

disbud To remove vegetative or flower buds.

disease Plant condition caused by a microorganism or by environmental conditions in which health is impaired.

dissociation Reversible degradation or separation of a complex substance into simpler constituents.

division A hierarchical ranking between kingdom and class; a group of similar classes. The highest category regularly used in plant taxonomy, identified by names ending in *-phyta*.

division Technique of vegetative propagation in which plants are separated into two or more pieces, each containing a portion of roots and stems.

dolomitic limestone Primarily calcium carbonate ($CaCO_3$) with a proportion of dolomite $[CaMg(CO_3)_2]$.

dormancy Inactive phase in the life cycle of plants where growth ceases.

dormant oil Lightweight oil sprayed on dormant plants to kill insects by suffocation.

double fertilization Simultaneous fusion of one sperm with an egg and a second sperm with the polar nuclei.

double leader Two main stems on the same tree.

double potting Placing a potted plant in a larger pot lined with sphagnum moss.

double-working Grafting technique in which the stock and scion are separated by an interstock.

drainage Removal of water from soil. Rate at which water flows through soil.

drainage tiles Hollow cylinders laid in a trench to drain excess water from gardens, lawns, or fields.

drill hole fertilization Technique for supplying fertilizer to trees by drilling holes in the soil and filling them with fertilizer.

drip irrigation Trickle irrigation.

drought tolerance Capacity of a plant to resist death or impaired growth due to water stress.

drupe A simple fruit containing a single seed that is surrounded by a thin exocarp, a fleshy mesocarp, and a stony endocarp.

dry fruit A type of fruit in which the pericarp is hard and brittle.

dwarf A genetic condition in which a plant grows slowly and remains small.

dwarfing rootstock A rootstock that makes the scion grow more slowly than if it were on its own roots.

ecosystem   Complex interacting system of organisms and their environments.

edaphic   Referring to soil conditions that affect plant growth.

eelworm   A nematode.

electromagnetic spectrum   The range of radiant energy with wavelengths between 0.001 and 100,000 nm.

embryo   Immature plant when part of the seed.

embryo sac   Female gametophyte in angiosperms.

encapsulated fertilizer   Slow-release fertilizer composed of granules of fertilizer embedded in a resin that dissolves slowly.

endocarp   Innermost layer of the mature ovary or fruit wall.

endodermis   Tissue, with cells having Casparian strips, that forms a ring about the vascular cylinder of roots.

endoplasmic reticulum (ER)   Membranous cell organelle ramifying through the cell.

endosperm   Tissue formed following fusion of a sperm with polar nuclei in the embryo sac and serving as a nutritive tissue for the embryo.

entomology   The study of insects and their relation to humans.

enzyme   A protein that serves as a catalyst in biological reactions.

epicotyl   Upper portion of the embryonic axis above the cotyledons that gives rise to the shoot.

epidermis   Outer layer of cells initially surrounding all plant organs.

epiphyte   Plant that can grow on another plant, but is not parasitic.

epigyny   Flower organization in which the sepals, petals, and stamens seem to grow from the top of the ovary.

ergastic substances   Nonliving constituent of protoplasm such as starch grains, oil droplets, and crystals.

erosion   Removal of soil by water or wind.

espalier   A plant trained to grow flat against a wall or trellis.

essential nutrient   An inorganic ion required by plants.

established   Referring to a plant whose roots have penetrated well into the soil and is developing normally.

ethylene   A simple hydrocarbon plant growth-regulating substance involved in fruit ripening and other processes.

etiolation   Condition of abnormal stem elongation, poor leaf development, lack of chlorophyll, and general succulence of the stem due to inadequate light.

eukaryote   Organism whose cells have membrane-bound organelles and a well-defined nucleus.

evapotranspiration   Diffusive loss of water vapor from plants and soil.

everbearing   As applied to small fruits, producing more than one crop of fruit per growing season.

exocarp   Outer layer of the fruit wall or pericarp.

external dormancy   Inability of a plant to grow due to unfavorable conditions including water, temperature, oxygen, or light. Quiescence.

fall vegetable gardening   Seeding cool-season vegetables in summer to obtain a crop in the fall.

family   A hierarchical ranking between order and genus; a group of related genera.

far red light   Radiant energy having wavelengths of 720 to 740 nm.

fascicle   Bundle of conifer needles.

fast-release fertilizer   Granular, powdered, or liquid fertilizer whose ingredients are immediately available to plants.

fat   A lipid that, at room temperature, is a solid.

fermentation   Process by which sugars are converted to ethyl alcohol and carbon dioxide, usually in the absence of oxygen.

ferredoxin   An electron-transferring, iron-containing protein that functions in photosynthesis.

fertilization   Fusion of two gametes or sex cell nuclei to form a diploid zygote or fertilized egg.

fertilizer   Substance that contains plant nutrients.

fertilizer analysis   List of the kinds of essential nutrients and their proportions in a mixture or compound.

fertilizer burn   Damage to plants caused by excessive fertilizer.

fertilizer salt   Chemical compound that includes one or more of the essential plant nutrients.

fiber   Slender, elongated, thick-walled cell.

fibril   Microscopic to submicroscopic cellulose thread that is part of the cellulose matrix of plant cell walls.

fibrous root   Root system in which both primary and lateral roots have approximately equal diameters.

field capacity   Amount of water that a soil can hold against gravity; expressed as a percentage of the dry weight of soil. The soil moisture potential at field capacity is $-\frac{1}{3}$ bar.

field percentage   Upper limit of available capillary water.

filament   Stalk of the stamen on which the anther is borne.

filler   Material added to fertilizer to increase volume.

flat   Shallow container used for growing numbers of plants.

fleshy fruit   A fruit with a soft, fleshy pericarp, including berry, pepo, drupe, pome, and hesperidium.

fleshy root   Root that stores reserve food supplies.

flocculation   Union of soil particles to form loose aggregates.

floret   Small flower that is found in the inflorescences of grasses and other plants.

floriculture   The study of the growing, marketing, and arranging of flowers.

florigen   A general term to include the several identified and unidentified substances that appear to function in flower induction.

flower   Reproductive organ of angiosperms with four major parts: sepals, petals, stamens, and carpels.

flower border   A narrow flower bed.

foliar feeding   Technique of supplying nutrients to plants through leaves and stems, usually by spraying or dipping.

follicle   Dry, dehiscent fruit.

foot-candle   A psychometric measure of light intensity. Now superseded by the lux, or meter candle (1 fc = 10.7 lux).

forcing   Process of activating bloom in bulbs and other plants out of season by manipulation of the environment.

fork   Narrow angle between two branches of a tree.

form   The overall shape of a plant.

forma   A taxonomic category in which the members differ only slightly from other members of the same species or variety.

formal flower bed   Symmetrically arranged bed of flowers.

foundation planting   Shrubs or ground cover planted next to a structure.

free-standing bed   Flower, vegetable, or shrub planting accessible from all sides; an island planting.

friable   Term applied to soils whose consistency is loose, porous, and easily crumbled.

frond Fern leaf.

frost hardy Able to be exposed to temperatures at or somewhat below freezing without injury.

frost heaves Upheaval of soil caused by alternate freezing and thawing of the soil.

frost pocket Depression in the soil surface of variable size into which cold air drains but from which it cannot escape.

frost tender Susceptible to damage or death if exposed to temperatures slightly below freezing.

fructose A six-carbon sugar with a molecular structure slightly different from glucose.

fruit A ripened ovary containing seeds and with other structures attached.

fruit load Amount of fruit borne by a plant.

fruit set Development of fruits following pollination of flowers.

fruit wall Outer part of a fruit derived from the ovary wall (pericarp) or from the pericarp plus other structures associated with the ovary.

fungicide Chemical used to kill fungi and control fungus-caused diseases.

fungus A nonphotosynthetic organism in a kingdom parallel to the plant and animal kingdoms.

fumigant Compound with high vapor pressure that in the gaseous state is used to control diseases in greenhouses and in soils.

gall An abnormal swelling on a plant leaf, stem, or root.

gamete Any cell that is capable of fusing with another cell to form a new individual.

gametophyte In a plant that has alternate sexual and asexual generations, the generation that has a single set of chromosomes (n) and produces gametes as reproductive bodies.

gene A segment of a DNA double helix that acts as a template for the production of a particular kind of RNA; governs particular hereditary characteristics of an organism.

genera Plural of genus.

genetic dwarf A plant that is a dwarf owing to its genetic makeup rather than to grafting on a dwarfing rootstock.

genome One complete set of chromosomes; a chromosome complement.

genotype The genetic constitution, latent or expressed, of an organism; the total of all the genes present in an individual.

genus A hierarchical ranking between family and species; a group of related species.

geotropism Growth movements in which the direction of movement is determined by a response to the force of gravity. Also called gravitropism.

germination Beginning of active growth of an embryo with the rupture of the seed coats and emergence of a new seedling plant; sprouting of a seed.

gibberellin Naturally occurring plant hormones involved in elongation, enhancement of flower, fruit, and leaf size, vernalization, and other processes.

girdle To restrict the function of phloem in a band around the circumference of a plant. To remove from a woody stem a ring of bark extending inward to the cambium.

glucose A six-carbon sugar; the most common monosaccharide.

gluten Amorphous protein occurring in the starchy endosperm of some cereal grains. Involved in the leavening of bread.

glycolysis Process in which sugar is changed anaerobically to pyruvic acid with the liberation of a small amount of useful energy.

Golgi body Cell organelle composed of disk-shaped sacs and involved in membrane formation, secretion, and cell wall formation. Also called dictyosome or Golgi apparatus.

grading Changing the slope level of the soil in an area.

grafting To join a root or stem of one plant (the scion) to the root or stem of another (the stock) so that by tissue regeneration they form a union and grow as one plant.

graft union The point at which a scion from one plant is joined to a stock from another plant.

grana *(sing.* granum) Disc or sac-like structure found in chloroplasts composed of stacked membranes and containing the chlorophyll and carotenoid pigments associated with photosynthesis.

granular fertilizer A fertilizer in a pelletized form.

gravitational water Water in excess of capillary water held at soil moisture of less than −¹⁄₃ bar.

greenhouse effect Heating of the air in a translucent or transparent structure owing to the energy of the sun; increase in temperature due to the trapping of infrared (heat) rays inside a structure.

green manure crop A grass or other fast-growing plant sown over a future planting area and turned under before it reaches maturity to provide organic matter in the soil.

ground cover Usually, low-growing plants that form matlike growth over an area, but technically any planting that covers the surface of the soil to reduce soil erosion and inhibit the growth of other plants.

growing medium Any substance in which plants are rooted or grown such as soil, water, or soilless mixes of sand, peat moss, and other ingredients.

growing season The period from the last freeze in the spring to the first freeze in the fall; ranges from about 90 to 365 days in the continental United States.

growth habit The height, spread, and form of a plant.

grub Soil-inhabiting larva of beetles.

guard cell Specialized epidermal cell that occurs in pairs around a stoma and causes opening and closing of the stoma through changes in turgor.

guttation Exudation of water through the leaves via structures called hydathodes.

gymnosperm A plant having seeds that are not enclosed within the ovary, such as conifers and *Gingko.*

habitat Natural environment of an organism.

haploid Possessing one of each pair of chromosomes; having half the number of chromosomes characteristic of somatic cells.

harden Development of plant parts with age to a point at which they can withstand environmental stresses.

hardening off Treatment of tender plants to adapt them gradually to survive more adverse environmental conditions.

hardpan Soil layer impervious to water and air and through which roots cannot penetrate.

hardwood Wood of a dicot tree.

hardwood cutting A cutting taken in late fall or early spring from the mature growth of a woody plant.

hardy Capable of withstanding freezing temperatures.

heading back Removing the terminal portion of a shoot.

heavy soil Soil composed predominately of clay particles that have a high resistance to tillage.

hedge A number of plants set closely together to form a line.

heel in To cover roots of plants temporarily to prevent drying out until they are planted.

hemicellulose Substances, including pentosans, in cell walls.

herb Culinary or medicinal plant. Usually nonwoody plant with relatively short life.

herbaceous   Exhibiting the nonwoody character.

herbaceous cutting   Cutting taken from herbaceous plants such as geranium, coleus, or house plants.

herbaceous perennial   Plant in which the aerial portion is killed by frost, but the rootstock can regenerate the plant under favorable growing conditions.

herbicide   Chemical used to kill plants.

hesperidium   A fruit with a leathery rind, such as citrus fruits.

heterosis   Hybrid vigor in which offspring are more vigorous than either parent.

heterotroph   Organism that obtains energy by degradation of organic matter. Opposite of autotroph.

heterozygous   Having contrasting genes in a gene pair.

hexose   A six-carbon sugar.

hill   Seeds or plants set closely together.

hilum   Scar left on seed where it was attached to the seed stalk (funiculus).

holdfast   Structure on a climbing vine that anchors the plant to a vertical surface.

home horticulture   Growing ornamentals or edible plants in and around a home, usually noncommercially.

homozygous   Having identical gene pairs.

hormone   Chemical produced by a plant in small amounts that regulates plant growth and development.

horticulture   The science of intensive cultivation of useful plants.

host   Organism in or on which another organism lives.

hot cap   Paper or plastic dome set over a plant to protect it from frost and to increase the daytime growing temperature.

humic acid   Compound formed during the decomposition of organic matter.

humidity   Amount of water vapor in the air.

humus   Decomposed organic matter in which the carbon-to-nitrogen ratio is 10:1 to 15:1.

hybrid   Offspring of two parents differing in one or more genes.

hybridization   The production of hybrids.

hydathode   Pore or gland that releases liquid water.

hydrated lime   Burned lime that has reacted with water to form calcium hydroxide [$Ca(OH)_2$].

hydrolysis   Chemical breakdown of larger molecules into component parts by insertion of water at the place of breakage.

hydrophyte   Plant that lives in water.

hydroponics   Technique of growing plants in an aqueous nutrient solution with or without a solid substrate.

hygroscopic water   Soil water that exists as a thin film around soil particles and is unavailable to plants.

hypha   Single filament of a fungus.

hypobaric storage   Cold storage method for plants in which atmospheric pressure is reduced to depress respiration and lower production of the ripening compound ethylene.

hypocotyl   That portion of the embryo or plant that is just below the cotyledons and connects the stem to the root.

hypogynous   Flower type in which the sepals, petals, and stamens are attached to the receptacle below the ovary.

imbibition   Absorption of water by seeds.

imperfect flower   Flower lacking either stamens or carpels.

incompatible   Plants incapable of crossbreeding or grafting together properly.

incomplete flower   Flower lacking one of the four major parts: sepals, petals, stamens, or carpels; may or may not be imperfect.

indehiscent   Fruit type in which the fruit wall does not split at a seam at maturity.

indeterminate   Characterized by relatively unlimited growth or growth that continues after initial fruit set.

indoleacetic acid (IAA)   A natural growth-regulating compound, known as auxin.

inflorescence   A flower cluster with precise arrangement.

initial   Cells in a meristem that remain permanently meristematic and form tissues of particular structure and function.

insecticide   Chemical that kills insects.

insolation   Radiation received from the sun.

integrated pest management   A system of insect, weed, and disease control that combines biological, physical, cultural, and chemical techniques.

integument   One of the layers that encloses the ovule and is the precursor of the seed coat.

intercalary   A meristematic tissue or growth in regions other than the apical meristem.

intercellular space   Space between cells.

interfascicular cambium   Cambium that arises between vascular bundles.

internode   Portion of a stem between successive leaf-bearing nodes.

interphase   Stage of cell division between mitotic phases.

interplanting   Sowing seed of a quick-maturing plant between seeds of a slower growing plant.

interstock   Stem section grafted between a stock and scion to permit grafting of otherwise incompatible tissues and to confer desirable characteristics on the plant.

invasive root   Vigorous root that grows where it is not wanted.

ion   An atom or molecular group that has lost or gained electrons and has an electric charge.

ionization   Process of ion formation.

iron chlorosis   Iron deficiency in plants characterized by yellowed leaves whose veins remain green.

irrigation   Supplying water to plants, whether by spray, flooding, or other means.

juvenility   Phase of plant development in which the plant is incapable of sexual reproduction.

kinetin   A purine that acts as a cytokinin. Probably not natural.

kingdom   The highest hierarchical ranking, dividing all living organisms into animals, plants, or fungi.

Krebs cycle   The series of enzymatic reactions starting from the oxidation of pyruvic acid resulting in hydrogen ion formation, electron flow, and carbon dioxide release.

lamella   Layer of cellular membranes including photosynthetic and mitochondrial membranes.

lamina   Leaf blade.

lankiness   Elongation of stem internodes, usually as a result of insufficient light.

larva   Immature developmental stage of some insects.

latent heat of soil   Relatively uniform temperature of the soil over time.

lateral   A side branch of a shoot or a root.

lateral meristem   Meristem that gives rise to a secondary tissue such as the vascular cambium or the phellogen.

laterite A red, iron-containing soil of the tropics that is very hard.

lath house Structure covered with thin strips of wood used to grow shade-requiring plants.

lava rock Coarse aggregate made from ground volcanic rock.

lawn substitute A ground cover planted where lawn grasses do not grow well.

layering Technique of vegetative propagation in which new plants are produced from adventitious roots before the new plant is severed from the parent plant.

LD_{50} The amount of a chemical that will kill 50 percent of the test population. The higher the LD_{50}, the lower the presumed toxicity of the chemical.

leaching Downward movement through soil of substances dissolved in water. The gradual removal of substances from soil, plants, or other material by dissolving in water.

leaf Plant organ that is usually the principal photosynthetic organ.

leaf arrangement Organization of leaves on a stem.

leaf base Portion of the leaf blade that joins to the leaf stalk (petiole).

leaf blade The usually flattened portion of the leaf.

leaf bud cutting Cutting that includes a short section of stem with attached leaf.

leaf cutting Cutting composed of the leaf blade and petiole.

leaflet Expanded leaflike part of a compound leaf.

leaf margin Edge of a leaf.

leaf mold Partly decomposed leaves used as a soil amendment.

leaf primordium Lateral outgrowth from the apical stem meristem that will develop into a leaf.

leaf scar Mark left on a stem after a leaf abscisses.

leaf stalk Portion of the leaf that joins the leaf blade to the stem; petiole.

leaf vegetable A vegetable grown primarily for its edible leaves (cabbage, lettuce, spinach).

leggy Common term describing an etiolated plant with elongated stems and usually small leaves.

legume Member of the pea-bean family. The fruit of a member of this family.

lenticel Structurally modified portion of the cork or bark of woody plants that allows gas exchange between the atmosphere and the interior of the plant.

leucoplast Colorless cellular inclusion or plastid.

life cycle The entire sequence of phases in the growth and development of an organism.

light compensation point That level of irradiance at which there is no net exchange of carbon dioxide, where photosynthesis equals respiration.

light duration Total number of hours in a day during which light is received by a plant.

light intensity Brightness or flux of light.

light reactions That portion of the photosynthetic process in which light is captured and converted into chemical energy.

light saturation That level of irradiance above which there is no further increase in net photosynthesis.

light soil Soil composed predominately of sand with a low resistance to tillage.

lignin Complex polymer derived from phenyl propanes found in xylem cell walls.

limbing out Removal of branches from a tree.

lime Ground limestone used to raise soil pH and alter cation exchange capacity. Consists primarily of calcium carbonate ($CaCO_3$) with varying amounts of calcium magnesium carbonate [$CaMg(CO_3)_2$].

line Uniform plant cultivar that is reproduced by seed.

lipid Any of several fats and oils.

loam Soil having large proportions of both sand and clay.

loamy potting soil Potting soil having equal parts of loam, peat moss, and either sand, perlite, or vermiculite.

long-day plant Plant that requires a dark period shorter than its critical dark period to induce flower formation.

low-maintenance plant Plant that requires a minimum of care or attention.

lux Metric unit of measurement of light intensity equal to the illumination on a surface 1 meter distant from a standard candle (10.7 lux = 1 fc).

luxury consumption Nutrient absorption by a plant in excess of that required for optimum growth and productivity.

macroelement Element required by organisms in large amounts; macronutrient.

macromolecule Molecule of large molecular weight, such as proteins, nucleic acids, and polysaccharides.

macropore space Large space between particles or aggregates of soil.

mass planting Planting of closely spaced groups of plants.

maturity Phase of plant development in which the plant is capable of sexual reproduction.

mealybug Insect that attacks plants; small, usually white, and covered with protective waxy fibers.

medium Material used for rooting or supporting plant roots.

meiosis Cell division characterized by a reduction in the chromosome number to the haploid level.

meristem Region of rapidly growing and dividing cells.

meristematic cell Cell that is the source of other cells.

mesocarp Central portion of the fruit wall or pericarp.

mesophyll Tissue consisting primarily of parenchyma cells between the upper and lower epidermal layers of leaves.

metabolism The overall sum of chemical processes in organisms.

metaphase Stage of mitosis or meiosis in which the chromosomes lie in the central plane of the spindle.

microclimate The climate of a specific area produced by conditions, such as elevation, orientation, and plant cover, in that area that make it different from the climate in nearby areas.

microelement Element required by organisms in small amounts; micronutrient.

microgametophyte Male gametophyte.

microorganism Organism visible only under magnification.

micropore space Small space between particles or aggregates of soil.

micropyle Opening in ovular integuments through which pollen tubes can enter.

microsome Cell organelle that may be involved in cell wall formation and in mitosis.

middle lamella Layer of pectinaceous substance that binds primary wall of adjacent cells.

mildew Fungus disease of foliage characterized by a white powdery layer.

minimum tillage Soil management system in which a winter crop is killed by herbicides and the new crop seeded directly into the residue without plowing or tilling.

misting Spraying plant leaves with water.

mite Sucking invertebrate related to spiders.

miticide Chemical used to kill mites.

mitochondria (*sing.* mitochondrion) Membranous cell organelle that contains the enzymes of the Krebs cycle and the electron transport chain.

mitosis Process of nuclear division.

mixed bud   Bud containing undeveloped tissues of both leaves and flowers.

modified central leader   Form of fruit trees in which the central leader is cut back to the nearest scaffold branch to restrict tree height.

monocarp   Plant that grows vegetatively for one or more years, but flowers only once before dying.

monocotyledon, monocot   One of the two classes of angiosperms, characterized by a single cotyledon and frequently strap-shaped leaves with parallel venation. See dicotyledon.

monoculture   System of agriculture or horticulture in which the same species or cultivar of plant is grown by itself, usually for a number of years.

monoecious   Bearing reproductive structures of both sexes on the same plant, but not in the same flower.

monosaccharide   A simple sugar such as a pentose or hexose.

morphogenesis   Sum of all developmental and differentiation processes.

morphological symptom   Visible alteration of structure produced by chemicals or disease.

morphology   The study of the form and structure of an organism throughout its life cycle.

mosaic   A group of diseases caused by viruses in which leaves become mottled.

mound layering   Technique in asexual propagation in which new shoots are initiated from a crown buried in the soil. Also called stool layering.

muck   Organic soil composed primarily of decayed plant parts.

mulch   Material used to cover soil to conserve moisture or prevent weed growth.

multiple fruit   A cluster of matured ovaries, such as a pineapple fruit.

mutation   Permanent, spontaneous alteration in the genetic composition of an organism.

mycelium   Mass of fungal hyphae.

myco-   Pertaining to fungi.

mycorrhizae   A symbiotic union of specific fungi and plant roots which may be endotrophic (hyphae within plant cells) or ectotrophic (fungi surrounding the root).

NAD   Nicotinamide adenine dinucleotide, a respiratory coenzyme.

NADP   Nicotinamide adenine dinucleotide phosphate, a coenzyme functioning in both photosynthesis and respiration.

natural system   A classification system for organisms that attempts to show the evolutionary and phylogenetic relationships among them.

nematocide   Chemical that kills nematodes.

nematode   Microscopic invertebrate worm that damages roots.

net photosynthesis   Photosynthetic activity minus respiratory activity as measured by carbon dioxide exchange.

net venation   Arrangement of veins in a leaf that resembles a network; characteristic of dicot leaves. Also called reticulate venation.

nitrification   Conversion of ammonium ions or ammonia to nitrate ions.

nitrogen cycle   Changes in nitrogen compounds.

nitrogen fixation   Process by which gaseous nitrogen is converted into nitrogenous compounds. May involve nonbiotic processes or the activity of bacteria or blue-green algae alone or in association with flowering plants.

node   That part of the stem where leaves are attached.

nodule   Enlargement or swelling on roots that may contain bacteria that fix nitrogen.

nonselective herbicide   Chemical that can kill all plants.

nucleic acid   Organic macromolecule consisting of nucleotides joined through phosphate groups. Both DNA and RNA are nucleic acids.

nucleolus   Spherical body composed of RNA that is found within the nucleus.

nucleus   Membrane-bound cell organelle that contains chromosomes. Also the central part of an atom.

nut   Dry, indehiscent fruit, usually one-seeded.

nutrient   Any substance used in plant growth and development and obtained from the environment.

nutrient deficiency   Absence or insufficiency of some inorganic ion needed for normal growth and development.

offset   Young plant produced at the base of another.

offshoot   Short, usually horizontal stem produced near the crown of a plant.

oil   A lipid naturally occurring in a liquid state.

olericulture   The science and technology of vegetable production.

ontogeny   Developmental life history of an organism.

opposite leaves   Leaves arising from opposite sides of the same node.

order   A hierarchical ranking between class and family; a group of related families.

organ   Structure composed of different tissue systems.

organelle   Membrane-bound structure within the cytoplasm of a cell.

organic   Referring to living organisms, to substances produced by organisms, and to the chemistry of compounds containing carbon atoms.

organic fertilizer   Fertilizer made of organic matter, such as manure and compost.

organism   An individual, living creature.

ornamental   Plant grown for beauty.

ornamental horticulture   The branch of horticulture dealing with the cultivation of plants for their esthetic value, including floriculture, landscape horticulture, cultivation of house plants, and turf growing.

osmosis   Diffusion of water and contained solutes through a semi-permeable membrane driven by differences in the potential of solutions on either side of the membrane.

osmunda fiber   Roots and rhizomes of ferns in the genus *Osmunda* used as a potting medium or soil amendment.

ovary   Basal portion of a carpel; becomes a fruit upon maturation.

overwatering   Applying excessive water to plants at too frequent intervals leading to soil saturation and anaerobiosis.

ovule   Structure in the carpel that contains the female gametophyte with embryo sac and supporting tissues.

oxidation   Chemical reaction in which the net positive valence of an element is increased.

oxidative phosphorylation   Formation of ATP that occurs in the electron transport chain in the respiratory process of the mitochondria.

palisade cell   Elongated, photosynthetic cell that forms the upper portion of the leaf mesophyll.

palmate leaf   Compound leaf with all leaflets arising from one point at the end of the petiole.

panicle   Branched inflorescence bearing loose flower clusters.

parallel venation   Leaf venation pattern in which the principal veins are parallel. This venation pattern is characteristic of monocots.

parasite   Organism that lives on or in another organism and obtains its nutrients therefrom.

parenchyma cell   Thin-walled cell having large central vacuole. The basic plant cell type.

parthenocarpy   Fruit development without fertilization of the egg cells. Parthenocarpic fruits are usually seedless.

pathogen   Organism that causes disease.

pathology   The study of plant diseases, their biological effects, and their control.

peat   Organic soil composed of plant residues in various stages of decomposition.

peat pot   Container made of compressed peat and filled with soil or soilless mixture in which seedlings are started.

peat moss   Product derived from one or more bog plants in various stages of decomposition which is dried, sometimes ground, and used as a soil amendment.

pectic substances   Hydrophilic substances containing pectins and other compounds derived from the middle lamellae of plants.

pedicel   Stem of an individual flower.

peduncle   Short stem of a flower cluster.

pelleted seed   Seed enclosed in a coating that makes it easier to sow and may also contain nutrients.

perennial   Plant capable of living for an indefinite number of years.

perfect flower   Flower containing both male and female structures.

perianth   Sepals and petals of a flower considered collectively.

pericarp   Fruit wall usually consisting of three layers.

pericycle   Cell layer in roots inside the endodermis and from which lateral roots arise.

periderm   Tissue system, usually corky, that replaces the epidermis as the plant ages.

perigynous   Flower type in which the receptacle forms a cuplike structure around part of the ovary.

perlite   White, granular substance derived from silica and used in potting media in place of sand.

permanent sod   Soil management system in which the ground cover may be mowed but is not subjected to tillage.

permanent wilting point or percentage   Amount of water a soil holds at a potential that makes it unavailable to plants, usually -15 bars.

permeable   Able to allow substances to move through.

peroxisome   Microbody containing enzymes of the glyoxylate cycle.

pesticide   Any substance used to kill plant or animal pests of plants.

petal   Structures comprising the corolla.

petiole   Leaf stalk attaching the leaf blade to the stem.

pH   Symbol defined as the log reciprocal of the hydrogen ion concentration. A measure of acidity and alkalinity.

phellem   Cork. A protective tissue composed of dead cells with suberized, water-repellent walls; part of the periderm.

phellogen   Cambium that produces phellem or cork cells.

phenotype   The physical appearance of an organism resulting from the interaction between its genetic constitution and its environment.

phloem   Principal tissue that conducts materials made in the leaves down to the rest of the plant. Consists of sieve tubes, fibers, sclereids, and phloem parenchyma.

phosphorylation   Reactions in which phosphate is added to a compound to produce one that may possess high potential energy. The addition of phosphate to ADP.

photoperiod   The light-to-dark or day-to-night ratio in 24 hours.

photoperiodism   Development responses of plants to photoperiod. A mechanism that evolved in organisms to measure time.

photorespiration   Respiratory utilization of products of photosynthesis activated by light.

photosynthate   The carbohydrates and other compounds produced in photosynthesis.

photosynthesis   The linked chemical, physical, and biological processes by which green plants manufacture carbohydrates from CO_2 in the presence of light.

photosynthetically active radiation (PAR) Radiant energy captured by the photosynthetic system in the light reactions; usually defined as the wavelengths between 400 and 700 nm.

phototropism Growth movements in which the direction of the growth is determined by the wavelength, direction, and intensity of light.

phyllotaxy Arrangement of leaves about a stem.

phylogeny The study of the evolutionary relationships among plants.

physiology The study of the activities of organisms.

phytochrome A pigment involved in the reception of those red and far red wavelengths that regulate many processes in plants including flower induction, dormancy, seed germination, and morphogenesis.

pigment Any chemical capable of absorbing specific wavelengths of radiation.

pinching Removal of portions of stems usually to reduce apical dominance and obtain bud break below the part removed.

pinnate leaf Compound leaf with leaflets arranged on both sides of the midrib.

pistil Female reproductive organ in the flower consisting of the stigma, style, and ovary.

pistillate flower Imperfect flower containing only pistils and no anthers.

pith Tissue occupying the center of stems or roots and consisting primarily of parenchyma cells.

placenta That part of an ovary wall to which ovules or seeds are attached.

plant breeding The science of crossing plants to obtain new cultivars or varieties.

plant cell sap The liquid within plant cells, usually in the vacuoles.

plant food Nonscientific term for fertilizer or nutrients.

plant key An arbitrary method for separating different plants by use of characters of the plants in opposition.

plant pathogen Organism that causes disease in plants.

plant propagation Techniques used to increase the numbers of a species or its varieties and lines.

plant residue Unharvested or unused parts of plants.

plant toxicity Poisonous effects of substances on plants.

plasma membrane Cell membrane.

plasmodesmata Cytoplasmic threads that extend through pores and connect the protoplasts of adjacent living cells.

plasmolysis Collapse of cell vacuoles as a result of water loss. Usually apparent as wilting.

plastic mulch Thin layer of plastic sheeting used to cover an area in which plants are grown to increase water retention and heat absorption and decrease weed growth.

plastid Cell organelle that is the site of various metabolic activities.

plugging Method of lawn establishment in which small cylinders of sod are inserted into prepared soils.

plumule Bud of an embryo that will give rise to a stem.

polar nuclei Two haploid nuclei in the embryo sac that fuse with a sperm to form the endosperm tissue.

pollarding A training method for deciduous trees in which branches are pruned back almost to the main trunk at frequent intervals.

pollen grain Microspore containing the male gametophyte (sperm) nuclei.

pollen tube Tube formed by a pollen grain that grows through stigma and style to the egg sac in the ovule.

pollination Transfer of pollen from an anther to a pistil of the same or another flower.

polyploidy State where a cell contains more than two sets of chromosomes.

polysaccharide Carbohydrate polymer consisting of many monosaccharides joined together in straight or branched chains. Starch and cellulose are glucose polysaccharides.

pome A simple, fleshy fruit, such as apple, pear, and quince.

pomology The science and practice of fruit cultivation.

pore space Spaces between soil particles or aggregates.

postemergence herbicide Herbicide that kills established weeds.

pot bound Growing in a limited space that restricts the spread of the root system.

potting compost An English term for a growing medium.

potting up Transplanting a seedling into a pot.

preemergence herbicide Herbicide that kills plants at the stage of germination or early seedling growth. Usually ineffective against established plants.

primary growth Growth originating from a meristem, but not from a cambium.

primary plant body Those parts of a plant derived directly from a meristem and not a cambium.

primary root The first root of a plant developed from the radicle in the embryo.

primary wall Outer or first-formed wall layers of a cell after its formation.

prokaryote Organism whose cells lack membrane-bound organelles and a nucleus and do not carry out regularized cell divisions, and are usually considered to be evolutionarily primitive. Includes bacteria and blue-green algae. All other organisms on earth are eukaryotic.

propagate To produce new plants from seeds or by nonsexual means.

prophase Stage in mitotic division of cells characterized by shortening of chromosomes as a prelude to chromosome movement in the metaphase stage.

proplastid Plastid in its early stages of development.

prop root Adventitious root arising from a stem above the soil line that serves to support the plant.

protective layer Layer of cells in the abscission zone of a leaf that, after leaf abscission, forms a water-impermeable barrier.

protein A complex, usually large organic compound composed of many amino acids linked into a long chain by peptide bonds.

protoplast Living contents of a cell consisting of protoplasm and its plasma membrane.

pruning Removal of parts of a plant.

puddled soil Soil in which structure has been lost, with almost no pore spaces, so that aeration and water movement are poor.

pup Common name for small plants formed on stems or roots.

raceme An inflorescence in which the main axis is elongated but the flowers are borne on pedicels that are about equal in length.

radicle Part of the embryo of a seed that gives rise to the root following germination.

reaction wood Wood with more or less distinctive anatomical characteristics, formed in parts of leaning or crooked stems and in branches. Referred to as compression wood in conifers and tension wood in dicotyledons.

receptacle That part of the axis of a flower stalk that bears the floral organs.

red light Radiant energy at a predominant wavelength of 660 nm.

reduction division Process by which the number of chromosomes in a cell is reduced from two sets (2n) to one set. Meiosis.

refoliate To grow new leaves after being leafless.

relative humidity Amount of water vapor present in the air, expressed as a percentage of the maximum water vapor that the air could hold at the same pressure and temperature.

renovation pruning   Severe pruning used to rejuvenate and reshape an overgrown or badly formed plant.

repotting   Transferring a plant to a larger container when the plant becomes pot-bound or if destructive soil insects are present.

resistance   Ability of a plant to withstand attack by insect pests or diseases or to withstand environmental stresses.

respiration   A cellular process in which organic substances are oxidized with release of energy. The complete breakdown of sugar or other organic compounds to carbon dioxide and water is termed aerobic respiration.

rest   State of suspended growth or outwardly visible activity due to internal physiological factors. It is broken by exposure to temperatures of 7° C or lower for an extended period of time (chilling requirement). Also called physiological dormancy.

rhizobia   Bacteria of the genus *Rhizobium* which may associate with the roots of many leguminous plants in a symbiotic relationship as a result of which elemental nitrogen is fixed or converted to ammonia.

rhizoid   Structure of rootlike form and function, but lacking xylem and phloem.

rhizome   Horizontal stem that grows partly or entirely underground; often thickened and serving as a storage organ.

ribonucleic acid (RNA)   Type of nucleic acid formed on chromosomal DNA and involved in protein synthesis.

ribosome   Small, dense, globular structure in cellular cytoplasm often associated with membranes of endoplasmic reticulum; involved in protein synthesis.

ringing   Removing a ring of bark extending inward to the cambium.

rock garden   A combination of rocks and plants that creates a natural looking area for the cultivation of plant species native to rocky or alpine regions.

root   One of the primary organs of most vascular plants, serving to anchor the plant in the soil, to absorb water and minerals, and to serve as a storage organ.

root ball   Soil attached to the roots of a plant that is in a container or otherwise out of the ground.

root cap   Thimblelike mass of cells covering and protecting the growing tip of a root.

root cutting   Cutting made from sections of roots alone.

root hair   Extension of the epidermal cells on young roots immediately behind the root tip.

rooting   Formation of roots on a cutting taken from a plant.

rooting hormone   Mixture usually containing natural or synthetic auxins that stimulates root formation on cuttings of plants.

rooting medium   Any material in which roots may form on cuttings taken from a plant, such as sand, perlite, peat moss, or water.

root pressure   Pressure developed in roots as the result of osmosis which causes guttation from leaves and exudation from cut stems, and may be involved in the rise of water in plants.

rootstock   The plant that bears the roots of the new plant in a budding or grafting operation.

root tuber   Thickened root that stores carbohydrates.

root vegetable   A vegetable grown primarily for its edible root (radish, turnip, carrot) or tuber (potato).

root zone   Volume of soil or growing medium containing the roots of a plant.

rosette   A plant form in which the plant has a shortened stem with leaves that overlap and radiate outward from a central point.

rotary tiller   A machine that turns the soil by means of revolving arms called tynes.

rotation   The practice of growing different crops in recurring succession on the same plot of land.

runner   An above-ground stem; a slender stolon with elongated internodes, produced as a natural means of vegetative reproduction.

rust   A fungus disease requiring two host plant species for a complete life cycle and characterized at one point in the life cycle by rust-colored pustules on the leaves of the affected plant.

saline soil   An alkali soil with more than 2000 ppm soluble salts, but relatively low sodium.

saline-sodic soil   An alkali soil with more than 2000 ppm soluble salts and high sodium.

samara   Indehiscent, dry fruit with either one or two seeds, in which the pericarp bears a flattened winglike outgrowth.

sand   One of the three basic soil particles, with a size range of 0.05 to 2.0 mm in diameter.

sandy soil   Light soil with a high proportion of sand. Soil mix consisting of 1 part loam, 1 part peat moss or leaf mold, and 2 parts sand or perlite.

sap   Fluid contents of the xylem and sieve elements of phloem. Fluid contents of the vacuole are referred to as cell sap.

saprophyte   Organism that absorbs nutrients from dead plant and animal remains.

scaffold branch   A main fruit-bearing branch.

scale   An insect pest with a shell-like covering that attaches to a plant and sucks plant juices.

scale leaf   Modified leaf that protects structures.

scarification   The chemical or physical treatment given to some seeds in order to break or weaken the seed coat sufficiently to permit germination.

scientific name   Botanical name consisting of a genus and a species name in Latin assigned to each recognized and described kind of organism.

scion   The twig or bud to be grafted onto the roots of another plant, the stock, in a budding or grafting operation.

sclereid   A sclerenchyma cell that has a thick, lignified secondary wall with many pits, is variable in form, and may or may not be living at maturity.

sclerenchyma   A supporting tissue composed of sclerenchyma cells, including fibers and sclereids.

screening plant   Plant used to block a view or to separate areas.

scutellum   The single cotyledon of a grass embryo; specialized for absorption of nutrients from endosperm tissue.

secondary growth   Type of growth characterized by an increase in thickness of stem and root and resulting from formation of secondary vascular tissues by the vascular cambium.

secondary phloem   Phloem tissue formed by the vascular cambium during secondary growth in a vascular plant.

secondary root   A branch or lateral root.

secondary thickening   Deposition of secondary cell wall materials. Increase in thickness in stems and roots.

secondary vascular tissue   Vascular tissue (xylem and phloem) formed by the vascular cambium during secondary growth in a vascular plant.

secondary wall Innermost layer of cell wall with a highly organized microfibrillar structure, formed in certain cells after cell elongation has ceased.

secondary xylem Xylem tissue formed by the vascular cambium during secondary growth in a vascular plant.

seed Structure formed by the maturation of the ovule of seed plants following fertilization; embryo and food-storing tissues surrounded by one or more protective layers or seed coats.

seed coat Outer layer of the seed, developed from the integuments of the ovule.

seed leaf The first leaf (cotyledon) or set of leaves produced by the seedling, usually with a different shape from true leaves.

seedling Young plant developing from a germinating seed.

seed potato Segment of a potato tuber containing at least one eye or bud which is planted to start a potato plant.

seed tape Strip of degradable plastic tape in which vegetable or flower seeds are embedded.

selective herbicide Chemical that kills only certain groups of plants.

self-fertility Ability of a plant to set viable seed or fruit with pollen from the same plant.

self-incompatibility Inability of pollen to fertilize eggs of the same plant.

self-sterility Inability of a plant to set viable seed or fruit with pollen from the same cultivar.

semidwarf A fruit tree that at maturity is intermediate in size between dwarf and standard or full size.

semihardwood cutting Cutting made from the partially matured new growth of a woody plant.

semipermeable membrane Membrane that allows free movement of water in both directions, but restricts passage of solute molecules in solution.

senescence The aging and death of a plant or any of its parts.

sepal A member of the outermost set of floral leaves, typically green or greenish and more or less leafy in texture; collectively the calyx.

separation Use of bulbs and corms in propagation utilizing the naturally detachable parts.

sessile Without a petiole (referring to leaves); without a pedicel (referring to flowers and fruits).

sexual reproduction Reproduction of plants through a sexual process involving meiosis and fusion of gametes.

shade house A garden structure covered with plastic, netting, or lath under which plants requiring shade are grown.

shading Material, such as whitewash, lath, or bamboo blinds, applied to glazing to decrease light entry and heat buildup in a greenhouse or similar structure.

sheath Base of a leaf that wraps around the stem, as in grasses. A tissue layer surrounding another tissue, as a bundle sheath layer.

shock Wilting and leaf drop following root loss during transplanting or other sudden environmental stress.

shoot The above-ground portions of a vascular plant including stem and leaves.

short-day plant Plant that requires a day (or light period) shorter than a critical daylength to induce flower formation. Conversely, a long-night plant, requiring a night (or dark period) longer than its critical dark period.

shrub Perennial woody plant of relatively low stature and typically with several stems arising at or near the crown.

side dressing   A narrow band of fertilizer, compost, or other material placed around a plant or along a row, not touching the plant shoot.

sieve element   The fundamental type of cell in phloem which is long, slender, and thin walled and has cytoplasm but no nucleus at maturity.

sieve tube   A series of sieve tube members arranged end to end and interconnected by sieve plates.

silique   The fruit characteristic of the mustard family (Cruciferae); two-celled, the valves splitting from the bottom and leaving the placenta with the false partition stretched between.

silt   One of the three basic soil particles with a size range of 0.002 to 0.05 mm in diameter.

simple fruit   Fruit derived from one carpel or several united carpels.

simple leaf   Leaf with a single blade.

single element fertilizer   Fertilizer containing only one of the essential elements for plant growth.

slip   Cutting.

slow-release fertilizer   Fertilizer formulation in which particles are coated with a slowly dissolving substance to permit the predictable slow solubilization of the encapsulated nutrients.

small fruit   Collective name for plants that bear edible fruits and are not trees and are usually of small size.

sodic soil   An alkali soil with high sodium, but low soluble salts.

softwood   Wood of conifer trees.

softwood cutting   Cutting taken from new, succulent growth of plants.

soil   The superficial weathered layer of the earth's crust composed of inorganic particles, organic matter, microorganisms, water, and air.

soil aeration   Process by which soil air is exchanged for atmospheric air.

soil ball   Soil plus contained roots of a plant.

soil borne   An organism living in soil. Usually refers to disease or pest organisms.

soil drench   A liquid poured over the root zone of a plant.

soil horizon   Layer of soil in a soil profile.

soil management   Practices employed to maintain soil in a condition for growing plants.

soil pasteurization   Heating of soil to kill harmful organisms.

soil permeability   Ease with which materials penetrate through bulk soil.

soil solution   Aqueous portion of soil including dissolved substances that can be taken up by plants.

soil structure   Arrangement of soil aggregates.

soil test   Analysis to determine nutrient levels, acidity, and presence of potentially toxic substances.

soil texture   Relative proportions of particles of different sizes in terms of sand, silt, and clay.

spadix   Fleshy inflorescence with a spike of male and female flowers.

species   A hierarchical ranking of organisms, consisting of freely interbreeding individuals and varieties, with many common characteristics. The basic taxonomic category.

specific epithet   The second word in a scientific name.

specimen plant   Ornamental plant grown by itself in a landscape.

spermatophyta   That division of the plant kingdom including plants that reproduce by seeds.

sphagnum   A bog moss used as peat.

spike   An inflorescence in which the axis is elongated and flowers are sessile.

spine   Hard, sharp structure, usually a modified leaf.

spongy parenchyma   Leaf mesophyll cells.

sporophyte   The diploid (2n) phase of a plant's life cycle.

spur   Stem with shortened internodes that bears flowers and/or leaves.

spur-type tree   Fruit tree with many spur branches capable of bearing fruit.

stabilizer   Compound that retards the decomposition of another material.

stamen   Male part of a flower consisting of an anther that produces pollen and a filament bearing the anther.

staminate flower   Flower in which anthers are formed without pistils.

standard   A cultivated tree that matures at full size, as contrasted with a dwarf variant.

starch   A polysaccharide polymer consisting of unbranched (amylose) or branched (amylopectin) chains of glucose molecules.

starter solution   A fertilizer, high in phosphorus, used to hasten growth of seedlings.

stele   The central vascular cylinder of roots and stems.

stem   Vegetative axis of a plant derived from the epicotyl of the embryo; usually above ground and bearing lateral shoots, leaves, and flowers.

stem cutting   Cutting of a shoot containing buds.

stem section cutting   Cutting composed of a short segment of stem containing at least one node.

stem tip cutting   Cutting composed of the top of a shoot.

stigma   That portion of the pistil that receives pollen.

stipule   Leaflike appendage at the base of the petiole.

stock   The lower portion of a graft.

stolon   Above-ground stem that grows horizontally and is capable of forming roots at its nodes. A runner.

stoma   Opening in a leaf through which gas exchange occurs. Plural: stomata.

stone fruit   Fruit containing a single seed contained within hard endocarpic layer. Usually fleshy as in plum, peach, and apricot.

stratification   Chilling of moist seeds to break dormancy.

stress   Any physical or chemical condition that can limit the growth and development of plants.

stroma   Ground substance of chloroplasts where the fixation of carbon dioxide occurs.

style   That portion of the pistil between the stigma and the ovary through which a pollen tube grows.

suberin   Chemical that waterproofs cell walls in cork.

subsoil   Layer of soil directly beneath the topsoil characterized by lower fertility, smaller proportion of organic matter, and different texture and structure from the topsoil.

subspecies   Subdivision of the taxonomic category of species.

subsurface irrigation   Application of water to plants through seepage from underground pipes.

succulent   Plant with thickened leaves or stems structurally and functionally adapted for water conservation. Also, the young, tender growth of plants.

sucking insect   Insect with mouth parts capable of sucking sap from plants, such as aphids, scale insects, and leafhoppers.

sucrose   A disaccharide composed of one molecule each of glucose and fructose. Cane and beet sugar.

sun scald   Injury caused by excessive sunlight.

superior ovary   Ovary that is separate from the calyx.

surface irrigation   Application of water directly to the soil surface by flooding or moving the water through trenches.

surface root   Root that grows horizontally along the soil surface.

symbiosis   Close association of two or more dissimilar organisms that may be parasitic or mutually beneficial.

systematics   The study of the kinds and diversity of living things and the relationships among them.

systemic pesticide   Pesticide that is absorbed into a plant and moves to all parts of the plant.

tap root   Primary root of a plant formed as a direct continuation of the radicle of the embryo. Fleshy root growing vertically into the soil; the edible portion of carrot or parsnip.

taxon   Any taxonomic unit of classification.

taxonomy   The science of the classification, naming, and identification of organisms.

TCA cycle   Tricarboxylic acid cycle, or Krebs cycle, for the respiratory breakdown of pyruvate.

telophase   The last stage in mitosis and meiosis during which the chromosomes become reorganized into two new nuclei.

temperate fruit   Fruit plant that requires a cool period and is deciduous.

temperature inversion   Condition at night in the lower atmosphere which is the reverse of normal daytime conditions. During the day the warmest air is usually at the surface of the ground and temperatures decline with increasing altitude. During a temperature inversion surface layers cool, and there is warm air above the cooler surface air.

tendril   Slender coiling structure, usually a modified leaf or part of a leaf, which aids in support of the stem.

tension wood   Reaction wood in dicotyledons formed on the upper sides of branches and leaning or crooked stems.

terminal bud   Bud located at the tip of a stem.

terrarium   Transparent glass or plastic container retaining high humidity used for displaying and growing plants indoors.

testa   Seed coat.

tetraploid   Twice the usual, diploid (2n) number of chromosomes, that is, 4n.

texture   Visual impact of a plant due to the size of its leaves; coarse-textured plants have large leaves and fine-textured plants have small leaves. Refers also to the proportions of sand, silt, and clay in the soil.

thatch   A layer of stems and roots (both dead and living) that accumulates between the surface of a turf and the soil.

thinning   Removal of older stems to promote new growth. Removal of excess fruits to improve the size and quality of the remaining fruits. Removal of seedlings spaced too closely for optimum growth.

thorn   Hard, woody, pointed branch.

thrips   Minute, winged insects that damage plants by rasping the surface of the leaves and lapping the exuded sap.

thylakoid   Saclike, membranous structure within the chloroplast; stacks of thylakoids make up the grana.

tilth   Physical condition of soil as related to its ease of tillage, fitness as a seedbed, and its resistance to seedling emergence and root penetration.

tip burn   Death and browning of leaf tips, common on indoor plants in low humidity environments.

tip layering   Layering in which rooting takes place near the tip of the current season's shoot.

tissue Organized group of cells with similar origin and function.

tissue culture Growing of masses of unorganized cells on agar medium or in liquid suspension. Useful for the rapid asexual multiplication of plants.

tomato cage Wire mesh cylinder used to support a tomato plant.

tonoplast Membrane surrounding the vacuole.

top dressing Application of fertilizer over the soil surface.

topiary Training of a shrub by pruning or shearing to develop a controlled shape.

topping Removal of the central leader of a tree to make the head fuller.

top soil Uppermost layer of soil, usually characterized by a higher quantity of organic matter and nutrients than the subsoil.

topworking Grafting procedure by which branches of trees are exchanged for a more desirable cultivar.

totipotency Ability to generate or regenerate a whole organism from a part.

trace element Elements such as boron, iron, copper, zinc, and manganese necessary in small amounts for plant growth.

tracheid Elongated, thick-walled conducting and supporting cell of xylem tissue with tapering ends and pitted walls without perforations.

training System of pruning and tying plants to make them conform to a particular size or shape; used on fruit trees to aid harvesting and on ornamentals for decorative effects.

translocation Movement of dissolved materials in cell sap from one plant organ or tissue to another, as the movement of sugar from leaves to stems.

transpiration Loss of water vapor from plant parts, most of which occurs through leaf stomata.

transpirational pull Tension that is generated by transpiration and is the major force in the rise of water in plants.

transplant A seedling plant grown in a cold frame, greenhouse, or indoors for later planting outdoors. Also, to dig up and move a plant to another location.

tree Perennial woody plant generally with a single stem or trunk.

tribe A subdivision of a subfamily.

trichome Outgrowth of the epidermis, variable in shape, size, and function; includes hairs and scales.

trickle irrigation Method of supplying water to plants involving flexible water pipes inserted at intervals with small microtubes that run to the base of plants.

troph, tropho Suffix or prefix meaning feeder or feeding; autotrophic, for example, means self-nourishing.

tropism Response to an external stimulus in which the direction of the movement is usually determined by the direction from which the most intense stimulus comes; phototropism, geotropism, thigmotropism are examples.

true leaves Second and subsequent sets of leaves produced by a seedling.

tube cell In male gametophytes, the cell of the pollen grain that develops into the pollen tube.

tube nucleus One of the nuclei of a pollen grain thought to influence the growth and development of the pollen tube, but is not a gamete.

tuber Thickened underground stem, for example, white potato, in which carbohydrates are stored.

turf Low dense sod of lawns, including the above-ground parts, upper roots, and rhizomes of plants with attached soil particles.

turgor Condition resulting from the osmotic uptake of water into the vacuole so that the cytoplasm is firmly pressed against the cell wall.

twig A stem, one year old or less.

umbel   An inflorescence in which the pedicels arise from a common point and are about equal in length.

understock   Host plant for a grafted scion, a branch or shoot from another plant; may be a fully grown tree or a stump with a living root system.

undifferentiated   In a meristematic state or resembling a meristem.

vacuole   Part of the cell bounded by the tonoplast membrane and filled with cell sap, an aqueous solution of inorganic salts, organic molecules, and crystals.

vapor pressure   Pressure exerted by water vapor.

vapor pressure gradient   Difference between the actual water vapor pressure and the vapor pressure required to saturate air at the same temperature.

variegation   Genetically controlled patterning of leaves with white or green patches.

variety   A subdivision of a species, usually differing from the species in stable minor characteristics.

vascular bundle   The conducting tissue system.

vascular cambium   Meristematic cell layer that gives rise to the secondary vascular system.

vegetable   Edible portion of a herbaceous plant.

vegetative   Relating to growth not involved in sexual reproduction. Includes stems, leaves and roots.

vegetative reproduction   Propagation of new flowering plants by means other than by seeds. Usually results in new plants genetically identical to the parent plant.

vein   Vascular bundle in a leaf or flower.

venation   Arrangement of veins in a leaf blade.

vermiculite   Coarse aggregate material made from expanded mica having a high cation exchange capacity and high water-holding capacity and used as a rooting medium and a soil additive.

vernalization   Subjecting a plant to a regime of cool temperatures to promote or enhance growth or flowering.

vessel   Long, continuous tube of xylem cells through which water and minerals move.

vine   Plant with elongated stems that cannot support upright growth.

virus   Submicroscopic, obligate intracellular parasite, composed of nucleic acid and protein that can be reproduced only by the genetic material of a living cell.

viscosity   Resistance to flow of a liquid.

visible light   That part of the electromagnetic spectrum to which the human eye can respond; wavelengths between 380 nm and 750 nm.

volatilization   Conversion of a solid or liquid into a gas or vapor.

volunteer   A plant that develops from natural reseeding.

wall pressure   Pressure that a cell wall exerts against the turgor of the cell contents. It is equal and opposite to the turgor potential.

warm-season vegetable   Vegetable that grows best when day temperatures are between 18° and 32° C.

water-holding capacity   Ability of a growing medium to hold water against gravitational pull.

water potential   Sum of the solute potential and wall pressure potential. In soils, the matric potential is also included.

water sprout   Vertical, usually vigorous shoot produced on the trunk or branch of a tree.

water table   Upper horizon of free water in soil.

weather   Short-term atmospheric conditions including temperature, relative humidity, wind speed and direction, sky conditions, precipitation, and atmospheric pressure.

weed   Plant not valued in the place where it is growing.

wetting agent   Chemical that decreases surface tension and increases adhesion of a liquid.

wick watering   Technique for watering potted plants in which water is moved from a reservoir to the substrate through a wick.

wilt   Drooping of stems and foliage due to loss of water and decreased turgidity of cells. May be caused by water stress or disease.

wilting coefficient   The amount of water remaining in soil which is unavailable to plants; usually -15 bars. Frequently called the permanent wilting point and expressed as the percentage of the dry weight of soil.

winter annual   Frost-hardy flowering plant grown for winter bloom in regions with mild winters.

winter desiccation   Injury to plants caused by moisture loss of foliage in winter when evapotranspiration is greater than water uptake from cold or frozen soils.

wood   The secondary xylem of woody perennials.

wrapping   The practice of covering the trunk of young trees with paper or cloth to prevent sun scald or to protect from injury or infection.

xanthophyll   Yellow carotenoid pigments that are part of the photosynthetic apparatus.

xerophyte   Plant adapted for growth in dry or arid habitats.

xylem   Vascular tissue composed of tracheids, vessels, parenchyma cells, and fiber cells through which most of the water and minerals are conducted from roots to leaves.

yellows   Disease syndrome caused by viruses in which leaves become yellow and curl and the plants are stunted.

yield   Amount of produce obtained from horticultural or agricultural plants.

zone of elongation   That section of the young root or shoot just behind the apical meristem in which the cells are enlarging and elongating rapidly.

zygote   The diploid cell resulting from the fusion of male and female gametes. The fertilized egg cell.

INDEX

597

INDEX **607**